*The Physics of*
# Engineering Solids

Second Edition

# The Physics of
# Engineering Solids

### T. S. Hutchison
### and D. C. Baird
*Royal Military College of Canada*

*John Wiley and Sons, Inc.    New York  ·  London  ·  Sydney*

# Preface to the Second Edition

The purpose of the second edition of *The Physics of Engineering Solids* remains the same as that of the first: to acquaint the undergraduate engineer with the fundamental properties of the solid state.

Again the book falls into two main divisions. Chapters 1 to 7 are concerned with the consequences of the periodic nature of atomic packing in solids and the nature of lattice defects. Chapters 11 to 17 are concerned with the quantum properties of electrons in solids. An elementary introduction to quantum principles, discussed in Chapters 8 to 10, is interposed between the two main divisions of the text.

In response to modern emphasis we have expanded the discussion of a number of topics, notably, semiconductors and optical properties of dielectrics and semiconductors. We have introduced new chapters on internal friction, radiation damage, lattice vibrations, and superconductivity.

Acknowledgement is made throughout the text to several authors where we have followed their presentations of particular topics rather closely. We are indebted to Paul van Nest and Ken Smee for the preparation of the table of magnetic susceptibilities and checking of the problems and to Mrs. Jean E. Malach for typing the manuscript.

T. S. Hutchison

D. C. Baird

*Kingston, Ontario, Canada*
*May 1967*

# *Preface to*
# the First Edition

The invasion of engineering practice by the methods, discoveries, and man-power of the physical sciences which has occurred over the last two decades is now being reflected in the teaching curricula of most engineering schools. The most spectacular aspects of this invasion lie in the introduction of nuclear power and the ever-growing use of electronic devices of a solid state nature. There is no doubt that the engineering students now in our schools and universities will, throughout their professional lives, make almost exclusive use of such devices for the measurement and control of nuclear and electrical power, radiation, heat, liquid and gas flow, temperature, acceleration, strain, etc., in the engineering systems with which they are associated.

To assist in the discovery and development of solid state instruments, it is necessary in most cases to have a knowledge and working familiarity with quantum mechanics to a greater degree than that usually acquired at the undergraduate level. This applies to students of physics and chemistry as well as engineering. In order, however, to make intelligent use of existing devices and to forecast new uses this is not so. A sound grasp of the fundamental principles on which the physics of the solid state is based should suffice. This is also true of the current use of electronic tubes which can be intelligently employed without a specialist's knowledge of electron ballistics and thermionic emission. Familiarity with the fundamental principles of these latter two topics is, however, essential.

Therefore, the purpose of this textbook is to acquaint the undergraduate engineer with the fundamental properties of the solid state. These properties fall into two categories. One aspect is purely geometrical and deals with the packing characteristics of atoms in a solid. These packing characteristics and the defects from perfection which occur govern to a great extent the mechanical properties of the solid. They also govern the possible types of alloying of several elements. In addition, the interaction of defects and electrons are responsible for many of the characteristics of semiconductors and luminescent solids. The second fundamental aspect of the physics of the solid state concerns the allowed energies of electrons in solids. An understanding of this aspect requires a knowledge of quantum mechanics. The book then falls into two parts. Chapters 1 to 7 are concerned with the consequences of the periodic nature of atomic packing in solids. Chapters 8 to 10 introduce the quantum principles, and Chapters 11 to 17 introduce the consequences of these principles when applied to electrons in solids.

We have made no attempt to avoid a certain amount of repetition in the chapters introducing wave mechanics, since it is here that the imagination of the student will be most severely taxed. In the chapters that follow, we introduce a number of solid state devices in current use and discuss these in terms of simple physical models that depend on the energy band structure. We have, of course, omitted from our discussion a number of types of engineering solids. For instance, we have made no reference to ceramics, organic solids, agglomerated solids, and a number of others that are undoubtedly of technical importance. We have also omitted descriptions of a number of important physical phenomena. Examples of these are dipole relaxation, internal friction, corrosion, and radiation damage. Throughout we have limited our selection to the aspects of solids that are of technical importance, and for which there exists a relatively simple physical model.

A group of problems follow each of the chapters, these being for the most part exercises on the topics of the chapters. An attempt has been made to introduce into the problems some association of theory with practice. As far as possible, however, the problems have been kept elementary, in keeping with the intention that this is a second- or third-year book and will be studied in a busy curriculum.

Courses in mathematics and physics at the level given in the first and second years of most engineering schools should suffice as introductory material to most of this work.

In a book of this nature, which is not original, we owe a great deal to the books already published. In particular we would like to record our special indebtedness to the books by Professors Barrett, Sproull, Kittel, and Dekker.

T. S. Hutchison
D. C. Baird

*Kingston, Ontario, Canada*
*February 1963*

# Contents

## Chapter 5    Elastic and Plastic Properties of Solids    116

*The Physics of*
# Engineering Solids

# 1

# *The Structure of Crystalline Solids*

## 1.1 The Solid State

Attractive short-range forces exist between gas atoms or molecules. There-fore when the atoms or molecules of a gas are brought close together by limiting the available volume, the attractive forces lower the pressure below the value expected by perfect gas behavior. Also, at sufficiently low tempera-tures, when the thermal motion of the atoms or molecules is weak, the interatomic or intermolecular forces cause the atoms or molecules to con-dense. The gaseous and condensed states are represented in Fig. 1.1 by the well-known pressure-volume curves for an actual gas.

In the figure, at temperature $T_3$ the gaseous state is maintained at all pressures. If, however, we consider compression of the vapor along the $T_1$ curve, then at the point $C$ the atoms or molecules come into the attractive range of one another. The *attractive* forces maintain the pressure at a constant value as the volume is being reduced. Full condensation is revealed at point $B$ with the atoms now "in contact." At this volume powerful

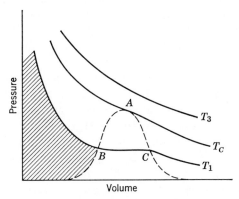

**Fig. 1.1**  The compression of an actual gas at temperatures $T_1 < T_c < T_3$.

shorter-range *repulsive* forces between the atoms produce strong resistance to further compression and the pressure rises steeply.

For the *critical* temperature $T_c$ the horizontal portion is reduced to a single point *A*, the *critical* point. Points along *BA* represent a condensed state of matter, and points along *CA* represent a vapor state. There is no spatial or regular structure just to the right of *A* along *AC*. Thus considerations of continuity around *A* preclude the possibility of *AB* representing a state of long-range order. The condensed state along *AB* is that of a liquid. For a temperature of $T_1$, points representing the solid state lie only within the shaded portion.

There are thus two condensed states of matter, the solid and liquid states. In the liquid state the spatial order is almost nonexistent, whereas in the solid state of most materials the regularity of atomic pattern or spatial order extends over distances hundreds or thousands of times the diameter of the atoms. Such solids are *crystalline*. Most of the physical properties of crystals owe their existence to this long-range order. However, there are a few properties which do not depend on long-range order and here the similarities of the two condensed states are apparent. The specific volume of a solid metal just below its melting point, for example, is only five per cent different from the specific volume of the liquid metal above the melting point. The enormous difference in regularity of atomic arrangement between a liquid and a solid must therefore be brought about by the vacating of comparatively few crystalline atomic sites.

## 1.2   Energies of Interaction Between Atoms

The attractive and repulsive forces between atoms are dependent on the distance between the atoms, since the attractive force is longer-range than the repulsive. If the attraction is represented by a positive force and repulsion by a negative, then Fig. 1.2*a* shows the dependence on the distance between the atoms. The actual force between the atoms is the sum of these two forces.

The energy of interaction between the atoms is given by $F\,dx$, where $F$ is the total force which closes the distance between the atoms by an increment $dx$. It is conventional to make the energy zero at infinite separation of the atoms. The work done by the atoms in moving together is then subtracted from this zero energy. A negative value of energy of interaction will therefore represent an attractive or binding force between the atoms. The energy of interaction is illustrated in Fig. 1.2*b*. The energy minimum $E$ is the energy required to dissociate the atoms of the solid into the separated or gaseous state. This binding energy will therefore be approximately equal to the latent heat of vaporization. Table 1.1 gives a few values of binding energy. The

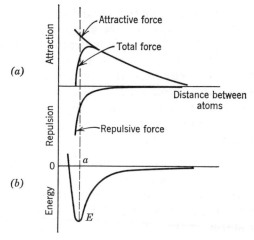

**Fig. 1.2** Forces and energies between atoms as functions of separation of the atoms. *E* is the energy of interaction at the equilibrium separation.

separation *a* of the atoms in the solid will be the distance at which the energy is a minimum.


## 1.3   The Origin of the Binding Energy

Qualitatively, the protons and neutrons of the atom are clustered together in a dense nucleus of dimension $\simeq 10^{-15}$ m and the electrons surround the core in a cloud which extends out to a distance of the order of $10^{-10}$ m. The

**Table 1.1**  Approximate Binding Energies of Solids (in Electron Volts per Atom)

| Bond | | | |
|---|---|---|---|
| Metallic | Na | Cu | Fe |
| | 1.1 | 3.5 | 4.3 |
| Covalent | C (graphite or diamond) | Ge | Si |
| | 7.4 | 3.9 | 4.6 |
| | LiF | NaCl | KBr |
| Ionic | 10.8 | 7.9 | 6.9 |
| | He | Ne | A |
| van der Waal's | 0.002 | 0.02 | 0.08 |

electrons, which are in constant motion around the nucleus, are distributed with a high density near the nucleus, the density falling off with distance.

The binding energy of solids is entirely dependent on the distribution of positive charge over the inner ion core and of negative charge over the space occupied by the outer electrons. It is primarily the *electrostatic Coulomb interaction between positive and negative regions which accounts for the cohesion of solids*. A study of the binding energies of solids is thus fundamentally concerned with the distribution of charge. The conditions which modify the distribution are as follows.

1. The outer electrons repel one another because of their like charges.
2. The positive ions repel one another.
3. The outer electrons are attracted to the positive ions.
4. Localization of the outer electrons is limited because of an associated increase in their kinetic energy.

Condition (4) is a quantum condition and will be discussed in the chapter on wave mechanics. By the rules of wave mechanics, electrons may have only "allowed values" of energy. Also, by the Pauli Exclusion Principle there is room for only two electrons in a similar allowed energy or quantum state while within the same field of force. These four conditions lead to four broad classes of bond between the atoms. The bonds differ in strength and directional characteristic.

## *Classification of Atomic Bond*

Atoms of different elements have different spatial distributions of outer electrons. These atoms are accommodated in a solid so that the energy, subject to the quantum rules just given, is a minimum. We will now comment briefly on the nature of the bonds which arise as a consequence of these considerations.

### 1.4   van der Waal's or Molecular Bond

In the inert gas atoms and in saturated molecules like $CH_4$ (where all four bonds of carbon are occupied by hydrogen atoms) the electrons participate in their own nuclear fields. These atoms are chemically inactive since chemical activity involves interactions between the outer electrons of one atom and the electron cloud of another. The electrons are, however, in motion around the nucleus and the electrostatic field fluctuates with the movement of the electrons. When two atoms approach one another, the electronic motions are correlated so that electrical charge surges from one

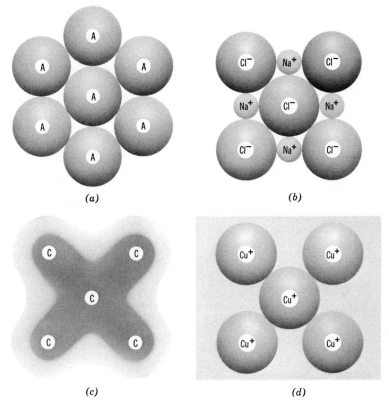

**Fig. 1.3** Pictorial representation of electron distribution in (*a*) van der Waal's bond, (*b*) ionic bond, (*c*) covalent bond, (*d*) metallic bond.

atom toward regions of low charge in the other. Thus although the average electric dipole (made up of a separated +ve and −ve charge) is zero, the instantaneous dipole is not zero and this results in an attraction between the atoms. The force is called a *van der Waal force*. It is weak, and solids which are bonded only by such forces have low melting and boiling points. Table 1.1 gives the order of magnitude of each class of bond that we will discuss and Fig. 1.3 gives a pictorial representation of the electron distribution.

## 1.5 Ionic Bond

In atoms which do not have electron clouds that are strongly associated with their own nuclear fields there is a strong tendency to lose or distort outer portions of the electron cloud. Sodium, for example, has a single outer electron which has a spatial distribution more remote from the nucleus than the other electrons. Chlorine, on the other hand, has an electron distribution in which one other electron can be accommodated in the outer shell of the distribution. If this occurs, the outer shell is filled and the electron distribution then resembles, for the chlorine ion, one of the inert gas atoms (argon). When, therefore, a sodium atom meets a chlorine atom, an electron is transferred. The positive and negative ions then attract electrostatically and are bound together by an *ionic bond*.

The energy of the bond will be given approximately by the work done by the force of attraction in bringing the chlorine and sodium ions to their equilibrium distance apart. We can estimate the bond strength. The force between charges of $+e$ and $-e$ when a distance $r$ apart is given by Coulomb's law:

$$F = \frac{1}{4\pi\epsilon_0} \frac{e^2}{r^2} \tag{1.1}$$

The potential energy $V$, which is $\int F \, dr$, is then

$$V = \frac{1}{4\pi\epsilon_0} \frac{e^2}{r} \quad \text{joules}$$

$$= \frac{1}{4\pi\epsilon_0} \frac{e}{r} \quad \text{eV} \tag{1.2}$$

Substituting the values $\epsilon = 1.6 \times 10^{-19}$ coulomb and $r = 2.81 \times 10^{-10}$ m for NaCl gives a binding energy of approximately 5 eV. Comparison with the values of Table 1.1 leads to the conclusion that binding energies in ionic crystals are largely electrostatic.

Equation 1.2 shows that if each ion donates or accepts only one electron (i.e., has a valency of one), then the binding energy is less if the ions are further apart. This is shown in Table 1.2 for the two ionic crystals NaCl and NaI. It also follows that ionic bonding between divalent ions will be greater than between univalent ions at the same distance apart. Comparison between BaO and NaCl shows that this is so.

**Table 1.2   Types of Ionic Bond**

| Crystal | Separation of Ions | Valency | Melting Point |
|---------|-------------------|---------|---------------|
| NaCl | $2.8 \times 10^{-10}$ m | 1 | 1074°K |
| NaI | $3.2 \times 10^{-10}$ m | 1 | 933 |
| BaO | $2.8 \times 10^{-10}$ m | 2 | 2206 |
| SiC | | 4 | 3773 |

In trivalent and tetravalent ionic binding the electric field of one ion can distort the field of the other. Then an excess of positive charge is built up in one ion opposite an excess of negative charge in the other; this is called *polarization*. More electrons are involved in the binding and the polarized bond is stronger. The polarized bond will obviously be more directional in nature than a nonpolarized ionic bond for a univalent ion. SiC is an example of a polarized ionic bond in which the electron sharing between the two ions is almost complete enough to designate it *covalent* (Section 1.6).

## 1.6  Covalent Bond

The characteristic feature of the covalent bond is that electrons are shared between atoms rather than transferred from one to another. Simple covalent bonds occur between atoms in the molecules $H_2$, $CH_4$, and $CCl_4$. Let us consider the distortion of the electron cloud when two hydrogen atoms approach to form a molecule. In Fig. 1.4a, b, and c a proton is successively

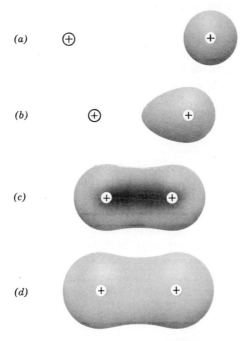

*(a)*

*(b)*

*(c)*

*(d)*

**Fig. 1.4**  The proton on the left is successively moved toward a hydrogen atom. In (*b*) and (*c*) the electron cloud is pulled toward the left. In (*d*) the presence of a second electron corresponds to the junction of two hydrogen atoms. The electrons now spend less time between the nuclei because of quantum energy restrictions.

moved closer to a hydrogen atom. Polarization of the electron field is shown in *b* and *c*, and in *c* the electron energy is lowered by moving from its equilibrium distance from *B* to a distance which is closer to *A*. The *covalent bond* is the attraction of the protons to the electron they share. If the other electron is now added, then the Exclusion Principle makes it energetically less favorable for both electrons to spend most of their time between the protons, and the interatomic distance increases to the value found in the hydrogen molecule.

A quantum state of two atoms has room for two electrons according to the Exclusion Principle. The covalent bond is therefore primarily an electron-pair bond and is generally highly directional in nature. Only a certain number of electrons can be accommodated between pairs of atoms forming a covalent bond. Commonly, an atom with $n$ electrons in an outer shell can bond with $8n$ neighboring atoms in order to share electrons in covalent bonds. The halogen elements with $n = 7$ will therefore form saturated molecules of two atoms. When $n = 6$, a chain structure, as in selenium, is common. If $n = 5$, there exists an ability to bond with three atoms, and this is often done by forming a layer structure, as in arsenic. Graphite has $n = 4$ and also forms a layer structure, leaving the fourth electron partially free and providing electrical conductivity.

The covalent bond is that encountered in organic chemistry, in hard metallic carbides and in diamond, germanium, and silicon. In the last three cases each atom is held to four neighboring atoms by strongly directional covalent bonds.

### 1.7   Metallic Bond

In metals, positively charged ion cores are held together by their attraction to the free electrons which form a cloud between them. The free electrons are not localized on an atomic scale and impart high electrical and thermal conductivity to the metal. There are more allowed quantum states than there are electrons, and in many ways the metallic bond is like an unsaturated covalent bond. As a consequence the metallic bond is much less directional than the covalent bond, and thus the main reason for a particular structure becomes packing efficiency. Many metals are therefore close-packed. The lack of quantum restriction of the electrons also removes any restriction on the kind of neighbor a metallic atom can have. Thus metals have the characteristic of forming alloys.

We have now introduced the main classes of interatomic bond. These, as we have seen, vary in strength and in directionality. The actual structure found for a particular material is a consequence of the type of bond. Before describing the structure of certain materials of importance in solid state engineering we will give an elementary discussion of the nomenclature of crystal structure.

## Nomenclature of Crystal Structure

In order to describe atomic positions in a crystal it is first necessary to have a set of reference points. The reference points must be arranged in an infinitely repeated identical pattern in three dimensions. These reference points form a *space lattice*. The crystal structure is then assembled by placing atoms or groups identically around the points of the space lattice.

## 1.8 Space Lattices: Unit Cell

Suppose we have an arrangement of atoms in two dimensions, as depicted by the circles in Fig. 1.5a. First choose a point *P* and then every other point which has the same environment as *P*. These points are good atomic reference positions and repeat indefinitely in the same pattern. They form a space lattice. In three-dimensional space it is obvious that the lattice points are

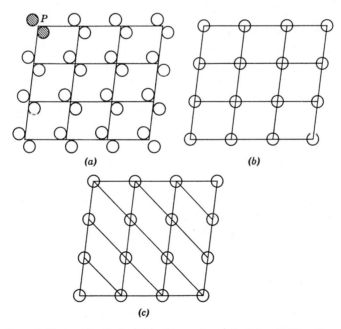

**Fig. 1.5** Space lattices. Identical unit cells are shown in (*a*) and (*b*) with a different choice in (*c*).

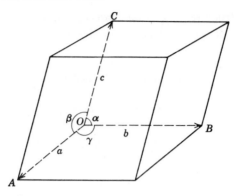

**Fig. 1.6**   Unit cell of the most general type.

the intersections of three intersecting families of parallel planes. The planes divide space up into small identical parallelepipeds. Each elementary parallelepiped is called a *unit cell*.

The points of the space lattice need not be atomic sites, although in some crystals, particularly metals where a single atom is often the unit of pattern, it is obviously convenient to make the points of the space lattice and the atomic sites coincide. Figure 1.5 shows that the space lattice of *a* is also a good choice to describe the atomic pattern of *b*, in which the atom is the unit of pattern. It is obvious that many space lattices and unit cells can be chosen as reference networks for a particular atomic arrangement. For example, in Fig. 1.5*c*, which has an identical atomic arrangement to *b*, a different choice of unit cell has been made. It should be noted that there is in *a*, *b*, and *c* a one-to-one correspondence between lattice points, that is, points where the space lattice lines cross, and unit cells. Unit cells with this property are called *primitive*.

Let us now illustrate in Fig. 1.6 a unit cell of the most general type. The edges *OA*, *OB*, and *OC* are called the fundamental translation vectors *a*, *b*, and *c*, respectively, while the angles $\widehat{BOC}$, $\widehat{AOC}$, and $\widehat{AOB}$ are $\alpha$, $\beta$, and $\gamma$, respectively. For any point in the lattice having the coordinates *xyz* measured parallel to the unit vectors, there will be a similar point at $x + pa$, $y + qb$, $z + rc$, where $p$, $q$, and $r$ are whole numbers.

### 1.9   Bravais Lattice

Space lattices are classified according to their symmetry. In 1848 Bravais showed that fourteen classes of lattice were sufficient in three dimensions. We will not justify this finding but merely show the lattices in Fig. 1.7. A unit

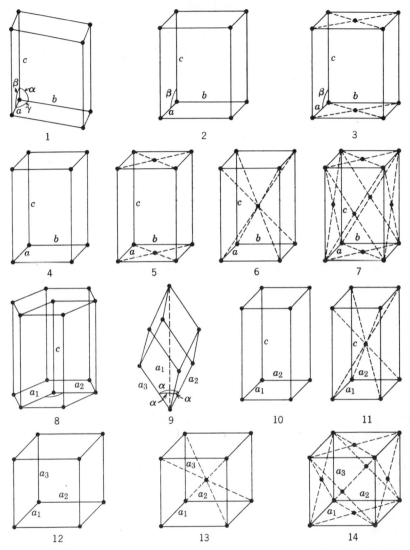

**Fig. 1.7** Possible space lattices of the seven crystal systems. 1. Triclinic, simple. 2. Monoclinic, simple. 3. Monoclinic, base-centered. 4. Orthorhombic, simple. 5. Orthorhombic, base-centered. 6. Orthorhombic, body-centered. 7. Orthorhombic, face-centered. 8. Hexagonal. 9. Rhombohedral. 10. Tetragonal, simple. 11. Tetragonal, body-centered. 12. Cubic, simple. 13. Cubic, body-centered. 14. Cubic, face-centered.

## Table 1.3

| System | Axes and Interaxial Angles | Examples |
|---|---|---|
| Triclinic | Three axes not at right angles, of any lengths<br>$a \neq b \neq c*$ $\qquad$ $\alpha \neq \beta \neq \gamma \neq 90°$ | $K_2CrO_7$ |
| Monoclinic | Three axes, one pair not at right angles, of any lengths<br>$a \neq b \neq c$ $\qquad$ $\alpha = \gamma = 90° \neq \beta$ | $CaSO_4 \cdot 2H_2O$<br>(gypsum) |
| Orthorhombic<br>(rhombic) | Three axes at right angles; all unequal<br>$\alpha \neq b \neq c$ $\qquad$ $\alpha = \beta = \gamma = 90°$ | $\alpha$-S<br>Ga<br>$Fe_3C$<br>(cementite) |
| Tetragonal | Three axes at right angles; two equal<br>$a = b \neq c$ $\qquad$ $\alpha = \beta = \gamma = 90°$ | $\beta$-Sn (white)<br>$TiO_2$ |
| Cubic | Three axes at right angles; all equal<br>$a = b = c$ $\qquad$ $\alpha = \beta = \gamma = 90°$ | Cu, Ag, Au<br>Fe<br>NaCl |
| Hexagonal | Three axes coplanar at 120°, equal<br>Fourth axis at right angles to these<br>$a_1 = a_2 = a_2 \neq c$ $\quad$ $\alpha = \beta = 90°,$ $\quad \gamma = 120°$ | Zn, Cd<br>NiAs |
| Rhombohedral<br>(trigonal) | Three axes equally inclined, not at right angles;<br>all equal<br>$a = b = c$ $\qquad$ $\alpha = \beta = \gamma \neq 90°$ | As, Sb, Bi<br>Calcite |

* In this table $\neq$ means "not necessarily equal to, and generally different form,"

cell of each lattice is shown and it can be seen that not all of the unit cells are primitive. There are two kinds of lattice named monoclinic, three kinds of orthorhombic space lattice, only one kind of hexagonal, and so on. There are, in fact, seven different classifications of lattice known as *crystal systems.* Table 1.3 gives the seven systems with the relationship between the fundamental translation vectors and the angles between the axes.

All crystal structures can be referred to these fourteen Bravais lattices. The simplest crystals are obtained by placing single atoms at lattice points. Atoms or groups may also, of course, be placed symmetrically with respect to each of the points.

## 1.10   Nomenclature of Crystal Directions

It is necessary in crystallography to have a system of notation for directions in a crystal. The standard notation will now be described. Suppose in

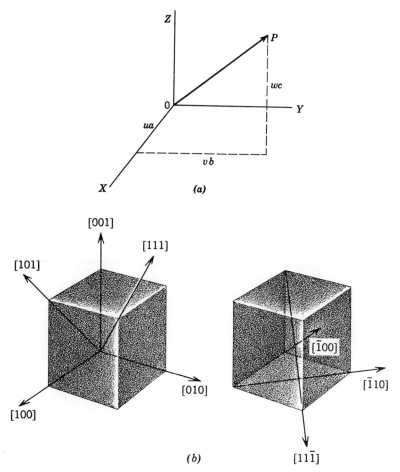

**Fig. 1.8** Notation for directions in crystals. (*a*) *OP* is the direction *uvw* if *u*, *v*, and *w* are the smallest integers. (*b*) Some important directions in crystals.

Fig. 1.8 that we wish to indicate the direction *OP*. The translation from *O* to *P* can be accomplished by going along the *X*-axis a distance *u* times the unit distance *a*, then in the *Y* direction a distance *v* times the unit distance *b*, then in the *Z* direction a distance *w* times the unit distance *c*. If *u*, *v*, and *w* are the smallest integers that will accomplish the desired translation, the direction *OP* is written [*uvw*] with the square brackets shown being widely adopted. Figure 1.8 gives the notation for some important directions and also indicates the method of dealing with negative directions. A full set of equivalent directions is indicated by carets: ⟨*uvw*⟩.

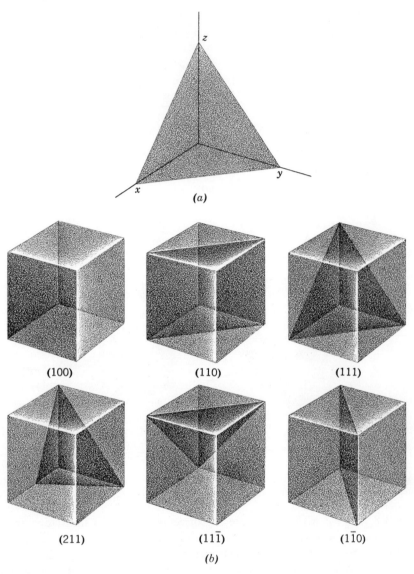

**Fig. 1.9**  Miller index nomenclature for crystal planes.  In (b) some important planes are indexed.

## 1.11   Nomenclature of Crystal Planes:  Miller Indices

It is also necessary to have a system of notation for crystallographic planes. The use of *Miller indices* for this purpose is universal.  Suppose that in Fig. 1.9 we wish to refer to the shaded plane.  This plane cuts the three crystallographic axes in the three intercept lengths $x$, $y$, and $z$.  First express the intercepts as fractions $x/a$, $y/b$, and $z/c$ of the unit distances $a$, $b$, $c$ along the respective axes.  Next take the reciprocals of the fractions just found.  After this has been done and the reciprocals reduced to the smallest integers $h$, $k$, $l$, having the same ratios, then $(hkl)$ are the Miller indices of the plane. They are always shown in parenthesis.  Figure 1.9 shows some important planes and also indicates how to deal with planes that cut an axis on the negative side of the origin.  Braces $\{hkl\}$ signify all the planes that are equivalent in a crystal, such as the cube faces of a cubic crystal: that is, $\{100\} \equiv (100) + (010) + (001) + (\bar{1}00) + (0\bar{1}0) + (00\bar{1})$.

### Simple Crystal Structures

We will now illustrate some of the simplest crystal structures found in technologically important solids.  For each structure a *conventional* unit cell of the space lattice is drawn with the *primitive* unit cell outlined.  The choice of conventional unit cell is one of convenience.  For instance, when we come to study the face-centered cubic structure, it will be seen that the conventional cell has cube axes, whereas the primitive cell does not.  It should be noted that, since there is a one-to-one correspondence between primitive unit cells and space lattice points, then if each unit assembly of atoms at each lattice point is a single atom, there must be just one atom per unit cell.  The conventional unit cells, however, often contain more than one atom.

## 1.12   Cesium Chloride Structure

The CsCl structure is shown in Fig. 1.10.  The Bravais space lattice is simple cubic with a molecule, consisting of one Cs atom and one Cl atom, per unit cell.  Each kind of atom has eight nearest neighbors.  The coordination number is said to be eight.  This is an open structure so that it is not favored on grounds of packing efficiency.

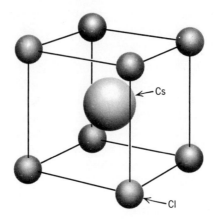

**Fig. 1.10** The cesium chloride structure: the unit cell with one molecule. Examples: TlBr, TlI, $NH_4Cl$, CuZn ($\beta$ brass), AlNi.

## 1.13 Body-Centered Cubic Structure

The simplest crystal structure found among the elements is called body-centered cubic. In Fig. 1.11 the *conventional* unit cell is shown and the three axes of the *primitive* unit cell are marked by dashed lines. Completion of the dashed line cube gives the primitive unit cell, which has one atom. The conventional unit cell, on the other hand, contains two atoms. This can readily be seen since the eight corner atoms are each shared by eight neighboring cells, whereas the central atom is uniquely associated with the cell drawn. The coordinates of the atoms in the conventional cell are 000 and

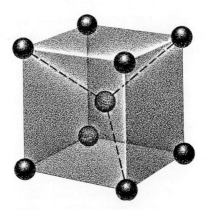

**Fig. 1.11** Conventional unit cell of body-centered cubic structure. Dotted lines show edges of primitive cell. Examples: Fe($\alpha$), Li, Na, K, Rb, Cs.

$\frac{1}{2} \frac{1}{2} \frac{1}{2}$. The coordination number is eight. Considerations of directionality of bond prevent the structure from being a close-packed nature.

## 1.14 Face-Centered Cubic

Figure 1.12 shows the unit cell of the face-centered cubic structure. The coordinates of the atoms are 000 and 0 $\frac{1}{2}$ $\frac{1}{2}$. The eight corner atoms of the conventional unit cell are each shared by the eight neighboring unit cells, while the six atoms at the middle of the cube faces are each shared by two unit cells. Thus there are one plus three, that is, four atoms per conventional unit cell. This structure can be considered to be constructed in the following way. Suppose atoms are closely packed in a single first layer, their positions being marked ○ in Fig. 1.13. A second layer can then be laid down on top of the first layer in two ways. Once one of the hollows in the first layer marked + has been chosen for the first of the second layer atoms, then all other hollows marked + must be used. There is, of course, another set of hollows in the first layer which can be utilized instead of the + hollows. The size of the atom, however, precludes the second layer atoms from going into a mixture of the two sets of hollows. The two-layered structures with the second layer atoms in either position are identical. When we look for possible positions for the atoms of the third layer, two nonidentical choices are available. First, we may select hollows in the second layer, marked □, which are directly above the first-layer atoms. This gives rise to a crystal structure which is called *hexagonal close-packed* and which will be considered

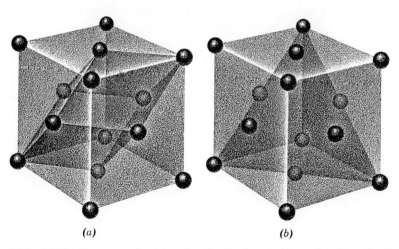

*(a)*           *(b)*

**Fig. 1.12** (*a*) The face-centered cubic unit cell with the primitive cell inside. (*b*) Close-packed plane shown. Examples: Ag, Al, Au, Cu, Co($\beta$), Fe($\gamma$), Ir, Ni($\beta$), Pb, Pt, Sr, Th.

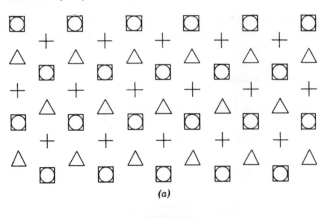

(a)

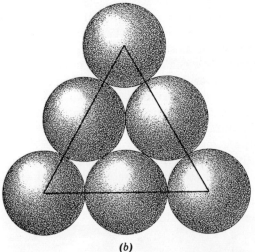

(b)

**Fig. 1.13**   Illustration of close packing of atoms. (*a*) ○ —First-layer atoms. + —Second-layer atoms, first choice. □ —Third-layer atoms in hexagonal close-packed structure. △ —Third-layer atoms in face-centered cubic structure. (*b*) Close-packed octahedral plane of Fig. 1.10.

later. Second, we may envisage the third-layer atoms in the positions marked △. This choice forms the *face-centered cubic structure*. The packing in the face-centered cubic structure is called *ABCABC*, whereas in the hexagonal close-packed structure the packing is *ABABAB*.

The face-centered cubic structure is common in metals where there is little or no directionality in the atomic bond. Considerations of packing efficiency dictate the structure. The coordination number is twelve in both hcp and fcc crystal structures.

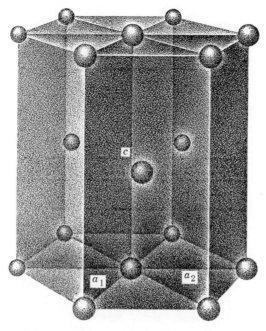

**Fig. 1.14**  Hexagonal close-packed unit cell.  The darker shading shows the primitive cell within the conventional cell.  Examples:  Be, Cd, Mg, Nd, P, Re, Ru, Ti, Zn.

## 1.15  Hexagonal Close-Packed Structure

This structure is shown in Fig. 1.14.  As has been described, it consists of close-packed layers of atoms placed one above the other with the atoms of each layer nestling in the hollows of the lower layer.  The conventional cell contains six atoms.  The atomic sites do not, however, form a space lattice since they do not transform into one another by the simple symmetry operation of replacing a vector $r$ from an origin by $-r$.  A portion of the primitive cell, which is simple hexagonal and contains two atoms per lattice point, is shown in Fig. 1.12.  Ideally the coordination number is twelve and the axial ratio $c/a_1 = 1.633$.  In metals there is often distortion and the ratio differs slightly from this value.

## 1.16  Diamond Cubic Structure

The atoms of certain elements are held together in the solid by strongly covalent bonds at tetrahedral angles of $109\frac{1}{2}°$.  Each atom has four nearest

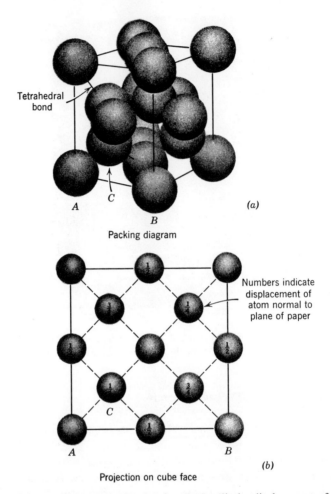

Tetrahedral bond

A

C

B

(a)

Packing diagram

Numbers indicate
displacement of
atom normal to
plane of paper

C

A                    B

(b)

Projection on cube face

**Fig. 1.15** Diamond cubic conventional unit cell. In (b) the displacement of the atoms normal to the plane of the paper is given in fractions of the unit cell edge. Examples: Si, Ge, Sn (gray). (After Wykoff)

neighbors and twelve next nearest neighbors, which is a consequence of each atom sharing one of its outer electrons with each of four neighbors. The typical structure so formed is that of diamond, shown in Fig. 1.15a and b. The space lattice is face-centered cubic with pairs of atoms at 000 and $\frac{1}{4}\frac{1}{4}\frac{1}{4}$ forming a pattern unit. As can be seen from the figure, this is not a close-packed structure, the directional nature of the covalent bonds overweighing considerations of packing economy.

## 1.17 Sodium Chloride Structure

The sodium chloride structure shown in Fig. 1.16 is typical of ionic bonding. The Bravais lattice is face-centered cubic with the unit of atomic pattern consisting of one sodium and one chlorine ion separated by one-half the body diagonal of the cube. The ions are in the positions

$$\text{Na:} \quad 000, \quad \tfrac{1}{2}\tfrac{1}{2}0, \quad \tfrac{1}{2}0\tfrac{1}{2}, \quad 0\tfrac{1}{2}\tfrac{1}{2}$$
$$\text{Cl:} \quad \tfrac{1}{2}\tfrac{1}{2}\tfrac{1}{2}, \quad 00\tfrac{1}{2}, \quad 0\tfrac{1}{2}0, \quad \tfrac{1}{2}00$$

Since each ion has six nearest neighbors of the opposite kind, the coordination number is six.

## 1.18 Zinc-Blende Structure

We have already seen that the diamond cubic structure is a consequence of the carbon valency of four. We may expect to find the same structure in compounds where one atom has more than four electrons and the other the same number less than four, so that a total of four valency electrons to each atom is maintained. If the compound is of the form AX, this structure can

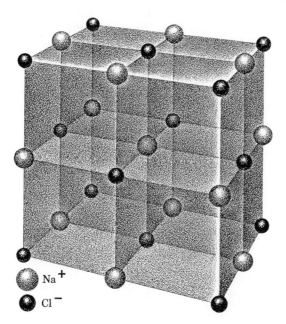

Na$^+$

Cl$^-$

**Fig. 1.16** Sodium chloride unit cell. Examples: NaCl, KCl, BaO, MgO, NiO, MnO, PbS, PbTe.

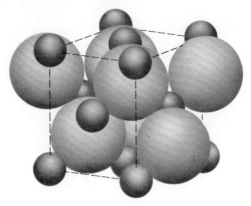

**Fig. 1.17**   The zinc-blende structure. Examples: αZnS, αCdS, βAgI, SiC. (After Azaroff)

be produced in two ways. The first is the cubic zinc-blende structure shown in Fig. 1.17, with four zinc and four sulfur atoms per conventional unit cell.

## 1.19   Wurtzite Structure

The second method by which a structure is formed where each atom of one kind, in a compound AX, is surrounded by four of another is shown in Fig. 1.18. This is the hexagonal βZnS or wurtzite structure, which differs only from the zinc-blende structure in the stacking sequence of the sulfur layers.

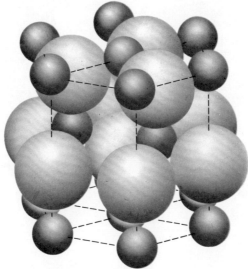

**Fig. 1.18**   The wurtzite structure. Examples: βZnS, βCdS, MgTe, CdSe. (After Azaroff)

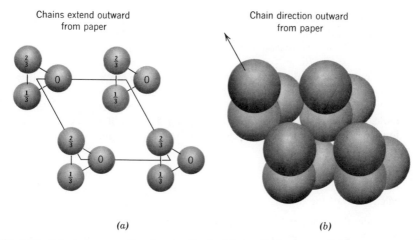

Chains extend outward
from paper

Chain direction outward
from paper

*(a)*                    *(b)*

**Fig. 1.19**  Selenium conventional unit cell.  In (*a*) the displacement of the atoms normal to the plane of the paper is given in fractions of the appropriate unit cell parameter. (After Wykoff)

## 1.20  Selenium Structure

The important materials selenium and tellurium have crystal structures that can also be described as hexagonal.  Here the covalent bonds between neighboring atoms hold the atoms in spirals around the long hexagonal axes. The crystal structure is shown in Fig. 1.19.

## References

Phillips, F. C., *An Introduction to Crystallography*, 3rd ed., John Wiley and Sons, New York, 1963.
Wyckoff, R. W. G., *Crystal Structures*, 2nd ed., Interscience, New York, 1963.
   Many texts on X-ray diffraction give material on crystal structures.

## Exercises

1. By reference to Tables 3.1 and 10.2, specify the electron distributions which characterize each of the following classes of elements:
   (*a*) The alkali metals.
   (*b*) The good conductors Cu, Ag, and Au.
   (*c*) The transition elements with:
$$Z = 21 \text{ through } 28$$
$$39 \text{ through } 46$$
$$57 \text{ through } 78$$
$$89 \text{ on}$$

2. The Coulomb electrostatic energy is given by $\alpha(14.40/R)$ in eV per A where $\alpha$, the Madelung constant, takes into account all nearest neighbors in the lattice. Show that this is reasonable. The value of $\alpha$ for the sodium chloride structure = 1.7476.

   Calculate the binding energy of NaI for which the nearest neighbor distance is 3.24 A. Express the energy in eV per molecule and also in kilocalories per mole. The experimental value of the binding energy is 162.3 kilocalories per mole. Calculate the repulsion energy (Section 1.3, condition 4) which accounts for the difference between the calculated and experimental values of binding energy.

3. For the sodium chloride structure list the first three nearest neighbor distances with the corresponding numbers of nearest neighbors. Show how to make a calculation of the total Coulomb energy for the complete structure.

4. The line of intersection of two planes is given by the cross-product of the two normals to the planes. For a cubic crystal, show that the line of intersection of the planes $(h_1k_1l_1)$ and $(h_2k_2l_2)$ is given by the following scheme:

$$
\begin{array}{ccccccc}
h_1 & k_1 & l_1 & h_1 & k_1 & l_1 \\
& \times & \times & \times & \\
h_2 & k_2 & l_2 & h_2 & k_2 & l_2
\end{array}
$$

   What are the lines of intersection of the following pairs of planes in copper:

   (a) (111) and (101)
   (b) (200) and (321)
   (c) (1$\bar{1}$0) and (222)

5. Calculate the interatomic distances in the [110], [111], and [210] directions in $\alpha$Fe and Cu.

6. Show that the ratio volume of atoms : volume available is given for the various structures by:

   (a) Simple cubic            $\dfrac{\pi}{6}$ (52%)

   (b) Body-centered cubic     $\dfrac{\pi 3^{1/2}}{8}$ (68%)

   (c) Face-centered cubic     $\dfrac{\pi 2^{1/2}}{6}$ (74%)

   (d) Hexagonal close-packed  $\dfrac{\pi 2^{1/2}}{6}$ (74%)

   (e) Diamond cubic           $\dfrac{\pi 3^{1/2}}{16}$ (34%)

7. From the following table of atomic weights and lattice parameters, calculate the densities of the elements in solid form.  Compare with measured values.

αFe:  Atomic weight = 55.85;  $a$ = 2.861 A.
Cu:  atomic weight = 63.57;  $a$ = 3.708 A.
Zn:  atomic weight = 65.38;  $a$ = 2.659 A:  $c$ = 4.934 A.
Diamond:  atomic weight (carbon) = 12.01;  $a$ = 3.560 A.

8. Show that in an ideal hexagonal close-packed structure that

$$\frac{c}{a} = \frac{8\frac{1}{2}}{3\frac{1}{2}} = 1.633$$

Using the data of Exercise 7, compare with the measured ratio in zinc.

9. Give the coordinates of the principal voids in the body-centered cubic structure and compute the radii of the interstitial atoms which can fit into these voids.

10. Calculate the density of packing, in atoms per square meter, for the following planes:

(a) (110) plane in αFe.
(b) (111) plane in Cu.
    (110) plane in Cu.
(c) (001) plane in Zn.

# 2

# *X-Ray, Electron, and Neutron Diffraction in Crystals*

The external symmetry shown by many crystals, particularly those naturally grown, led investigators many centuries ago to postulate that the fundamental atoms of which the crystals were composed must be arranged in a characteristic pattern. The direct exploration of the atomic arrangement, however, had to await the discovery of waves which would interact with atoms and have wavelengths comparable to the atomic spacing in crystals. Such waves, called X-rays and of wavelength of the order of 1 A ($10^{-10}$ m), were first used in this connection about 1912 in the pioneer X-ray diffraction experiments of von Laue and W. H. and W. L. Bragg.

Some fifteen years later the first experiments on diffraction of electrons by crystals were carried out. Electrons penetrate crystals to only small depths, and as a consequence the technique of electron diffraction has had its greatest use in the examination of surfaces and thin films.

With the availability of sources of neutrons from the chain-reacting atomic pile, the investigation of crystals by neutron diffraction has become possible. The penetration depth is great for neutrons, and, moreover, differences between the neutron and X-ray scattering powers of atoms have led to the growth of the technique of neutron diffraction as a useful supplement to X-ray diffraction.

This chapter will contain a brief outline of some of the properties of X-rays, electrons, and neutrons which are of significance in diffraction, followed by a description of the diffraction techniques currently used in the study of solids.

## 2.1 Emission of X-Rays

X-rays are electromagnetic radiation with wavelengths of the order of 1 A. If a beam of electrons, emitted usually from a hot filament, are accelerated on to a positive metallic electrode by a high voltage, the loss of energy occurs in two important ways: (*a*) by emission of *white* X-radiation, and (*b*) if the voltage is sufficiently high, by the emission of X-radiation *characteristic* of the target material.

## White Radiation

White radiation, as the name implies, is of continuously varying wavelength from one end of the allowed spectrum to the other. The maximum energy which the electron can impart to an atom of the target is $eV$, where $e$ is the electronic charge and $V$ the accelerating voltage. If this energy is completely converted into X-radiation, the shortest wavelength which will be emitted from the target will be given by the Einstein conversion formula

$$eV = \frac{he}{\lambda} \qquad (2.1)$$

where $\lambda$ is the wavelength of the emitted X-rays, $c$ is the speed of light, and $h$ is Planck's constant. Substitution in (2.1) of numerical values from the Appendix gives

$$\lambda = \frac{12.4}{V}$$

with $\lambda$ in angstrom units (A) and $V$ in kilovolts (kV).

Figure 2.1 shows the distribution of intensity of white X-radiation as a function of wavelength for different applied accelerating voltages. As can be seen, the point of sharp cutoff on the short wavelength end of the spectrum depends on the accelerating potential. High-voltage machines give shorter possible wavelengths.

White X-radiation has its principal use in medical and industrial radiography. X-rays from the target are made to penetrate the specimen under investigation. Behind the specimen is a fluorescent screen or photographic film to record the intensity. Variations in density of the specimen give corresponding variations in density of the photographic film, enabling the operator to detect, for example, bone fractures in the medical application or porosity in castings in the metal industry.

## Characteristic Radiation

If the accelerating voltage applied to the electrons is raised above that necessary to produce white radiation, the X-radiation characteristic of the element of which the target is composed may be emitted. Such radiation depends on the electron energy levels of the target atom. A discussion of

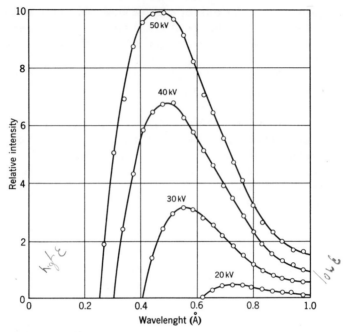

**Fig. 2.1** Relative intensity of white X-radiation as a function of wavelength for different applied accelerating voltages.

such levels in many-electron atoms is given in Section 11.2. It will be seen that these levels are sharply defined in energy. Transitions of electrons between the atomic levels results in absorption or emission of energy. Energy emitted is in the form of electromagnetic radiation, which is also sharply defined in wavelength. The characteristic wavelengths used in X-ray diffraction techniques are called the K$\alpha$ and K$\beta$. The distribution of intensity in the X-ray spectrum from a molybdenum target with an accelerating voltage of 35 kV is shown in Fig. 2.2.

## 2.2   Absorption of X-Rays

If X-radiation irradiates a specimen, absorption of energy may be brought about by the electrons of the atoms of the specimen being excited from one set of energy levels to other levels. The apparent absorption of incident X-rays increases abruptly as the critical wavelength for absorption. The dotted line in Fig. 2.2 shows the absorption of radiation by the element zirconium. The abrupt rise in absorption is called an *absorption edge*.

These considerations affect the choice of X-radiation for a particular diffraction analysis. For instance, the choice of an X-radiation whose $K\alpha$ wavelength is just under an absorption edge of the specimen irradiated would result in a good deal of absorption of the X-radiation by the specimen. The electrons of the atoms of the specimen then rearrange among the available energy levels, resulting in most cases in unwelcome re-emission from the specimen of *secondary X-radiation*. This is precisely what happens where an iron specimen is irradiated by characteristic radiation from a copper target. On the other hand, a beam of X-rays containing $K\alpha$ and $K\beta$ may be made much more monochromatic by passing the beam through a thin filter of a material whose absorption edge lies between the $K\alpha$ and $K\beta$ wavelengths. It is obvious from Fig. 2.2 that zirconium would filter out much of molybdenum $K\beta$ radiation without affecting the intensity of the

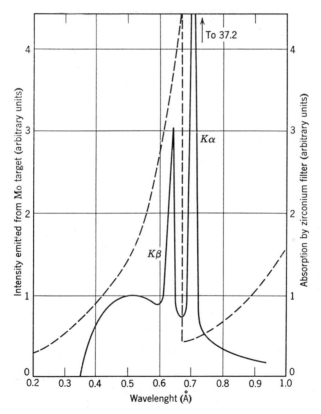

**Fig. 2.2** Full line: characteristic X-radiation from a Mo target with 35 kV applied voltage. Dotted line: absorption of X-radiation by a zirconium filter.

**Table 2.1**

| Target | Filter | Thickness in mm | Per cent $K\beta$ Absorbed |
|:------:|:------:|:---------------:|:--------------------------:|
| Mo | Zr | 0.063 | 96 |
| Cu | Ni | 0.016 | 98 |
| Co | Fe | 0.015 | 99 |
| Cr | V  | 0.015 | 99 |

K$\alpha$ to the same extent. Table 2.1 lists the characteristics of several filters for the production of monochromatic X-rays.

## 2.3   The Geometry of Diffraction

X-rays are scattered by the electrons surrounding the nucleus of an atom. The scattered waves from the atoms in a crystal lattice may combine in phase in particular directions. In these directions there will be intense diffracted X-ray beams. There are two ways of calculating diffraction directions: that due to von Laue and that due to Bragg. Both are informative and will be discussed.

### von Laue Treatment

Let us now imagine each atom of a crystal scattering, with reduced intensity, a certain amount of incident X-radiation. The atoms are arranged in a pattern. Suppose in Fig. 2.3 a row of atoms with interatomic distance $a$,

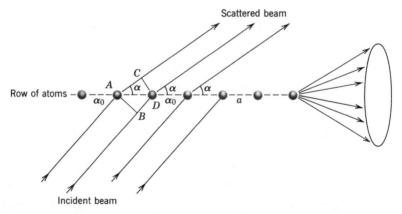

**Fig. 2.3**   Laue calculation of geometric condition for diffraction.

and $AB$ and $CD$ the positions of wave crests in the incident and scattered beams, respectively. A diffracted beam will be observed if the phase difference $AC - BD$ is a whole number of wavelengths. Then only will crest meet crest in the scattered beam.

The condition for a diffracted beam is then

$$a(\cos \alpha - \cos \alpha_0) = n_1\lambda \qquad (2.2)$$

with $n_1 = 0, 1, 2, \ldots$ .

The diffracted beam in which condition (2.2) is met forms, for a single value of $n_1$, a cone, as shown in the figure. In three dimensions for a unit cell of parameters $a$, $b$, and $c$, the conditions for diffraction will be

$$a(\cos \alpha - \cos \alpha_0) = n_1\lambda$$
$$b(\cos \beta - \cos \beta_0) = n_2\lambda$$
$$c(\cos \gamma - \cos \gamma_0) = n_3\lambda$$

We can write these conditions more neatly in vector form. Suppose $\mathbf{s}_0$ and $\mathbf{s}$ are unit vectors in the incident and diffracted beam directions, respectively. Then the first equation of (2.2) may be written

$$a_O(\mathbf{s} - \mathbf{s}_0) = n_1\lambda \qquad (2.3)$$

where $\mathbf{s}_0$ and $\mathbf{s}$ are unit vectors in the incident and scattered directions, respectively. This treatment of the geometric condition for diffraction from a periodic array of atoms was first presented by von Laue.

### The Bragg Treatment

W. L. Bragg considered the conditions for diffraction by means of a model which, although not immediately obvious, gives very simple and correct mathematical results. Bragg found that the diffracted beams can be accounted for by making the assumption that the X-rays are specularly reflected from atomic planes in the crystal. Again the condition is imposed that the phase difference between the incident and diffracted beam must be a whole number of wavelengths. The mathematical development assumes the truth of Snell's law, which states that for mirror reflection the incident and reflected beams and the normal to the reflecting plane are all coplanar, and that the angle of incidence is equal to the angle of reflection.

Suppose that in Fig. 2.4 the horizontal parallel lines $AA$ and $BB$ represent planes of atoms which partly reflect incident X-radiation. The path difference for rays $LMN$ and $L_1M_2N_2$, reflected from adjacent planes, is the length $PM_2Q$, which is equal to $2d \sin \theta$. The reflected rays from adjacent planes will be in phase, and their amplitudes will reinforce if this path difference is

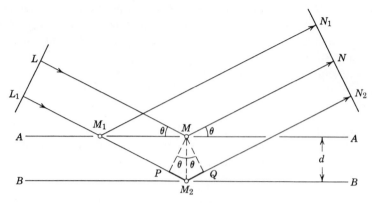

**Fig. 2.4**  Geometry of X-ray reflection from atomic planes.

equal to an integral number of wavelengths. Thus the Bragg condition for diffraction is

$$n\lambda = 2d \sin \theta \qquad (2.4)$$

with *n* an integer. The Bragg equations reduce to the von Laue equations, which is a justification for the model which led to the Bragg equations.

Equation 2.4 is the familiar equation for the optical diffraction grating in experiments on visible spectra. There *n* was the order of the spectra. In Equation 2.4 if the diffracted beam arises from the *n*th order reflection from a set of atomic planes of true spacing *d*, we may think of the beam as a first-order reflection from a set of planes parallel to the true lattice planes but with a spacing which is $1/n$ of the true spacing. This device leads to great simplification in interpretation.

## 2.4  The Intensity of the Diffracted Beam

The von Laue or Bragg equations give the conditions for diffraction of X-rays by a crystal. The actual intensity of the diffracted beam depends on how efficiently each atom scatters the beam and on how the atoms are grouped in the unit cell.

### The Atomic Scattering Factor

The scattering of X-rays is almost entirely by the cloud of electrons which surrounds each nucleus in the crystal. If all parts of the electron cloud scattered in phase, then the total scattering from an atom would simply be the scattering from one electron multiplied by the number of electrons per atom.

This is not the case since the size of the atom is of the order of the X-ray wavelength, and therefore out-of-phase addition of amplitude takes place in the scattered beam. The ratio of the scattering amplitude of the atom to that of a single electron is called the *atomic scattering factor f*. It is a measure of the effectiveness of interference in the scattered beam and a little consideration will convince the reader that it must depend on the angle through which the incident beam is scattered.

Let us consider a scattering object consisting of just two electrons, one of which is at the origin $O$ in Fig. 2.5 and the other at the end $M$ of vector $\mathbf{r}$. Then the linear phase difference $\Delta$ between wavelets from $O$ and $M$ is given by Equation 2.3:

$$\Delta = (\mathbf{s} - \mathbf{s}_0) \cdot \mathbf{r}$$

where $(\mathbf{s} - \mathbf{s}_0)$ is a vector difference and the dot product with $\mathbf{r}$ is required. The phase difference in angular measure is $(2\pi/\lambda)\Delta$ or $2\pi[(\mathbf{s} - \mathbf{s}_0)/\lambda] \cdot \mathbf{r}$. We have written this in the general form to show that diffraction for a group of electrons, no matter how complicated the distribution, depends only on the vector $[(\mathbf{s} - \mathbf{s}_0)/\lambda]$. Provided $[(\mathbf{s} - \mathbf{s}_0)/\lambda]$ has the same value, two experiments with quite different incident and scattered X-ray directions will give the same phase difference. The vector $[(\mathbf{s} - \mathbf{s}_0)/\lambda]$ bisects the angle between $\mathbf{s}_0$ and $\mathbf{s}$ and has length $2 \sin \theta/\lambda$, where $\theta$ is the Bragg angle.

We can relate the phase difference directly to the Bragg form by noting in Fig. 2.5 that if $d$ is the distance between atomic planes, then from Equation 2.4 the angular phase difference is $(2\pi/\lambda) (2d \sin \theta)$. These equalities of phase angle also relate the von Laue (2.3) and Bragg (2.4) equations.

Let us now suppose that we are no longer dealing with a two-electron object, but with an atom in which the density of electrons is spherically

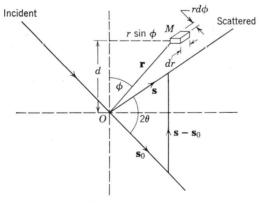

**Fig. 2.5** Calculation of the phase difference of X-rays scattered by an electron at $O$ and at $M$.

symmetrical about the nucleus. The density $\rho(\mathbf{r})$ at a distance $\mathbf{r}$ from $O$ will depend on the length of the vector $\mathbf{r}$. It is apparent from the figure that the number of electrons at $\mathbf{r}$ is $\rho(\mathbf{r}) \, drr \, d\phi 2\pi r \sin \phi$ and that the phase difference between X-rays scattered from these electrons and rays scattered by an electron at $O$ will be constant at the value $(4\pi/\lambda)d \sin \theta$ or $(4\pi/\lambda)r \cos \phi \sin \theta$.

There is an important theorem which relates amplitudes of scattered waves to the phase difference. It will be encountered in a number of physical models throughout the text. *If an object contains n electrons at vectors* $\mathbf{r}_1, \mathbf{r}_2, \ldots \mathbf{r}_n$, *then the amplitude of rays scattered from all of these electrons, taking as unity the amplitude scattered by one electron at O, is given by the summation*

$$\sum_{n=1}^{n} \exp \left\{ -2\pi i \frac{(s - s_0)}{\lambda} \cdot \mathbf{r}_n \right\} \tag{2.5}$$

In our problem the summation gives $f$, the atomic scattering factor. Thus

$$f = \int \rho(r) \, drr \, d\phi 2\pi r \sin \phi \exp \left( -\frac{4\pi i}{\lambda} r \cos \phi \sin \theta \right) \tag{2.6}$$

Writing the exponential in trigonometric form

$$f = \int \rho(r) 2\pi r^2 \sin \phi \sin \left( \frac{4\pi}{\lambda} r \cos \phi \sin \theta \right) \, dr \, d\phi \tag{2.7}$$

Integration over the $\phi$ terms gives

$$f = \int_0^{\infty} 4\pi r^2 \rho(r) \frac{\sin \left[ (4\pi/\lambda) \sin \theta \right]}{[4\pi/\lambda] \sin \theta} \, dr \tag{2.8}$$

A plot of $f$ against $\sin \theta / \lambda$ is shown in Fig. 2.6 for N and Cu. Clearly no phase difference will exist for X-rays scattered in the forward or $s_0$ direction.

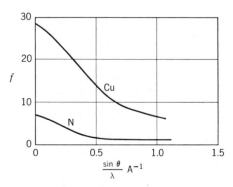

**Fig. 2.6**  The atomic scattering factor $f$ of copper and nitrogen as a function of scattering angle. At $\theta = 0°, f = Z$.

This can be seen by putting $\theta = 0$ when the value of $f$ becomes

$$f = \int_0^\infty 4\pi r^2 \rho(r)\, dr \tag{2.9}$$

But $4\pi r^2 \rho(r)\, dr$ is the number of electrons in a spherical shell of thickness $dr$ and radius $r$. Thus the integral equals the total number of electrons in the atom or the atomic number $Z$.

### The Structure Factor

In a crystal a group of atoms surrounds each lattice point. These atoms will each scatter some of the radiation and again the scattered amplitudes will not generally be in phase. The factor which gives the total scattered amplitude at an angle, associated with the Miller indices $hkl$ of the reflecting plane, is called the *structure factor F(hkl)*. In order to obtain $F(hkl)$ we have again to first calculate phase differences.

The X-rays scattered from each individual atom have an amplitude $f$ times that scattered by a single electron. Suppose that an atom is located at $(xyz)$ and that the unit cell edges are $a$, $b$, and $c$. Figure 2.7 shows the $yz$-plane. A set of planes (dashed lines) with Miller indices $(hkl)$ divides $a$ into $h$ equal parts, $b$ into $k$ equal parts, and $c$ into $l$ equal parts. For diffraction, the distances $a/h$, $b/k$, $c/l$ must each correspond to a phase difference of $2\pi$. A distance $y$ in the $b$ direction must therefore correspond to a phase angle $2\pi y(b/k)$.

The total phase angle between X-rays scattered from an atom at the origin $O$ and X-rays scattered from an atom at $(xyz)$ is thus

$$\left(2\pi x \frac{h}{a} + 2\pi y \frac{k}{b} + 2\pi z \frac{l}{c}\right)$$

The total structure factor $F(hkl)$ is now obtained by multiplying the atomic

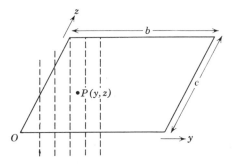

**Fig. 2.7**   The $yz$ plane of a unit cell of edges $a$, $b$, and $c$. Edge $b$ is divided into $k$ equal parts and side $c$ into $l$ equal parts by the plane $(hkl)$.

scattering factor $f_j$ for each atom of the unit cell by its respective phase factor and adding all the products. Then

$$F(hkl) = \sum_j f_j \exp\left\{2\pi i\left(\frac{hx}{a} + \frac{ky}{b} + \frac{lz}{c}\right)\right\} \qquad (2.10)$$

A double summation is implied. One is over the different positions of the atoms in the unit cell and the other is over the different atomic elements in the unit cell.

## 2.5   X-Ray Diffraction Methods

We have seen from the Bragg equation 2.4 that $\lambda$, $d$, and $\theta$ must have simultaneous specific values to satisfy the equation. In practice this matching of the parameters is accomplished in three standard ways.

### Laue Method

In the *Laue method*, Fig. 2.8, a single crystal specimen is held stationary while irradiated with *white X-radiation*. A photographic film is placed to receive the rays diffracted through the crystal or (see Fig. 2.11) those diffracted in a back reflection direction. Because the crystal is fixed in position the angles $\theta$ are also fixed. The Bragg condition (Equation 2.4) can be satisfied

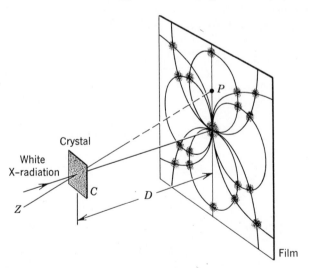

**Fig. 2.8**  Laue method. A set of planes lying parallel to a common zone axis *ZCP* give rise to a series of spots on a given ellipse.

since a range of wavelengths is present. If the photographic film is at a distance $D$ from the crystal, it will show reflection spots at various distances $R$ from the direct beam. Here

$$R = D \tan 2\theta \qquad (2.11)$$

Each spot will be due to all the orders of reflection $n = 1, 2, 3, \ldots$ from a single plane. Thus each spot can be considered to be a reflection from planes of spacing $d$, $d/2$, $d/3$, $\ldots$. The Laue photograph gives a series of values of $\theta$ for different crystal planes, together with the orientation of each $R$ relative to horizontal and vertical directions on the photograph. The Laue method gives only the symmetry, the axial ratios $a/b$, $c/b$, and the axial angles $\alpha$, $\beta$, and $\gamma$. The method does not give the size of the unit cell, only its shape, because it gives a measure of angles only, not of spacings.

### Rotating Crystal Method

In the *rotating crystal* method, a single crystal is rotated in a beam of monochromatic X-rays. The rotation makes it possible for the Bragg law to be satisfied. Not every plane can reflect; for example, a plane which always contains the incident beam during the whole rotation cannot reflect, nor could one whose spacing is so small that $\lambda/2d > 1$. The reflected spots, on a cylindrical film whose axis is the rotation axis of the crystal, lie on parallel lines. Since the wavelength is known, the spacing $d$ may be calculated from Equation 2.4. Reflections from planes in different orientations may overlap on the film, and to make the identification of the spots less ambiguous, two modifications of the apparatus are often employed—the *oscillation* method and the *Weissenberg* method. In the oscillation method the number of planes which can reflect is restricted by oscillating the crystal through a small angle. In the Weissenberg method, while the crystal rotates, the film is translated parallel to the axis of rotation, the two motions being synchronized.

The oscillation and Weissenberg methods are used in complete crystal structure analysis.

### Powder Method

In the *powder method*, a finely powdered specimen is placed in a mono-chromatic beam. The specimen is often rotated. Certain of the many crystallites are correctly oriented to satisfy Equation 2.4. The powder method, convenient because single crystals are not required, is used for accurate determination of lattice parameters in crystals of known structure and for the identification of elements and compounds.

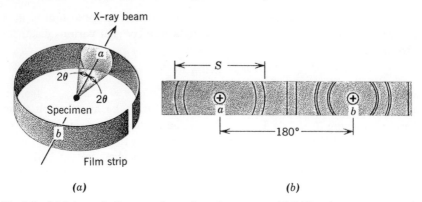

**(a)**                                                    **(b)**

**Fig. 2.9**   (a) Schematic diagram of use of powder camera. (b) Diffraction pattern recorded on film strip.

Figure 2.9a shows a small cylindrical powder specimen mounted at the center of a cylindrical camera. A narrow incident beam of monochromatic X-rays, often Kα radiation, irradiates the sample. Each type of atomic plane with its characteristic spacing $d$ produces a diffracted cone of X-rays of vertex angle $4\theta$. The cone of X-rays is intercepted by a narrow strip of film which is fitted inside the circular camera. Development of the film after exposure will reveal a diffraction pattern shown in Fig. 2.9b. The distance $S$ on the film between diffraction lines corresponding to a particular plane is related to the Bragg angle by the equation

$$S = 4\theta R \tag{2.12}$$

where $R$ is the known radius of the camera. A list of $\theta$ values can thus be obtained from the measured values of $S$. Since the wavelength is known, substitution in Equation 2.4 gives a list of spacings $d$. Each spacing $d$ is the distance between neighboring planes $(hkl)$.

In the simple case of a *cubic* structure the relationship between $d$ and the lattice parameter $a$ is given by the equation

$$d = \frac{a}{\sqrt{h^2 + k^2 + l^2}} \tag{2.13}$$

Some simple examples of this relationship are shown in Fig. 2.10.

Combined with the Bragg law, Equation 2.13 gives for the *cubic* system

$$\sin^2 \theta_{hkl} = \frac{\lambda^2}{4a^2}(h^2 + k^2 + l^2) \tag{2.14}$$

The corresponding relation for the hexagonal system is

$$\sin^2 \theta_{hkl} = \frac{\lambda^2}{4}\left[\frac{4(h^2 + k^2 + hk)}{3a^2} + \frac{l^2}{c^2}\right] \tag{2.15}$$

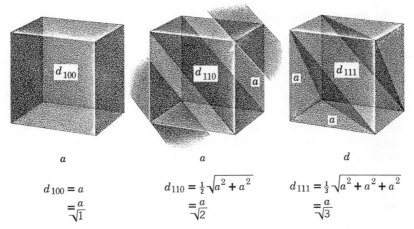

$$d_{100} = a$$
$$= \frac{a}{\sqrt{1}}$$

$$d_{110} = \tfrac{1}{2}\sqrt{a^2 + a^2}$$
$$= \frac{a}{\sqrt{2}}$$

$$d_{111} = \tfrac{1}{3}\sqrt{a^2 + a^2 + a^2}$$
$$= \frac{a}{\sqrt{3}}$$

**Fig. 2.10**   Spacings in a cubic crystal calculated from equation 2.13.

Clearly, if the values of $\theta$ for which diffracted beams exist can be measured and associated with particular planes, substitution in these equations will give a number of values of the lattice spacings. With systems of lower symmetry than hexagonal, it is rarely possible to carry out a structure analysis by the powder method alone.

The values of spacing given by measurement of the higher angle lines, that is, greatest $\theta$, are the most accurate. This can be shown by differentiating the Bragg relationship with respect to $\theta$.

We have

$$\frac{d}{d\theta}(n\lambda) = 2\frac{\Delta d}{\Delta \theta}\sin\theta + 2d\cos\theta$$

and for monochromatic radiation when the left-hand side is zero

$$\frac{\Delta \theta}{\Delta d} = -\frac{1}{d}\tan\theta \tag{2.16}$$

Equation 2.16 shows that the variation in $\theta$ for a small change in $d$ becomes very large as $\theta$, the Bragg angle, approaches $90°$. Accurate determinations of parameters are thus best made by back reflection methods.

## 2.6   The Uses of X-Ray Diffraction Techniques

So far we have dealt with the principles of X-ray diffraction and have made little mention of its practical uses. Although a vast number of diffraction techniques are now in use, we will select only a few which are of special interest to the solid state engineer.

### Crystal Structure Determination

The first task in structure determination is to index the X-ray pattern. This amounts to trying to account for all of the angles measured from a film such as in Fig. 2.9*b* by a formula such as (2.14) or (2.15). The pattern is indexed by assigning appropriate (*hkl*) indices to each diffraction line or spot. Missing values of (*hkl*) are then a guide to zero values of the structure factor *F(hkl)*. The *International Tables for X-ray Crystallography* should then be consulted for the (*xyz*) positions of atoms in the unit cell. If *a*, *b*, and *c* are known as well as the positions (*xyz*) for each atom, then a substitution in the structure factor formula (2.10) should give agreement with measured intensities of the diffraction lines or spots.

Suppose, for example, that body-centered cubic α-iron is being examined. The atomic positions in the unit cell are 000 and $\frac{1}{2}a$, $\frac{1}{2}b$, $\frac{1}{2}c$. Substitution in the structure factor gives

$$F(hkl) = f_{Fe} \exp\left[2\pi i(h \cdot 0 + k \cdot 0 + l \cdot 0)\right]$$
$$+ f_{Fe} \exp\left[2\pi i(h \cdot \tfrac{1}{2} + k \cdot \tfrac{1}{2} + l \cdot \tfrac{1}{2})\right]$$
$$= f_{Fe}\{1 + e^{\pi i(h+k+l)}\}$$

Hence

$$F = 2f_{Fe} \quad \text{when} \quad h + k + l \text{ is even}$$

and

$$F = 0 \quad \text{when} \quad h + k + l \text{ is odd}$$

Thus the X-ray diffraction pattern from α-Fe will contain only the lines (110), (200), (211), (220), (321), (400), etc.

The equivalent positions, number of atoms per unit cell, and "rule for allowed reflections" for fcc and hcc crystals are given in Table 2.2. Although the basic ideas of structure analysis have now been discussed, the subject can be complex and is appropriate only in a specialized text.

**Table 2.2**    Calculation of Structure Factor in fcc and hcp Crystals

| Structure | Number of Atoms | Positions | Rule for (*hkl*) |
|---|---|---|---|
| Face-Centered Cubic | 4 | $000, \frac{1}{2}0\frac{1}{2}, 0\frac{1}{2}\frac{1}{2}, \frac{1}{2}\frac{1}{2}0$ | All even or all odd |
| Hexagonal Close-Packed | 2 | $000, \frac{1}{3}\frac{2}{3}\frac{1}{2}$ | All *hkl* except if $h - k = 0, 3, 6, 9$ then *l* must be even |

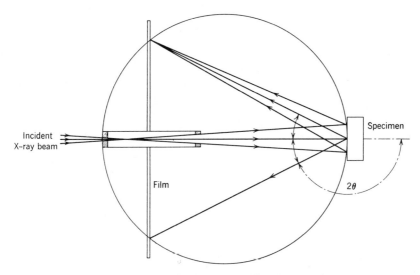

**Fig. 2.11** Back reflection X-ray diffraction technique.

*The Determination of the Orientation of a Single Crystal by the X-Ray Method.* Many physical properties are dependent on the crystallographic direction in which they are measured. It is therefore of importance to be able to determine the orientation of a single crystal or an individual crystal in a polycrystalline aggregate. The most convenient method is to employ the X-ray back-reflection Laue technique. The apparatus is similar to that shown in Fig. 2.11. White radiation is used, usually from a tungsten or molybdenum target. A back-reflection Laue pattern of iron is shown in Fig. 2.12. It will be seen that the Laue spots lie on hyperbolas. The spots on each of these rows are reflections from various planes of a given zone, that is, planes parallel to a line that is the zone axis. A cone of reflected rays is formed for each zone of planes in the crystal, the cone intersecting the flat film in a hyperbola. It follows that if the proper Miller indices can be assigned to the zones, the orientation of the single crystal can be deduced. There are standard methods and charts to carry out the procedure.

A camera such as that shown in Fig. 2.11 is suitable also for use with monochromatic X-rays. Highly precise lattice parameter determinations can then be made in the back reflection region (Equation 2.16). Such changes in parameter may be the result of alloying, the introduction of defects, or thermal expansion.

*Detection of X-Rays by the Geiger-Müller Tube.* Thus far we have limited the discussion of X-ray diffraction equipment to that using photographic film as a means of detection. With the photographic film an entire pattern

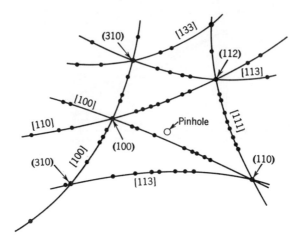

**Fig. 2.12**   Back reflection Laue pattern from an iron single crystal.  The main diffraction spots and zone axes are indexed.  (After Barrett)

may be recorded at once, and thus all the reflections are on a strictly comparable basis.

In certain instances, however, particularly in commercial X-ray powder techniques, it is more convenient to use the Geiger-Müller tube as a detector. With this tube the inherent sensitivity to X-rays is much greater than with film.  When X-ray quanta of sufficient energy enter the Geiger tube, voltage pulses are produced that may be shaped and counted by electronic circuits. The tube is automatically scanned around the specimen to give all $\theta$ values, and the integrated intensity is automatically drawn as a function of angle by a chart recorder.

### X-ray Diffraction Topography

Imperfections can markedly change many physical properties of a crystal. These imperfections can be of a varied nature.  They may be dissolved or precipitated impurities, atoms out of position in the lattice, or line faults known as dislocations.  Dislocations occur in all natural and grown crystals. The location and study of such defects are of great importance in the metallurgical and semiconductor industries.  This is particularly true in the semiconductor industry, where a high degree of crystal purity and perfection is necessary for useful performance.

The integrated intensity of a particular X-ray diffraction line and its width are strongly influenced by gross crystal perfection, and studies have been made on line-broadening effects of dislocation densities in the range $10^{10}$ to $10^{16}$ per m².

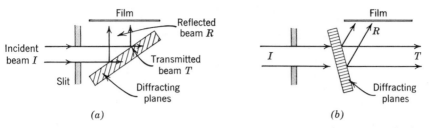

**Fig. 2.13** X-ray diffraction topography. (*a*) Berg-Barrett method in back-reflection position. (*b*) Berg-Barrett method in Laue position.

Recently topographical X-ray diffraction methods have been developed in which dislocations can be individually resolved in crystals where the density is less than $10^{10}$ m$^{-2}$. The basis for detection of individual dislocations is the difference in intensities of X-rays diffracted or transmitted from regions near a dislocation and from regions of perfect crystal structure. The methods yield an unmagnified topographical projection on high-resolution X-ray sensitive photographic emulsion. The resolution is of the order of $10^{-6}$ m and optical magnification of the film pattern is possible. Large crystal areas can be scanned and the interior structure examined to depths of the order of $10^{-3}$ m.

Figure 2.13*a* and *b* show two schemes using the Berg-Barrett technique. Incident X-rays are reflected by the atomic planes (*hkl*) of a specimen set at the appropriate Bragg angle. The film is within a distance of $10^{-2}$ m from the crystal face. A line source of X-rays of Kα radiation is used often with a considerable amount of horizontal divergence.

Figure 2.14 taken with the reflection technique shows a topograph with the ($\bar{2}20$) and ($1\bar{1}1$) planes in the reflecting positions. The presence of dislocations on these planes is clearly seen and dislocation geometry can be studied. Figure 2.15 taken with the specimen in the Laue geometry, and for a (220) reflection, shows an X-ray image of a silicon wafer containing copper precipitated particles at a concentration of less than $10^{23}$ Cu atoms m$^{-3}$.

## 2.7  Electron Diffraction

The relationship between the momentum of a particle and its associated wavelength is dealt with in Chapter 8. It is sufficient at this stage to note that electrons of mass $m$ and velocity $v$ have a momentum $mv$ and an associated de Broglie wavelength $\lambda$ given by

$$\lambda = \frac{h}{mv} \tag{2.17}$$

where $h$ is Planck's constant.

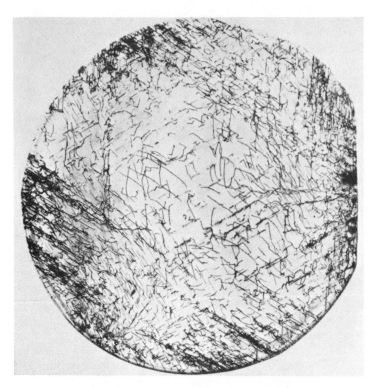

**Fig. 2.14** ($\bar{2}$20) and (1$\bar{1}$1) X-ray topograph of silicon wafer. (From A. E. Jenkinson and A. R. Lang, *Direct Observations of Imperfections in Crystals*, Interscience, New York, 1962.)

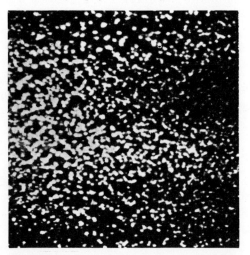

**Fig. 2.15** X-ray image of crystal wafer of zero dislocation density containing copper precipitates; 220-type reflection. (From G. H. Schwuttke, *Direct Observations of Imperfections in Crystals*, Interscience, New York, 1962.)

If a stream of electrons is accelerated by an applied electrical potential, the kinetic energy of the electrons $\frac{1}{2}mv^2$ is given by

$$\frac{1}{2}mv^2 = eV \tag{2.18}$$

where $V$ is the electrical potential and $e$ the electron charge.

From Equations 2.17 and 2.18 we have

$$\lambda = \sqrt{\frac{150}{V}}$$

with $\lambda$ expressed in angstroms and $V$ in volts. For example, for $V = 50\,\text{kV}$, $\lambda = 0.05\,\text{A}$.

In contrast with X-rays, a beam of electrons is scattered by the atomic nuclei as well as by the outer atomic electrons. The scattering factor $f$ again decreases with increasing angle of incidence $\theta$, as in X-rays. The scattering efficiency by atoms of electrons is, however, considerably greater than that of X-rays, and although the penetration depth of electrons in most solids is small ($\simeq 500\,\text{A}$ for 50 kV electrons), sufficient material exists in the thin layer to diffract the incident beam.

Figure 2.16 shows a transmission electron diffraction pattern from gold foil. The rings subtend an angle of $4\theta$ with the incident beam, and thus lattice spacings can be calculated if the camera geometry is known.

The problems that have been successfully studied by electron diffraction are illustrated by the following examples.

1. Investigation of surface oxides of metals.

2. Studies of orientation, lattice parameter, and perfection of evaporated thin films.

3. Since the regularity of atomic arrangement a thin film varies over regions of crystal imperfection, diffraction studies made in the electron microscope reveal dislocation patterns. These will be shown in Section 5.20.

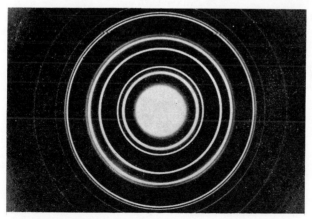

**Fig. 2.16.** Electron diffraction pattern of gold foil.

### 2.8    Neutron Diffraction

The relationship between wavelength and momentum of a neutron is similar to that for electrons given in Equation 2.17. The mass of the neutron, however, is about 2000 times that of the electron. Thus a wavelength of about 1 A is associated with neutrons of energy only 0.1 eV.

Neutrons are chiefly scattered by the nuclei of atoms, and since the wavelength of the neutron is much greater than the dimension of the scattering nucleus ($\simeq 10^{-15}$ m) the atomic scattering factor is practically independent of the scattering angle.

The factors that make diffraction by neutrons a useful supplementary tool to solid studies by X-rays are twofold. First, the scattering of neutrons by light elements is, in contrast to X-rays, quite often relatively strong. Second, the magnetic moment of the neutron interacts with the magnetic moment of the scattering atom, modifying the diffraction pattern in a way that gives

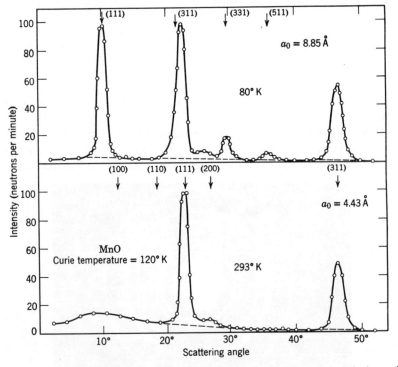

**Fig. 2.17**  Neutron diffraction patterns of MnO at temperatures below and above the Curie temperature. (After Shull et al.)

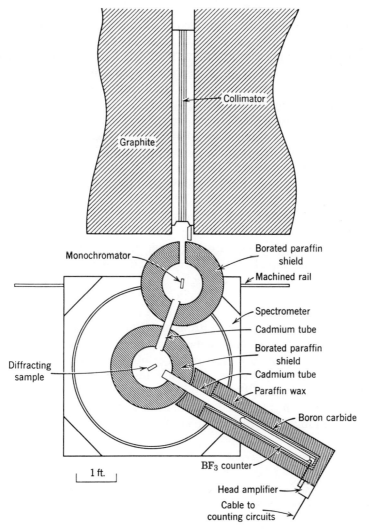

**Fig. 2.18**   The technique of neutron diffraction.  (From G. E. Bacon, *Neutron Diffraction*, Clarendon Press, Oxford, 1955)

information about the number of atoms grouped in a common magnetic pattern.

The first factor has enabled the crystallographer to deduce the positions of hydrogen and carbon atoms in a number of organic crystals by the technique of neutron diffraction.  The second factor has proved useful in the detection of antiferromagnetism (see Chapter 15).  In an antiferromagnetic solid the magnetic moments of pairs of atoms are aligned antiparallel and hence appear different to an incident neutron. The neutron diffraction pattern of MnO is shown in Fig. 2.17 taken at two different temperatures. At room temperature, which is above the Curie temperature for MnO, the long-range magnetic ordering is destroyed by thermal agitation, and the pattern is typical of a structure of the NaCl type. At a temperature below the Curie temperature the *magnetic* unit cell is twice the size of the *chemical* one. This is because in antiferromagnetic MnO the Mn atoms at positions 000 and 100 have oppositely directed magnetic moments and thus appear to the neutrons to be different atoms; similarly, the atoms at 010 and 001 have moments directed opposite to the one at 000. Thus if the MnO is held below the Curie temperature of 120°K, additional diffraction lines appear, typical of the larger cell.

Figure 2.18 shows apparatus for crystal structure investigation by neutron diffraction. Neutrons from the reactor are slowed down in the graphite thermal column. Very few are lost while their energy decreases to the equilibrium value equal to the thermal energy of the carbon atoms. A distribution of energies and consequently of wavelengths is present in the neutron beam. Neutrons of a suitable wavelength are then selected by the single crystal monochromator, which reflects according to the Bragg relation. The reflected monochromatic neutrons are then used to investigate the solid under test. The scattered neutron beam can be detected with a counter filled with boron trifluoride gas. The boron is often enriched in $B^{10}$ for better absorption. The diffracted neutrons cause disintegration of the $B^{10}$ into the lighter elements $Li^7$ and $He^4$. These move rapidly through the gas and the resulting ionization is recorded electronically as the counter is moved slowly through the range of diffraction angles $\theta$.

### References

Bacon, G. E., *Neutron Diffraction*, 2nd ed., Oxford, New York, 1962.

Buerger, M. J., *Crystal Structure Analysis*, John Wiley and Sons, New York, 1960.

Guinier, A., *X-ray Diffraction in Crystals, Imperfect Crystals and Amorphous Bodies*, W. H. Freeman, San Francisco, Cal., 1963.

Klug, H. P., and L. E. Alexander, *X-ray Diffraction Procedures*, John Wiley and Sons, New York, 1954. (Contains A.S.T.M. identification procedures.)

### Exercises

1. (a) What is the wavelength associated with an electron of kinetic energy 10 keV?

    (b) What is the wavelength associated with a neutron of 300°K ($KE = \frac{1}{2}kT$)?

    (c) What is the minimum wavelength in X-ray white radiation if the applied voltage on the tube is 30 kV?

2. The fraction of the incident radiation intensity transmitted by a shield of thickness $x$ is $e^{-\mu x}$ where $\mu$ is the *absorption coefficient*. Calculate the thickness of lead shield to reduce the intensity to 50 per cent of its incident value for (a) neutrons of wavelength 1.08 A for which $\mu$ for lead is $3 \times 10^{-1}$ m$^{-1}$; (b) X-rays of wavelength 1.54 A for which $\mu$ for lead is $2.4 \times 10^5$ m$^{-1}$.

3. First-order X-ray diffraction from the (100) planes in NaCl occurs with MoK$\alpha$ radiation ($\lambda = 0.709$ A) at a Bragg angle of 7.3°. If the density of the NaCl crystal is 2160 kg m$^{-3}$, calculate Avogadro's number. Atomic weight Na = 23; Cl = 35.5. (*Hint:* In Fig. 1.16 the cube of side $d_{100}$ contains $\frac{1}{2}$ atom Na and $\frac{1}{2}$ atom Cl.)

4. X-ray back-reflection experiments with an aluminum specimen and CuK$\alpha_1$ radiation ($\lambda = 1.5405$ A) indicate that the Bragg angle of the (422) ring changes by 0.3° as the aluminum specimen is raised in temperature by 100°C. Calculate the mean coefficient of thermal expansion of aluminum. Lattice parameter $a$ for aluminum = 4.041 A.

5. The table shows the measured $\theta$ values in a tantalum powder diffraction pattern using CuK$\alpha_1$ X-radiation:

| Line | $\theta°$ |
| --- | --- |
| 1 | 19.611 |
| 2 | 28.136 |
| 3 | 35.156 |
| 4 | 41.564 |
| 5 | 47.769 |
| 6 | 54.119 |
| 7 | 60.876 |
| 8 | 68.912 |
| 9 | 81.520 |

(a) Calculate the spacings, $d$. (b) Index the lines with the indices ($hkl$). (c) Calculate the lattice parameter $a$ from each $d$ value. (d) Plot $a$ against $\cos^2 \theta$ and extrapolate to $\theta = 90°$ to get a best value of the lattice parameter. This procedure eliminates a number of systematic errors.

6. Confirm the "rule for allowed reflections" given in Table 2.2 for face-centered cubic and hexagonal close-packed structures in pure elements. Confirm that the allowed reflections of the diamond structure (Fig. 1.15) satisfy ($h + k + l$) = $4n$ where $h$, $k$, and $l$ are even and $n$ is an integer or else $h$, $k$, and $l$ are odd. Write out the first six low-angle reflections for diamond.

# 3

# *Alloys*

We have already seen that elements in the solid form possess a characteristic atomic arrangement (Chapter 1). It is now of interest to discuss the effect on this atomic arrangement of introducing atoms of a second element. We will first discuss the effect of the addition of small amounts of the second element before proceeding to a brief discussion of alloying in binary systems.

If, for example, we take pure copper, which has a face-centered cubic lattice, and introduce a small amount of zinc, we obtain a homogeneous solid called α brass. After the surface of this solid has been polished to a fine finish and etched, the microscopic appearance is little different from that of the pure copper. The X-ray diffraction powder photographs also show little difference from that of pure copper, although a calculation of lattice parameter would reveal that the parameter has slightly increased to accommodate the larger zinc atoms. Here we are dealing with a *substitutional* solid solution of zinc in copper in which some of the lattice positions occupied by copper atoms in the pure copper have now been taken by zinc atoms. The substitutional type of solid solution is by far the most common in alloys.

If, however, the second element is much smaller in atomic radius than the solvent atom, a type of alloy may be formed in which the solute atom fits into the interstices between the solvent atoms. Such a solid solution is called *interstitial*. Technologically, the most important of such alloys is austenitic steel, in which carbon atoms are in interstitial solution in γ iron.

## 3.1 Hume-Rothery Rules for Solubility

The rules of Hume-Rothery identify the important factors which favor or oppose solid solubility. These rules are empirical.

### *Size Factor*

If an element *B* is added to an element *A*, the lattice of *A* must be distorted to accommodate the atoms of *B*. It is not surprising to find that the extent

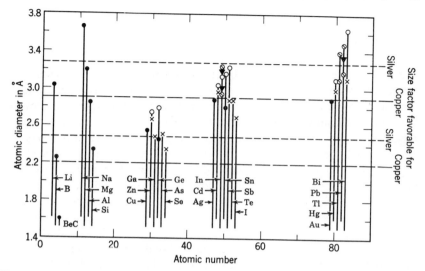

**Fig. 3.1** Atomic diameters of elements plotted against atomic number with size factors favorable for solution in copper and silver. (After Hume-Rothery)

to which *A* can dissolve *B* atoms depends on the difference in atomic radii. The effective atomic radius of an element is often taken as one-half of the closest distance between the centers of atoms in the crystal of the pure material. If the other factors, yet to be discussed, are favorable, extensive solid solubility is expected if the atomic radii differ by less than 14 per cent. Silver and gold atoms, for example, have nearly identical radii and form a continuous series of solid solutions.

It is more difficult to assign a ratio between solute and solvent atomic radii to categorize interstitial solid solution. The common interstitial solids—carbon, hydrogen, nitrogen, boron, oxygen—may ionize in solution, making uncertain the effective radius. We may in many cases, however, expect extensive interstitial solid solution if the radius of the solute atom is less than about 60 per cent of the solvent atom.

Figure 3.1 shows the atomic diameters of some of the elements plotted against atomic numbers with the size factors favorable for solution in copper and silver.

### Crystal Structure Factor

For extensive solid solution of one element in another it is often found that the crystal structures should be similar.

### Relative Valency Factor

For extensive solid solubility the chemical valence of two elements should not differ by more than one. Other factors being equal, it is often found that a metal of lower valency is more likely to dissolve one of higher valency than vice versa. Suppose we consider the system copper-silicon. The atom of higher valency, that is, silicon, crystallizes so that each atom has four nearest neighbors (see Chapter 1). If an atom of silicon is replaced by a copper atom, which has only one valence electron, there will be insufficient electrons to form the tetrahedral bonds, and the solid solution will be very restricted. On the other hand, the univalent elements copper, silver, and gold can dissolve elements of higher valency to a much greater degree.

If the factors discussed thus far are unfavorable, they lead to atomic bonds of one element being unmatched by bonds of the other. Distortions occur which are energetically unfavorable and limit the solid solubility.

### Electronegative Valence Factor

Hume-Rothery lists one more factor which may limit solid solubility even if the other factors are reasonably favorable. It is sometimes found that stable intermediate compounds are formed at the expense of the primary solid solution. The general rule for the formation of such compounds is that the solute element be electronegative and the solvent be electropositive, or vice versa. For example, in Group VIA the elements sulfur, selenium, and tellurium (see Table 3.1) form stable sulfides, selenides, and tellurides, and consequently the solid solubility of these elements in metals is low. Group VA elements such as phosphorus, arsenic, and antimony are less electronegative and slight solubility in metals is possible. Group IVA elements, being still less electronegative, are able to enter into solid solution in some metals to a certain extent.

In most cases where formation of such compounds takes place, the solid solubility of one element in another increases with temperature. It is then possible to precipitate the compound out of solution by decreasing the temperature. This is also the case in some ternary alloys. For example, the elements Mg and Si will remain in solution in Al at high temperatures, but will precipitate out as the stable compound $Mg_2Si$ when the temperature is lowered. A critical dispersion of the precipitated particles of compound will often harden the alloy, making the process, known as "precipitation hardening," one of industrial importance.

**Table 3.1**  Periodic Classification of the Elements

| Group / Periods | IA | IIA | IIIB | IVB | VB | VIB | VIIB | VIIIB | IB | IIB | IIIA | IVA | VA | VIA | VIIA | VIIIA |
|---|---|---|---|---|---|---|---|---|---|---|---|---|---|---|---|---|
| 1 | $H_1$ | | | | | | | | | | | | | | | $He_2$ |
| 2 | $Li_3$ | $Be_4$ | | | | | | | | | $B_5$ | $C_6$ | $N_7$ | $O_8$ | $F_9$ | $Ne_{10}$ |
| 3 | $Na_{11}$ | $Mg_{12}$ | | | | | | | | | $Al_{13}$ | $Si_{14}$ | $P_{15}$ | $S_{16}$ | $Cl_{17}$ | $Ar_{18}$ |
| 4 | $K_{19}$ | $Ca_{20}$ | $Sc_{21}$ | $Ti_{22}$ | $V_{23}$ | $Cr_{24}$ | $Mn_{25}$ | $Fe_{26}$ $Co_{27}$ $Ni_{28}$ | $Cu_{29}$ | $Zn_{30}$ | $Ga_{31}$ | $Ge_{32}$ | $As_{33}$ | $Se_{34}$ | $Br_{35}$ | $Kr_{36}$ |
| 5 | $Rb_{37}$ | $Sr_{38}$ | $Y_{39}$ | $Zr_{40}$ | $Nb_{41}$ | $Mo_{42}$ | $Te_{43}$ | $Ru_{44}$ $Rh_{45}$ $Pd_{46}$ | $Ag_{47}$ | $Cd_{48}$ | $In_{49}$ | $Sn_{50}$ | $Sb_{51}$ | $Te_{52}$ | $I_{53}$ | $Ne_{54}$ |
| 6 | $Cs_{55}$ | $Ba_{56}$ | $La_{57}$* $Lu_{71}$ | $Hf_{72}$ | $Ta_{73}$ | $W_{74}$ | $Re_{75}$ | $Os_{76}$ $Ir_{77}$ $Pt_{78}$ | $Au_{79}$ | $Hg_{80}$ | $Tl_{81}$ | $Pb_{82}$ | $Bi_{83}$ | $Po_{84}$ | $At_{85}$ | $Rn_{86}$ |
| 7 | $Fr_{87}$ | $Ra_{88}$ | $Ac_{89}$† | $Th_{90}$ | $Pa_{91}$ | $U_{92}$ | | | | | | | | | | |

\* Rare earth series: $Ce_{58}$, $Pr_{59}$, $Nd_{60}$, $Pm_{61}$, $Sm_{62}$, $Eu_{63}$, $Gd_{64}$, $Tb_{65}$, $Dy_{66}$, $Ho_{67}$, $Er_{68}$, $Tm_{69}$, $Yb_{70}$, $Lu_{71}$.

† Actinide Series: $Th_{90}$, $Pa_{91}$, $U_{92}$, $Np_{93}$, $Pu_{94}$, $Am_{95}$, $Cm_{96}$, $Bk_{97}$, $Cf_{98}$, $E_{99}$, $Fm_{100}$, $Mv_{101}$, $No_{102}$.

Thus far we have merely listed some of the factors which limit solid solubility. In order to describe the nature of alloys formed when elements are mixed in sizable proportions, we must first be able to say something of the energies involved. To do this we must describe the parameters which define the energy and elicit some of the relationships between these parameters. In short, we must discuss some elementary thermodynamics of solids.

## 3.2  Thermodynamics of Solids

In this section we will assume a certain familiarity with elementary thermodynamics and develop only those parts which are fundamental to the study of solids. The ideas will be illustrated with reference to binary alloys.

In a binary alloy of a certain composition the *components*, which in this case are the two elements, may be liquid if the temperature is high enough. The liquid mixture is called a liquid *phase*. On lowering the temperature partial solidification may take place and two phases—liquid and solid—coexist together. In the solid state one component may be in solution in the other, making a solid solution phase. Or an intermetallic compound phase may form. It is necessary at the outset of our discussion of binary alloys to try to define the conditions that govern the choice of phase in which an alloy of a certain composition will exist at a certain temperature. In many cases this is not known in detail. We can, however, give a thermodynamic condition that defines the equilibrium state of a solid state system.

Suppose that a system of volume $V$ at a pressure $P$ has internal energy $E$ and entropy $S$. The internal energy is the sum of the kinetic and potential energies of the atoms present, and in an isolated system it would be constant. Suppose here that the system is not isolated but can exchange energy with its surroundings. In alloy formation heat can be absorbed or rejected in the melting or solidifying processes.

Then from the first law of thermodynamics, if $dQ$ is the heat absorbed by the system from its surroundings, we have

$$dQ = dE + P\,dV \tag{3.1}$$

Here the term $dE$ represents energy associated with the internal rearrangement and $P\,dV$ gives the external work done by the system. Both are a consequence of absorbing energy $dQ$.

Let $dS_1$ and $dS_2$ be the entropy change in the system and in its environment, respectively. The second law of thermodynamics then ensures that there is an entropy increase, that is, $dS_1^{\cdot} + dS_2 > 0$. The change in entropy of the environment $dS_2$ is associated with the heat transfer $dQ$ at the temperature $T$.

From the definition of entropy we have, for a spontaneous process to take place,

$$dS_2 = \frac{-dQ}{T} \tag{3.2}$$

Since in general the heat capacity of the system is much smaller than that of its total environment, if $dQ$ is *reversed* and comes from the *system to the environment* the rise in temperature of the environment is infinitesimally small. The entropy change $dS_2$ is then that of an essentially reversible process. Thus

$$dS_1 - \frac{dQ}{T} > 0$$

and from Equation 3.1 this reads

$$dE + P\,dV - T\,dS_1 < 0 \tag{3.3}$$

This is the condition that defines, for the system itself, in which direction the physical-chemical change will proceed. When the condition

$$dE + P\,dV - T\,dS_1 = 0 \tag{3.4}$$

is reached, the system is in equilibrium and all further infinitesimal changes are reversible.

### Free Energy

We can now define the equilibrium condition for a particular temperature $T$. The quantity $E + PV - TS$ is called the *Gibbs free energy G*. If $E$, $S$, and $V$ are functions of temperature and pressure, then

$$dG = dE + P\,dV + V\,dP - T\,dS - S\,dT \tag{3.5}$$

At a particular temperature and pressure

$$dG = dE + P\,dV - T\,dS \tag{3.6}$$

Thus the condition for equilibrium of a thermodynamic system at a particular temperature and pressure can be written

$$dG = d(E + PV - TS) = 0 \tag{3.7}$$

Or, in other words, the Gibbs free energy must be a minimum. Solid state systems are generally not in a state of equilibrium because of the slowness of rearrangement of atoms in a rigid solid. We can say, however, that as far as is possible under the conditions prevailing, the system will continually change in the direction of minimization of free energy.

Generally, in solids the product $PV$ remains constant and Equation 3.7 can be written

$$d(E - TS) = 0 \qquad (3.8)$$

The quantity $E - TS$, which is called the *Helmholtz free energy F*, is then a minimum. Throughout the rest of the text we will use either $G$ or $F$. It should be remembered that for solid state systems these are practically equivalent.

### Phase Changes

The *phase* in which an element, alloy, or compound exists may be loosely defined as the state of aggregation of the atoms. This is ambiguous and the following examples may be helpful in its clarification.

The liquid state and vapor state of an element are discernibly different in appearance, and if they exist together the system is referred to as a *two-phase* system. At the *triple point* of an element the *vapor, liquid,* and *solid* phases coexist and there are, of course, three phases. Now let us consider the mixing of two elements. If both exist as vapors, then, when mixed, the respective elements are indistinguishable and the mixed vapors are referred to as a single phase. Similarly, liquids that mix, such as glycol and water, form a single phase. Oil, on the other hand, does not mix with water, and thus forms an oil phase and a water phase. In solid systems two elements may mix intimately together and form a single phase. Complete solid solubility at all compositions of two elements is, however, rare; in general, there exists a phase in which some part of the first element is dissolved in the second, another phase in which some part of the second element is dissolved in the first, and a third phase in which a mixture of these two other phases is present.

We can see from Equation 3.8 that at low temperatures the free energy is close to the internal energy $E$, so that minimization of the free energy implies a lowering (or increasing negatively) of $E$. This takes place by the formation of strong interatomic bonds and a tendency toward the solid state.

As the temperature is raised the negative $TS$ term gains in importance and will contribute appreciably to the lowering of the free energy if $S$ has a large value. This occurs, as we shall see, when *disorder* exists in the phase. Thus a tendency toward the more disordered liquid phase exists as the temperature is raised.

At still higher temperatures disorder is preferred so that the intermediate liquid phase then transforms to the completely disordered vapor phase. A pressure-temperature graph of the different phases is shown in Fig. 3.2.

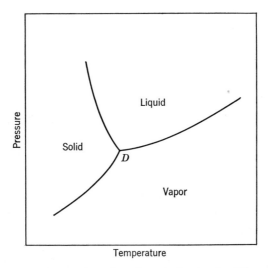

**Fig. 3.2** Pressure versus temperature of an element, showing the different phases. $D$ is the triple point.

In the figure two phases coexist in equilibrium along the $P$, $T$ boundary between them. Three phases coexist at $D$, the triple point. A transition across the phase boundaries of the figure implies, as we have seen, a change in the internal energy or bond strength. Such changes are called *first-order changes*. First-order changes may also occur at low temperatures in solids which transform from one crystal structure to another. The more closely packed structure, or the one of lowered or more negative internal energy, is generally preferred at the lower temperatures.

### Entropy

We have indicated that the entropy term is related to the atomic disorder in the various phases. We will now discuss this a little more fully. Generally, thermodynamic changes in solids are *irreversible*. If, for example, a liquid is supercooled, then once it begins to freeze it is impossible to reverse the freezing process by an infinitesimal change in temperature. In fact, the temperature would have to be raised above the freezing point to remelt the solid portion already formed. The entropy criterion for an irreversible heat transfer from a system is

$$dS_{\text{system}} > \frac{dQ}{T}$$

We next expand the meaning of the term entropy to include its relation to atomic disorder.

Boltzmann first suggested a relationship between the entropy of a system in a given state and the probability of existence of the state. Planck put this in mathematical form.

$$S = k \ln p \qquad (3.9)$$

where $p$ represents the probability of a given state and $k$ is the Boltzmann constant, which equals $1.380 \times 10^{-23}$ joule $°K^{-1}$. As we will see later, the probability is calculated by making a summation over all the molecules of the system. The summation can, of course, be made only by statistical methods since even in a small piece of solid material the numbers of atoms and molecules are enormous. We will encounter the calculation of the number of possible configurations of a system in a number of different associations throughout the text. In Chapter 4 we will compute the number of ways that vacancies can be distributed among atomic sites in a crystal. In Chapter 13 the number of ways in which vibrational modes may be distributed among the atoms of a crystal will be presented. In Chapter 15 we will discuss the number of ways in which a system of atoms have particular spin values. In all cases the entropy is directly related to the number of possible energy configurations.

Since it will be appropriate to our discussion of binary alloys, we now calculate the entropy associated with the random mixing of the atoms of two elements. Suppose in unit volume of a crystal there are $N_0$ lattice sites on which are arranged $n_B$ atoms of element $B$ and $n_A$ atoms of element $A$. The entropy of mixing $\Delta S_m$ will be the entropy $\Delta S_{A,B}$ associated with the solution of $A$ and $B$ minus the entropy $\Delta S_A$ associated with the $A$ atoms alone, minus the entropy $\Delta S_B$ associated with the $B$ atoms alone.

Thus

$$\Delta S_m = \Delta S_{A,B} - \Delta S_A - \Delta S_B \qquad (3.10)$$

From Equation 3.9 we have

$$\Delta S_m = k[\ln p_{A,B} - \ln p_A - \ln p_B] \qquad (3.11)$$

The term $p_{A,B}$ is the number of ways of arranging $n_A$, $A$ atoms and $n_B$, $B$ atoms on $N_0$ sites if $A$ atoms can be distinguished from $B$ but not from one another. Suppose, for a moment, that we were able to distinguish one atom from another and that each site could hold only one atom. Then, of course, $p_{A,B}$ would be $N_0!$ The number $p_{A,B}$ will be less than this since we cannot distinguish between the $A$ atoms and between the $B$ atoms. The number of ways of arranging distinguishable $A$ atoms among $n_A$ sites is $n_A!$ Also, the number of ways of arranging the distinguishable $B$ atoms among $n_B$ sites is $n_B!$ The number of ways of arranging $n_A$ atoms of $A$ and $n_B$ atoms of $B$ on $N_0$ sites when the only possible distinction is between $A$ and $B$ is therefore given by dividing $N_0!$ by $n_A!$ and by $n_B!$

Thus

$$P_{A,B} = \frac{N_0!}{n_A!\, n_B!}$$

The values of $p_A$ and $p_B$ are both unity since all of the ways of arranging $n_A$ atoms of $A$ are indistinguishable. We thus have

$$\Delta S_m = k[\ln p_{A,B} - \ln(1) - \ln(1)]$$

$$= k \ln\left[\frac{N_0!}{n_A!\, n_B!}\right] \qquad (3.12)$$

For the large numbers always encountered, Stirling's approximation can be used. This is

$$\ln N! \simeq N \ln N - N \qquad (3.13)$$

Thus

$$\Delta S_m = N_0 k\left[\frac{n_A}{N_0} \ln \frac{N_0}{n_A} + \frac{n_B}{N_0} \ln \frac{N_0}{n_B}\right] \qquad (3.14)$$

We can simplify this equation by letting the atomic fraction of $A$ atoms be $X_A$ and the atomic fraction of $B$ atoms be $X_B$. Then

$$X_A = \frac{n_A}{N}$$

and

$$X_B = \frac{n_B}{N_0}$$

giving

$$\Delta S_m = -N_0 k[X_A \ln X_A + X_B \ln X_B] \qquad (3.15)$$

This is the well-known "entropy of mixing" equation. Figure 3.3 shows a plot of the entropy $\Delta S_m$ against composition.


## 3.3   Free Energy of Binary Systems

We are now equipped to investigate some aspects of the free energy associated with the mixing of $A$ and $B$ atoms. We have seen that a system will rearrange to minimize the free energy. Were we aware of all the factors which contribute to the free energy we would be able to calculate exactly the nature and composition of the different phases in which a binary alloy would exist if in equilibrium. This is beyond quantitative calculation at the present time. What we can do is to relate theory and experiment in a semi-quantitative manner. Let us first introduce one more thermodynamic

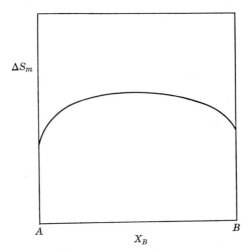

**Fig. 3.3**   Entropy of mixing $\Delta S_m$ versus composition $X_B$ for a binary alloy of two elements $A$ and $B$.

quantity which will simplify the algebra. We can write

$$dG = dE + P\,dV - T\,dS$$

as

$$dG = dH - T\,dS \tag{3.16}$$

where $H$ is called the *enthalpy*.

### Dilute Solution of B in A

Suppose the atomic fraction $X_A$ of $A$ atoms is mixed with $X_B$, the atomic fraction of $B$ atoms. Then the Gibbs free energy of the mixture is given by

$$\Delta G_m = X_A\,\Delta H_A + X_B\,\Delta H_B + N_0 kT[X_A \ln X_A + X_B \ln X_B] \\ - TX_A\,\Delta S_A - TX_B\,\Delta S_B$$

Let us find out how the free energy changes on addition of a small number of $B$ atoms. We must differentiate to get $\partial G_m/\partial X_B$, a quantity called the *chemical potential*. The terms $\ln X_A$ and $\ln X_B$ will vary very little with a small change in composition. The term $X_A$ will vary with a change in $X_B$ with a negative slope of unity since

$$1 - X_A = X_B$$

Thus

$$\frac{\partial G_m}{\partial X_B} = -\Delta H_A + \Delta H_B + N_0 kT \ln\left(\frac{X_B}{1 - X_B}\right) - T\Delta S_A - T\Delta S_B \tag{3.17}$$

For a dilute solution of $B$ in $A$ we have

$$\Delta H_A \quad \text{and} \quad \Delta S_A \simeq 0 \quad \text{and} \quad 1 - X_B \simeq 1$$

Also for a dilute solution of $B$ in $A$, the atoms of $B$ will be far apart and will not interact with one another to any great extent. The terms $\Delta H_B$ and $\Delta S_B$ will therefore be negligible. The change in free energy with composition for a very dilute alloy thus depends almost entirely on the $N_0 kT \ln [X_B/(1 - X_B)]$ term.

We will examine this term more closely. If $X_B \to 0$, then $\ln X_B \to -\infty$ and thus, regardless of the magnitude of the other terms, $\partial G_m/\partial X_B$ must be negative. Therefore the introduction of solute into a solid solvent will always reduce the free energy. Thus there always exists a strong tendency for a pure material to dissolve small amounts of available impurity. We will later plot diagrams of free energy versus composition and have just discovered that the ends of the free energy line must always curve sharply upward.

In order to construct a free energy versus composition diagram we must know how both the enthalpy and entropy terms behave. The enthalpy term is volume dependent. However, in a solid the volume changes little and thus the enthalpy is dominated by the internal energy. Strong internal bonds are characterized, as discussed before, by large negative internal energy. In a mixture of $A$ and $B$ atoms, the $A$ atoms may be more strongly bonded to $B$ atoms than to one another. Then the introduction of $B$ atoms to an $A$ solid would result in a lowering of the enthalpy, and we might expect a minimum at about the 50-50 atomic per cent composition. If, on the other hand, $A$-$A$ bonds are stronger than $A$-$B$ bonds, then addition of $B$ atoms to $A$ atoms would raise the enthalpy. An *ideal* variation occurs when $A$-$A$ bonds are similar in strength to $A$-$B$ bonds and the enthalpy varies linearly with composition between its two end values.

The following discussion treats the variation of free energy with composition for the negative, positive, and ideal enthalpy behavior. The entropy term in the free energy is, of course, lowered by addition of $B$ atoms to $A$ atoms.

### Negative and Ideal Enthalpy versus Composition

Figure 3.4$a$ shows the variation of enthalpy $H$, entropy term $-TS_m$, and the free energy $G$, with composition for the case of a *negative* enthalpy variation. Figure 3.4$b$ shows these terms for an *ideal* enthalpy variation. In both cases a single minimum occurs in the free energy, showing that the solution of $B$ atoms in $A$ is stable.

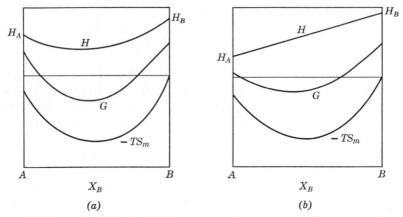

**Fig. 3.4** (a) $H$, $-TS_m$, and $G$ plotted against composition $X_B$ for a binary alloy in which there is a *negative* variation of enthalpy with composition. The $A$—$B$ bonds are stronger than $A$—$A$ bonds. (b) $H$, $-TS_m$ and $G$ plotted against composition $X_B$ for a binary alloy in which there is an *ideal* variation of enthalpy with composition. The $A$—$B$ bonds are equal in strength to the $A$—$A$ bonds.

### Positive Enthalpy versus Composition

The case where the enthalpy varies in a positive manner with composition is more interesting and will be discussed for a high and low temperature.

At high enough temperatures the $-TS_m$ term is sufficiently negative to overcome the positive enthalpy term at all compositions and so $G$ has a minimum and the solution is always stable. This is shown in Fig. 3.5$a$.

At low enough temperatures the $-TS_m$ term may be overcome by the positive enthalpy variation. Since we have already seen that the free energy always slopes upward toward the end points of the composition ranges, there must now result a double minimum in the free energy versus composition diagram. Figure 3.5$b$ shows the double minimum for a low enough temperature.

It is instructive to discuss the stability of two compositions $X_1$ and $X_2$. The alloy of composition $X_1$ is more stable than pure $A$ or pure $B$ and will therefore exist. At a composition $X_2$ the free energy would be lowered if the alloy decomposed into two different solutions, one of composition $e$ and the other of composition $f$. We decide on the two stable compositions $e$ and $f$ in the following way. Anticipating a fuller discussion in Section 4.4, it can be stated that the variation of free energy with composition or, in other words, the chemical potential must be equalized across a portion of solid to inhibit mixing or unmixing. The stable compositions $e$ and $f$ will thus occur where common tangents to the $G$ curve exist. These are the compositions of equal chemical potential.

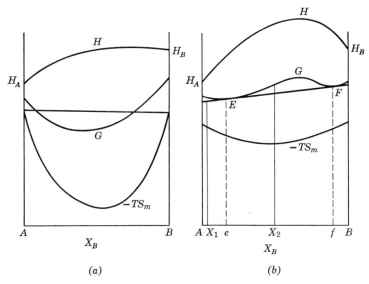

**Fig. 3.5**   (*a*) High temperature variation of $H$, $-TS_m$, and $G$ with composition. $A$—$B$ bonds $>$ $A$—$A$ bonds.  (*b*) Low temperature variation of $H$, $-TS_m$, and $G$ with composition.  $A$—$B$ bonds $>$ $A$—$A$ bonds.

### 3.4   Comparison of Free Energy and Phase in Equilibrium

We can now qualitatively argue the kind of phase which should exist in equilibrium at various temperatures for a binary alloy.  This argument is not, however, produced in detail.  The scheme which will be followed is to draw *free energy versus composition* diagrams for various temperatures and to recognize the stable phases at the different temperatures.  This information is then transferred to a temperature versus composition or *phase diagram* in which the stable phases are separated by boundary lines.

#### Solutions Miscible in all Proportions

Figures 3.6*a*, *b*, *c*, and *d* show free energy versus composition curves at different temperatures for a completely miscible binary alloy in which the melting point temperatures of all the alloys of intermediate composition lie between the melting points of the pure elements.  The stable phases are recognized by a free energy minimum at each of the temperatures considered, and in Fig. 3.7 these stable phases are labeled on a phase diagram of temperature versus composition.

It must be emphasized again that these phases are the equilibrium phases.

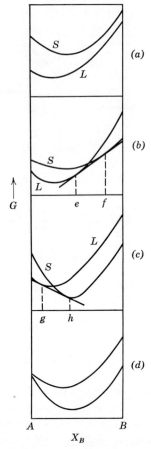

**Fig. 3.6** (a) At temperature $T_1$ above the melting points of A and B. S is the solid and L the liquid curves of G versus $X_B$. (b) At $T_2$ between the melting point of B and the melting point of A. S curve dips below L curve. Liquid phase stable between compositions A and e. Between e and f liquid phase of composition e coexists with solid phase of composition f. (c) At a lower temperature $T_3$ between the melting point of B and the melting point of A. Liquid phase stable from composition A to g. Liquid and solid coexist from g to h. Solid solutions exist from h to B. (d) At $T_4$ the melting point of A. S and L curves meet at the A composition. At all other compositions solid solutions are stable.

Because of the slow rates of atom migration in solids, equilibrium is seldom if ever achieved.

The copper-nickel system reveals solid solubility (see Fig. 3.8). In this type of phase diagram the upper curved line is called the *liquidus* line and represents the limit of the liquid phase, and the lower curved line is called the *solidus* and represents the limit of the solid phase. Points in the area

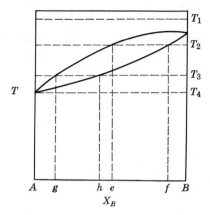

**Fig. 3.7** Phase diagram showing the stable phases at various temperatures and compositions for a completely miscible binary alloy. The temperatures $T_1, T_2, T_3$, and $T_4$ are those of the free energy diagrams of Fig. 3.6.

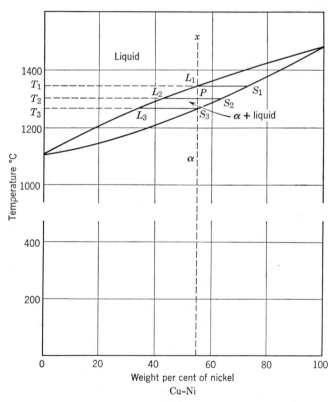

**Fig. 3.8** Binary phase diagram with complete miscibility.

between the lines represent composition-temperature combinations in the form of mixtures of solid and liquid phase. If an alloy of arbitrary composition, say about 55 per cent nickel, is cooled very slowly from the liquid phase (point $x$) and equilibrium is maintained, the solidification will take place in the following sequence. When the temperature has fallen to $T_1$ solidification begins, the solid first formed being of composition $S_1$, which is richer in nickel than 55 per cent. The remaining melt will thus be enriched in copper. At a lower temperature $T_2$ further solidification takes place, the composition of the solid in equilibrium with liquid being $S_2$. If the cooling is sufficiently slow, the original solid deposit will have time to absorb copper from the liquid to change its composition from $S_1$ to $S_2$. Finally, at temperature $T_3$ no liquid remains, and the solid has attained the uniform composition of $x$.

It is readily understood that if the cooling is too rapid to permit diffusion of copper from the liquid into the forming solid, each layer of solid that is deposited differs in composition from the preceding layer. This is called *coring*. Coring is often found in practice and may be removed by suitable annealing at a high enough temperature and for sufficient time to allow diffusion of atoms to homogenize the solid.

### Binary Eutectic

It is rare to find, as in the last example, two elements in the solid state which are completely soluble in one another. Partial solubility is much more common. The following investigates two elements, ordinarily solid, which are completely soluble in one another when in the liquid state but are only partially soluble when in the solid state. We will suppose that the two elements $A$ and $B$ have different crystal structures. In such a case we must draw free energy curves corresponding to each type of crystal. Figures 3.9$a$, $b$, and $c$ show free energy curves drawn as a function of composition for three different temperatures. Only one liquid $L$ curve need be drawn since $A$ and $B$ are soluble in one another in the liquid state. Individual free energy curves $S_\alpha$ and $S_\beta$ must, however, be drawn for the $\alpha$ crystal structure, which is similar to the pure $A$ structure, and for the $\beta$ structure, which is similar to the pure $B$ structure. The detail of the curves is given in the captions of Fig. 3.9. A phase diagram designating the stable phases at different temperatures and compositions can now be deduced from the individual free energy diagrams. This diagram is called a *eutectic*, signifying partial solubility only in the solid state. Figure 3.10 shows the aluminum-silicon phase diagram, which is typically eutectic in nature. Also included in Fig. 3.10 are a series of photomicrographs which show the structures of several phases at room temperature which will be discussed next.

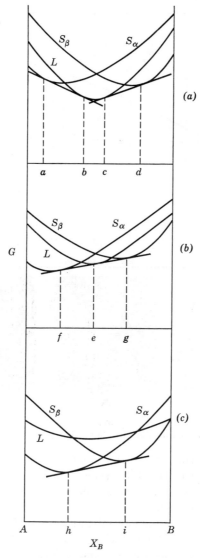

**Fig. 3.9** (a) At $T_1$ just below the lower melting point. Between composition $A$ and $\alpha$ a solid solution of $\alpha$ exists. Between $a$ and $b$ solid solution $\alpha$ is in equilibrium with liquid. Between $c$ and $d$ liquid coexists with solid solution $\beta$. Between $d$ and $B$ solid solution $\beta$ exists. (b) At $T_2$, the *eutectic* temperature. At composition $e$ a mixture of $\alpha$ solid, $\beta$ solid and liquid coexist. (c) At $T_3$ below the *eutectic* temperature. Between $A$ and $h$ solid phase $\alpha$ exists. Between $h$ and $i$ solid $\alpha$ coexists with solid $\beta$. Between $i$ and $B$ solid $\beta$ exists.

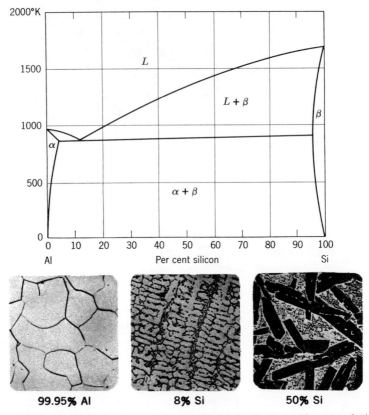

**Fig. 3.10** Aluminum-silicon phase diagram. (From A. G. Guy, *Elements of Physical Metallurgy*, Addison-Wesley Pub. Co., Reading, Mass., 1951)

At 99–100% Al. This shows the grain structures of the pure metal. There is a little segregation of Si to the grain boundaries. This is an α solid solution.

At say 8% Si This shows the α + β eutectic microconstituent, which is an intimate mixture of α and β and is one phase, surrounding the white α solid solution crystals. These crystals are long and fernlike or *dendritic*. They have been formed by slow solidification of the α phase on close-packed planes.

At say 50% Si Here the α + β eutectic microconstituent is intermingled with black lumps of β solid solution. The β solution is similar in crystal structure to that of pure Si. As we have seen, this is essentially diamond cubic and is not close-packed. Dendritic growth does not readily take place in such a structure.

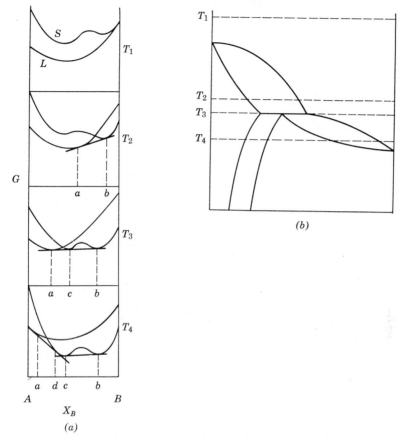

**Fig. 3.11** (*a*) Free energy versus composition curves at three temperatures $T_1$, $T_2$, and $T_3$. The binary alloy shows a peritectic reaction at the peritectic temperature $T_3$. (*b*) The equilibrium phase diagram deduced from (*a*).

### Binary Peritectic

With this kind of phase diagram there is a solid reaction in which liquid plus phase $\alpha$ transforms to another phase $\beta$. This is the *peritectic* reaction. Figure 3.11 shows the free energy curves and the deduced phase diagram. The peritectic reaction can occur if one component of the binary alloy has a much lower melting point than the other component. The reader is left to work out the detail from the diagram. Peritectic reactions are found in the important steel or iron-carbon system and in the brass or copper-zinc system.

### Binary Phase Diagram with Intermediate Phases

We have already stated that one of the factors limiting the solubility of one solid in another is a tendency in some instances toward formation of a

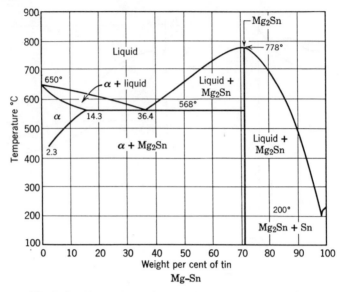

**Fig. 3.12**   Binary phase diagram with an intermediate phase.

chemical compound. Thus magnesium, for example, forms compounds of the type MgX with S, Se, or Te, of the type $Mg_2X$ with Si, Ge, Sn, or Pb, and of the type $Mg_3X$ with $As_2$, $Sb_2$, or $Bi_2$. The nature of an equilibrium diagram which contains an intermediate compound is illustrated by the magnesium-tin system shown in Fig. 3.12. The compound $Mg_2Sn$ contains 29.08 per cent by weight of magnesium. The complete phase diagram consists of two eutectic diagrams placed together, with the dividing line coming at the compound composition.

The main features of binary equilibrium phase diagrams have now been demonstrated. More complex systems are, of course, produced by increasing the number of components to more than two, but no new fundamental principles are involved.

## 3.5   The Lever Rule

The *lever rule* is a simple rule by which the relative proportions of two phases in a binary alloy can be quickly deduced from the composition of the alloy and the compositions of the two phases. Suppose that we have an alloy of two components $A$ and $B$, the weight concentrations (i.e., fractions by weight) being $C$ and $1 - C$, respectively. The alloy is a mixture of two phases, 1 and 2, in which the concentrations of $A$ are respectively $C_1$ and $C_2$

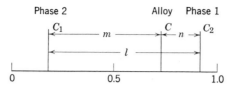

**Fig. 3.13**   The lever rule.

(see Fig. 3.13).   Let the proportion of phase 1 in the alloy be $x$ so that the proportion of phase 2 is $1 - x$.   The problem is to find $x$ and $1 - x$ in terms of $C$, $C_1$, and $C_2$.   If the total weight of alloy is $W$, the weight of $A$ is $CW$. The weight of $A$ in phase 1 is $xC_1W$, and the weight of $A$ in phase 2 is $(1 - x)C_2W$.   Hence $CW = xC_1W + (1 - x)C_2W$, so that

$$x = \frac{C - C_2}{C_1 - C_2} = \frac{m}{l}$$

$$1 - x = \frac{C_1 - C}{C_1 - C_2} = \frac{n}{l} \tag{3.18}$$

and

$$\frac{x}{1 - x} = \frac{C - C_2}{C_1 - C} = \frac{m}{n}$$

Equation 3.18 expresses the lever rule.   Application of the rule in Fig. 3.8 for a temperature $T_2$ and composition $x$ shows that the two phases, liquid and solid which are present, are in the ratio

$$\frac{\text{weight of solid of composition } S_2}{\text{weight of liquid of composition } L_2} = \frac{PL_2}{PS_2}$$

## 3.6 Nonequilibrium Solidification

So far we have discussed only equilibrium phases which occur in binary alloys.   Under the usual conditions of solidification, most alloys are not in equilibrium.   This is because of the slow rates of diffusion of atoms in solids. We have already mentioned coring as a consequence of nonequilibrium solidification.   Eutectic nonequilibrium phases are often produced by rapid cooling from the melt, and nonequilibrium peritectic constituents are almost always formed.   Equilibrium is approximated only by long annealing at the highest temperature within the phase limits.   At this point it is constructive to enuciate the physical principles governing the rate of approach to equilibrium.

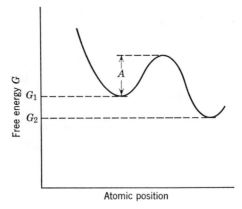

**Fig. 3.14**   Free energy plotted as a function of atomic position.

## 3.7   The Rate of Approach to Equilibrium

In actual physical systems an irreversible process often causes changes which inhibit the continuation of the process. The reaction is stopped by an activation energy barrier. At higher temperatures the atoms may be thermally activated over the barrier, and the reaction can then continue.

Let us represent the free energy as a function of atomic position, as in Fig. 3.14. The free energy can be reduced from $G_1$ to $G_2$ if thermal activation is sufficient to overcome the activation barrier $A$. The relative chance of an atom acquiring this energy is $e^{-A/kT}$. Obviously, this chance is increased by raising the temperature.

Another way of saying the same thing is as follows. If $q$ is the energy per atom, the fraction of atoms possessing energy greater than $q$ is $e^{-q/kT}$. Expressed per mole the fraction is $e^{-Q/kT}$, where $Q$ is the energy per mole and

$$R = kN$$

where $N$ is Avogadro's number.

The rate $r$ of the reaction, which is dependent on the barrier $A$, is thus given by

$$r = Ze^{-Q/RT} \tag{3.19}$$

where $Z$ is a constant.

## 3.8   Metastability

Often the activation energy barrier is high enough that the reaction cannot take place under possible thermal activation. Such a system will then remain in a state of local equilibrium with only a negligible chance of being activated over the barrier into the lower and more stable free energy configuration. The system is said to be *metastable*. A well-known example is diamond, which will exist at all readily attainable temperatures without transformation into graphite, the more stable form of carbon. Thus stable and metastable equilibriums are dependent only on the relative energies involved, and in nature most systems are, in fact, metastable. Martensite, the main hardening constituent of steels, is metastable relative to a mixture of ferrite and cementite, other phases in the carbon-iron diagram. Metals and alloys contain dislocations, discussed in Chapter 5, which are also metastable with respect to the perfect lattice. It is the ease or difficulty of motion of these dislocations which give the metal its characteristic strength. A supercooled liquid is metastable relative to the solid phase. We can introduce a fundamental characteristic of solidification by further reference to this last example.

### 3.9   Nucleation

In the gaseous or vapor phase there is no regularity of pattern or order among the atoms. If the temperature is sufficiently reduced, the atoms will condense into the solid phase and take up the most favored positions in the force fields of the neighboring atoms. There is then a long-range regularity of pattern or order. The long-range order in crystalline solids is evident from the physical character of, say, X-ray diffraction or anisotropy of yield strength and other properties.

The liquid state is interpolated between the two so that at the *triple point temperature*, where all three phases coexist, some continuity between long-range order in the crystal and no order in the vapor can be accommodated by the structure.

In the liquid, thermal motion produces random statistical fluctuations of atomic grouping. It is generally assumed that some of these groups are structurally quite similar to the embryo of a small solid crystal. Let us examine the criteria by which one can decide whether such an embryo crystal grows or perishes.

#### *Homogeneous Nucleation*

There is a free energy difference between liquid and solid. The free energy is temperature dependent and is, of course, zero at the temperature at which the crystal and the liquid can coexist. If $f$ is the free energy difference per unit volume, then for a spherical embryo of radius $r$ the free energy difference between solid and liquid embryo due to the difference in *volume* will be

$\frac{4}{3}\pi r^3 f$. The atoms of the crystal embryo are not in registry with those of the surrounding liquid and thus a *surface* energy term also exists. If $\gamma$ is the surface energy per unit area, then the surface term will be $4\pi r^2\gamma$.

Thus the free energy $b$ required to create a crystal nucleus of radius $r$ in a supercooled liquid is given by

$$b = \tfrac{4}{3}\pi r^3 f + 4\pi r^2\gamma \qquad (3.20)$$

Above the equilibrium temperature of liquid and solid the energy $b$ will increase with $r$. This merely states that it is unlikely at higher temperatures that solid exists in the liquid. Below the equilibrium temperature the volume term $\frac{4}{3}\pi r^3 f$ is negative, and the free energy $b$ increases with $r$ up to a critical size before decreasing. This behavior is sketched in Fig. 3.15.

The critical size of nucleus $r_c$ is found by differentiating to get $\partial b/\partial r$ and equating to zero. Then it is quickly shown that

$$r_c = \frac{2\gamma}{f} \qquad (3.21)$$

and $B$, the maximum value of $b$, is given by

$$B = \frac{16\pi\gamma^3}{3f^2} \qquad (3.22)$$

If we now used this value of $B$ in a rate equation such as (3.19) we would neglect consideration of the arrival of atoms at the appropriate critical size nucleus. We will see in Chapter 4 that such diffusion of atoms is also a

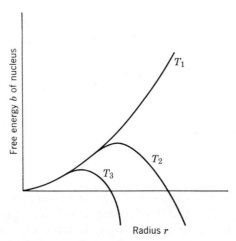

**Fig. 3.15**  The free energy $b$ associated with the creation of a nucleus, in homogeneous nucleation, for different radii of nucleus.

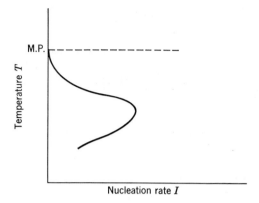

**Fig. 3.16**  The nucleation rate $I$ versus temperature $T$ in homogeneous nucleation.

thermally activated process.  A migration energy, which we will call $M$, is involved.  Thus the nucleation rate $I$ will be given by an equation in which

$$I \quad \text{is proportional to} \quad e^{-(B+M)/kT} \tag{3.23}$$

Now let us consider qualitatively what this relation implies.  We have seen that below the melting point of a solid the factor $e^{-B/kT}$ increases.  The diffusion term $e^{-M/kT}$, however, decreases since thermal activation is necessary for the migration of atoms through the solid.  The rate $I$ will therefore first increase as the temperature falls and then decrease as migration of the atoms ceases.  Figure 3.16 shows the dependence of $I$ on $T$.

### Heterogeneous Nucleation

In almost all practical cases, where inhomogeneities occur in the melt or on the walls of the container, homogeneous nucleation does not occur.  Rather, dust particles, sharp points on the container walls and other localities act as *heterogeneous* nucleation centers.  In a pure metal, in which such centers have been carefully eliminated, supercooling of about 100 degrees occurs before homogeneous nucleation takes place.  Heterogeneous nucleation also accounts for the formation of liquid droplets from the vapor phase.

It is possible to show that the relative ease with which heterogeneous nucleation takes place in comparison with homogeneous nucleation is mostly accounted for by considering differences in interfacial tension.  Let us envisage, as in Fig. 3.17, a spherical cap of solid phase $\alpha$ forming on a solid nucleating surface while surrounded by a liquid phase.  If $\gamma_{\alpha L}$, $\gamma_{SL}$, and $\gamma_{\alpha S}$ are, respectively, the $\alpha$-liquid, solid-liquid, and $\alpha$-solid interfacial tensions,

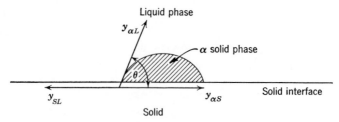

**Fig. 3.17**   An α solid nucleus growing on a solid from the liquid.  The interfacial tensions are shown by the arrows.

then from the diagram we have

$$\gamma_{SL} = \gamma_{\alpha S} + \gamma_{\alpha L} \cos \theta \qquad (3.24)$$

As the spherical cap or nucleus develops it covers a larger area on the nucleating surface.  The high energy $S$-$L$ surface is replaced by the lower energy $\alpha$-$S$ interface.  Thus in Equation 3.20 for homogeneous nucleation we must now include a negative term which is the free energy per unit area of growing $\alpha$-$S$ interface.  The free energy $b$ is reduced by $\gamma_{\alpha S} - \gamma_{SL}$, which is equal to $\gamma_{\alpha L} \cos \theta$.  Thus heterogeneous nucleation occurs much more readily than homogeneous nucleation.  In practical cases most metals solidify with only a few degrees of supercooling.

### Accommodation Stresses

If a new phase grows in a solid then the total free energy $b$ must contain still another term, the elastic strain energy.  This occurs because the volume of unit mass of the new solid phase will generally not coincide exactly with the volume of unit mass of the solid matrix.  Then accommodation stresses are generated and the free energy raised.  These accommodation stresses account, for example, for alloy hardening in martensite, the hard constituent of quench-hardened carbon steels.

### 3.10   Thin Films

A special kind of nucleation and growth is involved in the technique of producing thin films by vacuum evaporation.  The film may be continuous or, in the case of evaporation of the noble metals, it may be condensed in "island films" of up to $10^{-8}$ m in thickness.  Under certain growth conditions the evaporated and condensed films have preferred crystal orientations.  In *epitaxial* films the crystal orientation is determined by the orientation and crystal structure of the underlying substrate.

Commonly, molecules or atoms at thermal energies are evaporated at a definite angle onto a cold or heated solid substrate. At close distances to the surface of the substrate the atom enters an attractive field and at still closer, a repulsive field. The repulsive forces arise because the electronic cloud of the evaporated atom penetrates the electronic clouds of the surface atoms. The repulsive forces will therefore have the periodicity of the crystal structure of the substrate, which can affect the crystal of the evaporated layer as in epitaxy. Migration takes place over the surface with an activation energy which is associated with surface diffusion. The atoms may also be thermally released or de-adsorbed from the surface. Permanent condensation commonly occurs at nucleation centers, which may be clusters of condensed atoms, irregularities in the substrate surface, or "seed" crystals of a different material.

Most metals condense in crystalline form, with the crystallite size increasing with the temperature of the substrate. Amorphous layers have been formed in the deposition of some dielectrics and metals such as antimony at low substrate temperatures.

The manufacture of thin films is of great importance in the electronics industry. Reference will be made to their uses in the appropriate chapters.


## 3.11   The Preparation of Very Pure Materials

The presence of quite small numbers of foreign atoms in a solid element markedly affects many of the physical characteristics of the element. This is not surprising since it may be easily calculated that in a solid with, say, one foreign atom per thousand lattice atoms, few points in the solid, if it is homogeneous, are more distant from a foreign atom than about eight atomic spacings.

*Zone refining* is a powerful method for the purification of metals and some intermediate compounds. It has made possible the purification of germanium and silicon to the degree necessary for use in transistors and other solid state electronic devices. The principles of the method will be outlined in a manner following the original work of Pfann (1958).

In a binary alloy the presence of solute may lower or raise the freezing point temperature of the solvent. If the freezing point is lowered, the equilibrium phase diagram will take the form at low solute concentrations shown in Fig. 3.18. Here $K_0$, the distribution coefficient, which is the ratio of solute concentration in solid to solute concentration in liquid, is less than unity. In the solidification of a dilute alloy of this nature, the solute will be concentrated in the last regions to freeze.

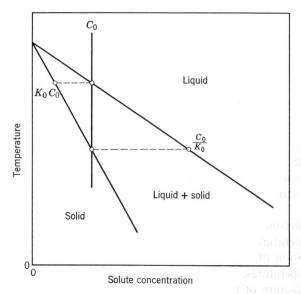

**Fig. 3.18** Equilibrium phase diagram at low concentration of solute that lowers the melting point of the solvent.

Let us consider a rod of constant cross section and uniform concentration $C_0$ of solute along its length. This may be produced in a number of ways, for example, by rapid freezing from the melt, as in chill casting. Now suppose that, as in Fig. 3.19, a molten zone of short length $l$ is made to pass from left to right along the rod. This may be done by moving the rod in a suitable refractory through a small furnace or alternatively and more commonly by moving the furnace. At $x = 0$ the first solid to freeze is of concentration $K_0 C_0$. If $K_0 < 1$, the liquid is enriched in solute by the solidification. As the zone progresses, the liquid continues to be enriched unit it attains the solute concentration $C_0/K_0$. When this condition is reached, the concentrations of solute in the solid entering and leaving the molten zone are identical.

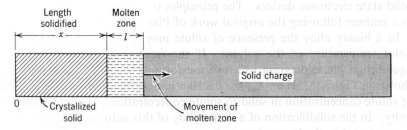

**Fig. 3.19** Molten zone passing along length of metal as in zone refining.

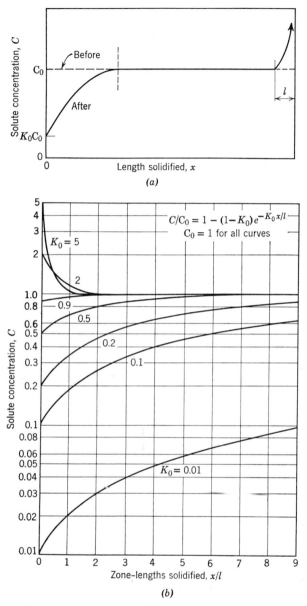

Fig. 3.20 (a) Solute concentration at different distances along metal rod after a single pass of the molten zone. (b) Solute concentrations after a single pass for $C_0 = 1$ and various values of $K_0$. (After Pfann)

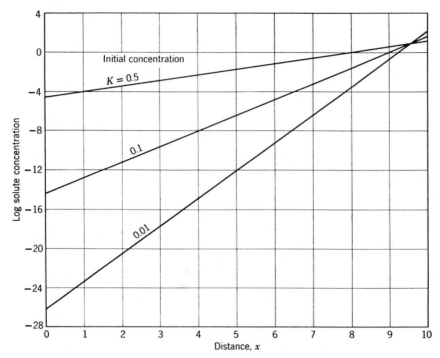

**Fig. 3.21**    Ultimate distribution attainable by zone refining for several values of $K$, for an ingot 10 zones long. $K$ is the effective value of the distribution coefficient $K_0$ appropriate to nonequilibrium conditions. (After Pfann)

The concentration $C$ of solute at a position $x$ in the zone melted bar is given, except in the last zone, by the equation*,

$$\frac{C}{C_0} = 1 - (1 - K_0)e^{-K_0 x/l} \tag{3.25}$$

Equation 3.25 giving solute concentration as a function of $x$, is plotted in Fig. 3.20$a$. In Fig. 3.20$b$ the zone-melting curves with $C_0$ equal to unity are drawn for various values of $K_0$ and for lengths solidified of up to nine times the zone length. Both Figs. 3.20$a$ and 3.20$b$ give the concentrations after a single pass of the molten zone. As can be seen for small values of $K_0$. considerable purification can be effected in the initial portion of the rod by even single-pass zone melting.

Much greater purification is attained by passing the zone repeatedly down the solid bar always in the same direction. This is often done by

* See W. G. Pfann, *Zone Melting*, John Wiley and Sons, New York, 1958.

returning the furnace quickly to the starting point after completion of a slow zone pass. During each pass the molten zone picks up solute on its way and deposits it at the end of the rod. After repeated passes in one direction, a distribution of solute is reached that cannot be further changed. Figure 3.21 shows the ultimate distribution after multiple zone refining for various $K_0$ values. From the diagram with $K_0 = 0.1$ and the zone length one-tenth of the bar length, we see that the ultimate concentration at $x = 0$ is less than $C_0$ by a factor of $10^{14}$. In addition, since the concentration at the starting end is decreased by a factor of the order of $K_0$ for each pass (see Fig. 3.20$b$), at least fourteen passes are required to reach the ultimate distribution.

Whereas impurities with $K_0 < 1$ are transported with the liquid zone, impurities with $K_0 > 1$ move in the opposite direction. If both types of impurity are present, in order to obtain a highly refined rod it is necessary to crop both ends and use only the central portion.

For germanium it has been possible by the zone-refining process to reduce impurities to a level less than one impurity atom in $10^{10}$ germanium atoms. Since however, ultimate purity is dependent on the relevant value of $K_0$, such refinement is not always possible.

### References

Hume-Rothery, W., and G. V. Raynor, *The Structure of Metals and Alloys*, 3rd ed., The Institute of Metals, London, 1954.
Most texts on metallurgy discuss alloys.

### Exercises

1. The size factor favors solid solubility for each of the following alloys. Consider the relative valency effect and say whether or not solubility will be favored or restricted. Solute follows solvent.

| K  | — | Rb | Mg | — | Cd | Ag | — | Sn |
|----|---|----|----|---|----|----|---|----|
| Rb | — | Cs | As | — | Sb | Sn | — | Ag |
| Ag | — | Au | Se | — | Te | Pd | — | Pt |
| Cu | — | Si | Cu | — | Ge | Ag | — | Mg |
| Si | — | Cu | Ge | — | Cu | Mg | — | Ag |

2. In the compound CuZn there are two atoms and three valency electrons (one from the copper and two from the zinc). The electron-atom ratio is thus $3:2$.

The following compounds are grouped according to their electron-atom ratios. Work out the effective valencies for each element.

| Ratio 3:2 | 21:13 | 7:3 |
|---|---|---|
| CuBe | $Cu_5Zn_8$ | $CuZn_3$ |
| AgMg | $Cu_5Cd_8$ | $CuCd_3$ |
| AgZn | $Cu_9Al_4$ | $Cu_3Sn$ |
| AgCd | $Cu_9Ga_4$ | $Ag_3Sn$ |
| AuZn | $Cu_9In_4$ | $Ag_5Al_3$ |
| CoAl | $Cu_{31}Si_8$ | $Au_5Al_3$ |

For a number of these compounds calculate the percentage by weight of the elements. Refer to a table of atomic weights.

3. Decide whether the carbon atoms are interstitial or substitutional in the iron-carbon alloy whose characteristics are given.

> Per cent weight of carbon = 0.8
> Structure: face-centered cubic
> Lattice parameter $a$ = 3.583 A
> Density of alloy = 8142 $kgm^{-3}$

4. The copper-nickel equilibrium diagram of Fig. 3.8 shows complete solid solubility. Liquid copper-nickel alloys containing, respectively, 80 per cent, 50 per cent, and 10 per cent by weight of nickel are cooled from the melt. Give the compositions of the first solid to form in each case. If one kilogram of the 50 per cent nickel alloy is used, how much solid can be filtered out at 1300°C?

5. Consider the Al-Si phase diagram of Fig. 3.10. Determine the percentage of $\alpha$ solid solution in the eutectic microconstituent following solidification. Using the 70 per cent by weight silicon alloy, determine the phases and percentages of each at (a) 900°K and (b) 700°K.

6. Sketch roughly the form of the temperature-time dependence for these alloys of Fig. 3.10 as they lose heat at a constant rate and transform from the liquid to the solid phase.

(a) 0 per cent Si.
(b) 10 per cent Si.
(c) the eutectic composition.
(d) 60 per cent Si.
(e) 100 per cent Si.

7. From Fig. 3.8 estimate the value of Ko for a very dilute alloy of copper in nickel. Suppose that a rod of nickel containing 0.1 per cent by weight of copper is zone refined, the molten zone being about one-tenth of the rod length. Estimate the ultimate purity attainable and the minimum number of passes.

8. A crystal surface is in a supersaturated vapor. An island monolayer, assumed circular, grows across the surface. Show that the critical radius $r_c$ for growth is given by

$$r_c = \frac{\sigma}{\epsilon}$$

where $\epsilon$ is the free energy gained per unit area when adsorbed molecules become attached to the island and $\sigma$ is the free energy per unit length of boundary step surrounding the island. Show also that the turning value of the free energy is given by $\pi\sigma^2/\epsilon$.

9. A small spherical crystal of radius $r_c$ is in equilibrium with its liquid. Write down an expression for the enthalpy change on melting and, by equating the free energy change on melting to zero, show that the melting point of the crystal is lower than the melting point $T_M$ in a large crystal by

$$T_M \frac{2\gamma V}{r_c L_M}$$

where $\gamma$ the crystal-liquid interfacial energy, $V$ the molar volume, and $L_M$ the latent heat per mole are all essentially independent of temperature.

# 4

## *Diffusion in Solids*

In Chapter 3 we saw that all phase changes in alloys involve a redistribution of the atoms present. This is true of many physical changes in solids, the kinetics of such changes being controlled by the migration of the participating atoms. This migration is called *diffusion*.

The hardening of steels is an industrial process based on the diffusion of carbon and other elements through iron. The production of age-hardened alloys depends on the dispersal of hardening compounds in a metallic matrix, the dispersal being brought about by diffusion. The basis of powder metallurgy is the diffusion at elevated temperatures and pressures of atoms from one grain to another. Crystals in a polycrystalline aggregate can grow in size under suitable conditions by the diffusion of atoms.

Surface oxidation is a phenomenon dependent on the diffusion penetration of a solid by oxygen atoms. At elevated temperatures and in the presence of an electric field the ions of the alkali halides can diffuse through the solid carrying electrical charges and thus leading to ionic conductivity.

In modern technology the production of germanium and silicon of extremely high purity and the doping of these elements with minute quantities of known impurities are the basis of semiconductor device fabrication. More recent techniques involve the growth of thin epitaxial films of semiconductor and magnetic elements. All of these processes involve diffusion. The sophistication of solid state devices is increasing at a very rapid rate, and the fabrication of these devices requires an increasing understanding and control of diffusion processes. Because of the present and future technological importance of diffusion, we will include in the discussion a fair amount of mathematical detail.

In a discussion of diffusion it is important to distinguish at the outset between macroscopic flow of atoms and the individual atomic movements which constitute it. In the ensuing treatment the term diffusion will mean the macroscopic flow.

Thermal agitation supplies an atom at occasional intervals with sufficient energy to enable it to climb the potential barrier between one atomic site and the next. The directions of the collisions between neighboring atoms are quite random, the resulting path of an individual migrating atom being therefore a haphazard zigzag. If, however, we consider a cross-sectional plane through a solid bar with a higher concentration of solute atoms or defects on one side of the plane than on the other, more solute atoms or defects will, in general, cross the plane from one side to the other than in the opposite direction, simply because more of them are available for such movement on the higher concentration side. There will be a statistical drift down the concentration gradient. Although as we shall see, this is not the most fundamental way of looking at diffusion, it is generally true.

In 1885 Fick proposed a set of equations to describe this mass flow by diffusion. These equations are the analogues of Fourier's heat flow equations. We will develop these equations for two particular sets of circumstances.

## 4.1 Steady State Flow

First let us discuss the Fick equations for the case in which the concentration gradients do not change with time over the region of flow. This is often the case for, say, flow of gases through metals where a constant pressure of gas is maintained on one side of a metal specimen, the gas being removed on the other. Hydrogen, nitrogen, and oxygen, for example, diffuse rapidly through many metals at elevated temperatures. In such instances, solubility is necessary for diffusion, an insoluble gas being able to pass only through pores and cracks and not through the solid metal.

Suppose in Fig. 4.1 that the two vertical lines represent adjacent atomic planes 1 and 2 distant $a$ apart in a solid. Each plane is of unit area. The concentrations $c_1$ and $c_2$ of solute atoms are the fractions of the total numbers of atoms on the respective planes. Let us also suppose that a concentration gradient $\partial c/\partial x$ of solute atoms exists in the direction marked, that is, $c_1 > c_2$. The argument which follows will apply equally well to defects.

There are $c_1 N$ and $c_2 N$ *solute* atoms on the respective planes if $N$ is the number of atoms on the planes. If the frequency of jumping, by thermal action, of solute atoms from each plane is $n$ times per second, then in unit time $nc_1 N/2$ solute atoms will jump from plane 1 to plane 2. In the same time $nc_2 N/2$ will jump from plane 2 to plane 1. Thus the net number $J$ of atoms transferred per second from plane 1 to plane 2 is $\frac{1}{2}nN(c_1 - c_2)$, that is,

$$
\begin{aligned}
J &= \tfrac{1}{2}nN(c_1 - c_2) \\
&= -\tfrac{1}{2}nNa\,\frac{\partial c}{\partial x} \quad \text{where} \quad c_1 - c_2 = -a\,\frac{\partial c}{\partial x} \\
&= -D_1\,\frac{\partial c}{\partial x}
\end{aligned}
\tag{4.1}
$$

where $D_1$ is the *diffusion coefficient* or *diffusivity*. $D_1$ is measured in units of square meters per second. It is dependent on temperature and frequently varies with concentration. When this is so the concentration must be known at each point $x$ in the solid in order to apply Equation 4.1.

## 4.2 Nonsteady State Flow

We shall now set up a much more general equation than (4.1) to describe nonsteady states of flow where the average concentration in a given region varies with time. This is the normal circumstance when solute atoms or defects migrate through a solid solvent.

Consider the two atomic planes of Fig. 4.1 to be in this case a distance $l$ apart, where $l$ is greater than one atomic distance. If the concentration of solute atoms on plane 1 is $c$, the concentration on plane 2 is $c + (\partial c/\partial x)l$. The *rate of exit* of solute atoms from the shaded volume element across plane 1 is $-\frac{1}{2}nNa(\partial c/\partial x)$. In addition, the *rate of entry* across plane 2 is $\frac{1}{2}nNa(\partial/\partial x)[c + (\partial c/\partial x)l]$. Thus the rate of accumulation of solute atoms in the volume element is

$$\frac{1}{2}nNa\left[\frac{\partial}{\partial x}\left(c + \frac{\partial c}{\partial x}l\right) - \frac{\partial c}{\partial x}\right]$$

that is,

$$\frac{1}{2}nNal\frac{\partial^2 c}{\partial x^2}$$

Since there are $l/a$ planes in the volume element, the rate of accumulation on any particular plane of the element is given by

$$\frac{\partial}{\partial t}(Nc) = \frac{1}{2}nNa^2\frac{\partial^2 c}{\partial x^2}$$

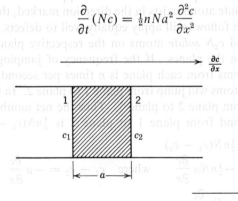

**Fig. 4.1** Derivation of Fick's laws.

Thus

$$\frac{\partial c}{\partial t} = \tfrac{1}{2}na^2 \frac{\partial^2 c}{\partial x^2}$$

or

$$\frac{\partial c}{\partial t} = D\frac{\partial^2 c}{\partial x^2} \tag{4.2}$$

where $D$ $(=\tfrac{1}{2}a^2 n)$ is the diffusion coefficient. Equation 4.2 expresses Fick's law in a more general form.

Where diffusion is not unidirectional but the solid is isotropic with respect to diffusion, the following partial differential equation applies:

$$\frac{\partial c}{\partial t} = D\left(\frac{\partial^2 c}{\partial x^2} + \frac{\partial^2 c}{\partial y^2} + \frac{\partial^2 c}{\partial z^2}\right) \tag{4.3}$$

or

$$\frac{\partial c}{\partial t} = D\,\nabla^2 c$$

Cubic crystals fulfill the isotropic condition, whereas hexagonal, rhombohedral, and tetragonal crystals require two diffusion coefficients.

These equations are developed in this simple form to give meaning to the concept of diffusivity. Later development will expand the meaning of $D$.

As in other theories in physics, the differential equation must be solved for particular boundary conditions appropriate to the situation. As an example we will quote the solution of Equation 4.3 for one set of boundary conditions. Consider diffusion across a plane interface between adjoining columns of solid solution and solid solvent. If the columns of solution and solvent are sufficiently long so that no appreciable change in composition occurs at their outer ends during the course of the observations, the columns can be regarded as of infinite length.

Under these conditions

$$c = \frac{c_0}{2}\left[1 - \frac{2}{\sqrt{\pi}} \int_0^{x/2\sqrt{Dt}} e^{-y^2}\, dy\right] \tag{4.4}$$

where $c$ is the concentration of solute in solvent after time $t$ at a distance $x$ from the interface, $c_0$ being the initial concentration, $D$ the coefficient of diffusion, and the second term in the bracket is the *probability integral*, values of which may be found in most books on statistics and probability. Figure 4.2 shows the concentration $c$ as a function of penetration $x$ measured from the interface, for various times of diffusion. The solution of Equation 4.3, which is quoted in (4.4) is only applicable if $D$ is a constant, independent of composition. Coefficient $D$ does usually vary with composition and the penetration curves are, as a consequence, distorted from those of Fig. 4.2.

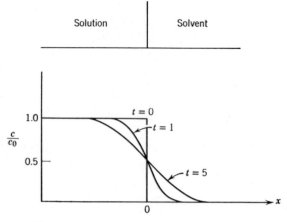

**Fig. 4.2**   Boundary diffusion. The concentration of solute in the solution is $c_0$ at time $t = 0$.

## 4.3   Variation of $D$ With Composition

Equation 4.3 assumes $D$ to be constant. In most diffusing systems, however, a variation of $D$ with composition is found. It would therefore be more generally correct to rewrite Equation 4.2 as

$$\frac{\partial c}{\partial t} = \frac{\partial}{\partial x}\left(D\,\frac{\partial c}{\partial x}\right)$$
(4.5)

to take account of a possible variation of $D$ with $c$. As can be seen immediately, Equation 4.5 becomes (4.2) if $D$ is truly constant. This would occur for diffusion of atoms through a lattice of like atoms, that is, for self-diffusion. Very dilute systems also approximate this condition of constancy of $D$. In general, the variation of $D$ with composition should be experimentally investigated. Quite often this has not been done, and the published values of $D$ represent an average value over the range investigated. To set up a truly satisfactory model for diffusion we must be able to account for $D$ in terms of atomic properties of the diffusing atoms. Then only can we give the full significance of the diffusion coefficient.

## 4.4   The Chemical Potential

In our discussion so far we have implied that $D$ is a measure of the tendency of the system of diffusing atoms to yield to a difference in composition.

Indeed, if we relate measured values to Equation 4.3 then, although this is convenient, we must accept the fact that we are merely setting up a phenomenological model of diffusion. There is a more fundamental way of treating the problem. We have seen in Section 3.2 that all systems, including solid state systems, will, as far as is possible under the conditions prevailing, change in the direction of minimization of free energy. Let us look at diffusion in this more fundamental way. We will follow the argument of Le Claire.[*]

Let us suppose that a solid system contains a number of components in the concentrations $c_1, c_2, c_3, \ldots$ . The free energy of the system changes by an amount $\delta F$ because of a change $\delta c_1$. The quantity $\partial F/\partial c_1$ is then a measure of the potential to change because of composition change. This quantity is called the *chemical potential* $p_1$.

$$p_1 = \frac{\partial F}{\partial c_1}$$

and

$$dF = \frac{\partial F}{\partial c_1} dc_1 + \frac{\partial F}{\partial c_2} dc_2 + \cdots \tag{4.6}$$

The free energy cannot be a minimum if there exists in the solid a potential to change. The equilibrium condition therefore can only be attained when the individual chemical potentials $p_1$ are the same at every point in each phase throughout the whole system. Thus diffusion occurs down a chemical potential gradient, not necessarily down a concentration gradient. In most solid systems, of course, it is a difference in concentration that causes a difference in potential, so that the conditions of equalization of potential and equalization of composition are equivalent. But this is not always so since we can readily define the potential to include factors other than composition, such as temperature, pressure, electrical field and so on. Then "uphill" diffusion against the concentration gradient is possible and has been observed in solid systems. These cases are rare but serve to demonstrate that the fundamental manner in which diffusion should be discussed is by consideration of the chemical potential.

## 4.5 Atomic Mobility

Having introduced the parameter of chemical potential, let us rewrite the simple Fick equation (4.5) and introduce another quantity, *the mobility*, which is much used in atomic diffusion models and in charge diffusion models of semiconductors.

[*] A. D. Le Claire, *Progress in Metal Physics*, Vol. I, Butterworth, London, 1949, p. 306.

The mobility $\mu$ of a diffusing atom is its average velocity per unit driving force. The driving force is, from elementary physics, the negative derivative of the potential with respect to distance. Thus the force on $i$ atoms is $-\partial p_i/\partial x$. If $V_i$ is the average velocity of $i$ atoms, then

$$\mu_i = -v_i \frac{\partial x}{\partial p_i} \tag{4.7}$$

Let us suppose that there are $n_i$ atoms of character $i$ per unit volume. Then the number crossing unit area perpendicular to $x$ in unit time is the "current density" $J_i$ where

$$J_i = n_i v_i$$

$$= -n_i \mu_i \frac{\partial p_i}{\partial x} \tag{4.8}$$

## 4.6   The Dependence of Diffusion on Temperature

It is found experimentally that for a great number of diffusion phenomena, the coefficient of diffusion varies with temperature according to an exponential law.

$$D = D_0 \exp\left(-Q/kT\right) \tag{4.9}$$

$D_0$ is simply called the pre-exponential factor and is relatively independent of temperature. We will discuss its nature at a later point.

$Q$ is called the activation energy for diffusion, $k$ is the Boltzmann constant, and $T$ the absolute temperature.

Equation 4.9 is a phenomenological equation. We will try to obtain the meaning of the equation by considering it in terms of the free energy. Let us design a very simple model relating atomic position and free energy and then apply an elementary statistical argument.

## 4.7   Rate Theory of Diffusion

Let us suppose that the free energy of a lattice atom in positions $A$ and $B$, separated by a distance $a$, is represented by the ordinate in Fig. 4.3. Both $A$ and $B$ are equilibrium positions, and between them the free energy rises to a maximum. The atom, in order to change position, must acquire thermal energy greater than the barrier height.

The average number of atoms per unit volume $n$ which jump from position $A$ to position $B$ or back again per second is given by Maxwell-Boltzmann statistics.

$$n = \alpha v_0 \exp\left(-\frac{\Delta F}{kT}\right) \tag{4.10}$$

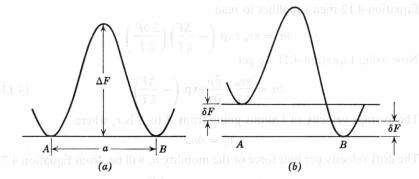

**Fig. 4.3** (*a*) Free energy as a function of position between two atomic sites $A$ and $B$. (*b*) Tipping of free energy contour by a concentration gradient.

Here $v_0$ is the average frequency of atomic vibration or the number of attempts on the energy barrier per second (about $10^{13}$ s$^{-1}$ in many solids). The factor $\alpha$ depends on the geometry of the diffusion path and on the detailed atomic mechanism. We will discuss this factor with reference to a specific mechanism in section 4.14.

Let us now suppose that a concentration gradient exists between $A$ and $B$, being higher at $A$. There will be a chemical potential and a free energy gradient. The increase in free energy $\delta F$ associated with the concentration gradient will be given by the product of the driving force on the atom and the distance over which the atom would have to move to surmount the barrier between $A$ and $B$. The force is given by $\partial p/\partial x$ and the distance is $a/2$. Thus

$$\delta F = \left(\frac{\partial p}{\partial x}\right)\left(\frac{a}{2}\right) \qquad (4.11)$$

The barrier height is diminished by $\delta F$ on the high concentration side, which accounts for the dropping of the minus sign. On the $B$ side the barrier is increased by the same amount $\delta F$.

More atoms are now thermally activated from $A$ to $B$ than from $B$ to $A$, and the difference $\delta n$ in number per unit volume per second is obtained from Equation 4.10. We have

$$\delta n = \alpha v_0 \left[\exp\left\{-\left(\frac{\Delta F - \delta F}{kT}\right)\right\} - \exp\left\{-\left(\frac{\Delta F + \delta F}{kT}\right)\right\}\right] \qquad (4.12)$$

In most cases $\delta F \ll kT$ and we can just use the first two terms of the exponential series without serious error; thus

$$e^x = 1 + x + \cdots$$

Equation 4.12 then simplifies to read

$$\delta n = \alpha v_0 \exp\left(-\frac{\Delta F}{kT}\right)\left(\frac{2\,\delta F}{kT}\right)$$

Now using Equation 4.11 we get

$$\delta n = \frac{\alpha v_0}{kT}\,a\,\frac{\partial p}{\partial x}\exp\left(-\frac{\Delta F}{kT}\right) \tag{4.13}$$

The average velocity of $i$ atoms going from $A$ to $B$ is $v_i$ where

$$v_i = \delta n a$$

The drift velocity per unit force or the mobility $\mu_i$ will be, from Equation 4.7,

$$\mu_i = \frac{\alpha v_0}{kT}a^2\exp\left(-\frac{\Delta F}{kT}\right) \tag{4.14}$$

We now have an equation which relates the mobility of atoms which make jumps between two positions in a lattice to the difference in free energy of the atom in these two positions. Our plan now is to choose a particular diffusion mechanism and relate this fundamental equation (4.14) to the empirical equation (4.9). Before we do so it is profitable to derive a relationship between the mobility and diffusivity.

## 4.8    The Einstein Relation between Mobility and Diffusivity

We will derive this relation for an ideal solution. In such a solution Boltzmann statistics apply. Interactions between the diffusing atoms are negligible. This means that the mathematics will be directly applicable to weak solutions or to self-diffusion. The relation, which was first developed by Einstein, is also applicable to the diffusion of electrons and holes in semi-conductors where the densities of the diffusing charge carriers are low enough so that little interaction occurs.

In an ideal solution the number of atoms of a particular kind crossing a plane in the direction of flow $x$ per second is given, from Equation 4.8, by $-(\partial p_1/\partial x)\mu_i n_i$ where $n_i$ is the number of $i$ atoms per unit volume. This number is also given by $D_i(dn_i/dx)$ since this constitutes the definition of $D_i$, the diffusion coefficient. Thus

$$\left(\frac{\partial p_i}{\partial x}\mu_i\right)n_i = D_i\left(\frac{dn_i}{dx}\right).$$

The concentration $n_i$ of such atoms at $x$ will therefore be

$$n_i = \text{constant}\,\exp-\left(\frac{\partial p_i}{\partial x}\right)\left(\frac{\mu_i x}{D_i}\right)$$

But if Boltzmann statistics apply, the concentration is also proportional to $\exp -[(\partial p_i/\partial x \; x)/kT]$. We can therefore equate the exponents and obtain the Einstein relation

$$D_i = \mu k T \tag{4.15}$$

We should note at this point that the mobility and diffusivity relate to a particular kind of atom, and thus in a binary alloy (of two components) the rates of diffusion will be the same only if the mobilities are the same. This is not always the case. Indeed it is only when an atom of type 1 exchanges position directly with an atom of type 2 that the mobilities are exactly equal and this particular simple exchange mechanism is seldom favored. We will discuss the importance of the mobility difference in Section 4.16.

### 4.9   Self-Diffusion in a Metal

We are now ready to discuss a particular diffusion mechanism. Our task is to find the real meaning of the coefficients $D_0$ and $Q$ in the experimental relation given by Equation 4.9. The development will continue to Section 4.14. We choose a simple mechanism which is of very wide applicability. It is the vacancy diffusion mechanism found in almost all close-packed solids. We will treat diffusion in a dilute substitutional binary alloy. The treatment is also applicable directly to self-diffusion in a close-packed metal such as copper.

Figure 4.4 shows the atomic mechanism in self-diffusion or diffusion in a dilute substitutional alloy. The diffusion atom changes place with an associated vacancy. Let us now discuss, in turn, the different factors of Equation 4.14 with relation to this particular diffusion mechanism.

### 4.10   The Geometric Factor $\alpha$

In a face-centered cubic metal like copper there are six directions in which an atom can jump. Each is equally probable. The geometrical factor $\alpha$ thus contains the fraction $\frac{1}{6}$. If there are $m$ equally likely directions, then $\alpha$ contains the factor $1/m$.

Also in the vacancy diffusion mechanism an atom in position $A$ can only jump to position $B$ when $B$ is vacant. The factor $\alpha$ must therefore also contain the probability of position $B$ being vacant. That is, the factor $\alpha$ will contain the vacancy concentration in the solid.

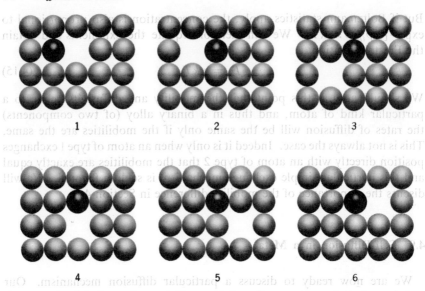

**Fig. 4.4** Migration of a solute atom associated with a vacancy.

## 4.11 Lattice Imperfections

Before we attempt the calculation of the number of vacancies, let us list the different types of lattice defect which might be encountered in diffusion and related phenomena. *Foreign atoms* in a pure element may be regarded as lattice defects. Their solubilities have been discussed in Chapter 3. In this chapter we will describe the role in diffusion of *vacancies* and *interstitial atoms*. The major sinks to which migrating atoms diffuse are the surface, grain boundaries, and line faults called *dislocations* which are encountered in crystals. These defects and their associated properties will be treated in Chapter 5. In Chapter 14 we will consider the diffusion of *electrons* and *holes* in our discussion of semiconductors.

## 4.12 Vacant Lattice Sites and Interstitial Atoms

The two simplest types of lattice vacancy are illustrated in Fig. 4.5*a* and *b*. The *Schottky defect* in (*a*) is a simple lattice vacancy or missing atom in the lattice. The missing atom may have been transferred to the surface of the crystal or to a dislocation (see Chapter 5) or to some other sink associated with a disordered portion of the lattice. If, however, the missing atom is transferred to an interstitial site in the lattice, a *Frenkel defect*, shown in *b*,

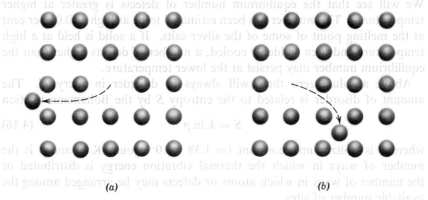

**Fig. 4.5** Lattice vacancies. (*a*) Schottky defect. (*b*) Frenkel defect.

results. Vacancies and interstitials often exist in pairs. In addition, interstitials may interact with one another to form stable clusters, rather like diatomic or triatomic molecules. Similarly, vacancies can cluster in groups which range in size from pair combinations to large voids in the lattice.

A further very important property of vacancies and interstitials is their tendency to associate with impurities in the solid. A binding energy may therefore exist between vacancies, between interstitials, and between these imperfections and impurities. Obviously, below a certain temperature the imperfection and impurity will remain bound and we must consider the diffusion properties of the combination. At higher temperatures the combination may separate and we must consider the imperfection and impurity separately. We now consider the equilibrium number of defects with particular reference to vacancies.

## 4.13 The Equilibrium Number of Defects

Thermal energy in a solid exists as nearly elastic vibrations of the lattice atoms. The vibrations interact with one another, and in fact may combine at a localized region of the lattice to produce a large displacement on one or two atoms. This can cause atoms to jump from normal to interstitial positions, thereby producing both interstitial atoms and vacant lattice sites. If the lattice vibrations are in thermal equilibrium, which they will be if the solid remains at a constant temperature for sufficient time, the density of imperfections so produced can be determined by the laws of statistical mechanics. We will reproduce such a calculation for Schottky defects since it is illustrative of concepts of wide application in the physics of solids.

We will see that the equilibrium number of defects is greater at higher temperatures. This number has been estimated to be as high as 0.01 per cent at the melting point of some of the silver salts. If a solid is held at a high temperature and then suddenly cooled, a number of defects higher than the equilibrium number may persist at the lower temperature.

Above absolute zero there will always be disorder in a crystal. The amount of disorder is related to the entropy $S$ by the Boltzmann relation

$$S = k \ln p \qquad (4.16)$$

where $k$ is Boltzmann's constant $(= 1.38 \times 10^{-23}$ joule $°K^{-1})$ and $p$ is the number of ways in which the thermal vibration energy is distributed or the number of ways in which atoms or defects may be arranged among the available number of sites.

The first choice for $p$ leads to an expression for the *thermal entropy*, whereas the second leads to an expression for the *configurational entropy*. In our calculation of the equilibrium number of Schottky defects at a particular temperature, we will first calculate the configurational entropy of such defects.

It is possible to take $n$ atoms from $N$ lattice sites in $N!/(N - n)! \, n!$ different ways. Thus the configurational entropy increase $S_c$ because of the presence of the $n$ Schottky defects, is given by

$$S_c = k \ln \frac{N!}{(N - n)! \, n!}$$

$$= k[\ln N! - \ln (N - n)! - \ln n!]$$

To deal with terms like $\log n!$, we use Stirling's formula $\log n! = n \log n - n$. It is substantially true if $n > 10$. Thus

$$S_c = k[N \ln N - (N - n) \ln (N - n) - n \ln n] \qquad (4.17)$$

Now if $E_f$ is the work done to move a single atom from a lattice site to the surface, that is, the energy of formation of a Schottky defect, then the energy to form $n$ such defects is $nE_f$.

It remains now to impose the condition characterizing equilibrium. This is the condition of making the free energy $F$ a minimum. Here

$$F = nE_f - TS_c$$

$$= nE_f - kT[N \ln N - (N - n) \ln (N - n) - n \ln n]$$

The condition for $F$ to be a minimum by adjustment of the number is given by $\partial F/\partial n = 0$. This leads to

$$E_f = kT[\ln (N - n) - \ln n]$$

that is,

$$E_f = kT \ln \frac{N - n}{n}$$

Thus the equilibrium ratio of the number of vacancies to the number of atoms in lattice positions at temperature $T$ is given by

$$\frac{n}{N - n} \simeq \frac{n}{N} \simeq e^{-E_f/kT} \tag{4.18}$$

If we insert $E_f \simeq 1$ eV and $T \simeq 1000°$K in the equation, the proportion of vacancies is of the order of 0.001 per cent.

It is often more favorable to form pairs of positive and negative vacancies. This is especially true in ionic crystals since the surface of the crystal will then be electrostatically neutral. The number of ways in which $n$ separated pairs can form is $[N!/(N - n)! \, n!]^2$, and a calculation similar to the one earlier gives the fractional number of pairs as

$$\frac{n}{N} = e^{-E_{2v}/kT} \tag{4.19}$$

where $E_{2v}$ is the energy of formation of a pair.

The energy of formation of lattice defects gives an extra contribution to the heat capacity of a crystal. With silver bromide, for example, the heat capacity increases linearly but very little with temperature up to about 500°C. Between this temperature and the melting point at 700°C defects are formed thermally, and the heat capacity increases to about three times its value at 500°C.

It should be again emphasized that, as in the formation of alloys (Chapter 3), although the equilibrium state describes the condition toward which the system tends, in solids with low rates of diffusion it is seldom if ever attained.

In the derivation given of Equation 4.18 we have referred only to the configurational entropy of the crystal. However, close to the defect, the vibrational frequencies of the neighboring atoms are slightly altered. These arrangements of different frequencies around the vacancy introduce additional randomness, and we should include an *entropy* of formation of the defect $S_f$. Making the adjustment, which is small in our model, Equation 4.18 reads

$$\frac{n}{N} \simeq e^{-(E_f - TS_f)/kT}$$

or

$$c_v \simeq \frac{n}{N} \simeq e^{-E_f/kT} e^{S_f/k} \tag{4.20}$$

where $c_v$ is the concentration of vacancies.

## 4.14   Diffusion with a Vacancy Mechanism

Now let us summarize our whole procedure with reference to the vacancy diffusion model. We started with the experimental equation

$$D = D_0 e^{-Q/kT}$$

We then made a free energy model of an atom in two positions in a lattice and obtained the equation

$$\mu_i = \frac{\alpha v_0}{kT} a^2 e^{-(\Delta F/kT)}$$

Introducing the Einstein relation $D_i = \mu kT$ gives

$$D_i = \alpha v_0 a^2 e^{-(\Delta F/kT)} \tag{4.21}$$

The diffusion coefficient depends on the geometric factor $1/m$ and concentration of vacancies $c_v$. Hence

$$D_i = \frac{c_v}{m} v_0 a^2 e^{-\Delta F/kT} \tag{4.22}$$

Finally, after our discussion of energy and entropy of formation we can now justifiably replace $\Delta F$ by plausible energy and entropy terms. For an atom to diffuse because of a vacancy mechanism these terms will be:

1. An energy of formation of the vacancy $E_f$.
2. An entropy of formation of the vacancy $S_f$.
3. A migration energy for the vacancy $E_m$.
4. A migration entropy for the vacancy $S_m$, since a small amount of disorder is also associated with the change in position of the vacancy.

The complete equation for vacancy diffusion in copper now reads

$$D_i = \frac{v_0}{m} a^2 e^{(S_f+S_m)/k} e^{-(E_f+E_m)/kT} \tag{4.23}$$

and a comparison with the empirical equation (4.9) gives

$$D_0 = \frac{v_0}{m} a^2 e^{(S_f+S_m)/k} \tag{4.24}$$

and $Q$, the activation energy, the value

$$Q = E_f + E_m$$

$D_0$ is usually of the order $10^{-2}$ to $10^{-1}$ m$^2$ s$^{-1}$.

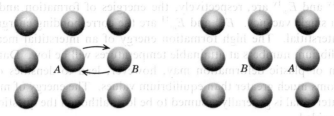

**Fig. 4.6** Direct interchange mechanism of diffusion.

## 4.15 Other Diffusion Mechanisms

Huntingdon and Seitz first attempted to calculate the activation energy for self-diffusion in copper. They considered three mechanisms.

1. The vacancy mechanism we have just discussed.

2. A mechanism in which two adjacent atoms trade places by direct interchange. This is shown in Fig. 4.6.

3. A mechanism in which a cubic interstitial migrates by pushing one of its neighbor atoms into another interstitial position. This is shown in Fig. 4.7.

Calculations were made of the energies of an atom in the various intermediate positions. These calculations have since been repeated by computer techniques in which many more neighboring atoms can be included.

For mechanism 1,

$$Q = E_{if}^{1v} + E_m^{1v}$$
$$= (1.5 \pm 0.5 \text{ eV}) + (1.0 \pm 0.5 \text{ eV})$$

For mechanism 2,

$$Q = 10 \text{ eV}$$

For mechanism 3,

$$Q = E_f^{1I} + E_m^{1I}$$
$$= (4 5 \pm 1.0 \text{ eV}) + (0.16 \pm 0.1 \text{ eV})$$

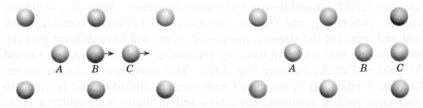

**Fig. 4.7** Interstitial mechanism of diffusion in a cubic crystal.

Here $E_f^{1v}$ and $E_m^{1v}$ are, respectively, the energies of formation and migration of a single vacancy. $E_f^{1I}$ and $E_m^{1I}$ are the corresponding energies for a single interstitial. The high formation energy of an interstitial means that the equilibrium numbers at attainable temperatures will be low. Damage by radiation or plastic deformation may, however, lead to densities of interstitial atoms much greater than equilibrium values. The energy of migration for an interstitial is generally assumed to be low, although the question is not finally decided.

Since the measured activation energy $Q$ for self-diffusion in copper has the value 2.05 eV, the mechanism is undoubtedly one of vacancy migration.

A great deal of caution must be exercised in attributing diffusion in a particular system to a specific defect or impurity-defect combination. Often, for instance, the defects are associated in pairs or larger clusters. The binding energy $U$ between the pairs has then to be subtracted from the formation energy, giving for two vacancies the value $E_f^{2v} - U$.

The lines along which future theoretical work on diffusion will be carried have now been outlined. The subject is of the greatest technical importance since the fabrication of modern solid state electronic devices depends on diffusion mechanisms. Nuclear reactor technology is also fundamentally concerned with diffusion.

## 4.16   The Kirkendall Effect

We have been careful in our theoretical treatment of diffusion to attribute a diffusion coefficient $D_i$ to a particular component of an alloy. It is not a priori certain that various components diffuse at equal rates, that is, have equal mobilities. Of course, in a direct interchange mechanism (cf. Section 4.15, mechanism 2) the rates must be equal. If, however, vacancy diffusion is taking place, then atom $A$ may change places with a vacancy more easily than atom $B$. There may be a difference in free energy barrier.

Let us suppose that a gold bar is intimately joined to a nickel bar, and inert markers, often molybdenum wires, are initially across the interfacial plane (see Fig. 4.8*a*). After a diffusion anneal of many hours at a high temperature, say 1200°K, interdiffusion will have taken place. Since $D_{Au}$ is greater than $D_{Ni}$ (where $D_{Au}$ and $D_{Ni}$ are, respectively, the diffusion coefficients for gold and nickel in the system), more gold atoms will have diffused past the inert markers than nickel atoms, and the markers will have moved toward the gold end of the bar (see Fig. 4.8*b*). This movement is known as the Kirkendall effect. It is associated with vacancy diffusion and is found in most close-packed substitutional alloys and in many body-centered cubic metal alloys.

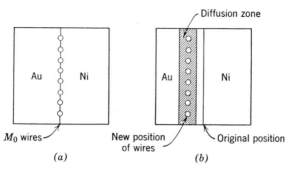

**Fig. 4.8** (*a*) A gold-nickel diffusion couple with marker wires. (*b*) After high temperature diffusion the marker wires have shifted position.

We can make a calculation of the appropriate diffusion coefficient. Suppose that the markers are at a distance $x$ from the gold end and have a velocity $v$. The number of gold atoms which diffuse per second across a unit area perpendicular to $x$, which is fixed relative to the gold end of the bar, is $(\delta n_{Au})_x$ where

$$(\delta n_{Au})_x = -D_{Au}\left(\frac{\partial n_{Au}}{\partial x}\right) + n_{Au}v \qquad (4.25)$$

The first term on the right is the diffusing number of gold atoms across the interface to the right, and the second term is the number swept past the markers as they move to the left. $n_{Au}$ is the number of gold atoms per unit volume.

We can now move the reference unit area plane to the position $x + \delta x$ and rewrite Equation 4.25:

$$(\delta n_{Au})_{x+\delta x} = -\left[D_{Au}\left(\frac{\partial n_{Au}}{\delta x}\right) + n_{Au}v\right] + \frac{\partial}{\partial x}\left(-D_{Au}\frac{\partial n_{Au}}{\partial x} + n_{Au}v\right) \qquad (4.26)$$

Since the numbers of gold atoms in both equations refer to times of one second, the *rate* of *accumulation* $\partial n_{Au}/\partial t$ at $x$ will simply be given by the difference (4.26) − (4.25):

$$\frac{\partial n_{Au}}{\partial t} = \frac{\partial}{\partial x}\left(D_{Au}\frac{\partial n_{Au}}{\partial x} - n_{Au}v\right) \qquad (4.27)$$

We can write a similar equation for the nickel atoms:

$$\frac{\partial n_{Ni}}{\partial t} = \frac{\partial}{\partial x}\left(D_{Ni}\frac{\partial n_{Ni}}{\partial x} - n_{Ni}v\right) \qquad (4.28)$$

As many gold atoms accumulate on the plane at $x$ per second as nickel atoms are lost from the plane, and hence the addition of these last two equations must equal zero.

$$\frac{\partial}{\partial x}\left[D_{Au}\frac{\partial n_{Au}}{\partial x} + D_{Ni}\frac{\partial n_{Ni}}{\partial x} - v(n_{Au} + n_{Ni})\right] = 0$$

This equation holds right along the bar. But at the gold or nickel end $v = 0$ and

$$\frac{\partial n_{Ni}}{\partial x} = \frac{\partial n_{Au}}{\partial x} = 0$$

so that the quantity in parenthesis must be zero. We have therefore obtained a value for the velocity of the markers

$$v = \left(D_{Au}\frac{\partial n_{Au}}{\partial x} + D_{Ni}\frac{\partial n_{Ni}}{\partial x}\right)\left(\frac{1}{n_{Au} + n_{Ni}}\right) \qquad (4.29)$$

If we use $X_{Au}$ and $X_{Ni}$ as the volume fractions of gold and nickel, respectively, we can simplify this equation since

$$\frac{\partial n_{Au}}{\partial x}\left(\frac{1}{n_{Au} + n_{Ni}}\right) = \frac{\partial X_{Au}}{\partial x}$$

and

$$\frac{\partial n_{Ni}}{\partial x}\left(\frac{1}{n_{Au} + n_{Ni}}\right) = \frac{\partial X_{Ni}}{\partial x} = -\frac{\partial X_{Au}}{\partial x}$$

then

$$v = (D_{Au} - D_{Ni})\frac{\partial X_{Au}}{\partial x} \qquad (4.30)$$

Now substitute this value back in Equation 4.27

$$\frac{\partial X_{Au}}{\partial t} = \frac{\partial}{\partial x}\left[D_{Au}\frac{\partial X_{Au}}{\partial x} - X_{Au}(D_{Au} - D_{Ni})\frac{\partial X_{Au}}{\partial x}\right]$$

$$= \frac{\partial}{\partial x}\left[D_{Au}\frac{\partial X_{Au}}{\partial x} - X_{Au}D_{Au}\frac{\partial X_{Au}}{\partial x} + X_{Au}D_{Ni}\frac{\partial X_{Au}}{\partial x}\right]$$

$$= \frac{\partial}{\partial x}\left[(D_{Au}X_{Ni} + X_{Au}D_{Ni})\frac{\partial X_{Au}}{\partial x}\right] \qquad (4.30)$$

since

$$1 - X_{Au} = X_{Ni}$$

Now compare Equation 4.30 with the Fick equation

$$\frac{\partial c}{\partial t} = \frac{\partial}{\partial x}\left(\bar{D}\frac{\partial c}{\partial x}\right)$$

Pores

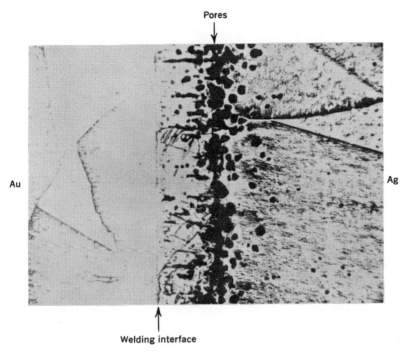

Au

Ag

Welding interface

**Fig. 4.9**  An Au-Ag diffusion couple after high temperature treatment. Pores have gathered on the more rapidly diffusing silver side of the interface. (From W. Seith, *Diffusion in Metals*, 2d ed., Springer, Berlin, 1955)

where $\bar{D}$ is the appropriate interdiffusion coefficient. We obtain

$$\bar{D} = X_{Au}D_{Ni} + D_{Au}X_{Ni} \tag{4.31}$$

In all cases marker movement is associated with a defect mechanism of diffusion. Figure 4.9 shows the Kirkendall effect in a Au-Ag couple. Pores, formed by the clustering of excess vacancies, collect in a zone which is at a particular composition, and this zone moves as diffusion proceeds. The growth of these pores may have serious technical consequences in welding and in the adhesion of clad or plated products which are diffusion bonded at high temperatures.

## 4.17  Interstitial Diffusion

A solute element whose atomic size and valency are not much different from the solvent atom usually has a diffusion coefficient which is within a factor of five of the self-diffusion coefficient of the solvent. The diffusion mechanism is then probably a vacancy mechanism.

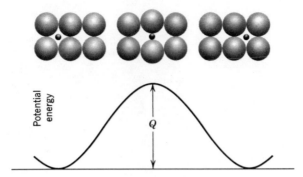

**Fig. 4.10**   Migration of an intersitial atom with the potential energy of the atom shown for each position.

On the other hand, solute elements which are much smaller in atomic size than the solvent element are generally supposed to occupy interstitial sites and diffuse through interstitial paths in the lattice. Figure 4.10 shows an interstitial atom in three positions with respect to neighboring solvent atoms and the measured energy associated with each position. Thus the elements carbon, nitrogen, and boron diffuse through iron at a rate which is five orders of magnitude faster than self-diffusion. Hydrogen diffuses at a rate eight orders of magnitude faster than self-diffusion. These small elements undoubtedly diffuse by interstitial paths.

### 4.18   Grain Boundary and Surface Diffusion

So far the remarks on diffusion have dealt almost exclusively with volume diffusion in single crystals. In polycrystalline material diffusion along grain boundaries is also possible. In addition, atoms residing on a crystal surface will be less tightly bound than those within the volume of the crystal, or even within the disorganized region of a grain boundary, and as a consequence they can diffuse more easily. Thus, as we would expect,

$$Q_\text{volume} > Q_\text{grain boundary} > Q_\text{surface}$$

As we will see in Section 5.20 on tilt boundaries, there is greater disorganization of the lattice in a high-angle boundary than in a low. It has been found, not surprisingly, that the activation energy for diffusion decreases with increase of boundary angle. Also in Section 5.20 we shall discover that low-angle tilt boundaries consist of line imperfections called dislocations fairly regularly spaced along the boundary and running at specific angles to it. Diffusion in such low-angle boundaries is greatest down the dislocation lines and is consequently orientation dependent. Often in grain boundary diffusion the activation energy is as low as only half that for volume diffusion.

## 4.19   Measured Diffusion Coefficients

We have seen that diffusion is generally dependent on composition and always dependent on temperature. Often practical values of diffusion coefficients are quoted as coefficients $D$ for substitution in the Fick equation (4.3). The variation of $D$ with composition is shown for alloys of copper at a temperature of 800°C in Fig. 4.11. The variation with temperature of $D$ for trace elements in silicon is shown in Fig. 4.12.

## 4.20   Experimental Methods for the Determination of $D$

The *steady state* method, in which solute is supplied at a constant known rate to one face of the solvent layer and removed at another known rate from the opposite face, is generally limited to systems in which the solute is volatile.

Carbon diffusivity in iron has been measured by the steady state method. A constant mixture of methane and hydrogen was passed across one face of a

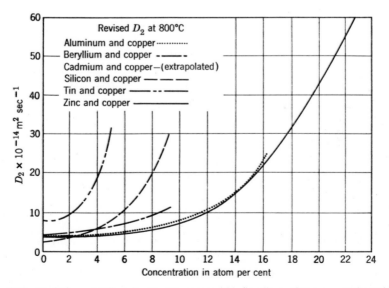

**Fig. 4.11**   Variation of diffusivity $D$ with composition in alloys of copper. (After Rhines and Mehl)

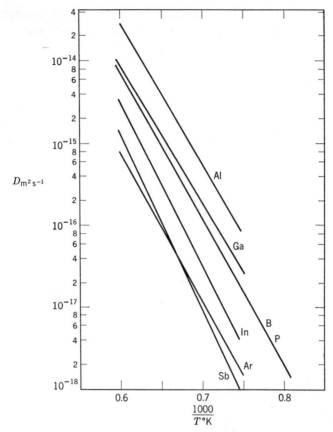

**Fig. 4.12** Diffusivity versus temperature for impurity doping elements in silicon. (Redrawn from S. N. Levine, *Principles as Solid-state Microelectronics*, Holt, Rinehart and Winston, New York, 1963).

γ iron (austenite) disk. The carbon in the methane diffuses into the austenite. The amount of carbon passing through the disk (i.e., $J$ in Equation 4.1) was determined by analysis of a hydrogen and water vapor stream flowing across the other face of the disk. The disk was later sectioned and analyzed for carbon at different penetrations giving $(\partial c/\partial x)$ as a function of $x$. The variation of diffusivity $D_1$ with concentration can then be calculated. This determination is of considerable metallurgical interest since austenite is surface hardened by the diffusion penetration of carbon in the *carburizing* process.

A number of precautions should be observed in making determinations of diffusion coefficients. The extent to which grain boundary diffusion affects the results should be determined by finding the dependence of coefficient on grain size. Intimate contact between the alloys or elements should be made by electroplating, welding, or mechanical rolling. Oxide layers will limit the diffusion cross section and precautions must be taken to avoid this difficulty.

The dependence of $\bar{D}$, the interdiffusion coefficient (Equation 4.31), on composition should be determined throughout the diffusion zone. Two direct methods are available.

## Chemical Methods

Thin layers are removed from the diffusion couple by careful machining or lapping. These layers are then analyzed for solute concentration by chemical or spectrographic analysis.

## Radioactive Methods

These methods depend on the availability of a radioactive isotope of the solute. In one method the solute is plated on to one surface of the solvent. The rate of penetration of the solute by diffusion into the solvent is then determined by observation of the rate of decay of surface radioactivity. The concentration gradient may also be determined by measurement of the radioactivity of thin slices removed from the diffusion couple.

The radioactive tracer methods are to be preferred. With the discovery of artificial radioactivity they are now of wide application. An obvious advantage over chemical methods is that coefficients of *self-diffusion* can be readily determined.

Any physical property which changes with diffusion can, of course, be used to determine diffusion coefficients. In our later discussion of the annealing out of damage of solids by radiation, we will refer to changes in electrical resistivity as such a property.

If the separate diffusion coefficients are required from measurements of $\bar{D}$, the interdiffusion coefficient, then Kirkendall determinations of velocities and compositions at marker positions must be made. Only then can Equations 4.30 and 4.31 be solved.

## 4.21 Measurement of Defect Annealing

Three main processes result in the production of enhanced numbers of defects in solids.

1. Radiation damage (Chapter 7).
2. Plastic deformation (Chapter 5).
3. Quenching from a high temperature when the number of defects in equilibrium at the high temperature remains at the lower temperature.

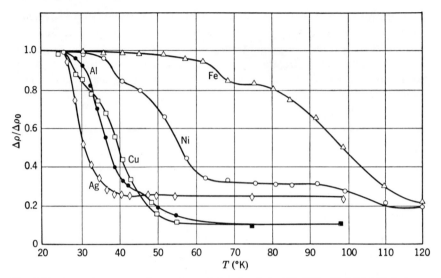

**Fig. 4.13**  Stage I recovery of several metals bombarded at 20.4°K with 1.5 MeV electrons. The recovery curve is of the isochronal type obtained by pulsing the samples to the specified temperatures and holding them there for 10 min. The samples are then quenched to 20.4°K for measurement. (Redrawn from R. M. Walker, *Radiation Damage in Solids*, p. 620, Academic Press, New York, 1962)

Often a physical property will change as the defect anneals out of the solid. Difficulty in satisfactory interpretation of the experimental data often results from a lack of knowledge of the kinds of defects involved in diffusion. Physical properties which have been used to follow defect annealing are electrical resistance, X-ray lattice parameter magnitude, measurement of stored energy in the lattice, and others. Very significant changes are brought about in semiconductor properties by introducing defects. These will be discussed in Chapter 15.

One of the least ambiguous series of experiments on defect annealing is electrical resistivity determinations of metals after bombardment with 1.5 MeV electrons at 20.4°K. In the results of Fig. 4.13 the specimens were pulsed in temperature up to a specified temperature, held there for ten minutes, and then quenched again to 20.4°K for measurement.

The radiation damage, which in this case consists of simple Frenkel pairs, raises the resistivity and as the defects anneal out the resistivity falls. It is seen that defect migration takes place at incredibly low temperatures. This is called Stage I recovery. The rate of recovery, moreover, is not constant, but defects are eliminated over specific temperature ranges giving a number of substages to the recovery curves. The model here is of interstitial-vacancy pairs, driven apart by the radiation, coming together to annihilate at a temperature appropriate to the migration activation energy.

If the defect concentration in a solid is greatly increased by radiation damage with energetic particles, diffusion rates may be greatly increased. Significant diffusion may then take place at low temperatures. Such "cold" microdiffusion effects can be of great importance in particle detection by solid state instruments. Two examples will be given.

Below about 400°C long-range order develops in the compound $Cu_3Au$. The order is absent above this temperature. Let us discuss what happens if a $Cu_3Au$ specimen is subjected to irradiation by neutrons. Diffusion is enhanced since excess vacancies are produced. The vacancy diffusion will tend to order a disordered specimen. The neutron bombardment, on the other hand, will disorder an initially ordered specimen. Figure 4.14 shows that both processes occur. Note that the bombardment is carried out at 80°C where normal diffusion without excess vacancies in $Cu_3Au$ would be negligible.

Another example of enhanced diffusion in the presence of defects is shown by experiments on copper bombarded by α-particles. Annealing at

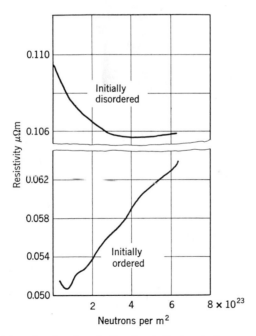

**Fig. 4.14** Resistivity of ordered and disordered $Cu_3Au$ during neutron irradiation at 350°K. (Redrawn from H. L. Glick, F. C. Brooks, W. F. Witzig, and W. E. Johnson, *Phys. Rev.* **87,** 1074, 1952)

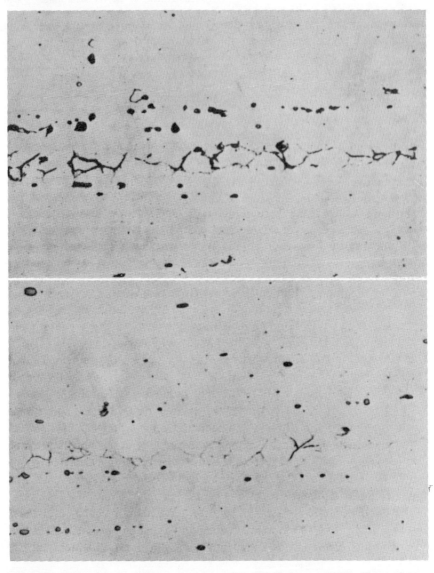

**Fig. 4.15** Copper bombarded by α-particles and heated 10 days at 425°C. Upper picture: heating in reactor. Lower picture: heating outside reactor. Center horizontal band in pictures is position of imbedded helium. (From A. N. Goland, Electron Microscopy Conference, Philadelphia, Pa., 1962)

high temperatures (above 400°C) precipitates out the helium (from the $\alpha$-particles) as gas bubbles. These can be seen with the electron microscope. The diffusion rate can be increased by providing excess vacancies by neutron irradiation. Figure 4.15 shows results on two solid specimens which have each received $\alpha$-particle bombardment. One specimen was heated in the reactor and the other outside. The reactor specimen shows a greater density of voids arising from the greater rate of migration and clustering of the helium in the presence of excess vacancies.

## 4.22  Property Changes with Isothermal and Isochronal Annealing

We will conclude this chapter with a discussion of the changes brought about in a physical property by diffusion. Let us suppose, as is often the case, that, on annealing at a temperature $T$, a given defect migrates to a number of sinks $s_1$, $s_2$, $s_3$, ... and thereafter has a negligible effect on a physical property. The sinks may be the surface, a dislocation, a vacancy if the migrating defect is an interstitial, and so on. If $n$ is the total number of defects per unit volume and $Q$ is the activation energy, then the number would be expected to follow a rate equation of the form

$$\frac{dn}{dt} = \phi(n, s_1, s_2, \ldots) \exp\left(-\frac{Q}{kT}\right) \tag{4.32}$$

The function $\phi(n, s_1, s_2, ..)$ describes the ways in which the defect is annihilated.

If a macroscopic physical property $M$, such as the electrical resistivity, depends on the number of defects in the solid and if the number of sinks remains constant, then

$$\frac{dM}{dt} = \phi(M, s_1, s_2, \ldots) \exp\left(-\frac{Q}{kT}\right) \tag{4.33}$$

This equation may be integrated to give

$$\int_{M_0}^{M} \frac{dM}{\phi(M, s_1, s_2 \ldots)} = \int_0^t \exp\left(-\frac{Q}{kT}\right) dt = \chi \tag{4.34}$$

In order to obtain the important quantity $Q$, the activation energy, the previous equation can be employed in two types of experiment. Annealing procedures are, in general, a combination of both types.

### Isothermal Annealing

Suppose a physical property, dependent on the number of defects, has an initial value $M_0$ and reaches a value $M$ in time $t_1$ at temperature $T_1$.

On repeating the experiment with the same or similar specimen, the value $M$ is reached in time $t_2$ at temperature $T_2$. Then from Equation 4.34

$$t_1 \exp\left(-\frac{Q}{kT}\right) = t_2 \exp\left(-\frac{Q}{kT_2}\right) \tag{4.35}$$

A value of $Q$ may be obtained from such physical data. Obviously also the *rates* of *change* at two temperatures lead to a determination of $Q$. The rates at the two temperatures

$$\left(\frac{dM}{dt}\right)_{T_1} \quad \text{and} \quad \left(\frac{dM}{dt}\right)_{T_2}$$

give

$$\left(\frac{dM}{dt}\right)_{T_1} \bigg/ \left(\frac{dM}{dt}\right)_{T_2} = \exp\left[-\frac{Q}{k}\left(\frac{1}{T_1} - \frac{1}{T_2}\right)\right] \tag{4.36}$$

### Isochronal Annealing

The physical property will also change if the specimen is maintained for a constant interval of time at varying temperatures. This is the *isochronal* method. Let us work out a relation between the results of the two kinds of experiment. We will consider two solid specimens, 1 and 2, with identical histories.

*Isochronal.* Specimen 1 is annealed at temperature $T_1$ for a certain fixed length of time. The physical property changes and has a value $M_1$ at the end of the time interval. The specimen is then raised in temperature very quickly to $T_2$ and kept for the same time interval, at the end of which the property has the value $M_2$. We summarize the results in the scheme:

| Time interval $\Delta t$ Constant | Temperature | Physical Property |
|---|---|---|
| | $T_1$ | $M_1$ |
| | $T_2$ | $M_2$ |
| | $T_3$ | $M_3$ |

From Equation 4.33 we can write for any given heat pulse

$$\Delta\phi_i = \Delta t \exp\left(-\frac{Q}{kT_i}\right)$$

or

$$\ln(\Delta\phi_i) = \ln \Delta t - \left(\frac{Q}{kT_i}\right)$$

$$= C' - \frac{Q}{kT_i} \tag{4.37}$$

since $C'$ is constant for an isochronal process.

*Isothermal.* Specimen 2 is annealed at a single temperature $T_A$ and $M$ is measured as a function of annealing time $\tau$. Again from Equation 4.33 we have

$$\tau_i = \phi_i \exp\left(-\frac{Q}{kT_A}\right)$$

If $\tau_i$ denotes the value of $\tau$ corresponding to $\phi_i$, that is, the length of time during which the property has changed by a certain amount,

$$\Delta\tau_i = \tau_i - \tau_{i-1}$$

$$= \Delta\phi_i \exp\left(-\frac{Q}{kT_A}\right)$$

or

$$\ln(\Delta\tau_i) = \ln(\Delta\phi_i) - \frac{Q}{kT_A}$$

$$= \ln(\Delta\phi_i) - C'' \tag{4.38}$$

since $Q/kT_A = C''$ is constant for an isothermal process.

We can now combine Equations 4.37 and 4.38 to give us a relationship between the two experimental ways of carrying out an annealing process.

$$\ln(\Delta\tau_i) = C - \frac{Q}{kT_i} \tag{4.39}$$

where

$$C = C' + C''$$

In terms of measured results this has the following meaning. Experimentally we get the $M$ versus $\tau$ relationship from specimen 2. We can then determine the $\tau_i$ corresponding to each $M_i$ measured on specimen 1. In practice we get the $\Delta\tau_i$ for each successive heat pulse, corresponding to temperature $T_i$. Then we plot $\ln(\Delta\tau_i)$ versus $1/T_i$. From Equation 4.37 we should get a straight line with the slope giving the activation energy. The line will be curved if two or more activation energies govern the defect migration. Figures 4.16a and b show the results of isochronal and isothermal annealing on a physical property. Figure 4.16c shows the relationship between the isothermal times and the isochronal temperatures.

We have discussed this relationship at some length because all diffusion work is done either isothermally or isochronally or by a combination of both. It is now possible to calculate annealing effects by means of a knowledge of the activation energy. Conversely, a proper analysis of experimental data can lead to a calculation of the activation energy and a subsequent indication of the diffusion mechanism involved.

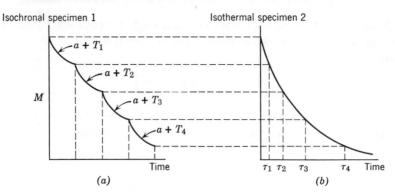

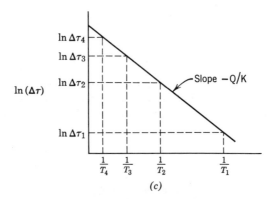

**Fig. 4.16**   (*a*) Isochronal data. (*b*) Isothermal data. (*c*) The relation between (*a*) and (*b*).

## References

Birchenall, C. E., *Physical Metallurgy*, McGraw-Hill Book Co., New York, 1959.
Cottrell, A. H., *Theoretical Structural Metallurgy*, E. Arnold, 1948.
Swalin, R. A., *Thermodynamics of Solids*, John Wiley and Sons, New York, 1962.

## Exercises

1. Produce a simple argument to show that the coefficient of diffusion $D$ (the net number of particles which flow in unit time through a unit plane perpendicular to a unit concentration gradient) is given by $\frac{1}{3}\bar{c}l$ where $\bar{c}$ is the average velocity and $l$ the mean free path. The most probable sum of $N$ equal positive or negative quantities is $\sqrt{N}$ one such quantity. Show that a particle migrates by random walk during time $t$ a distance $x$ where

$$x = \sqrt{Dt}$$

For interstitial diffusion of carbon in iron, $D = 10^{-21} \; m^2 \; sec^{-1}$. Calculate how far a carbon atom diffuses randomly in $10^8$ sec (3.3 years).

2. Write an expression for (a) the number of ways that $n$ atoms may be removed from $N$ lattice sites and (b) the number of ways these $n$ atoms may be put in $N'$ interstitial positions to form $n$ Frenkel defects. Show, by a calculation similar to that given in Section 4.3, that the number $n$ of Frenkel defects in equilibrium at temperature $T$ is given by

$$n \simeq (NN')^{\frac{1}{2}} e^{-W/2kT}$$

where $n \ll NN'$ and $W$ is the energy to remove an atom from a lattice site to an interstitial position.

If the energy of formation of a Frenkel defect in a silver halide is 1.5 eV, calculate the ratio of the number of defects to that at 100°K produced by quenching the halide specimen to that temperature after prolonged annealing at 600°K.

3. Estimate the atomic percentage of interstitials and vacancies at the melting point of copper. The formation energies are, respectively, 4.5 and 1.5 eV.

4. A piece of iron is held for 10 hours at 1700°K in an atmosphere of carburizing gases so that the concentration of carbon in the surface layers of the iron is 1.3 weight per cent. Plot the concentration of the carbon as a function of penetration depth at the conclusion of the carburizing process. The average diffusion coefficient of carbon in iron at 1700°K is $1.5 \times 10^{-11} \; m^2 \; sec^{-1}$. (*Hint:* Use Equation 4.4.)

5. Calculate the appropriate coefficients of diffusion $D$ at 300°K for the following cases:

| Diffusing Metal | Matrix | $D_0 \; m^2 \; sec^{-1}$ | $Q$ kcal mole$^{-1}$ |
|---|---|---|---|
| Copper | Aluminum | $2 \times 10^{-4}$ | 33.9 |
| Silver | Silver (volume diffusion) | $0.72 \times 10^{-4}$ | 45.0 |
| Silver | Silver (grain boundary) | $0.14 \times 10^{-4}$ | 21.5 |

6. In a number of examples of high temperature oxidation of metals, the rapidity of diffusion of metal ions through the oxide scale is so much greater than oxide through the scale that the latter may be neglected. A constant difference exists throughout the process between the metal concentration at the oxide surface and the metal concentration at the metal surface. Show that these observations suggest a parabolic relationship between thickness of oxide layer and time.

7. From the data of Sections 4.14 and 4.15 estimate the magnitude of the sum of the entropies of migration and formation for vacancy diffusion in copper.

8. Estimate from Fig. 4.12 the activation energies for diffusion of antimony and phosphorus in silicon. Estimate the penetration in one hour at 1400°K.

# 5

# *Elastic and Plastic Properties of Solids*

For most engineers the mechanical properties of a solid are of the greatest importance. Such properties describe the behavior of the solid when subjected to a deforming force and include measures of strength, hardness, ductility, and so on. If the deformation caused by the force is small, it is proportional to the force. This is *Hooke's law*. The theory of elasticity relates deformation to force and assumes the validity of the law. Above a certain limit of deformation, the *elastic limit*, the deformation is no longer a linear function of the deforming force. For much work of a technological nature, however, the deductions from elasticity theory are sufficiently good approximations and, in addition, the laws of elasticity still serve, and will probably always serve, as mathematical models against which the actual behavior of materials can be judged.

In this chapter we first discuss *elastic deformation* in isotropic and anisotropic solids. Later we discuss the behavior of materials subjected to forces which exceed the elastic limits, thus causing *plastic deformation*, and we will describe the influence of other factors such as temperature and purity.

## 5.1 Stress and Strain

In a test of the tensile or compressive strength of a solid material, a force is applied normal to a cross section of the specimen and a measurement made in the same direction as the force of the extension or reduction in specimen length, respectively. The normal stress $\sigma$ is equal to the magnitude of the force divided by the area normal to the force over which the force is applied. The strain $\epsilon$, produced by this stress, is then the fractional change in length of the specimen.

For small strains the strain is proportional to the stress and

$$\epsilon = \frac{\sigma}{E} \tag{5.1}$$

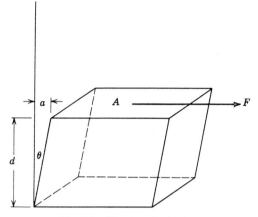

**Fig. 5.1** Simple cube in shear.

where the constant of proportionality $E$ is called *Young's modulus* and is a property of the material under test.

On the other hand, if the stress is applied tangentially to an imaginary plane in the material, a lateral displacement of the plane relative to another parallel plane constitutes a *shearing strain*. The magnitude $\gamma$ of shear strain is given by the quotient of the relative lateral displacement and the separation between the planes.

In Fig. 5.1 we have

$$\gamma = \frac{a}{d} = \tan \theta \tag{5.2}$$

In the elastic region the shear stress $\tau$ is related to the shear strain $\gamma$ by the equation

$$\gamma = \frac{\tau}{G} \tag{5.3}$$

where $G$ is the *shear modulus*.

## 5.2 Elastic Deformation in Isotropic Materials

The elastic properties of a single crystal are usually dependent on the crystallographic direction in the crystal, that is, they are *anisotropic*. Solids are usually encountered in the polycrystalline form, however, and if there is no preferred orientation of the individual crystals, the solid material may still follow closely the elasticity laws for an isotropic material. The laws are, of course, applicable to noncrystalline or amorphous materials, which we will discuss briefly.

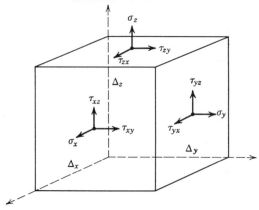

**Fig. 5.2**   Tensile and shear stresses acting on a cube of isotropic material.

Suppose a stress $\sigma_x$ is applied to a bar of isotropic material in the $x$ direction. There will be an elongation or strain $\epsilon_x$ in the $x$ direction and a consequent contraction in directions at right angles to the $x$ direction. If $\epsilon_y$ and $\epsilon_z$ are the strains parallel to the $y$ and $z$ directions, then

$$-\epsilon_y = -\epsilon_z = \nu\epsilon_x = \frac{\nu\sigma_x}{E} \qquad (5.4)$$

where $\nu$ is called Poisson's ratio and is a constant for the material under investigation. Many metals have values of $\nu$ of about 0.3.

Let us now examine the relationships in a cube of isotropic material. Rectangular axes $\Delta_x$, $\Delta_y$, and $\Delta_z$ are chosen, as in Fig. 5.2, and the tensile, compressive, and shearing stresses applied to the cube are also shown in the figure. The method of designating a particular stress is as follows. A compressive or tensile stress acting perpendicular to a plane whose normal is in the $\Delta_x$ direction is designated $\sigma_x$. A shear stress applied tangentially to a plane whose normal is in the $\Delta_x$ direction, the stress being in the $\Delta_y$ direction, is designated $\tau_{xy}$. The choice of suffix for the designation of strain follows similar rules.

In all, there are three stresses normal to the cube faces and six shear stresses acting across the cube faces. If the small cube is in equilibrium under the applied forces, the normal stress in the $\Delta_x$ direction must be balanced by a normal stress in the opposite direction. In addition, the shear stresses must balance at the edges of the cube. These two conditions mean that all relations such as the following exist.

$$\sigma_x = \sigma_{-x} \qquad (5.5)$$

$$\tau_{xy} = \tau_{yx} \qquad (5.6)$$

The six components of stress necessary and independent are $\sigma_x$, $\sigma_y$, $\sigma_z$, $\tau_{xy}$, $\tau_{yz}$, $\tau_{zx}$, and the components of strain are $\epsilon_x$, $\epsilon_y$, $\epsilon_z$, $\gamma_{xy}$, $\gamma_{yz}$, $\gamma_{zx}$.

If the coordinate axes are chosen so that the shear stresses on all faces of the cube are zero, a choice which is always possible, the stresses normal to the cube faces are called the *principal stresses* and are designated $\sigma_1$, $\sigma_2$, and $\sigma_3$. The cube of Fig. 5.2 would be elastically strained into the shape of a brick. The relationships between principal stresses and principal strains in an isotropic material are particularly simple. They are as follows:

$$\epsilon_1 = \frac{1}{E}\left[\sigma_1 - \nu(\sigma_2 + \sigma_3)\right]$$

$$\epsilon_2 = \frac{1}{E}\left[\sigma_2 - \nu(\sigma_1 + \sigma_3)\right] \tag{5.7}$$

$$\epsilon_3 = \frac{1}{E}\left[\sigma_3 - \nu(\sigma_1 + \sigma_2)\right]$$

## 5.3   Elastic Deformation in Single Crystals

So far we have dealt with isotropic materials. With single crystals the moduli relating stress and strain are dependent on crystallographic direction. Referring again to Fig. 5.2, the generalized Hooke's law relationships between stress and strain then take the form:

$$\begin{aligned}
\epsilon_x &= S_{11}\sigma_x + S_{12}\sigma_y + S_{13}\sigma_z + S_{14}\tau_{yz} + S_{15}\tau_{zx} + S_{16}\tau_{xy}\\
\epsilon_y &= S_{21}\sigma_x + S_{22}\sigma_y + S_{23}\sigma_z + S_{24}\tau_{yz} + S_{25}\tau_{zx} + S_{26}\tau_{xy}\\
\epsilon_z &= S_{31}\sigma_x + S_{32}\sigma_y + S_{33}\sigma_z + S_{34}\tau_{yz} + S_{35}\tau_{zx} + S_{36}\tau_{xy}\\
\gamma_{yz} &= S_{41}\sigma_x + S_{42}\sigma_y + S_{43}\sigma_z + S_{44}\tau_{yz} + S_{45}\tau_{zx} + S_{46}\tau_{xy}\\
\gamma_{zx} &= S_{51}\sigma_x + S_{52}\sigma_y + S_{53}\sigma_z + S_{54}\tau_{yz} + S_{55}\tau_{zx} + S_{56}\tau_{xy}\\
\gamma_{xy} &= S_{61}\sigma_x + S_{62}\sigma_y + S_{63}\sigma_z + S_{64}\tau_{yz} + S_{65}\tau_{zx} + S_{66}\tau_{xy}
\end{aligned} \tag{5.8}$$

The stress components are written as linear functions of strain as follows:

$$\begin{aligned}
\sigma_x &= C_{11}\epsilon_x + C_{12}\epsilon_y + C_{13}\epsilon_z + C_{14}\gamma_{yz} + C_{15}\gamma_{zx} + C_{16}\gamma_{xy}\\
\sigma_y &= C_{21}\epsilon_x + C_{22}\epsilon_y + C_{23}\epsilon_z + C_{24}\gamma_{yz} + C_{25}\gamma_{zx} + C_{26}\gamma_{xy}\\
\sigma_z &= C_{31}\epsilon_x + C_{32}\epsilon_y + C_{33}\epsilon_z + C_{34}\gamma_{yz} + C_{35}\gamma_{zx} + C_{36}\gamma_{xy}\\
\tau_{yz} &= C_{41}\epsilon_x + C_{42}\epsilon_y + C_{43}\epsilon_z + C_{44}\gamma_{yz} + C_{45}\gamma_{zx} + C_{46}\gamma_{xy}\\
\tau_{zx} &= C_{51}\epsilon_x + C_{52}\epsilon_y + C_{53}\epsilon_z + C_{54}\gamma_{yz} + C_{55}\gamma_{zx} + C_{56}\gamma_{xy}\\
\tau_{xy} &= C_{61}\epsilon_x + C_{62}\epsilon_y + C_{63}\epsilon_z + C_{64}\gamma_{yz} + C_{65}\gamma_{zx} + C_{66}\gamma_{xy}
\end{aligned} \tag{5.9}$$

The coefficients $S_{ij}$ are called the *elastic compliance constants* and $C_{ij}$ the *moduli of elasticity*. They differ for each material. The number of independent coefficients decreases as the symmetry of the crystal increases.

It may be shown that $S_{ij} = S_{ji}$ so that even in triclinic crystals the number of independent coefficients is twenty-one. In hexagonal crystals the number is five and in cubic crystals three. For hexagonal crystals the coefficients on the right hand side of equation 5.9 become:

$$
\text{Hexagonal}\ \begin{Vmatrix}
C_{11} & C_{12} & C_{13} & 0 & 0 & 0 \\
C_{12} & C_{11} & C_{13} & 0 & 0 & 0 \\
C_{13} & C_{13} & C_{33} & 0 & 0 & 0 \\
0 & 0 & 0 & C_{44} & 0 & 0 \\
0 & 0 & 0 & 0 & C_{44} & 0 \\
0 & 0 & 0 & 0 & 0 & \dfrac{C_{11} - C_{12}}{2}
\end{Vmatrix}
\tag{5.10}
$$

and for cubic crystals:

$$
\text{Cubic}\ \begin{Vmatrix}
C_{11} & C_{12} & C_{12} & 0 & 0 & 0 \\
C_{12} & C_{11} & C_{12} & 0 & 0 & 0 \\
C_{12} & C_{12} & C_{11} & 0 & 0 & 0 \\
0 & 0 & 0 & C_{44} & 0 & 0 \\
0 & 0 & 0 & 0 & C_{44} & 0 \\
0 & 0 & 0 & 0 & 0 & C_{44}
\end{Vmatrix}
\tag{5.11}
$$

Table 5.1 gives values of the elastic moduli of a number of cubic crystals.

In practice, single crystals are often prepared in cylindrical or bar form. The orientation of the longitudinal axis with respect to the major axes of the structure may be determined by X-ray diffraction techniques. Let us suppose that the longitudinal axis of a single crystal of the *cubic* system

**Table 5.1**   Elastic Moduli of Cubic Crystals at Room Temperature [Moduli in $10^{11}$ newtons m$^{-2}$ (or in $10^{12}$ dynes cm$^{-2}$)

| Crystal | $C_{11}$ | $C_{12}$ | $C_{44}$ |
|---------|------|------|------|
| Fe | 2.37 | 1.41 | 1.16 |
| W | 5.01 | 1.98 | 1.15 |
| Cu | 1.684 | 1.214 | 0.75 |
| Diamond | 9.2 | 3.9 | 4.3 |
| Si | 1.66 | 0.64 | 0.79 |
| Ge | 1.29 | 0.48 | 0.67 |
| Al | 1.08 | 0.82 | 0.28 |
| Pb | 0.48 | 0.41 | 0.14 |
| NaCl | 0.486 | 0.127 | 0.128 |

makes angles $\alpha$, $\beta$, and $\gamma$ with the cubic axis. It may be shown* that if the bar is pulled in a tensile test machine, the effective values of Young's and shear moduli are given by

$$\frac{1}{E} = S_{11} - 2[(S_{11} - S_{12}) - \tfrac{1}{2}S_{44}]$$
$$\times (\cos^2 \alpha \cos^2 \beta + \cos^2 \beta \cos^2 \gamma + \cos^2 \alpha \cos^2 \gamma) \quad (5.12)$$

and

$$\frac{1}{G} = S_{44} + 4[(S_{11} - S_{12}) - \tfrac{1}{2}S_{44}]$$
$$\times (\cos^2 \alpha \cos^2 \beta + \cos^2 \beta \cos^2 \gamma + \cos^2 \alpha \cos^2 \gamma)$$

For a *hexagonal* crystal with the specimen axis making an angle $\alpha$ with the $c$ hexagonal axis

$$\frac{1}{E} = S_{11}(1 - \cos^2 \alpha)^2 + S_{33} \cos^4 \alpha + (2S_{13} + S_{44}) \cos^2 \alpha(1 - \cos^2 \alpha)$$

$$\frac{1}{G} = S_{44} + [(S_{11} - S_{12}) - \tfrac{1}{2}S_{44}](1 - \cos^2 \alpha)$$
$$+ 2(S_{11} + S_{33} - 2S_{13} - S_{44}) \cos^2 \alpha(1 - \cos^2 \alpha) \quad (5.13)$$

The foregoing formulas enable us to calculate changes in dimensions of isotropic or crystalline solids when subject to stress, provided the changes are within the elastic range. In engineering practice it is generally assumed that deformations are elastic. This is a good first approximation, although, as we shall see later in the chapter, for large deformations a linear relationship between stress and strain does not exist.

## 5.4 Measurement of Elastic Constants

A measurement of the elastic constant may, of course, be made by direct observation of the strain due to a known applied stress. A more recent technique involves the determination of the velocity of sound waves in the crystal. These measurements are often made in the ultrasonic frequency range at, say, 30 to 50 MHz. A beam of sound waves, usually pulsed, is sent through the crystal in a particular direction. The velocity of sound is simply related to the appropriate modulus of elasticity. Suppose that a longitudinal ultrasonic wave is applied in the 100 direction in a cubic crystal.

* For transfer of axes problems see any standard text on elasticity, for example, C. Zener, *Elasticity and Anelasticity of Metals*, University of Chicago Press, Chicago, Ill., 1952.

Then

$$V_L = \sqrt{\frac{C_{11}}{\rho}} \qquad (5.14)$$

where $V_L$ is the velocity of the longitudinal wave and $\rho$ is the density of the solid. A transverse or shear wave will be propagated in the [100] direction in a cubic crystal with a velocity $V_T$ given by

$$V_T = \sqrt{\frac{C_{44}}{\rho}} \qquad (5.15)$$

## 5.5   Mechanical Tests in Materials

At this point it is pertinent to show some stress-strain diagrams in real solids. This will enable us to assess the degree of applicability of elasticity equations. Shown in Fig. 5.3 is the stress-strain behavior of polycrystalline mild steel.

Between the origin and the point $P$ there is essentially a linear relationship between stress and strain. The value of stress corresponding to $P$ is called the *proportional limit*. Just above $P$, and in ductile materials essentially at the same point, is $E$, the *elastic limit*, which is the greatest stress the material can withstand without permanent distortion. Both points are difficult to obtain with accuracy in practical tests. The point $Y$ is the *upper yield point* and $L$ the *lower yield point*. It is this little kink around $Y$ and $L$ that characterizes the diagram. Beyond the lower yield point, deformation increases rapidly with stress. The point $U$ is the *ultimate tensile strength* of the mild steel. Beyond this point the mild steel specimen appreciably narrows in diameter as deformation proceeds and finally breaks at the point $B$, which corresponds to the *fracture stress*.

Many materials such as rolled steel, hardened steel, cast iron, aluminum, copper, and most alloys do not show yield points. Shear stress-strain diagrams for various metals are shown in Fig. 5.4, and Fig. 5.5 shows an enlargement of a typical plot at low stress levels. A metal behaves plastically if the stress is increased beyond the value $E$, the elastic limit. Permanent distortion is produced and if the stress is then reduced to zero from the value at $X$, the path $XY$ is followed. It is often the practice to define as the elastic limit the point $X$ for which the permanent distortion at $Y$ is 2 per cent.

From external evidence, mostly furnished by microscopic examination, we can recognize that two different mechanisms of deformation must exist. These mechanisms are *slip* and *twinning*.

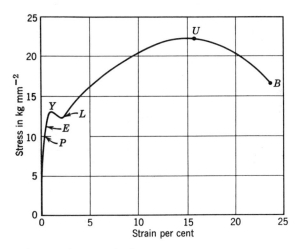

**Fig. 5.3**  Stress-strain diagram for mild steel in tension.

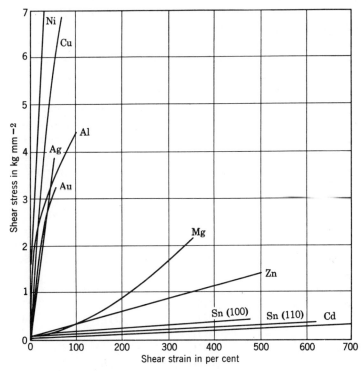

**Fig. 5.4**  Stress-strain diagrams for various metals.  (After Schmid and Boas)

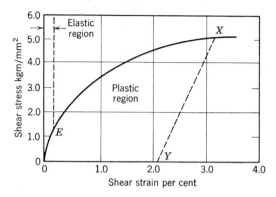

**Fig. 5.5**  Stress-strain behavior of nonferrous metals showing the initial plastic region.

## 5.6  Slip

In slip one portion of the crystal is displaced with respect to another by a shearing stress, the displacement taking place on a crystallographic plane called the *slip plane* and in a crystallographic direction called the *slip direction*.

The slip plane is always a plane of dense packing of atoms and the slip direction is always the one of maximum line density. The selection of operative plane on which slip takes place is quite often influenced by temperature; the slip direction, however, nearly always remains the same. The combination of slip direction and slip plane is called a *slip system*. The favored slip system is, of course, determined by the crystal structure of the solid. Face-centered cubic metals have only one class of slip system. The total strain may be carried on any or all of the four {111} planes. The plane which is first activated is that carrying the maximum resolved shear stress. Slip in body-centered cubic crystals is not so simple, and three different slip

**Table 5.2**  Slip Systems in Cubic and Hexagonal Crystals

| Structure | Slip Plane | Slip Direction | Number of Slip Systems |
|---|---|---|---|
| Face-centered cubic | {111} | $\langle 1\bar{1}0 \rangle$ | 12 |
| Body-centered cubic | {110} | $\langle \bar{1}11 \rangle$ | 12 |
| | {211} | $\langle \bar{1}11 \rangle$ | 12 |
| | {321} | $\langle \bar{1}11 \rangle$ | 24 |
| Hexagonal close-packed | {0001} | $\langle 11\bar{2}0 \rangle$ | 3 |
| | {10$\bar{1}$1} | $\langle 11\bar{2}0 \rangle$ | 3 |

systems have been found. Table 5.2 gives the observed slip systems in cubic and hexagonal crystals.

Let us suppose that in a certain solid the slip planes are of the type {111}. When slip occurs we might suppose that each (111) plane carries its share of the total slip deformation. This does not happen. Only certain active slip planes, quite often separated from one another in metals by distances of about 1 $\mu$, carry the displacement. Each unit displacement constitutes a motion of one plane laterally over its neighbor by one atomic distance, the active slip planes, however, carrying many such unit displacements. The edges of the slip planes at the polished surface of a deformed crystal become visible once the displacement has reached a large number of units, and the trace seen on the surface is called a *slip band*.

The applied stress necessary to produce plastic deformation in shear is called a *critical shear stress*. The critical shear stress is dependent on temperature, purity, previous mechanical history, and rate of deformation. The effects of these factors on the plastic behavior of metals will be discussed in succeeding sections.

### 5.7   Twinning

In a number of crystals (usually either hexagonal close-packed or body-centered cubic), and particularly at low temperatures, an important mechanism of deformation is *twinning*. This is a shearing motion of atomic planes over one another, the magnitude of translation of each plane being proportional to its distance from a particular plane in the lattice called the *twinning plane*. Figure 5.6 shows the shear movements for twinning in a body-centered cubic crystal. In the unit cube drawn in the upper part of the figure, the twinning plane which is the (211) is indicated by dot-dash lines. This plane stands perpendicular to the paper in the lower part of the figure, and the atom movements to form a twin are indicated by arrows. In slip we saw that considerable movement occurs on a few widely separated slip planes. In twinning a small displacement occurs on many neighboring planes. During deformation, twins may be produced very suddenly. They are also sometimes produced by annealing, probably as the result of growth from minute twinned regions produced by previous strain.

Measurements of a critical shear stress for twinning are complicated by the fact that slip in most metals at room temperature occurs at a lower critical stress than that necessary for twinning. The critical shear stress for slip rises with decreasing temperature, however, and twinning becomes relatively more likely. Thus deformation in $\alpha$-iron at temperatures around 80°K has been shown to be by twinning.

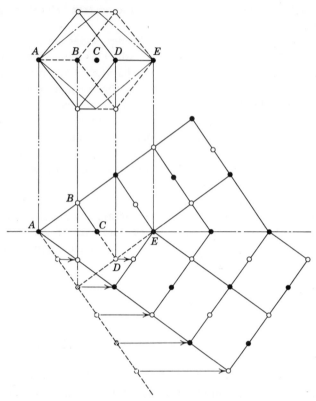

**Fig. 5.6** Shear movements of atoms (shown by arrows) for twinning in a body-centered cubic crystal. (After Barrett)

## 5.8 Estimation of the Magnitude of the Critical Shear Stress

In the previous sections we have seen that a strain occurs when a stress is applied to a solid, and that the magnitude of the strain per unit stress increment is much greater in the *plastic* deformation region than in the initial or *elastic* region.

Let us now give some consideration to an estimate of the expected magnitude of the critical shear stress or critical shear strain. We will reproduce a calculation by Frenkel (1926). Later refinements to this calculation have not changed Frenkel's estimate by a factor of more than about five.

Suppose in Fig. 5.7a that A and B represent atoms of two adjacent planes. The spacing between the planes is d. A shear stress τ is applied so that the planes are translated with respect to one another, the relative displacement being designated x. We make the assumption *that the A plane of atoms moves over the B plane as a whole just as one card moves over the next in a deformed deck.*

The first task is to obtain a realistic relationship between the shearing stress $\tau$ and the shear displacement $x$. The stress is, of course, zero at the equilibrium positions of the atoms shown by $A$ and $B$ in Fig. 5.7a. When the displacement is such that atom $A$ is directly over atom $B$, the planes are in unstable equilibrium and the stress is also zero. Let us suppose that the shear stress is a sinusoidal function of $x$ with period $a$, where $a$ is the inter-atomic spacing in the direction of shear. Then

$$\tau = K \sin \frac{2\pi x}{a} \tag{5.16}$$

which is shown in Fig. 5.7b. The constant $K$ can be determined from the condition that the initial slope (in Fig. 5.7b), that is, in the elastic region of very small strain, must agree with the shear modulus of the crystal. From (5.16) for small $x$ we have

$$\tau = K \frac{2\pi x}{a}$$

Also from the Hooke's law definition of $G$, the shear modulus, we have

$$\tau = \frac{Gx}{d}$$

Thus

$$\tau = \frac{aG}{2\pi d} \sin \frac{2\pi x}{a} \tag{5.17}$$

The stress $\tau$ may be increased to its maximum or critical shear stress value $\tau_M$, at which point the lattice becomes mechanically unstable and shear

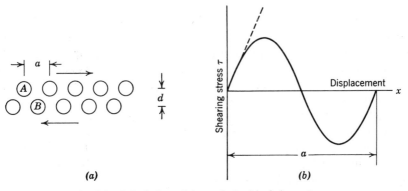

(a)                    (b)

**Fig. 5.7**   Calculation of theoretical critical shear stress.

occurs. After shear the *A* plane of atoms will be displaced relative to the *B* plane by one atomic spacing, that is, by *a*.

Thus in magnitude,

$$\tau_M = \frac{aG}{2\pi d} \tag{5.18}$$

If $a \simeq d$, the theoretical critical shear stress should be about $G/2\pi$. Even with refinements to the theory, which take the possible deformation of the atoms into account, $\tau_M$ cannot be much less than about $G/30$.

This value for $\tau_M$ is several orders of magnitude too high when compared with experimental measurements. Table 5.3 gives the comparison of shear

**Table 5.3**   Comparison of Shear Modulus and Elastic Limit

|  | Shear Modulus $(nm^{-2})$ | Elastic Limit $(nm^{-2})$ |
|---|---|---|
| Sn, single crystal | $1.9 \times 10^{10}$ | $1.3 \times 10^8$ |
| Ag, single crystal | $2.8 \times 10^{10}$ | $6 \times 10^5$ |
| Al, single crystal | $2.5 \times 10^{10}$ | $4 \times 10^5$ |
| Al, pure polycrystal | $2.5 \times 10^{10}$ | $2.6 \times 10^7$ |
| Al, commercial drawn | $\sim 2.5 \times 10^{10}$ | $9.9 \times 10^7$ |
| Duralumin | $\sim 2.5 \times 10^{10}$ | $3.6 \times 10^8$ |
| Fe, soft polycrystal | $7.7 \times 10^{10}$ | $1.5 \times 10^8$ |
| Heat treated carbon steel | $\sim 8 \times 10^{10}$ | $6.5 \times 10^8$ |
| Nickel-chrome steel | $\sim 8 \times 10^{10}$ | $1.2 \times 10^9$ |

modulus *G* with critical shear stress (or elastic limit) for a number of materials in different forms. We are driven to the conclusion that *shear or slip does not occur in soft crystals by the simple mechanism pictured above of one layer of atoms being displaced together in one sheet over an adjacent layer of atoms.* Some source of mechanical weakness of such a kind that slip can start from the source at very low applied stress must exist in real crystals. It is also obvious from the table that the presence of grain boundaries, cold work, and alloying components also increases the elastic limits.

X-ray experimental evidence has long shown that imperfections do occur in crystal lattices, and the idea that crystal weakness is associated with flaws is not a new one. The particular kinds of imperfections that occur in crystals and account for the low critical shear stress and a number of other mechanical properties are called *dislocations*.

Before we study the detailed nature of dislocations, let us speculate on the general form that this imperfection may take in a solid. Suppose a carpet lies on a floor and it is necessary to displace it by a short distance. In this analogy the carpet and the floor represent two adjacent planes of atoms and the requirement is to find with how small a force one may produce slip. There are, of course, two ways of proceeding. First, we can apply a force to one end sufficient in magnitude to cause the whole carpet to slip to the required position. The magnitude of the force depends on the force of attraction, gravitational in the analogy, and if the carpet is heavy the magnitude may be quite large. The second method of displacing the carpet over the floor is to make a small ruck or fold extending across the carpet. This corresponds to a fault in the atomic planes, which is a line imperfection or dislocation. It requires quite a small force to move the fold across the carpet. The displacement of the whole carpet caused by moving the fold right across the carpet is, on completion, indistinguishable from that produced by the first method.

In real crystals plastic deformation is caused by the movement of dislocations across slip planes in much the same manner as that suggested by the carpet analogy. Dislocations exist in the crystal and the critical shear stress is that force necessary to induce them to move.

## 5.9  Geometry of Dislocations

The actual form of the simplest types of dislocation, namely, the *edge dislocation* and the *screw dislocation*, will now be discussed. Dislocation theory will then be used to account for the mechanical properties of crystals.

### Edge Dislocation

Figure 5.8 shows a *positive edge dislocation*. In the diagram it is seen that an extra vertical half-plane of atoms exists in the upper half of the crystal. The termination of the extra plane is a dislocation, extending out from the paper in Fig. 5.8, and able to move on the horizontal plane containing it. This horizontal plane is the *slip plane*. If the extra half-plane is below the slip plane, the edge dislocation is said to be *negative*. The edge-type dislocation is always perpendicular to the direction of slip. Figure 5.9 shows a cubic crystal in which slip of one atom distance has occurred over the left portion of the slip plane but not over the portion of the slip plane to the right of the dislocation *EF*.

Figure 5.10 shows how a positive dislocation, if present, may move under a shearing stress across a slip plane. In the sequence *a*, *b*, *c*, and *d*, a positive dislocation moves to the right, whereas in *e*, *f*, *g*, and *h*, a negative dislocation

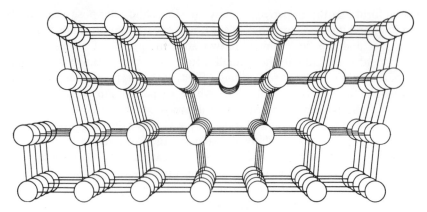

**Fig. 5.8**   Positive edge dislocation. (After Goldman)

moves to the left. It is to be noted that the resulting deformations are identical.

In a positive edge dislocation, as in Fig. 5.8, the atoms above the slip plane and just to the left of the dislocation will be attracted by the atoms below the slip plane, and on balance this attraction will be to the right. On the other hand, the atoms above the slip plane and just to the right of the dislocation will be attracted to the left. To a first approximation these two forces of attraction balance, and thus the external force required to move the dislocation will be quite small.

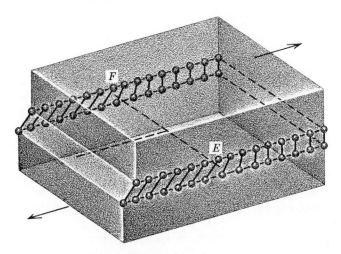

**Fig. 5.9**   Edge dislocation *EF* marking the boundary between a slipped region on the left and a region of no slip on the right. (After Cottrell)

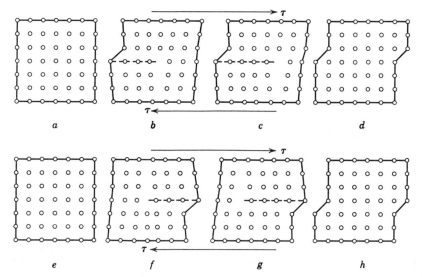

**Fig. 5.10** Movement of edge dislocation under a shearing stress: *a, b, c, d,* positive edge dislocation moving to right; *e, f, g, h,* negative dislocation moving to left. (After Taylor)

### Screw Dislocation

The second type of simple dislocation is the *screw dislocation* shown in Fig. 5.11. In Fig. 5.11*a* slip has occurred over the area *ABEF* in a direction parallel to the dislocation *EF*. Figure 5.11*b* shows the arrangement of atoms around a screw dislocation in a simple cubic structure. Here the two planes of atoms which meet on *ABCD* are viewed from above *ABCD*. Full circles denote atoms above plane *ABCD* and open circles atoms below *ABCD*.

### 5.10 The Burgers Vector

We have seen that the dislocation line represents the boundary between the slipped and unslipped portions of the crystal. The dislocation may either form a closed loop or intersect the surface of the crystal. It will therefore have portions which are pure screw and portions which are pure edge and be *hybrid* over intervening portions.

Figure 5.12*a* shows an unstrained cube. If we trace round the atom circuit shown by the heavy line this circuit closes. In *b* the cube has been plastically deformed by the shear stress *τ*. The dislocation segment which has contributed to the slip is pure edge in character at *E* and pure screw in character

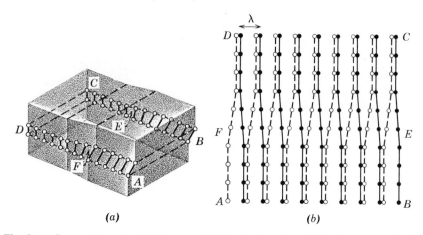

(a)                                    (b)

**Fig. 5.11**   Screw dislocation *EF* lying parallel to the direction of slip in a crystal.  In (*a*) slip has occurred over the region *ABEF*.  In (*b*) the atoms (in a cubic structure) above and below *ABCD* are viewed from above.  Full circles denote atoms above the plane *ABCD* and open circles denote atoms below that plane.  (After Cottrell)

at *S*.  If we now trace out the atom circuit we see that it no longer closes. It is incomplete at *E* by the segment *b*.  This is a characteristic of the dislocation called its *Burgers vector*.  The circuit at *S* shows that the screw component has the same Burgers vector.  The vector is, in fact, the same at all points along the dislocation line; it is parallel to the screw segment, perpendicular to the edge segment, and makes an angle with the hybrid segment.

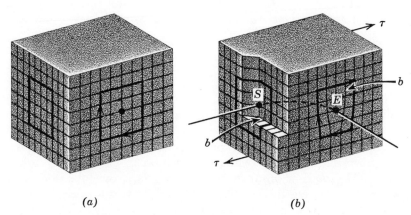

(a)                                    (b)

**Fig. 5.12**   (*a*) Unstrained cube.  (*b*) Strained in shear.  Atom circuit round the dislocation fails to close by the Burgers vector.  Pure edge at *E*, pure screw at *S*.

### 5.11   Force on a Dislocation

When sufficient force is applied to a crystal a dislocation will move, and the crystal is plastically deformed. The force acting on the dislocation will now be calculated.

Suppose that when a shear stress of magnitude $\tau$ acts on a slip plane of area $A$ that an element $dl$ of dislocation moves a distance $dS$; the area swept by the dislocation segment is $dS \cdot dl$. Now if the dislocation had swept over the entire slip plane $A$, the two half-crystals that meet on this plane would be displaced relative to one another by the amount $b$ which is the *Burgers vector*. In our present example the mean relative displacement of the half-crystals is taken to be $(dS \cdot dl/A)b$, a result which is intuitively plausible.

The applied force is $A\tau$ so that the work done when the slip takes place is given by

$$A\tau(dS \cdot dl/A)b = \tau b\, dS \cdot dl \tag{5.19}$$

If $F_S$ is the force in the direction of displacement $dS$ which acts on the dislocation, we can also write

$$\text{Work done by } F_S \text{ during slip} = F_S \cdot dS \tag{5.20}$$

Thus from (5.19) and (5.20) the force acting on a length of dislocation $dl$ is given by

$$F_S = \tau b\, dl \tag{5.21}$$

The force $F_S$ *per unit length of dislocation* is thus given by

$$F_S = \tau b \tag{5.22}$$

Force $F_S$ lies in the slip plane, is perpendicular to the dislocation line all along its length, and is directed toward the unslipped portion of the crystal.

### 5.12   Stress Fields of Dislocations

If we know the magnitudes and directions of the stresses introduced into a perfect lattice by the presence of a dislocation, then we can estimate the forces acting on a dislocation because of the presence of a second dislocation. It will then be possible to describe in a semiquantitative manner the behavior of networks of dislocations.

#### Screw Dislocation

The method of calculation of forces and energies will be demonstrated for the simpler case of a screw dislocation. The result for an edge dislocation, which is not very different, will simply be quoted.

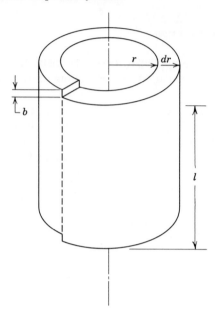

**Fig. 5.13**  Shell of deformed material surrounding a screw dislocation marked by dot-dash line.

Figure 5.13 shows a cylindrical crystal which has been sheared in the axial direction.  This is equivalent to introducing a screw dislocation, with Burgers vector $b$, along the crystal axis.  The displacement is in a peripheral length of $2\pi r$, and thus the shear strain is

$$\gamma = \frac{b}{2\pi r}$$

The shear stress is then given by

$$\gamma = G\gamma = \frac{Gb}{2\pi r}$$

The elastic energy $dE_S$ of the shell due to the presence of the dislocation is

$$dE_B = \tfrac{1}{2}G\gamma^2 \, dV$$

where $dV$ is the volume of the shell.  Thus

$$dE_S = \tfrac{1}{2}G\left(\frac{b}{2\pi r}\right)^2 2\pi rl \, dr$$

$$= \left(\frac{Gb^2}{4\pi}\right)\frac{dr}{r}\, l$$

The elastic energy $E_S$ per unit length of screw dislocation is

$$E_S = \int_{r_1}^{r_2} \left(\frac{Gb^2}{4\pi}\right) \frac{dr}{r}$$

$$= \left(\frac{Gb^2}{4\pi}\right) \ln \left(\frac{r_2}{r_1}\right) \tag{5.23}$$

where $r_1$ and $r_2$ are lower and upper limits for the radius of material strained by the presence of the dislocation. The choice of the limits $r_1$ and $r_2$ is not obvious. It is believed, however, that little error is introduced by simply making $\ln (r_2/r_1)$ equal to $4\pi$ and thus reducing $E_S$ to the simple value $Gb^2$ per unit length.

### Edge Dislocation

The strain energy $E_E$ per unit length of *edge* dislocation is obtained by a slightly more difficult calculation. It is

$$E_E = \frac{Gb^2}{4\pi(1 - v)} \ln \left(\frac{r_2}{r_1}\right) \tag{5.24}$$

where $v$ is Poisson's ratio, which in metals is about 0.3. If we again let $\ln (r_2/r_1)$ equal $4\pi$ we obtain

$$E_E \simeq \frac{Gb^2}{(1 - v)} \tag{5.25}$$

and thus is slightly greater than $E_S$.

There are two features of interest in these results. The energy is proportional to $b^2$. Thus the most stable dislocations (least energy) are these of minimum $b$, that is, in close-packed directions. The second feature is that the energy increases with length of dislocation. This is equivalent to saying that a *line tension* exists along the dislocation. The value of the tension $T$ is given by

$$T \simeq Gb^2 \tag{5.26}$$

since the elastic energy per unit length is always equivalent to the force.

## 5.13 Pinned Dislocations

Suppose that an edge dislocation moving in its slip plane encounters obstacles at $A$ and $B$ in Fig. 5.14. These obstacles may be impurity atoms, lattice defects, or other dislocation segments. Under the shear stress the dislocation will bow out so that it makes an angle $\theta$ with the line of the obstacles.

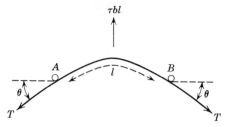

**Fig. 5.14**   Dislocation pinned at $A$ and $B$ bows out under a shear stress.

The force on the dislocation is balanced by the component of line tension

$$\tau bl = 2T \sin \theta$$

The dislocation will bow out until it becomes semicircular, at which point the stress to move the dislocation takes the maximum value $\tau_{\text{max}}$ where

$$\tau_{\text{max}} = \frac{2T}{bl}$$

$$= \frac{2Gb}{l} \tag{5.27}$$

The effectiveness of the obstacle as a pinning point thus depends on the distance $l$. Thus the strength of a material will depend on the state of dispersion of the obstacles.

### 5.14   Forces and Interactions between Dislocations

Let us now consider the magnitude of the forces that exist between dislocations. The result of the calculation will be quoted without proof for two *edge* dislocations with parallel Burgers vectors.

Following Cottrell, suppose that in Fig. 5.15 a positive edge dislocation lies along the $z$ axis with a Burgers vector $b$ along the $x$ axis. A second positive edge dislocation situated at $(x, y)$ lies parallel to the $z$ axis with its Burgers vector also parallel to the $x$ axis.

Then the components $F_x$ and $F_y$ of the force per unit length on the dislocation at $(x, y)$ because of the presence of the dislocation at the origin are given by

$$F_x = \frac{Gb^2}{2\pi(1 - v)} \cdot \frac{x^2(x^2 - y^2)}{(x^2 + y^2)^2} \tag{5.28}$$

and

$$F_y = \frac{Gb^2}{2\pi(1 - v)} \cdot \frac{y(3x^2 + y^2)}{(x^2 + y^2)^2} \tag{5.29}$$

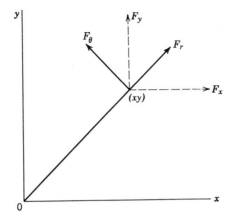

**Fig. 5.15**   Calculation of forces between edge dislocations.

In polar coordinates the components $F_r$ and $F_\theta$ are given by

$$F_r = \frac{Gb^2}{2\pi(1-\nu)} \cdot \frac{1}{r} \tag{5.30}$$

$$F_\theta = \frac{Gb^2}{2\pi(1-\nu)} \cdot \frac{\sin 2\theta}{r} \tag{5.31}$$

If the dislocations have opposite signs, the signs of these forces are reversed.

Equation 5.30, giving the force component on the line joining dislocations, shows that edge dislocations of the same sign repel each other along this line.

The variation of $F_x$ with $x$ from Equation 5.28 is shown in Fig. 5.16. $F_x$ is the component of force in the direction of slip and in Fig. 5.16 the unit of force is $Gb^2/2\pi(1-\nu)y$; $x$ is measured along the slip plane using $y$ as the unit of length. When $F_x$ is positive, it acts in the direction of increasing $x$.

When $x > y$, that is, $x > 1$ in Fig. 5.16, $F_x$ is positive for dislocations of the same sign which thus repel each other. When $x < y$, dislocations of the same sign attract each other.

The force between dislocations is zero at $x = y$, which is an unstable position, and also zero at $x = 0$. Thus an array of edge dislocations of the same sign will tend to align themselves on their respective slip planes so that they lie above one another along a line normal to the slip plane. The figure also shows that dislocations of opposite sign attract each other along the slip planes when $x > y$ and repel when $x < y$. The equilibrium is stable at $x = y$ and unstable at $x = 0$.

Pairs of screw dislocations have no stable positions since a screw dislocation may glide on any plane that contains it. Screw dislocations of the same sign thus repel each other to infinity, whereas those of opposite sign attract each other until they annihilate.

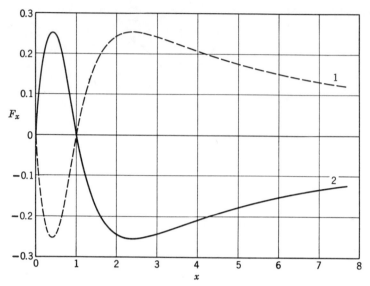

**Fig. 5.16** Variation of force between dislocations with distance apart. Curve 1 is for dislocations of the same sign and curve 2 for those of opposite sign. (After Cottrell)

Let us finally consider the interaction between edge dislocations of opposite sign on the *same* or on adjacent slip planes. As we have seen, the dislocations attract one another. If they are on the *same* plane the edge dislocations annihilate one another. If they are on an *adjacent* plane an *interstitial* atom or a *vacancy* results from the interaction. The three alternatives are illustrated in Fig. 5.17*a*, *b*, and *c*.

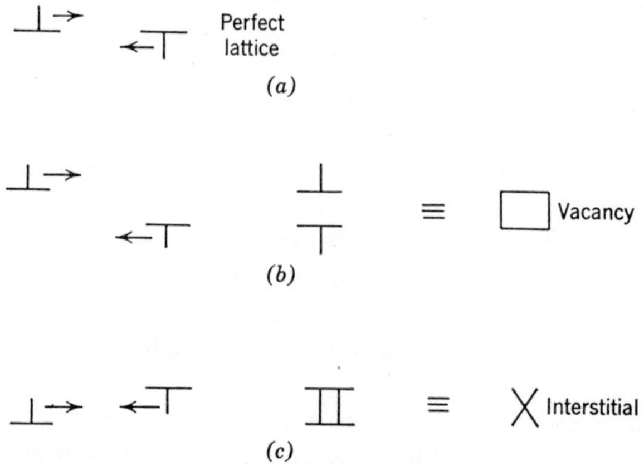

**Fig. 5.17** (*a*) Edge dislocations of opposite sign on the same slip plane. (*b*) and (*c*) Edge dislocations of opposite sign on adjacent slip planes.

## 5.15 Partial Dislocations: Stacking Faults

From Fig. 5.12 it is obvious that the Burgers vector of a *perfect* dislocation is limited in a crystalline structure to a few possible periodic distances in the lattice. The energy of a dislocation has been shown to be proportional to $b^2$ per unit length. Thus splitting of a dislocation of large $b$ into two other dislocations of vectors $b_1$ and $b_2$ would be energetically favored if

$$b_1{}^2 + b_2{}^2 > b^2 \qquad (5.32)$$

Such *partial* dislocations must together complete a unit slip displacement so that on adding vectorially

$$b_1 + b_2 = b \qquad (5.33)$$

These partial dislocations, being essentially of the same sign, repel one another so that a region where the normal crystal structure is interrupted is formed between them. Such a region is called a *stacking fault*. Since, of course, the perfect or normal lattice is that of the lowest energy, the stacking fault region is of higher energy. Thus the fault forms a ribbon between the partial dislocations and has an energy per unit area associated with it. This energy equals the work done by the force of repulsion between the partial dislocations. Stacking faults commonly occur in many metallic materials such as the face-centered cubic metals and alloys. We will consider two commonly occurring examples.

### Glissile Dislocations in a Face-Centered Cubic Metal

Figure 5.18*a* shows a perfect dislocation in a face-centered cubic structure. The Burgers vector is assumed to be in the $\langle 110 \rangle$ direction. Figure 5.18*b* shows the perfect dislocation split into two partial dislocations of vectors $b_1$ and $b_2$ with the stacking fault region between the partials. Figure 5.19 shows two adjacent atomic planes in a face-centered cubic structure. The distance *ab* between atoms is half the unit vector in the [110] direction and is

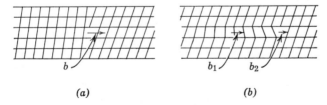

(*a*)             (*b*)

**Fig. 5.18** (*a*) Perfect dislocation in face-centered cubic structure. (*b*) Perfect dislocation split into two partial dislocations of vectors $b_1$ and $b_2$.

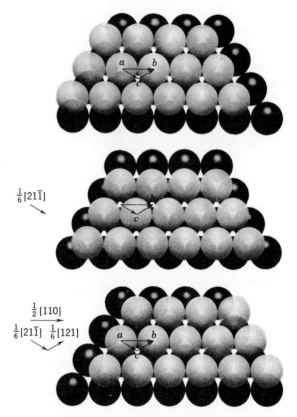

$\frac{1}{6}[21\bar{1}]$

$\frac{1}{2}[110]$

$\frac{1}{6}[21\bar{1}]$  $\frac{1}{6}[121]$

**Fig. 5.19**  In the face-centered cubic structure the partials $b_1(= \frac{1}{6}[21\bar{1}])$ and $b_2(= \frac{1}{6}[121])$ add vectorially to give the perfect Burgers vector $b(= \frac{1}{2}[110])$. (From Moffatt, Pearsall, and Wulff, *Structure and Properties of Materials*, Vol. 1, John Wiley and Sons, New York, 1964)

written $\frac{1}{2}[110]$. In slip of one plane past another the "through the valley route" zigzags in the $[21\bar{1}]$ direction *ac* and then in the [121] direction *cb*. The partials $b_1$ ($= \frac{1}{6}[21\bar{1}]$) and $b_2$ ($= \frac{1}{6}[121]$) add vectorially to $b$ ($= \frac{1}{2}[110]$) In Fig. 5.19 an edge dislocation of vector $b$, which has dissociated into partials $b_1$ and $b_2$, can move with the stacking fault on the slip plane.

A dissociated screw dislocation, on the other hand, must have partials which are partially edge in character. It can only move if the stacking fault, associated with the edge components, lies in the slip plane. In order to *change the direction of slip* the stacking fault must first be pinched. Then a new dissociation may be possible in which the new partials are on the new slip plane. The energy to do this is generally high enough so that this process of *cross-slip* is only possible at high applied stresses or at high

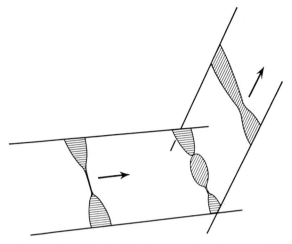

**Fig. 5.20**   Pinching of stacking fault during cross-slip of an extended dislocation.

temperatures.  Figure 5.20 shows the mechanism of cross-slip of a dissociated dislocation.  Dislocations with a stacking fault in a slip plane are often called *glissile dislocations*.

Table 5.4 shows a few values of stacking fault energies and widths.  Narrow stacking faults are naturally associated with high stacking fault energy.  The reader is reminded that this energy is balanced at a certain fault width by the work done in mutual repulsion of the two partials on the slip plane.

### Sessile Dislocations in a Face-Centered Cubic Metal

Face-centered cubic metals and alloys have nonequilibrium numbers of vacancies present after quenching (Section 4.13) or irradiation (Section 7.13).

**Table 5.4**   Stacking Fault Energies and Widths*

| Metal | Stacking Fault Energy (joules $m^{-2}$) | Stacking Fault Width (atomic distances) |
|---|---|---|
| Aluminum | $240 \times 10^{-3}$ | 1.0–2.0 |
| Copper | 160 | 1.5–3.5 |
| Gold | 10 | 11–36 |
| Stainless steel | 20 | 50 |
| α brass | 30 | 20 |

* After R. Berner, *Z. Naturf.*, **15a**, 689, 1960.

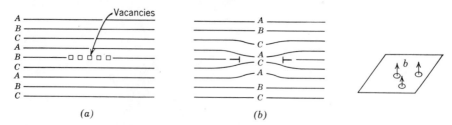

**Fig. 5.21** (*a*) A perfect lattice with vacancies in a saucer-shaped disc. (*b*) The disc can collapse to form a loop of sessile dislocation enclosing an area in which the stacking order differs from that of perfect face-centered cubic. (From Wulff, Hayden, and Moffatt, *Structure and Properties of Materials*, John Wiley and Son, New York, 1965)

Under certain conditions (Section 4.12) the vacancies cluster together to form disc-shaped cavities on close-packed planes. When these discs grow to about $10^{-7}$ m across, they often collapse to form dislocation loops. Figure 5.21*a* shows a perfect lattice with vacancies and Fig. 5.21*b* the situation after collapse of the vacancy disc. From the figure it can also be seen that, across the region of the stacking fault, the regular arrangement of the atoms of a face-centered cubic crystal is altered. These dislocation loops have Burgers vectors which are perpendicular to the plane of the loop. They are called *sessile* loops. Such loops cannot glide on the plane of the stacking fault and may only move by climbing to other planes by the emission or absorption of vacancies. This requires a diffusion mechanism and the necessary higher temperatures.

## 5.16   Dislocations Jogs

When two nonparallel dislocations intersect, a small step or *jog* is formed in either or both dislocations. Figure 5.22 shows a jog formed by an edge dislocation cutting through a screw, and Fig. 5.23 shows that cross-slip of a screw dislocation also forms a jog. In this case the jog is a short length of edge dislocation.

Suppose in Fig. 5.24 that a jogged screw dislocation is made to glide across the horizontal plane of the diagram. The jog trails behind since it cannot glide in this direction. Two parallel edge dislocations of opposite sign are left behind the moving screw parts of the dislocation. These *dislocation dipoles* have been observed in ionic crystals after plastic deformation.

If the parallel dislocations are one plane apart, they form lines of vacancies or interstitials. We have already discussed this scheme with the aid of Fig. 5.17. A simplified picture of the emission of vacancies from a moving jog is given in Fig. 5.25.

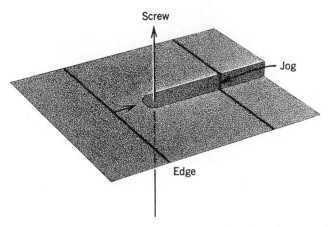

**Fig. 5.22** A jog being formed by an edge dislocation cutting through a screw dislocation.

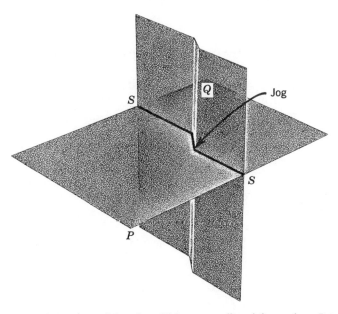

**Fig. 5.23** Part of the screw dislocation $SS$ has cross-slipped from plane $P$ to plane $Q$ forming a jog.

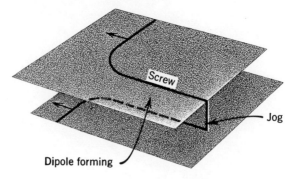

**Fig. 5.24** Motion of a jogged screw dislocation. The jog trails, and two parallel dislocations, called a *dipole*, are left behind. The dipole may collapse into a line of vacancies.

The restriction of dislocation motion by jogs and the production of point defects by intersecting dislocations are fundamental parts of modern theories of the hardening of metals by plastic deformation.

## 5.17   Estimates of the Density of Dislocations

Dislocations have energies which make it impossible for them to exist in thermal equilibrium in a crystal. They must therefore be introduced in a nonequilibrium manner during the solidification of the crystal, and continue to exist at lower temperatures.

Dislocation densities are quoted as the number which cross a unit area inside the crystal. The density may be from $10^9$ to $10^{12}$ per square meter in well-annealed polycrystalline metals, whereas the best germanium and silicon single crystals give density values below $10^6$ per square meter. In heavily deformed metals the densities increase to as high as $10^{15}$ or $10^{16}$ dislocations per square meter.

If a metal after severe deformation is heated in a calorimeter, it is possible

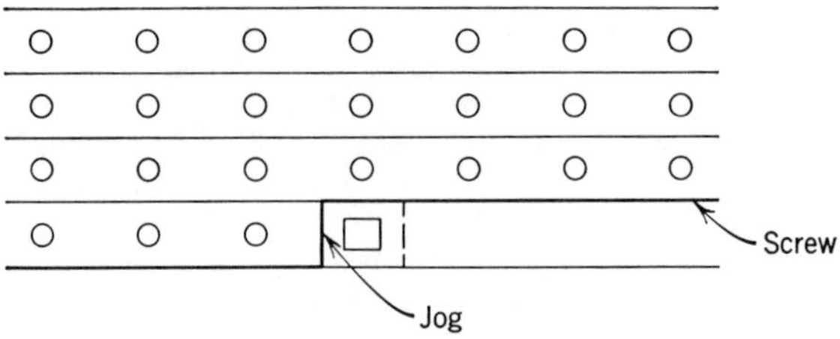

**Fig. 5.25** Simplified picture of the emission of vacancies from a jog on a moving screw dislocation.

to measure the release of energy associated with annealing. If the deformation is attributed to the introduction of dislocations, the dislocation density may be estimated from the calorimetric results.

Let us assume the measured maximum energy stored in the plastically deformed metal to be about 1 kilocalorie per kilogram. Most metals give stored energy values of about this magnitude. With a metal density of about $10^4$ kgm m$^{-3}$ the stored energy is then of the order of $4 \times 10^7$ joules m$^{-3}$. In order to estimate the number of dislocations per square meter, we must know the lattice energy per meter of dislocation, which we can calculate from Equation 5.23. If we let $r_2 \simeq 10^{-6}$ m and $r_1 \simeq 10^{-10}$ m, then $E_S$ is approximately $7 \times 10^{-9}$ joule m$^{-1}$. The total length of dislocation per cubic meter is then $4 \times 10^7/7 \times 10^{-9}$, that is, $6 \times 10^{15}$ m. Thus the number of dislocations which, on the average, cuts each square meter of internal crystal plane is about $2 \times 10^{15}$.

There are other less direct methods of estimating the density of dislocations in solids. Some of these involve measurement of X-ray line broadening, measurement of electrical resistivity, and measurement of saturation magnetic induction. These methods give order of magnitude estimates. Electron microscopy studies will be discussed later.

## 5.18 Dislocation Multiplication

Let us first make a rough estimate of the number of dislocations necessary to produce values of strain that are readily attainable in practice. We will use a greatly oversimplified model. Suppose in Fig. 5.26 that a solid after solidification contains dislocations which are on the average spaced a distance $l$ apart. Suppose now that this solid specimen is sheared and that each dislocation moves right across its slip plane from one boundary of the crystal to the other, a distance $L$. A dislocation generally will not move this

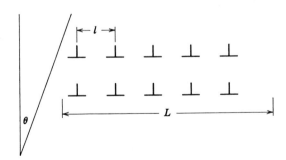

**Fig. 5.26** Calculation of possible strain by dislocation movement.

far, and our model should give an overestimate of the strain produced. As each dislocation moves across the slip plane, the atomic planes above and below are translated relative to one another by the Burgers vector $b$. The total translation will be given by $(L/l)b$. The shear strain is thus $Lb/l^2$. Suppose the dislocation moves across a complete grain of average dimension, say, $10^{-3}$ m, then with $b \simeq 10^{-10}$ m and $l \simeq 10^{-6}$, the strain would be $\simeq 10^{-1}$. Thus *if the same number of dislocations are present throughout the process of deformation*, the maximum strain we could expect in the foregoing case would be $\simeq 10^{-1}$. In practice, however, a well-annealed metal, with a dislocation density corresponding to $l \simeq 10^{-6}$ m, can be strained to many times the value $10^{-1}$. It is clear that the number of dislocations must increase during the deformation process. The multiplication factor can be as high as one thousand. A plausible model of dislocation multiplication has been proposed by Frank and Read (1950).

## 5.19  Frank-Read Dislocation Generator

Dislocations generally do not lie in a single slip plane. Instead they extend onto other neighboring slip planes by *jogs*. The dislocation is pinned at the points where it leaves the slip planes, and under the influence of an applied stress it bows out from the pinning point. The elastic energy of a dislocation loop of radius $r$ is $2\pi r$ times its energy per unit length and, from Equation 5.23, must be approximately

$$2\pi r \left(\frac{Gb^2}{4\pi}\right) \ln \left(\frac{r_2}{r_1}\right) \tag{5.34}$$

The energy of the crystal is at the same time decreased by the product (stress per unit length) (area of loop $\pi r^2$). The change in energy $\Delta E$ on introducing the loop is therefore given by

$$\Delta E = \frac{Gb^2 r}{2} \ln \left(\frac{r_2}{r_1}\right) - \pi r^2 \tau b$$

$E$ passes through a maximum when $\partial(\Delta E)/\partial r = 0$, which occurs when

$$\frac{2r}{b} = \frac{G \ln (r_2/r_1)}{2\tau \pi}$$

We can approximate $\ln (r_2/r_1)$ to $2\pi$, making the condition for the critical magnitude of loop radius simply

$$\frac{2r}{b} = \frac{G}{\tau} \tag{5.35}$$

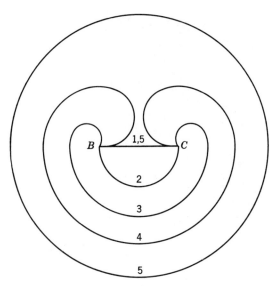

**Fig. 5.27** Dislocation multiplication by Frank-Read generator. The numbers indicate successive stages in position of dislocation loop.

If $l$ is the dislocation length between pinning points and if $2r > l$, further expansion of the loop decreases the radius, and from (5.35) would require a greater stress. The dislocation loop under such circumstances is stable and will remain bowed out at the particular radius appropriate to the stress level. When, however, the stress level is increased to a point beyond which $l/b = G/\tau$, the dislocation loop expands into a larger loop which completes itself, generates a new dislocation, and repeats the whole process. The stages of dislocation multiplication are shown in Fig. 5.27. This mode of multiplication, which is borne out by experiment, is called a *Frank-Read generator*.

### 5.20   Microscopic Evidence for the Presence of Dislocations

Three different experimental techniques which render dislocations "visible" and show them to have many of the geometric properties already attributed to them, have been devised. The techniques are:

1. Etching to show the point at which dislocation loops intersect a polished surface.

2. Decorating the dislocations within a transparent crystal by deposits of metallic atoms.

3. Detecting, by the electron microscope, the region of atomic rearrangement across a dislocation line in thin metallic foils.

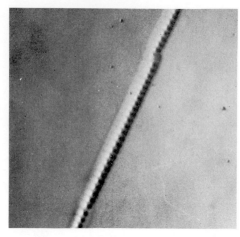

**Fig. 5.28**    Dislocation ends at low-angle tilt boundary made visible by etching. (After Vogel)

### Dislocation Etch Pits

In this technique a polished surface of the crystal is etched by special etches to reveal very fine detail. A surface replica is then made in a plastic material. This replica is often shadowed with layers of heavy metal atoms and examined by electron microscopy. The electron microscope photograph shows variations in replica density which reveal the topography of the original polished surface. Figure 5.28 shows pits which are etched in a polished metal crystal. The pits occur at the points of intersection of the surface and a wall of dislocations. The dislocations are lined up in a small angle grain boundary. We saw in Section 5.14 that like dislocations line up below one another to form a stable configuration. Figure 5.29 shows a cubic crystal with the boundary on a (010) plane and the rotation $\theta$ about a [001] tilt axis. Clearly from the diagram

$$\theta = \frac{b}{d} \qquad (5.36)$$

This model of a small angle boundary, which is due to Burger, can be quantitatively verified by measuring $\theta$ by an X-ray diffraction technique and counting the etch pits in the boundary.

### Dislocation Decoration

Mitchell and Hedges (1953) first photographed dislocation patterns within large transparent crystals of AgBr after producing print-out of the

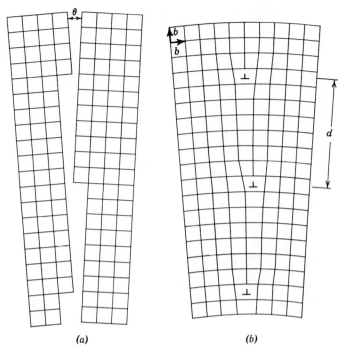

*(a)*        *(b)*

**Fig. 5.29** Low-angle tilt boundary envisaged as a line of edge dislocations. (After Burgers)

silver. The regular patterns of particles of photolytic silver clearly correspond to dislocation networks within the crystal. Figure 5.30 shows such a "chicken wire" three-dimensional crossing network of dislocations.

### Electron Microscope Dislocation Studies in Metals

In 1956 Hirsch and others showed that transmission electron microscopy through metallic foils thinned by beating or electropolishing can reveal the presence of dislocations. The specimen foils must be thinned to a few thousandths of an inch and the electron microscope operated at about 100 kv. A number of studies of dislocations including the taking of movie pictures to reveal rearrangement have already been made. Figure 5.31 shows dislocation networks at the surface of annealed stainless steel after fatigue bending. Figure 5.32 shows crossing dislocation lines in the basal plane of bismuth telluride.

It is clear that these techniques give beautifully detailed information on dislocation behavior, and they should prove powerful tools in the elucidation of the remaining problems of plastic deformation in solids.

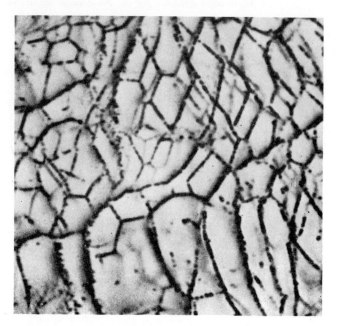

**Fig. 5.30** Dislocation network decorated by deposit of silver. (After Hedges and Mitchell)

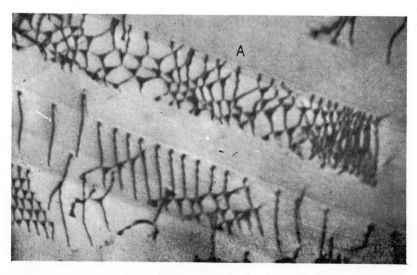

**Fig. 5.31** Electron microscope evidence of dislocation network in steel. (After Hirsch, Partridge, and Segall)

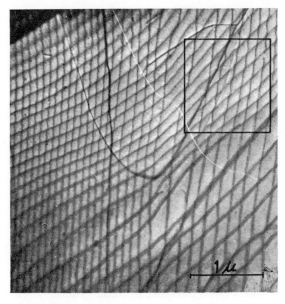

**Fig. 5.32** Crossing dislocation lines in bismuth telluride shown by electron microscope. (After Delavignette and Amelinckx)

## 5.21  Dislocation Motion

### *Dislocation Glide*

Glissile dislocations in face-centered cubic metals are extended, as we saw in Section 5.15, over a region of several or many atoms. In the absence of obstacles, the stacking fault of the dislocation moves in a potential energy field which has maxima and minima corresponding to the regular array of atoms in the slip plane. In close-packed metals these potential energy barriers are small and the expected critical yield stress is low. Several slip-systems are also available in the face-centered cubic metals which assist extended slip.

The dislocations themselves interact in several ways, all of which increase the yield stress. We have studied the following interactions:

1. Pure elastic interaction at long range (Section 5.14).

2. Action by dislocations on planes intersecting the glide plane, that is, jogs, etc. (Section 5.16).

3. Action of a dislocation which is more or less parallel to the moving dislocation. Several locking mechanisms can arise from this situation, one of which is shown in Fig. 5.33.

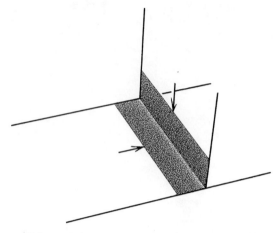

**Fig. 5.33**  Two parallel extended dislocations coalesce at the junction of their slip planes and form a sessile dislocation.

In the metals with crystal structure of lower symmetry fewer slip systems are available for extended slip.  In the hexagonal metals such as magnesium, or in solids with layered structures such as graphite, slip is usually confined to the basal plane.  These solids are hard on nonbasal slip systems and consequently are much stronger in the polycrystalline form than as single crystals.

In covalent crystals such as diamond or silicon the highly directional bonds must be severed in the course of dislocation glide.  Such motion is thus severely limited at low temperatures.

In ionic crystals such as sodium chloride the glide system favored is one in which like ions are not brought together.  The dislocations are narrow and the crystals are hard and brittle at low temperatures.

In metals of low symmetry, in both covalent crystals and ionic crystals the dislocations are narrow.  Although these substances are intrinsically harder than the ductile metals, the effect of impurities on the yield strength is less pronounced than in the ductile metals.  This is because a narrow dislocation is less confined to one plane and can cross-slip to another system if held up by a blocking impurity atom or other defect.

### Dislocation Climb

In another type of motion of a dislocation, *dislocation climb*, the movement is away from the glide plane.  Climb in metals and ionic crystals is highly temperature dependent.

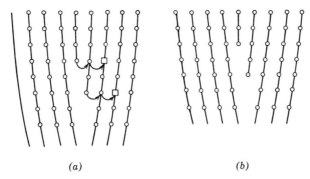

*(a)*                                        *(b)*

**Fig. 5.34**   Climb of edge dislocations in polygonal wall.   The arrows show the directions of migration of the atoms to the vacancies.

It has been shown (Section 5.14) in our discussion of the interaction between edge dislocations that they tend to line up in a small angle boundary. Thus densely tangled dislocations, following severe deformation, will line up into walls if there is enough thermal energy to enable the dislocation to climb out of its own slip plane.   There must also be enough strain energy present to activate the lining up process.   When small angle boundaries are formed in this way, the density of dislocations in the remainder of the crystal is then reduced.   This mechanism is called *polygonization*.   Figure 5.34 shows the formation of a polygonized boundary by climb of edge dislocations. A row of atoms must be added or subtracted from the half-plane of atoms that ends on the axis of an edge dislocation.   Thus polygonization is possible if:

1. The dislocations have edge components.
2. Vacancies are present in sufficient density.
3. A strain field is present sufficiently strong to pull the vacancies to the dislocations.

*Climb* is essentially a thermally activated diffusion process, whereas *cross-slip* is essentially a dynamic process produced by stress.   Climb is therefore important in metallic, ionic, and covalent crystals only at high temperatures.


## 5.22   Effect of Temperature on the Critical Shear Stress

Before we study the plastic behavior of crystals in greater detail let us consider the effect of temperature on the intrinsic hardness or strength.

### Thermal Assistance Past Dislocation Barriers

We begin by recalling our calculation of the theoretical critical shear stress $\tau_M$ for an ideal crystal. In Equation 5.18 we have

$$\tau_M = \frac{aG}{2\pi d}$$

Here $a$ is the lattice spacing in the slip plane, $d$ is the interplanar spacing, and $G$ is the shear modulus. The factor $a/d$ varies according to the nature of the interatomic bond; it is low in a layered structure in basal slip. The lowest possible shear stress $\tau_M$ will, of course, be the stress required to move one glissile dislocation in a perfect crystal.

Let us now suppose that a glissile dislocation is held up by an obstacle. It may be able to surmount the barrier with thermal assistance. If the dislocation width is $w$ and the length of dislocation which must be thermally assisted over the barrier is $l$, then the area of stacking fault which clears the barrier is $wl$. If $wl$ is large, there is little statistical probability that all the atoms in this area of stacking fault will be thermally activated together in the right direction. Thus the temperature dependence of yield stress in metals like copper with extended dislocations will be unlikely. On the other hand, metals like iron, tungsten, and molybdenum, with narrow dislocations and strong bonding, show much greater temperature dependence of yield strength. The experimental dependence for several metals is given in Fig. 5.35.

### Recovery

Any process of rearrangement of the dislocations in a deformed crystal that reduces the internal stress is called a process of *recovery*. We have already seen that cross-slip, climb, and polygonization involve redistribution of dislocations, mostly with thermal assistance, in order to accommodate the stress. These are processes of recovery.

### Recrystallization

If crystal boundaries, of larger angle than those normally associated with polygonal walls, exist at high enough temperatures and there is a sufficient vacancy population to promote climb, the boundaries may migrate through plastically deformed material and sweep up dislocation tangles. This mechanism is called *recrystallization*. It results in a set of new crystallites in the solid. Both thermal and strain energy are necessary. The higher the strain energy, within limits, the lower is the recrystallization temperature. *Cold-working*

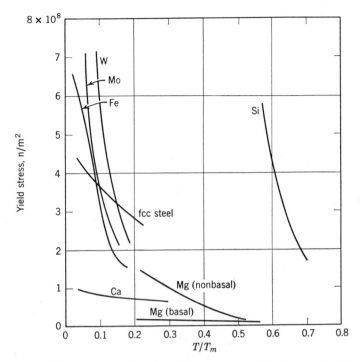

**Fig. 5.35** Yield stress as a function of temperature. The temperature is quoted as a fraction of the melting temperature. (Redrawn from Cottrell, *Mechanical Properties of Matter*, John Wiley and Sons, New York, 1964)

is mechanical deformation carried out at temperatures too low for recrystallization. *Hot-working* is deformation above the recrystallization temperature so that new strain-free crystallites form during the deformation.

## 5.23 Work Hardening of Crystals

Figure 5.36 shows the stress-strain behavior of a single crystal of face-centered cubic or hexagonal close-packed metal. Three stages of hardening are apparent.

*Stage* 1. The dislocations already present and those produced by operating sources, glide on a single set of parallel slip planes. There is little intersection of dislocations which ultimately escape from the surface of the crystal. Elastic interactions which account for the small amount of hardening found experimentally do, however, exist between the dislocations. With the microscope, we would expect to see fine lines appear on the polished surface

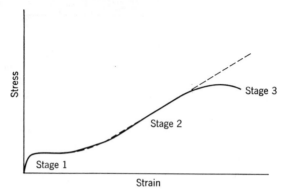

**Fig. 5.36**  Stress-strain behavior of a single crystal of face-centered cubic or hexagonal close-packed metal showing work hardening.

of a crystal in Stage 1.  These lines would, of course, be the traces in the surface of bundles of glide dislocations.

*Stage 2.*  This is the region of *work hardening.*  Let us illustrate the term by reference to Fig. 5.37, which shows stress versus strain for zinc when oriented for nonbasal slip.

The stress load is removed for half a minute after a strain corresponding to point *B* is reached.  When the load is reapplied, the stress-strain curve *DCE*

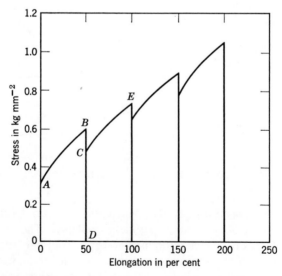

**Fig. 5.37**  Strain hardening in a zinc single crystal showing the effect of repeated loading. (After Haase and Schmid)

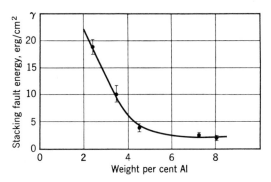

**Fig. 5.38** Stacking fault energy of Cu + Al alloys plotted against weight per cent Al. (From A. Howie, *Direct Observations of Imperfection in Crystals*, Interscience, New York, 1962)

is traced. Yielding now occurs at point *C*, which is at a higher stress than *A*. The critical shear stress has been increased by the previous strain. This process may be repeated in certain cases over strains of several hundred per cent.

A number of intersection effects arise from glide on several slip systems. Those that have been discussed are:

1. Crossing screw dislocations forming jogs (Section 5.16).

2. Intersection of glissile dislocations to form a sessile dislocation (Section 5.21).

3. The constriction of the stacking fault in dislocation intersection (Section 5.15).

*Stage* 3. In Stage 3 the strain rate of work hardening is reduced from the linear rate of Stage 2. In face-centered cubic metals this is due to stress-induced cross-slip. Since cross-slip is assisted by thermal activation and climb is completely dependent on thermal activation, the stress at which Stage 3 commences is lower at higher temperatures.

We shall now illustrate some of the ideas on dislocation behavior by showing stress-strain curves along with electron micrographs of dislocation arrangement in copper alloys. The alloying changes the stacking fault energy and width. The data are taken from the work of Howie.* Figure 5.38 shows that alloying with aluminum decreases the stacking fault energy of copper. Figure 5.39 shows stress-strain curves for copper and aluminum. Figure 5.40*a*, *b*, and *c* shows typical dislocation arrangements observed in Stages 1, 2, and 3. As can be seen, long straight dislocations with few intersections appear in Stage 1. Stage 2 is characterized by a ragged dislocation

* A. Howie, "Dislocation Arrangements in Deformed fcc Single Crystals of Different Stacking Fault Energy," p. 269, *Direct Observation of Imperfections in Crystals*, Interscience, New York, 1962.

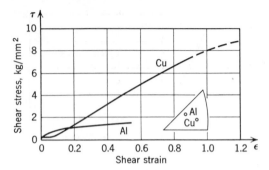

**Fig. 5.39**  Curves of resolved shear stress against shear strain for Cu and Al single crystals with tensile axes as shown.  (From Howie)

appearance which leads to the development of a rough cell-like structure. In Stage 3 the misorientations between neighboring parts of the crystal become great and it is difficult to see individual dislocations.

Figure 5.41 shows the stress-strain behavior of a Cu + 4.5 weight % Al alloy with a lowered stacking fault energy.  Stage 1 is now elongated and the initial yield stress is increased.  In Fig. 5.42a and b, respectively, Stage 1 and Stage 2 micrographs are shown.  For Stage 1 we see long dislocations lying on the same slip plane, and in Stage 2 there are dislocation locks, formed by interaction of the primary and conjugate slip systems.

The conclusion of Howie's work, of which we have shown only part, is that narrow dislocations show an increasing tendency, as deformation proceeds, to leave their slip planes and adopt more random arrangements.

We conclude this section by reference to the commercially important work hardening processes for many of the *austentic steels*.  These have wide stacking faults and deformation progressively locks the dislocations on the slip planes to which the dislocations are confined.

## 5.24   Effect of Rate of Strain on Deformation:   Creep

We have already seen that on raising the temperature of a plastically deforming metal, cross-slip and dislocation climb may become possible. At higher temperatures and greater degrees of deformation, large angle boundaries may migrate, producing a new set of strain-free grains.

A stress-strain curve, taken at a temperature where recovery or recrystallization can occur, may therefore be considered to be the result of a balance between thermal recovery or recrystallization and strain-hardening.  At low temperatures strain-hardening is alway more important.  At high temperatures recrystallization can occur at a comparable rate to strain-hardening,

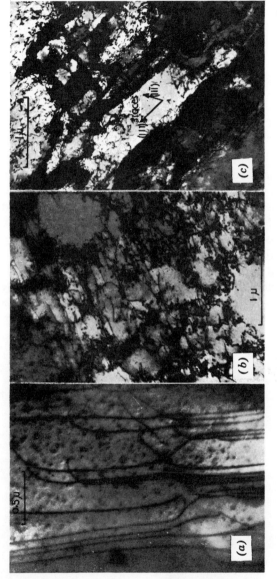

**Fig. 5.40** (*a*) Stage 1 in Cu (shear stress = 0.5 kg mm⁻²). (*b*) Stage 2 in Cu (shear stress = 5 kg mm⁻²). (*c*) Stage 3 in Cu (shear stress = 10 kg mm⁻²). (From Howie)

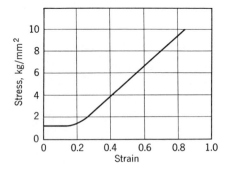

**Fig. 5.41**   Resolved shear stress versus strain for an alloy Cu + 4.5 weight per cent Al. (From Howie)

resulting in a horizontal stress-strain curve. A short time at a high temperature is equivalent to a long time at a lower temperature, as we have seen for all thermally activated processes. Often the activation energy is that of self-diffusion or vacancy migration. Figure 5.43 shows strain-hardening in aluminum at various temperatures.

Consideration of the effect of rate of deformation on the critical shear stress is partially a consideration of the balance between the opposing mechanisms— strain hardening and thermal recovery. Many solids when subject to a constant stress show a slow and progressive deformation as a function of time. This property is called *creep* and is of considerable technological

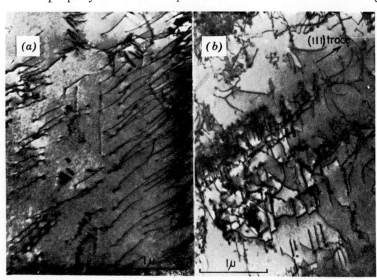

**Fig. 5.42**   (*a*) Stage 1 in Cu + 4.5% Al alloy ($\tau = 1$ kg mm$^{-2}$). (*b*) Stage 2 in Cu + 4.5% Al alloy ($\tau = 2$ kg mm$^{-2}$). (From Howie)

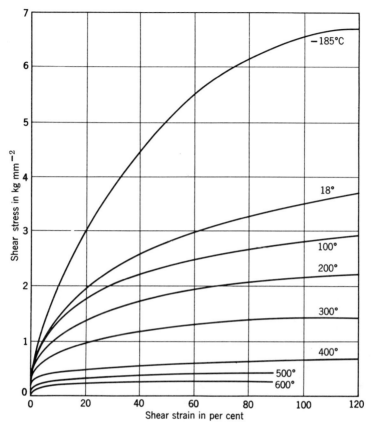

**Fig. 5.43** Strain hardening in aluminum at different temperatures. (After Boas and Schmid)

importance. Creep behavior is shown in Fig. 5.44. When the load is first applied there is an immediate elastic deformation. This is followed by a *primary stage* in which the creep rate slows to a minimum, followed by a *secondary stage* in which the strain slowly increases at this minimum rate. If the stress is sufficiently high, the creep condition reaches a *tertiary stage* in which the rate increases until fracture occurs. Creep is observed in metals, ionic crystals, and amorphous solids. In general, the temperatures at which metals creep are higher than those for plastics and rubbers. Since it is found that the metals with high melting points have high recrystallization temperatures, creep is low in these cases. Lead with a low melting point exhibits creep at room temperature. Alloying to raise the recrystallization temperature will increase the creep resistance.

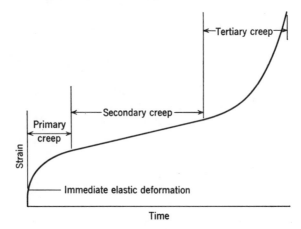

**Fig. 5.44**  Creep behavior at constant low level of stress.

## 5.25   Effect of Alloying on the Yield Stress

### Solute Hardening

Generally the addition of a substitutional solute to a solid will increase the hardness and yield strength.  The dependence of strength on alloying must be related to the distortion introduced in the matrix lattice.  We are reminded of the misfit parameter which appeared in the Hume-Rothery rule

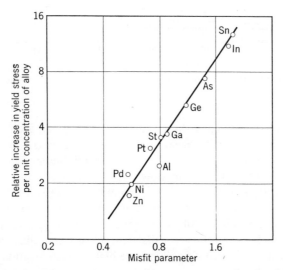

**Fig. 5.45**  Increase in yield stress per unit concentration for substitutional alloying elements in copper plotted against the misfit parameter. (Redrawn from R. L. Fleisher, *Acta Met.*, **9**, 996, 1961)

for solid solubility (Section 3.1). Figure 5.45 shows the effect on the strength of the difference in lattice parameter of solute and solvent. The hardening is called *solute hardening*; it is the result of an interaction between lattice strains and glide dislocations.

If the alloy is ordered so that the solute atoms occur on regular sites of the solvent lattice, elastic interactions with dislocations will be less than if irregular strain patterns are present in a disordered alloy.

The best known example of hardening by alloying is in the production of *martensite* in high carbon steels. Carbon in the steel is forced, by a special heat treatment, to remain in supersaturated solid solution. The body-centered cubic structure of iron is distorted into the tetragonal structure of martensite and the resulting strain fields impede the motion of glide dislocations. In addition, these strain fields produce fine-scale slip and twinning, and this also increases the yield stress of these steels.

### Precipitation Hardening

Some alloys are hardened by precipitation of an optimum size of precipitate from solid solution. This method is well illustrated by a 4 per cent alloy of copper in aluminum. If the alloy is held at a temperature above 780°K for several hours, the copper goes completely into solid solution. Subsequent aging at about 430°K allows the copper to precipitate out of solution as an intermediate compound. Aging for long times allows the precipitate to cluster into larger particles which are then further apart. The strength of the alloy goes through a maximum with time of aging. Clearly there is an optimum dispersion at which the glide dislocations are most impeded by the particles of precipitate. We have already made some reference to this problem (Section 5.19).

At an early stage of aging, the dimensions of the precipitate cannot be large. Suppose in Fig. 5.46a that a dislocation is pinned by finely dispersed particles condensed along its length. Then thermal activation can assist a small kink past the barrier, if the dimensions are not large. The loop will run out as in Fig. 5.46b and the dislocation is free.

At a later stage the precipitate has clustered into larger particles more widely dispersed. Thermal activation is now ineffective in assisting the

*(a)*                                    *(b)*

**Fig. 5.46**   (a) Dislocation with impurity × pinning. A small "kink" has thrown forward by thermal activation. (b) The dislocation loop has become free from the impurity pinning.

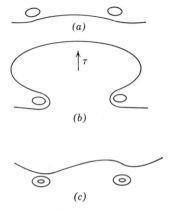

**Fig. 5.47**    (*a*) Loop of dislocation meeting precipitated particles. (*b*) The loop is bowed out by an applied shear stress. (*c*) The loop may pinch off around the obstacle and be free to move.

dislocation loops over the barriers.  As aging proceeds, a situation depicted in Fig. 5.47 is reached.  An applied stress may bow a dislocation past the precipitate clusters.  This is now a temperature-independent process.  We have shown (Section 5.19) that the stress needed to move a dislocation past obstacles distant $l$ apart is of the order of $Gb/l$.  Thus as $l$ increases with aging the alloy will soften.  The total behavior of yield stress with aging time will thus show a maximum strength at the time of optimum dispersion.

A fascinating example of the variation of strength or hardness with the dispersion of pinning obstacles is found in the work of Barnes[*] and others on radiation damage.  The inert gases xenon, krypton, and helium are frequent products of nuclear reactions in fissionable materials.  These elements are normally gaseous and occupy a large volume within the fissile metals.  They tend to cluster and to absorb vacancies.  Thus the distance between the gas bubbles increases with annealing time for temperatures at which vacancy migration is possible.

The effects on the mechanical properties are demonstrated by reference to an experiment in which microhardness tests are made on copper after irradiation with α-particles.  The α-particles displaced atoms close to the surface and came to rest as helium atoms at penetration distances of about $2 \times 10^{-3}$ m.  The results are shown in Fig. 5.48.  First, it is seen that the hardness is much greater where the helium atoms rest than in the region closer to the surface, where only displaced atoms are present.  Lattice distortion by the helium atoms is clearly greater than vacancy distortion.

    * R. S. Barnes, *Radiation Damage in Solids*, Academic Press, New York, 1962, p. 860.

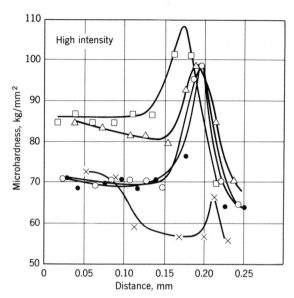

**Fig. 5.48** Microhardness of a copper block which has been bombarded with α-particles which have penetrated 0.2 mm where helium atoms deposit.

    ☐    as irradiated
    △    annealed at 200°C
    ●    annealed at 300°C
    ○    annealed at 700°C
    ×    annealed at 850°C

(From R. Barnes, *Radiation Damage in Solids*, Academic Press, New York, 1962).

There is also a difference in annealing behavior for the two regions. The shallow regions recover their original hardness of about 70 kgm per mm² in about 1 hour at 300°C, but the region containing the helium atoms does not recover after 1 hour at temperatures up to 700°C. Prolonged heating at 850°C, which clusters the helium bubbles, eventually softens the copper to a value lower than that before irradiation. The spacing between bubbles is then greater than $10^{-6}$ m. The hardening appears to be inversely proportional to the spacing between adjacent bubbles along the dislocations. The model used in the explanation of the effect is fully substantiated in this work by fine electron microscope observations of dislocations bowing out between anchoring bubbles.

### Strain-Aging in Steel

There is a force of attraction between impurity atoms and edge dislocations. Thus carbon atoms in mild steel will tend to condense along the line of a

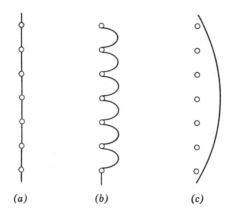

(a)  (b)  (c)

**Fig. 5.49** (*a*) Carbon atoms have condensed along the line of a dislocation. (*b*) Stress bowing out dislocation loops. The maximum stress corresponds to *Y* of Fig. 5.3. (*c*) The loop has torn clear and deformation proceeds at a lower applied stress.

dislocation, as in Fig. 5.49*a*. If a stress level is applied, then the dislocation may tear free of the carbon atoms and be free to move, as in *b*. Further strain continues then at a reduced stress, as in *c*. Condition *a*, in which the dislocation has picked up a carbon atmosphere, corresponds to the segment *AB* of the stress-strain diagram of Fig. 5.3. The steel is in the *strain-aged condition*. Condition *b* corresponds to the upper yield condition shown at *Y* in Fig. 5.3, and condition *c* describes the overstrained condition related to the flow region *CD*.

The carbon atoms will diffuse back to the dislocations from the overstrained condition. The activation energy is that of migration for carbon in mild steel. The stress-strain cycle can be repeated with the appearance of another yield point.

### 5.26   The Effect of Radiation Damage on the Yield Stress

A great deal of work has been done by various laboratories on this subject. As an example we will choose the early Oak Ridge work on neutron irradiation of copper.*

Figure 5.50 shows the increase of yield stress by neutron irradiation. Figure 5.51 shows the temperature dependence of the yield stress of reactor-irradiated copper after various doses. From the argument already presented, a qualitative explanation of the results is apparent. The mechanical changes brought about by subsequent annealing out of defects are matters of great concern to the nuclear engineer.

* T. H. Blewitt, *Radiation Damage in Solids*, Academic Press, New York.

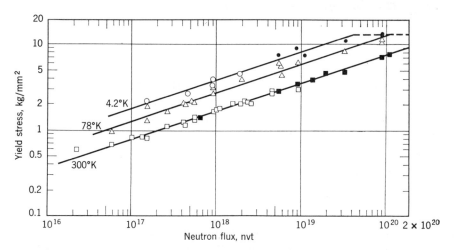

**Fig. 5.50** Effect of neutron irradiation on the yield stress of copper at various temperatures. (From T. H. Blewitt, *Radiation Damage in Solids*, Academic Press, New York, 1962)

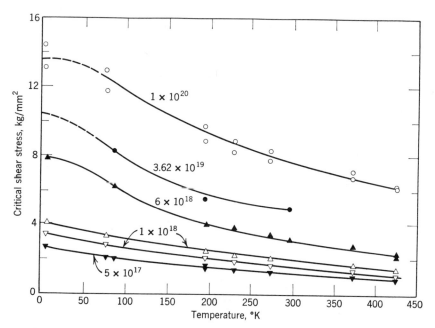

**Fig. 5.51** The temperature dependence of the yield of reactor-irradiated copper single crystals at various neutron doses. (From T. H. Blewitt, *Radiation Damage in Solids*, Academic Press, New York, 1962)

## 5.27  Fracture

By fracture we mean the separation of a solid into parts by the application of stress. The physical theories which have been developed are only partially successful in describing the phenomenon. We will concentrate on those parts of the subject for which a reasonably successful physical model exists.

### Brittle Fracture

At a certain stress level brittle materials like glass fracture suddenly. The theoretical strength was calculated in Section 5.8 and worked out to be about $E/10$, where $E$ is Young's modulus. Under tension glass can fracture at about 1 per cent of this value. In compression the strength of many brittle substances, such as stone, is much greater than in tension.

Griffith made a careful study of the breaking of glass and proposed that the fracture weakness was not an intrinsic property of the material but arose because of the presence of small cracks, often on the surface. These cracks act as stress raisers and can propagate through the brittle solid.

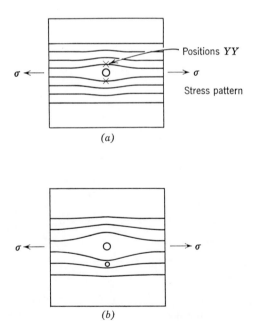

**Fig. 5.52**  (a) Plate under uniaxial tension. Stress is greater at the positions $YY$ close to a small hole in the plate. (b) A second hole is in the stress-enhanced region of the first.

Let us suppose that Fig. 5.52*a* shows a plate of glass under uniaxial tension $\sigma$ with a small hole of radius $r_0$ bored in the middle. The stress lines of equal value are shown across the plate. At positions such as $YY$ the stress is raised, and for a circular hole the factor is exactly 3. In Fig. 5.52*b* a smaller hole is in the stress-enhanced region of the first hole. The general stress is now $3\sigma$ and in the positions $YY$ of the second hole the level goes up to $3^2\sigma$. This provides an enhanced stress for a third yet smaller hole, and so on. The maximum stress $\sigma_c$ with $n$ holes is given by

$$\sigma_c \simeq 3^n \sigma \tag{5.37}$$

Now let the ratio of the diameter of each hole to the next be $R$ and the radius of the largest and smallest hole be $r_0$ and $r_n$, respectively. Then

$$r_0 \simeq R^n r_n \tag{5.38}$$

To a crude approximation, the ratio $R$ must be about $3^2$ for each hole to be in the stress-enhanced region of its larger neighbor. Thus we get the simple relation

$$\frac{\sigma_c}{\sigma} \simeq 3^n \simeq \sqrt{R^n} \simeq \sqrt{\frac{r_0}{r_n}} \tag{5.39}$$

If we conceive of a crack as a series of holes, then the stress at the tip of the crack of radius $r_n$ is raised above that of the widest part of the crack of radius $r_0$ by a factor which is roughly the square root of $r_0/r_n$. This is, of course, the reason why in good engineering practice sharp corners are rounded off.

It is comparatively simple to work out the conditions for propagation of such a crack. The calculation will not be given, but it is obvious that sharp cracks will grow under much lower stress conditions than those appropriate for the propagation of blunt cracks.

Numerous techniques are employed to reduce the presence and growth of surface cracks in brittle materials. The glazing of pottery is one of the most common examples. It is often less expensive to attempt to block crack propagation rather than eliminate the source. In fiberglass the fibers are glued together by a resin of lower elastic modulus than the glass, thereby providing a weak interface which stops the propagation of cracks.

### Fracture in Crystalline Materials

Fracture in brittle crystalline materials occurs by a mechanism not unlike that in glasses. Often such brittle fracture occurs at low temperatures and high rates of strain. Dislocation motion cannot accommodate the deformation, and the Griffith criterion for crack propagation is met at a certain level.

Crystals in brittle fracture often crack along planes of cleavage or along grain boundaries, which are preferred if impurities have segregated to the boundaries.

### Ductile Fracture

In ductile materials, fracture generally occurs because the specimen has necked down in cross section after extensive deformation. Cavities are formed in the necked region and cracks propagate toward the surface. At present the theories of crack propagation are qualitative in nature, and the transition between ductile and brittle fractures arising from temperature, deformation, and purity factors are not fully understood.

### Fatigue Fracture

This is a fracture failure of ductile materials subjected to cyclic stresses over many cycles. The current theories hold that cracks form and grow by plastic deformation. In a typical fatigue test, a bending load is applied to a rotating shaft of the material under test by a bearing carrying the load. The *fatigue limit* of plain carbon and low alloy steels is shown in Fig. 5.53. At this load shafts of these materials fracture after about $10^6$ cycles, the lifetime being essentially infinite at lighter loads. Most alloys and metals found in engineering practice do not, however, have this limit but fracture after a more or less specific number of stress cycles which is related to the applied load.

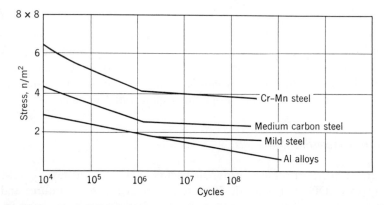

**Fig. 5.53** Fatigue fracture in low-alloy and carbon steels show fatigue limit (approximately $4 \times 10^8$ n/m$^{-2}$ in CrMn) not evident in aluminum alloys.

## References

Barrett, C. S., *Structure of Metals*, McGraw-Hill Book Co., New York, 1952.
Cottrell, A. H., *The Mechanical Properties of Matter*, John Wiley and Sons, New York, 1964.
Friedel, J., *Dislocations*, Addison-Wesley, Reading, Mass. 1964.
Weertman, J., and J. R. Weertman, *Elementary Dislocation Theory*, Macmillan, New York, 1964.

## Exercises

1. A platelike specimen of fine grained metal with no preferred orientation is subject to the principal stresses $\sigma_1$ and $\sigma_2$ lying in the plane of the free surface. Obtain an expression for the sum of the principal stresses in terms of the change in spacing of atomic planes lying parallel to the surface. Using copper $K\alpha$ X-radiation ($\lambda = 1.54$ A) with an aluminum specimen ($a = 4.08$ A), which diffraction ring would we use for the measurement of stress?

2. A cylindrical single crystal has a tensile stress $\sigma$ applied to each end. If the normal to a slip plane in the crystal makes an angle $\phi$ with the cylindrical axis and the direction of slip on the slip plane makes an angle $\lambda$ with the axis, show that the shear stress across the slip plane in the direction of slip is given by $\sigma \cos \phi \cos \lambda$. If the critical shear stress for copper is $10^6$ n m$^{-2}$ what is the minimum tensile applied stress to produce shear deformation?

3. Confirm that the stresses $\sigma_x{}^n$, $\sigma_y{}^n$, $\sigma_z{}^n$ acting on a plane whose normal makes direction cosines $\alpha$, $\beta$, $\gamma$ with the coordinate axes are given by

$$\sigma_x{}^n = \alpha\sigma_x + \beta\tau_{yx} + \gamma\tau_{zx}$$
$$\sigma_y{}^n = \alpha\tau_{xy} + \beta\sigma_y + \gamma\tau_{zy}$$
$$\sigma_z{}^n = \alpha\tau_{xz} + \beta\tau_{yz} + \gamma\sigma_z$$

4. Calculate the elongation of an aluminum crystal of [111] axis, $10^{-1}$ m long, $10^{-4}$ m$^2$ cross section when subjected to a tensile force of 0.1 n.
   For Al,

$$S_{11} = 15.9 \times 10^{-12} \text{ m}^2 \text{ n}^{-1}$$
$$S_{12} = -5.8 \times 10^{-12} \text{ m}^2 \text{ n}^{-1}$$
$$S_{44} = 35.2 \times 10^{-12} \text{ m}^2 \text{ n}^{-1}$$

5. How much heat in calories would be evolved by the complete annihilation of dislocations when 20 cc of cold-worked copper is annealed if the original dislocation density was $6 \times 10^{11}$ cm$^{-2}$. Assume a dislocation energy of 1 eV per A.

6. A single crystal of copper contains a low angle tilt boundary with the boundary on a (010) plane and the tilt axis parallel to the [001] direction. Calculate the tilt angle if the spacing of dislocations in the boundary is $1.5 \times 10^{-6}$ m.

7. A strip of iron of dimensions 1 × 2 × 15 cms is bent into a radius of 12 cms. What is the dislocation density if [111] edge dislocations line up with their Burgers vectors along the strip.

8. Show from energy considerations that in a body-centered cubic structure a [100] edge dislocation does not dissociate into two dislocations with Burgers vectors in the [111] directions. Show also that crossing [100] and [010] dislocations can dissociate into two dislocations with Burgers vectors parallel to the [111] directions.

9. What is the minimum stress required to activate a Frank-Read generator and produce slip in copper in the [110] direction? The dislocation loops are $\simeq 5 \times 10^{-6}$ m and the shear modulus is 300 kg mm$^{-2}$. If the velocity of dislocation motion is $10^3$ m sec$^{-1}$ show that the generator could produce 100 dislocations across a slip plane in one millisecond.

10. If the energy per unit area of stacking fault in copper is $S$ show that the equilibrium separation of the partials is $Ga^2/24\pi S$ where $G$ is the shear modulus and $a$ is the lattice parameter. Calculate the separation for aluminum for

$$S = 240 \times 10^{-3} \text{ joules m}^{-2}$$
$$G = 0.4 \times 10^{10} \text{ n m}^{-2}$$
$$a = 4.04 \times 10^{-10} \text{ m}$$

# 6

# *Internal Friction in Solids*

Vibrational energy in solids is damped out by many internal mechanisms collectively known as *internal friction*. In most cases the damping mechanism involves defects in the crystal lattice. In this chapter we shall discuss the principles of several classes of damping and relate these to possible defect interactions.

## 6.1  Relaxation Damping Mechanism

In this mechanism a solid is regarded as a system which, when subjected to a sudden stress, relaxes that stress at a characteristic rate. This dependence of strain on time is known as the anelastic effect to differentiate it from the time-independent strain in elastic theory.

A generally successful model was first proposed by Zener to simulate stress-strain behavior in real solids. It is called the "standard linear solid" and is shown in Fig. 6.1a. The model consists of the parallel arrangement of spring $S_2$ and the spring-dashpot series combination $S_1 D$.

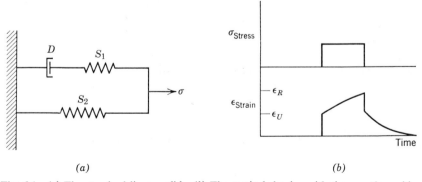

| | |
|:---:|:---:|
| *(a)* | *(b)* |

**Fig. 6.1** *(a)* The standard linear solid. *(b)* The strain behavior with time on the sudden application and removal of a stress.

173

Suppose that a stress $\sigma$ is suddenly applied; the system will then have an instantaneous displacement or unrelaxed strain $\epsilon_U$, depending solely on the spring constants. If the stress is maintained, then the dashpot relaxes, increasing the over-all strain to the value $\epsilon_R$. Conversely, when the stress is suddenly removed the springs will contract, resulting in instantaneous partial recovery. The complete release of all the energy in the springs must await the gradual relaxation of stress across the dashpot. The general features of *anelastic* behavior in real solids are thus simulated by the model, in which both the strain and rate of strain depend on the stress and rate of stress.

We can write this dependence in the form of a differential equation. If $\sigma$, $\dot{\sigma}$, $\epsilon$, and $\dot{\epsilon}$ are the stress, rate of change of stress, strain, and rate of change of strain, respectively, then the behavior of the standard linear solid may be written

$$\sigma + \tau_\epsilon \dot{\sigma} = M_R(\epsilon + \tau_\sigma \dot{\epsilon}) \tag{6.1}$$

where $M_R$ is the elastic modulus and $\tau_\epsilon$ and $\tau_\sigma$ are constants. The natures of $\tau_\epsilon$ and $\tau_\sigma$ are shown by testing under conditions first of constant strain and then of constant stress. Assuming $\epsilon = 0$, then Equation 6.1 reduces immediately to

$$\sigma + \tau_\epsilon \dot{\sigma} = 0$$

whose solution is

$$\sigma = \sigma_0 e^{-t/\tau_\epsilon}$$

where $\sigma_0$ is the initial stress and $t$ is time. Hence $\tau_\epsilon$ is the time which elapses between a stress value of $\sigma_0$ and a stress value of $\sigma_0/e$. In other words, $\tau_\epsilon$ is the *time constant* of the system or *relaxation time for constant strain*. Likewise $\tau_\sigma$ is the *relaxation time for constant stress*.

The proportionality between stress and strain after relaxation is complete (i.e., for times $t \gg \tau_\epsilon$ or $\tau_\sigma$) is given by the modulus $M_R$, which is therefore called the *relaxed modulus*.

Suppose that in a very short time $\delta t$ the stress increases from zero by the increment $\delta\sigma$ and an increment of strain $\delta\epsilon$ results. If $\delta t$ approaches zero, then the first term of each side of Equation 6.1 is close to zero and the relation between the increments of stress and strain is simply

$$\tau_\epsilon \, \delta\sigma = M_R \tau_\sigma \delta\epsilon \tag{6.2}$$

The ratio $\delta\sigma/\delta\epsilon$ is called the unrelaxed elastic modulus and will be denoted by $M_U$. Thus

$$\frac{M_U}{M_R} = \frac{\tau_\sigma}{\tau_\epsilon} \tag{6.3}$$

In much of the experimental work done on anelastic behavior of solids, the applied stresses are periodic. We will consider the periodic functions

$$\sigma = \sigma_0 e^{i\omega t}$$

and

$$\epsilon = \epsilon_0 e^{i(\omega t - \delta)} \tag{6.4}$$

where $\omega$ is the circular frequency and $\delta$ is the phase between stress and strain.

Equation 6.4 can be written

$$\epsilon = (\epsilon_1 - i\epsilon_2) \exp{(i\omega t)} \tag{6.5}$$

where $\epsilon_1$ and $\epsilon_2$ are, respectively, the components of strain in phase and in quadrature with the stress. Under these conditions the relation between stress and strain may be written

$$\epsilon = J^* \sigma \tag{6.6}$$

where $J^*$ is the *complex compliance* with in-phase and in quadrature components $J_1$ and $J_2$. Hence

$$J^* = J_1 - iJ_2 \tag{6.7}$$

where

$$J_1 = \frac{\epsilon_1}{\sigma_0}$$

and

$$J_2 = \frac{\epsilon_2}{\sigma_0} \tag{6.8}$$

The phase angle $\delta$ between stress and strain is, of course, given by

$$\tan \delta = \frac{\epsilon_2}{\epsilon_1} = \frac{J_2}{J_1} \tag{6.9}$$

For convenience we will rewrite Equation 6.1 in terms of compliances,

$$J_R \sigma + \tau_\sigma J_U \dot{\sigma} = \epsilon + \tau_\epsilon \dot{\epsilon} \tag{6.10}$$

This follows immediately from Equation 6.3 when written

$$\frac{M_U}{M_R} = \frac{\tau_\sigma}{\tau_\epsilon} = \frac{J_R}{J_U}$$

where $J_R$ and $J_U$ are the relaxed and unrelaxed compliances. Substitution of Equations 6.4 and 6.5 in (6.10) and selection of the real and imaginary parts gives

$$J_1 = J_U + \frac{J_R - J_U}{1 + \omega^2 \tau_\sigma^2}$$

and

$$J_2 = (J_R - J_U) \frac{\omega \tau_\sigma}{1 + \omega^2 \tau_\sigma^2} \tag{6.11}$$

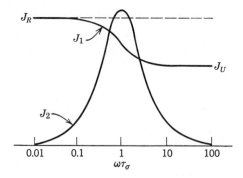

**Fig. 6.2**  The in-phase component of compliance $J_1$ and the out-of-phase component $J_2$ plotted against $\omega\tau_\sigma$. The damping loss, due to the phase lag, varies in the manner of $J_2$.

Figure 6.2 shown $J_1$ and $J_2$ plotted against the logarithm of $\omega\tau_\sigma$. The value of tan $\delta$ gives a measure of the damping losses due to the lag of strain behind stress. We can see from (6.11) that if $(J_R - J_U)$ is not large

$$\tan \delta \simeq \frac{(J_R - J_U)}{J_U} \frac{\omega\tau_\sigma}{1 + \omega^2\tau_\delta^2} \tag{6.12}$$

Thus the variation of damping loss with circular frequency is similar to that of the out-of-phase compliance component $J_2$.

The damping loss (or internal friction) maximum at a value of $\omega\tau^*$ equal to unity is an important characteristic of a relaxation mechanism which makes it amenable to test. If a cyclic periodic stress is applied to a test specimen at a circular frequency equal to the inverse of the relaxation time of the system, then the energy absorbed is a maximum, the dissipation of energy falling off with frequency above and below the critical value.

### 6.2  The Relation between Relaxation Time and Temperature

In a solid, the relaxation of internal stresses often involves the movement by diffusion of impurity atoms, lattice atoms, and defects. In these cases the stress and strain relaxation times are strongly temperature dependent. In many cases the temperature dependence is of the Arrhenius type, that is,

$$\tau^{-1} = \tau_0^{-1}e^{-H/kT} \tag{6.13}$$

where $\tau_0^{-1}$ is the product of a frequency factor and an entropy factor, as we discussed in Section 4.14. $H$ is the enthalpy of activation.

---

* We will drop the distinction between $\tau_\epsilon$ and $\tau_\sigma$ and write $\tau$. Often $\tau_\epsilon$ and $\tau_\sigma$ do not differ much in value.

The Arrhenius relation makes it possible to obtain a frequency spectrum of relaxation losses simply by changing the temperature over a few tens of degrees. This is much easier than varying the frequency of applied stress by many orders of ten. This becomes clear if we write Equation 6.13 as

$$\ln \omega\tau = \ln \omega\tau_0 + \left(\frac{H}{k}\right)\left(\frac{1}{T}\right) \tag{6.14}$$

There is a linear relation between the quantity $\ln \omega\tau$ and the reciprocal of temperature, $(1/T)$. Thus if $\tan \delta$, the damping loss, is plotted against $(1/T)$, the graph will have the same form as a plot against $\ln \omega\tau$. The form of such a graph is, of course, that of Fig. 6.2. Suppose that a measurement of damping loss is made and the peak loss occurs at a frequency of $v_1$ if the temperature is maintained at $T_1$. A repeat of the measurement at temperature $T_2$ reveals the peak loss at a frequency $v_2$. Then from Equation 6.14 it is easy to deduce

$$\ln \left(\frac{v_1}{v_2}\right) = \frac{H}{k}\left[\frac{1}{T_2} - \frac{1}{T_1}\right] \tag{6.15}$$

For a relaxation damping mechanism, recording of the frequencies and temperatures at which the internal friction maxima occur followed by a plot of $\ln v$ versus $(1/T)$ will thus give a straight line whose negative slope is $H/k$. Activation enthalpies for relaxation processes are often determined in this manner.

### Relaxation Mechanisms in Solids

In solids there are many relaxation mechanisms. We shall describe only a few in detail. Figure 6.3 shows a plot of $\tan \delta$, the internal friction, against the frequency of applied stress for a number of relaxations which can operate in solids at room temperature.

## 6.3  Snoek Relaxation in Body-Centered Cubic Metals

In $\alpha$ iron containing carbon or nitrogen in solid solution (interstitial impurity), a relaxation peak in internal friction occurs near room temperature at frequencies about 1 Hz. The interstitial positions occupied by the carbon or nitrogen atoms are the face centers and midpoints of the edges of the body-centered cubic cell. Such positions are midway between the iron atoms. Since the lattice is cubic, all of the face centers and edge midpoints are equally favored, and the equilibrium between the positions is established by thermal agitation. Suppose, however, that a stress is applied to the cell in the

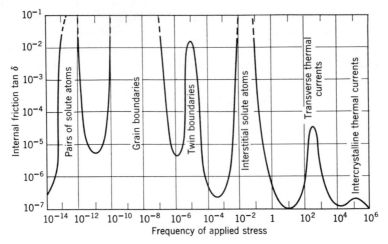

**Fig. 6.3**  The relaxation spectrum of a number of mechanisms in solids which operate at room temperature. Many other relaxation mechanisms are operative in specific solids. (From C. Zener, *Elasticity and Anelasticity of metals*, Univ. of Chicago Press, Chicago, Ill., 1952)

$z$ direction of Fig. 6.4, causing the iron atoms to move further apart along that axis. The favored positions for the carbon or nitrogen interstitial atoms will then be positions such as $C_1$ and $C_2$. In order to move to $C_1$ and $C_2$, the interstitial carbon or nitrogen atoms must be thermally activated.

The appropriate value for $\tau_0$ in Equation 6.13 is $0.45 \times 10^{-13}$ s. The activation energy is 0.13 eV per atom, giving, for a temperature of 300°K, a $\tau^{-1}$ value of about 2 Hz. Observations of the internal friction in steel wires, in slow oscillation experiments, should therefore disclose a relaxation mechanism due to the thermal motion of interstitial carbon atoms. In this example, if the temperature is raised to 450°K, insertion of the appropriate values in Equation 6.15 shows that the search for the damping maximum should be conducted in the kHz frequency range. There are many relaxation mechanisms of the Snoek type in body-centered cubic metals containing interstitial impurities.

## 6.4   Relaxation Mechanism in Silicon

Internal friction measurements at a frequency of 100 kHz on silicon show a peak at about 1300°K. Measurement at 300 Hz shifts the peak in temperature. These results are shown in Fig. 6.5. From the data, the calculated value of activation energy, using Equation 6.15, is about 3 eV. These measurements were made for longitudinal vibrations along a ⟨111⟩ direction.

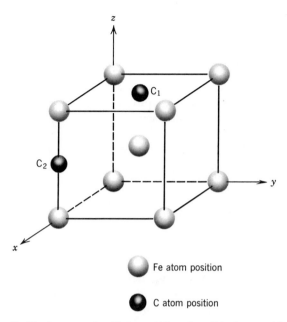

Fe atom position

C atom position

**Fig. 6.4** Unit cell of body-centered cubic iron. When the cell is elongated by a stress in the $z$ direction, the favored positions for interstitial carbon atoms are $C_1$ and $C_2$.

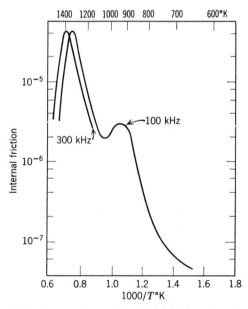

**Fig. 6.5** Internal friction of a longitudinally vibrating silicon crystal as a function of temperature. Length along axis. (Redrawn from P. D. Southgate, *Proc. Phys. Soc.,* London, **76,** 385, 1960)

Longitudinal vibrations along a ⟨100⟩ direction do not show this damping maximum.

It is believed that the relaxation mechanism is a consequence of the thermal hopping of an oxygen atom between equivalent sites. An impurity oxygen atom close to a Si–Si pair has six equivalent sites, forming in each case a noncollinear Si–O–Si configuration with the symmetry axis being ⟨111⟩ in nature. Rotation of the oxygen atom around the sites can occur at temperatures close to 1300°K. The smaller peak of Fig. 6.5 is attributed to a relaxation associated with electron-hole recombination.

### 6.5   Thermoelastic Relaxation Damping

Thermoelastic damping is important in metals where the thermal conductivities are high. In semiconductors and insulators the effect is small.

When a crystal is stressed suddenly its temperature changes, the temperature of the parts of the crystal under compression being raised and of those under tension being lowered. Since the stresses in polycrystals are not uniform but vary from grain to grain, it follows that in these the temperature resulting from this *thermoelastic effect* also varies from grain to grain. Now if the stresses vary slowly compared with the time required for heat to flow between regions having different temperatures, the temperature remains constant and the transfer of mechanical energy into heat, and vice versa, takes place reversibly. There is then no contribution to the internal friction. Similarly, if the stress oscillations take place so rapidly that no heat flows during a stress cycle, the process occurs adiabatically, for every grain behaves as if it were thermally isolated. The net conversion of elastic energy into heat during a complete cycle is also zero in this case. At intermediate frequencies there is a finite contribution to the internal friction from the thermoelastic effect. This effect is described successfully by a relaxation model. The frequency factor $\omega\tau/(1 + \omega^2\tau^2)$ in Equation 6.12 contains the circular frequency $\omega$ of the applied stress and $\tau$, the time for heat to flow, at the temperature of the specimen, across neighboring grain boundaries. Naturally, $\tau$ depends on the grain size and the rate of diffusion of heat. Maximum thermoelastic damping occurs when $\omega\tau = 1$.

### 6.6   Bordoni Peaks

Until recently a search for relaxations in solids by measurement of internal friction was not made at low temperatures. Since the lattice energy falls off quite rapidly below about one-third of the Debye temperature (see Fig. 13.6),

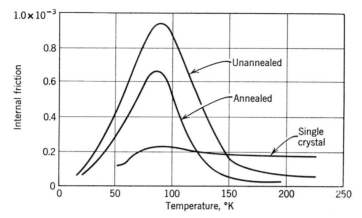

**Fig. 6.6** The Bordoni internal friction peak in copper at a frequency of applied stress of 30 kHz. A reduction of the degree of deformation of the specimen (by annealing) also reduces the height of the maximum but does not alter the temperature at which it occurs.

it was not expected that relaxation processes, which are generally thermally activated, would appear at low temperatures.

However, in 1954 Bordoni reported measurements of the internal friction of several metals at frequencies of about 40 kHz and at temperatures from 4°K up to room temperature. He found a large internal friction maximum at temperatures around 100°K; in copper, for example, at 30.3 kHz the peak temperature was 90°K. The height of the peak was increased by small amounts of plastic deformation of the specimen. The position remained unaltered. Annealing at high temperatures reduced the magnitude of the attenuation maximum. Figure 6.6 shows a plot of internal friction against temperature for copper in various conditions. Other measurements at different frequencies have shown that the peaks are relaxation peaks, since the frequency and peak temperatures are related by an equation of the type of (6.15). The activation energy is low, being about 0.085 eV for face-centered cubic metals.

It is believed that the Bordoni relaxation is characteristic of the dislocations in the materials. A portion of the dislocation moves under thermal influence and accounts for the relaxation process. This dislocation relaxation mechanism is not confined to metals but has been experimentally found in the alkali halides and in quartz.

To summarize, we have seen that point and other defects can produce anelastic relaxation behavior in solids. The process is one of *stress-induced* ordering. An equilibrium configuration of a defect or collection of defects changes in time under the applied stress to another configuration. When the stress is removed the change is reversed. We have seen that the *rate* of the

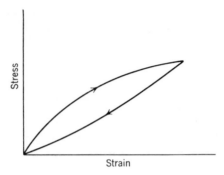

**Fig. 6.7**  A stress-strain hysteresis loop giving rise to anelastic behavior. The area of the loop represents the energy lost per half cycle of stress by internal friction. This energy is dissipated as heat.

change does not depend on the stress but on the mobility of the defect. The internal friction in a relaxation process is independent of stress amplitude. We will now study anelastic behavior in solids in which the internal friction is strongly stress amplitude dependent.

### *Hysteretic Mechanisms in Solids*

Except at very small stresses, the strain in most solids is not a single-valued function of the stress. The strain follows a different path on reducing the stress from that followed on increasing the stress from zero. A stress-strain hysteresis loop is formed (see Fig. 6.7) and the area of the loop represents mechanical energy which has been lost in the form of heat. The internal friction is the energy lost per cycle divided by the energy supplied per cycle.

### 6.7   Damping in Ferromagnetic and Ferroelectric Solids

One important class of phenomena of this nature is the amplitude-dependent losses in ferromagnetic (see Chapter 15) and ferroelectric (see Chapter 17) materials. As we shall see later, these materials are characterized by *domains*. Each domain is a region in which the magnetic or electric polarization is in a single direction. If a ferromagnetic or ferroelectric material is placed in either a magnetic or electric field, then the increase in over-all polarization is brought about by the growth of domains oriented in the direction of the field, at the expense of other domains less favorably oriented. The growth of magnetization or polarization is by motion of the domain wall.

The interaction of the periodically applied stress with the magnetization vector gives rise to *hysteretic magneto-mechanical* damping, which, at low frequencies, accounts for by far the largest part of the internal friction in ferromagnetic solids. The mechanism is a stress-induced irreversible motion of domain walls. It is intuitively expected that the damping will be dependent on parameters such as the applied stress, the applied magnetic field, and conditions such as impurity and internal stress which may lead to impeding of the motion of the domain walls.

Figure 6.8 shows the damping at 20 Hz in high purity iron as a function of shear strain for various applied magnetic fields. Let us assume an interaction between the stress and the domain wall and reserve discussion of the nature of the interaction until Chapter 15. As we have seen, hysteretic damping is a

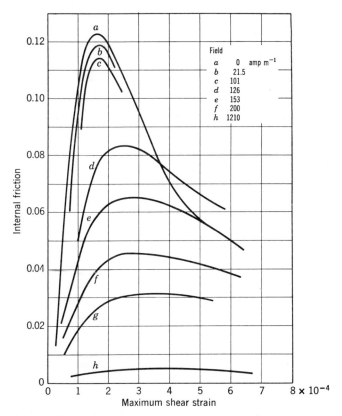

| Field | | |
|---|---|---|
| a | 0 | amp m$^{-1}$ |
| b | 21.5 | |
| c | 101 | |
| d | 126 | |
| e | 153 | |
| f | 200 | |
| h | 1210 | |

**Fig. 6.8** Magneto-mechanical damping in high purity iron as a function of maximum shear strain at 20 Hz. Measurements are made at various axially applied magnetic field strengths. (Redrawn from G. Sumner and K. M. Entwisele, *J. Iron and Steel Inst.*, London, **192**, 238, 1959)

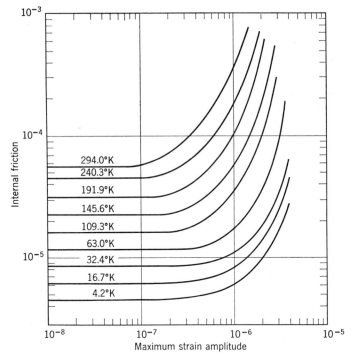

**Fig. 6.9** The internal friction of an annealed single crystal of copper as a function of maximum strain amplitude for various measurement temperatures. (Redrawn from H. L. Caswell, *J. Appl. Phys.*, **29**, 1210, 1958)

measure of the difference between the strain behavior on increasing the stress and the strain behavior on subsequently decreasing the stress. It is a measure of the irreversibility of the strain.

At low or zero field strengths, the strain cannot follow the stress in phase around the cycle. The strain causes domain wall motion with magnetic switching times which are relatively long. As a consequence the strain lags behind the stress. Thus at zero fields, hysteretic damping is large. At higher field strengths changes in magnetization are by rotation of the magnetic vector in the large domains. Switching times are much shorter. The strain, which is coupled to the magnetic vector, can then follow the stress much more closely in phase around the cycle. Hysteretic damping falls at higher field strengths, as shown in Fig. 6.8.

The damping versus strain curves all go through a maximum. Internal stresses nearly always exist in solids. These stresses impede the motion of domain walls. The applied stress (and the corresponding strain) has to increase to about the average internal stress value before appreciable motion of the domain walls can result. The damping thus rises with strain to a maximum. It decreases with greater applied strain because although the energy lost per cycle remains fairly constant, at greater strains the energy supplied per cycle increases. The internal friction is the ratio of the two and thus decreases.

As we have already noted, domain wall movement is influenced by internal stresses and imperfections in the lattice. The magneto-mechanical damping is strongly dependent on the degree of purity and metallurgical history of the solid specimen.

## 6.8   Hysteretic Damping due to Dislocation Motion

Another type of hysteretic loss, not yet fully understood, is concerned with the motion under cyclic stress of dislocations. Figure 6.9 shows the internal friction of an annealed copper single crystal. At a certain strain value, which decreases at higher temperatures, the damping increases rapidly with strain. There has been much speculation about the mechanism for this kind of damping. A moderately successful model due to Granato and Lücke is shown in Fig. 6.10.

The single crystal is assumed to contain a network of dislocations, with the network locking points strong enough to resist breakaway under stresses within the hysteretic damping range. The dislocations are further pinned by impurities or minor locking points. As the stress is increased in a half cycle, the dislocation bows out, as shown in the figure, and deformation strain occurs. At a particular value of stress the loop breaks from a minor locking point and the enlarged loop then tears away from the remaining pins until the network length is reached. At this point the strain increases with

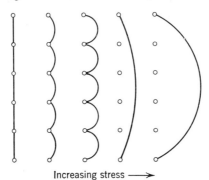

Increasing stress ⟶

**Fig. 6.10**   Granato and Lücke string model of a dislocation bowing out under increasing stress. The loops bow out from the pinning points until breakaway occurs. At reversed stress the long loop collapses back to be pinned in the original position.

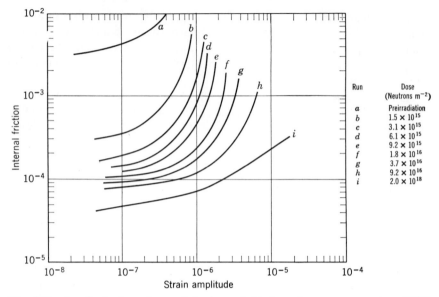

The figure legend reads:

| Run | Dose (Neutrons m$^{-2}$) |
|---|---|
| a | Preirradiation |
| b | $1.5 \times 10^{15}$ |
| c | $3.1 \times 10^{15}$ |
| d | $6.1 \times 10^{15}$ |
| e | $9.2 \times 10^{15}$ |
| f | $1.8 \times 10^{16}$ |
| g | $3.7 \times 10^{16}$ |
| h | $9.2 \times 10^{16}$ |
| i | $2.0 \times 10^{18}$ |

**Fig. 6.11** Amplitude dependence of the internal friction of a copper crystal at 375°K after neutron irradiation doses. (Redrawn from D. O. Thompson and V. K. Paré, *J. Appl. Phys.*, **36**, 243, 1964)

little extra stress. The return part of the half cycle, with the stress being reduced, causes the dislocation to collapse back until again pinned by the minor locking points. The stress-strain slope on the return will be less than that on the first half-cycle, resulting in a hysteresis loop.

Obviously, from the model, dislocation motion should be greatly affected by lattice defects and impurities, and this is found to be the case experimentally. Figure 6.11 shows the strain amplitude dependence of the internal friction of copper at 375°K after increasing neutron irradiation. The obvious interpretation is that the stress to break the dislocation from its pinning points has increased with the number of pins; in this case, they are presumably defects produced by the radiation.

There are other mechanisms of internal friction in solid materials. The few examples discussed in this chapter have been selected to demonstrate the more important characteristics of anelastic behavior.

### References

Mason, W. P., *Physical Acoustics and the Properties of Solids*, Van Nostrand, Princeton, N. J., 1958.

Zener, C., *Elasticity and Anelasticity in Metals*, Univ. of Chicago Press, Chicago, Ill., 1952.

## Exercises

1. What are the main experimental characteristics of a relaxation process?
2. Show that the maximum value of the damping loss is about twice the compliance defect $(J_R - J_u)/J_u$.
3. If the temperature of one part of a solid is suddenly changed, then time $\tau$ elapses before thermal equilibrium is again established over a distance $l$. Show that $\tau$ is given approximately by

$$\tau = l^2 \rho C/k$$

where $\rho$, $C$, and $k$, are, respectively, the density, specific heat, and thermal conductivity of the solid.

   Calculate $\tau$ for an aluminum rod $0.1 \times 1.0 \times 10$ cms oscillating in flexure at room temperature so that the upper and lower faces rise and fall periodically in temperature. Calculate the frequency of oscillation for maximum thermo-elastic damping.
4. How does the thermoelastic damping (in Exercise 3) vary with temperature at very low temperatures?
5. Using an attempt frequency of $2.10^{13}$ Hz and an activation energy for diffusion of carbon in iron of 0.13 eV per atom, calculate the frequency at which Snoek relaxation damping is a maximum in steel at the three temperatures $90°K$, $300°K$, and $500°K$.
6. Assuming a thermal attempt frequency of about $10^{12}$ Hz for all of the relaxation mechanisms of Fig. 6.3, estimate each of the activation enthalpies in eV per atom and in $k$ calories per mole.
7. A Bordoni damping maximum characterized by an activation energy of 0.085 eV per atom is found in copper at $90°K$ for an applied frequency of 30.3 kHz. Find the temperatures at which the maxima would occur at 100 kHz and at 10 MHz.
8. The attenuation $\alpha$ of a running wave in a solid is related to the damping loss $Q^{-1}$ by

$$\alpha = \pi f Q^{-1}/c$$

where $f$ and $c$ are, respectively, the frequency and velocity of the sound wave. Prove this relationship and express $\alpha$ numerically in db/$\mu$sec in terms of $Q^{-1}$.
9. An aluminum crystal is of thickness $10^{-2}$ m and has a damping factor $Q^{-1}$ of $10^{-3}$. Pulses of 15 mHz ultrasonic waves of pulse duration 1 $\mu$sec and repetition frequency 60 Hz are sent through the crystal. If the velocity of sound in aluminum is $5 \times 10^3$ m sec$^{-1}$, calculate the time interval between successive echoes from the bottom face of the crystal. Calculate also the ratio of the amplitudes of successive emergent pulse echoes.

# 7

# *Radiation Damage in Solids*

We saw in Chapter 4 that defects such as Schottky and Frenkel defects exist in all crystalline solids at temperatures above $0°K$. We have calculated the equilibrium number of such defects.

There are three possible ways to produce numbers of defects in a solid well above the equilibrium number. By quenching from a high temperature to a low temperature, the equilibrium number of defects appropriate to the high temperature may be retained at the lower temperature. By plastic deformation of the crystalline solid, defects may be produced. If the crystalline solid is subjected to radiation by energetic particles, atoms may be displaced by collision processes. The mechanism and magnitude of such displacements are the concerns of this chapter.

The motivation for carrying out defect studies is itself twofold. Quite often deleterious changes are caused in practical properties such as mechanical stability and electrical conductivity. The study therefore has great technological importance, particularly to the nuclear reactor engineer. Also, since irradiation can, in many cases, be made to introduce particular defects in controlled numbers, the study of radiation damage has become the most powerful method of investigating the nature of defects.

## 7.1  Types of Radiation and Interaction with Solids

The types of radiation of greatest interest in both technology and research are:

1. Neutrons.
2. Heavy charged particles such as protons, deuterons, particles, and fission fragments.
3. High energy electrons.
4. Gamma Rays ($\gamma$ rays).

These types of radiation interact with solids in the following ways:

1. Production of displaced atoms by collision.
2. Production of displaced or excited electrons, that is, ionization.
3. Production of fission spikes.
4. Production of thermal spikes.
5. Transmutation processes.

We will concern ourselves chiefly with the first two of these processes. In metals, because of their high electrical conductivity, ionization effects are of less importance. In insulators, on the other hand, ionization effects are of major importance. Both ionization and atomic displacement produce changes in the physical properties of semiconductors.

## 7.2   The Flux of Incident Radiation $\phi$

In order to discuss in a semiquantitative manner the effects of radiation on solids we must first define the number of incident radiation particles. Depending on the kind of experiment, the radiation may be in a collimated beam or distributed isotropically. Of course, in the majority of cases a mixture of the two extremes is likely. The *flux* is defined as the number of particles crossing unit area normal to the beam in unit time. If the beam is collimated and $n$ is the density of incident particles (number per unit volume) then the flux is simply given by $nv$, where $v$ is the velocity of the particles. If the beam is not collimated and $v$ is the velocity of a particle which travels at an angle $\theta$ to the normal to a small cross-sectional area $ds$, then the integrated flux $\phi$ is given by the integral $\int\int nv \cos \theta \, ds$. Over unit area this sum can be simply written in vector form $n\mathbf{N}$, where $\mathbf{N}$ is a unit vector normal to $ds$. If the flux of particles irradiates the solid for a time $t$, then the total exposure in numbers of particles will be $\phi t$ or $n\mathbf{N} \cdot vt$.

## 7.3   The Microscopic Cross Section $\sigma$

When an incident particle strikes an atom of the irradiated solid there may be an interaction between them. The chance that a particular reaction will take place is measured by its *cross section* $\sigma$. This means that we imagine, in a classical picture, an area $\sigma$ around the nucleus of the atom. If the bombarding particle passes through the area $\sigma$, the interaction takes place. If it misses the area $\sigma$, the interaction does not take place. Thus the cross section can be defined without a knowledge of the actual nature of the interaction.

Suppose that a collimated beam of incident particles of density $n$ and velocity $v$ impinge on a solid in which there are $N$ atoms per unit volume.

The flux $\phi$ is given by $nv$ and the number of interactions per unit volume per second by $\sigma N\phi$. In this definition $\sigma$ is called the *microscopic* cross section to distinguish it from $N\sigma$, the *macroscopic* cross section or the total cross section per unit volume.

## 7.4   The Differential Cross Section $d\sigma$

We can now broaden the definition of cross section by taking into account the angular distribution of scattered particles. We do this by first defining a differential cross section $d\sigma$, which varies with the angle between the incident and scattered particle.

Suppose in Fig. 7.1 that a beam of particles of flux $\phi_0$ encounters a target of unit area and thickness $\Delta x$. The target contains scattering centers (which may be atoms) of density $N$ per unit volume. For simplicity, we have assumed symmetrical scattering about the incident beam. There are $N\,\Delta x$ atoms in the target. Let the flux of particles in that part of the scattered beam which lies between angle $\alpha$ and angle $\alpha + d\alpha$ be $\Delta\phi_s$ These particles hit the shaded area $\Delta A$ in the figure, an area which subtends a solid angle $\Delta\omega$ with the target. $\Delta\omega$ is, of course, given by $\Delta A/r^2$. We can now define the differential cross-section $d\sigma$. The fractional chance of scattering into the solid angle $\Delta\omega$ is given by $\Delta\phi_s/\phi_0$. From our previous remarks on cross section we can also write this fractional chance as $N\,\Delta x\Delta\omega\,d\sigma$. Thus

$$\frac{\Delta\phi_s}{\phi_0} = d\sigma N\,\Delta x\,\Delta\omega \tag{7.1}$$

From Fig. 7.1 it is easy to see that

$$\Delta A = 2\pi r \sin\alpha r\,d\alpha$$

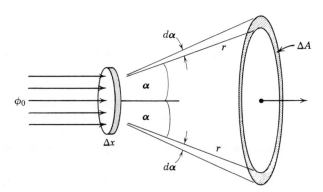

**Fig. 7.1**   Definition of differential cross section.

and that the solid angle $\Delta\omega$ is given by

$$\Delta\omega = \frac{\Delta A}{r^2} = 2\pi \sin\alpha\, d\alpha$$

Thus

$$\frac{\Delta\phi_s}{\phi_0} = d\sigma N\, \Delta x 2\pi \sin\alpha\, d\alpha \tag{7.2}$$

## 7.5  Dimensions of the Cross Section

The left-hand side of Equation 7.2 is dimensionless. If we write $[L]$ for a quantity having the dimensions of length, we can rewrite Equation 7.2 in dimensional form

$$[L]^0 = d\sigma[L^{-3}][L]$$

Thus the dimensions of the differential cross section must be $[L^2]$, or those of area. In nuclear physics and in radiation damage theory the unit of cross section is the *barn*, where

$$1 \text{ barn} = 10^{-28} \text{ m}^2 \tag{7.3}$$

## 7.6  The Total Scattering Cross Section $\sigma_{tot}$

In Section 7.5 we considered only the particles scattered at an angle $\alpha$ to the incident beam. In order to get the total number scattered around the target, we must integrate between the limits of $\alpha = 0$ to $\alpha = \pi$. The ratio $\phi_s/\phi_0$ of total scattered flux to incident flux is given by

$$\frac{\phi_s}{\phi_0} = N\, \Delta x \int_0^\pi d\sigma 2\pi \sin\alpha\, d\alpha$$

The integral is written as $\sigma_{tot}$. Thus

$$\frac{\phi_s}{\phi_0} = N\, \Delta x \sigma_{tot} \tag{7.4}$$

The total cross section is most easily obtained by experiment. This is done by first exposing a detector to the incident flux with no solid target in place. Without moving the detector a second exposure is then made with the target in place. If the measure of flux is then $\phi$, the total scattered flux $\phi_s$ is $\phi_0 - \phi$.

In this experiment it is obvious that the front part of the target will receive more radiation per unit time than does the back part. In our discussion so far we have simplified matters by referring only to *scattering* processes. This need not be the only means by which the flux is attenuated in the incident direction. *Absorption* and other processes may also occur. The cross sections for several processes will, in general, be additive. Suppose we called the total cross section for scattering $\sigma_{tot}$, as before, the cross section for absorption $\sigma_{ab.tot}$, and the cross section for capture $\sigma_{k.tot}$ Then if the flux $\phi$ is reduced by an amount $d\phi$ in passing through a thickness $dx$ of target, we have

$$d\phi = -\phi N(\sigma_{tot} + \sigma_{ab.tot} + \sigma_{k.tot} + \cdots)\, dx$$

Integrating over the whole target thickness $d$ gives

$$\int_{\phi_0}^{\phi} \frac{d\phi}{\phi} = -\int_0^d N(\sigma_{tot} + \sigma_{ab.tot} + \sigma_{k.tot} + \cdots)\, dx$$

or

$$\phi = \phi_0 \exp\left[-N(\sigma_{tot} + \sigma_{ab.tot} + \sigma_{k.tot})\, d\right] \tag{7.5}$$

In optics and sometimes in radiation experiments this equation is written in terms of intensities. The form is similar:

$$I = I_0 e^{-N\Sigma d} \tag{7.6}$$

where we have replaced the sum of the different cross sections by the symbol $\Sigma$.

## 7.7   The Interaction Mean Free Path of Penetration Depth

One other parameter comes frequently into the literature; this is the *interaction mean free path* or *penetration depth* $\lambda$. As we can see from Equation 7.5 or 7.6, the probability that an incident particle penetrates a distance $x$ into a solid without a scattering (or absorbing, capture, etc.) collision is $e^{-N\Sigma x}$. Then the probability $F(x)$ that the first collision occurs at some distance $<x$ is

$$F(x) = 1 - e^{-N\Sigma x} \tag{7.7}$$

The probability that the collision occurs between $x$ and $x + dx$ is $[\partial F(x)/\partial x]\, dx$. The expected or mean value of $x$, or the *penetration depth* $\lambda$, is therefore given by

$$\lambda = \int_0^\infty x \frac{\partial F(x)}{\partial x}\, dx$$

$$= \int_0^\infty x N\Sigma e^{-N\Sigma x} dx \qquad \text{from} \tag{7.7}$$

$$= \frac{1}{N\Sigma} \tag{7.8}$$

## 7.8   Orders of Magnitude

At this point some idea of typical orders of magnitude of the quantities may be introduced. Solids have densities $N$ of about $10^{29}$ nuclei m$^{-3}$. A typical reactor has a flux $\phi$ of thermal neutrons which may be $10^{17}$ neutrons m$^{-2}$ sec$^{-1}$. The process attenuating the flux of thermal neutrons is often one of capture by the nuclei of the surrounding material. Absorption by this means has a cross section which is typically about 1 barn. The average mean free path or the penetration depth of the thermal neutrons before capture absorption will then be about $10^{-1}$ m.

## 7.9   Choice of Differential Cross Section

Thus far we have considered the incident particles as points and the target elements or atoms as having a certain "target area;" this is a profitable way of visualizing the process at first, but it is oversimplified. Obviously, a process of absorption or any other kind of interaction must be a joint property of the incident particle and the interacting element. We have seen that we can make a choice of differential cross section without knowing in detail the interaction mechanism. We now wish to introduce the physical concept of defining the cross section so that it depends on the property which is changed by the interaction.* Suppose, for instance, that we are interested in the relation between the initial energy $E$ of incident radiation and energy $T$ transferred to "struck" atoms. We can define the differential cross section by the symbolic equation

$$d\sigma = K(E, T)\, dT \tag{7.9}$$

This means that the cross section of the struck particles is such that incident particles of energy $E$ transfer energy to "struck" particles so that their energy lies between $T$ and $T + dT$. We would have to know all about the physics of the "collision" in order to give the function $K$ a definite form. This cannot always be done, but we can define $d\sigma$ in terms of the experimental results. The total cross section for this mechanism of energy transfer would then be

$$\sigma_{\text{tot}} = \int_{\text{all } T} K(E, T)\, dT \tag{7.10}$$

* This development and those of a number of subsequent sections owe much to the review by D. K. Holmes, "Terms And Concepts in Radiation Damage Theory," Proc. Inter. School of Physics Enrico Fermi, *Radiation damage in solids*, Academic Press, New York, 1962, p. 182.

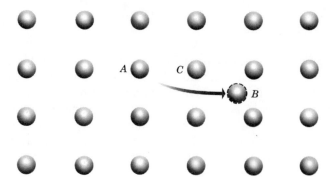

**Fig. 7.2**   Lattice atom *A* displaced by collision past position *C* to position *B*.

## 7.10   The Displacement Cross Section $\sigma_d$

We shall now calculate the magnitude of the energy *T* which must be transferred to an atom from an incident particle of energy *E* so that the atom can be displaced in the lattice. The simplest kind of displacement would move the atom to an interstitial position, leaving behind a vacancy. In Fig. 7.2 we have pictured an atom being displaced from position *A* to position *B* by a collision. The lowest or threshold value of this energy $T_d$ will be greater than the energy of formation of such a defect by thermal activation. In Section 4.13 we saw that the thermal formation probabilities were governed by factors such as $e^{-F/kT}$, where *F* is the formation energy. *F* is the difference in free energy of the atom in positions *A* and *B*. We saw that in infinite time the Frenkel defect was bound to be formed thermally if *T* is above 0°K. But to form the defect by a collision the energy must be supplied at once and is the energy of the barrier between positions *A* and *B*, which must exist somewhere about position *C* in the diagram. For a typical metal the difference in free energy of the atom in positions *A* and *B* is about 5 eV, whereas the threshold value of energy which must be transferred by a collision is about 25 eV.

Following Equation 7.10, we define the cross section for displacement $\sigma_d$ of the atom *A* in the manner

$$\sigma_d = \int_{T \geqslant Td} K(E, T)\, dT \tag{7.11}$$

The function *K* can be derived theoretically in only the simplest of cases. We will give values of displacement cross section and also their variation with incident energy in later sections.

In a discussion of the characteristics of radiation damage we believe it is most economical to classify the mechanisms according to the *nature of the radiation*. This is the division we shall follow.

*Damage by Non-Ionizing Radiation*

## 7.11  Damage by Neutron Radiation

Radiation damage by neutrons is encountered in the nuclear reactor. Neutron energies range from as high as 10 MeV down to thermal energies of the order of $10^{-1}$ eV. The uranium fission neutrons have energies of about 1.5 MeV, and in a well-moderated graphite reactor the pile neutrons are such that the number of neutrons per unit energy range is roughly inversely proportional to the value of the energy.

Neutrons interact with the nuclei of the atoms of the bombarded material. As a first approximation, which is reasonably true for low energies, the interaction potential is infinite for distances inside the sum of the neutron radius and the nucleus of the bombarded atom. The potential is zero outside this distance. This is, of course, just another way of expressing the fact that the scattering collision is not unlike that between two impenetrable spheres. We would expect the cross section to be $\simeq \pi R_N^2$, where $R_N$ is the nuclear radius. Experimentally, it is found that the cross section is considerably more sensitive to the nature of the potential than this simple picture implies. Experimental values of cross section are given in Fig. 7.3. We can see that most cross sections are in the range 1 to 10 barns. In neutron bombardment of solids of atomic weight greater than about 30, the scattering of neutrons of energy less than about $10^{-1}$ MeV is fairly isotropic. For higher neutron energies in the fission range of 1 to 2 MeV, the cross sections are also about 1 to 10 barns but, as shown in Fig. 7.4, there is a marked preference for scattering in the forward direction.

## 7.12  Calculation of the Number of Primary "Knock-On" Atoms

The initial step in the calculation of the amount of radiation damage is to estimate the number of atoms which are *first displaced* by the incident radiation. These are the *primary "knock-on" atoms*. The second step is to calculate the number of atoms which are displaced by these "primary" atoms. We start with the primaries, of which there are $N_d$ displaced by the neutrons of all energies per unit volume per second. Naturally the number $N_d$ depends on the energies of the neutrons. We have made a simplifying

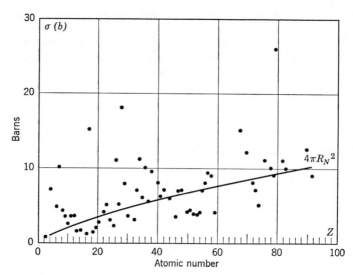

**Fig. 7.3** Cross sections for low energy neutrons for elements of atomic number $Z$. (After A. M. Weinberg and E. P. Wigner, *The Physical Theory of Neutron Chain Reactors*, Univ. of Chicago Press, Chicago, Ill., 1958)

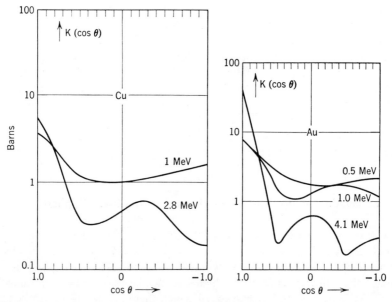

**Fig. 7.4** Neutron cross sections for Cu and Au. The angle $\theta$ is between the incident and scattered directions, for example, $\cos \theta = 1$ denotes scattering in the forward direction. (From G. Liebfried, *Radiation Damage in Solids*, Academic Press, New York, 1962)

assumption about these energies in a well-moderated reactor. Recalling this, there will therefore be the following two groups of primary "knock-on" atoms:

1. The atoms first displaced by the fast *fission neutrons* of about 1.5 MeV in energy before they begin to slow down by making their first collisions.
2. The atoms which are first displaced by *pile* neutrons, whose number distribution is proportional to $1/E$ if $E$ is the energy of the pile neutrons as they slow down to thermal values.

Suppose $\phi(E_0)$ is the flux of fast fission neutrons before they begin to slow down by making collisions. Let $\sigma_d(E_0)$ be the appropriate cross section at this energy. The number of primary knock-on atoms displaced in the first class is then $N\sigma_d(E_0)\phi(E_0)$, where $N$ is again the number of atoms per unit volume of target. If $\phi(T)$ is the flux of pile neutrons that have made at least one collision and $\sigma_d^*$ is an average value of displacement cross section between the energy limits, then the number of atoms displaced by the pile neutrons is $N\sigma_d^*\phi(T)$. Thus

$$N_d = N\sigma_d(E_0)\phi(E_0) + N\sigma^*\phi(T) \tag{7.12}$$

In a graphite reactor the fission flux is less than one per cent of the pile neutron flux, that is,

$$\frac{\phi(E_0)}{\phi(T)} < 0.01$$

Nevertheless, insertion of the correct cross sections makes

$$N\sigma_d(E_0)\phi(E_0) \simeq \tfrac{1}{6}N\sigma_d^*\phi(T)$$

so that the number of primary displaced atoms produced by the fast fission neutrons is about 15 per cent of those subsequently produced by the large pile flux. We will give an estimate of numbers after completion of the next step in the final calculation of displaced atoms.

## 7.13 The Cascade Process

In order to find the total number of displaced atoms, we shall make two simplifying assumptions which will assist the calculation but will not invalidate the general argument. These are:

1. The atoms of the lattice scatter like impenetrable spheres.
2. Atomic displacements are only possible above a sharp energy threshold value.

With the assumption of hard-sphere collisions between a neutron and an atom or between atoms, the application of conservation of momentum enables us to write an expression for the maximum fraction of energy transferred

$$\left(\frac{T}{E}\right)_{max} = \frac{4mM}{(m+M)^2} \tag{7.13}$$

If we start with a primary of energy $T$, then the number of displaced atoms in successive collisions and the corresponding energies of the struck atoms is given by

No. of displaced atoms in successive collisions     $1:2:4\cdots 2^s$

*Average* energy of struck atoms     $T\dfrac{T}{2}\dfrac{T}{4}\dfrac{T}{2^s}$

We must choose $s$, the number of steps in this cascade process, so that

$$\frac{T}{2^s} < 2T_d$$

where $T_d$ is the assumed sharp threshold value of energy below which an atom will not be displaced. Then in the $s$th collision, the required displacement energy can not be transferred. The total number $N_T$ of displaced atoms for different ranges of energy $T$ is now summarized in Table 7.1.

To illustrate the cascade process, suppose that a 1.5 MeV neutron is incident on a copper crystal. Then Equation 7.13, with the atomic weight of copper inserted, shows that energies up to $10^5$ eV may be transferred to the copper primary "knock-on" atom. Let us assume a threshold displacement energy $T_d$ of about 25 eV. Then from Table 7.1 the complete number of secondary, tertiary, and subsequently displaced atoms $N_T$ will be between 1000 and 2000. The displaced atoms will be lodged in the volume of crystal which can be reached by the cascade process. There are other processes which can carry the damage off into more remote regions, and these will be

**Table 7.1**  The Number $N$ of Displaced Atoms in Several Ranges
of Energy $T$

| Energy Range for $T$ | Total Number of Displaced Atoms $N_T$ |
|---|---|
| $T < T_d$ | 0 |
| $T_d < T < 2T_d$ | 1 |
| $\geqslant 2T_d$ | $T/2T_d$ |

**Table 7.2**   Copper Atoms Displaced by Various Radiations

| Type of Radiation | | $N_T$ (Order of Magnitude Only) |
|---|---|---|
| Electron | 1.5 MeV | 1 |
| Gamma | 1.5 MeV | 1 |
| Deuterons | 10 MeV | 5 |
| Pile neutrons | 1 MeV to $10^{-1}$ eV | 100 |
| Fission neutrons | | 1000 |

mentioned later. Thus a single incident 1.5 MeV neutron can displace more than 1000 atoms of copper. Table 7.2 shows some comparative numbers of copper atoms displaced by other radiations. The number of copper atoms displaced by an integrated flux of $10^{22}$ to $10^{23}$ fast neutrons over an area of 1 m² would therefore be about $10^{25}$ to $10^{26}$. This is about one atomic per cent since the number of copper atoms per m³ is about $4 \times 10^{28}$.

## 7.14   Replacement Collisions

Fast moving atoms can, in addition to producing Frenkel pairs, interchange with normal lattice atoms. The incoming atom replaces the struck atoms and the latter becomes interstitial. If the struck atom has sufficient momentum, it may cause other replacements. Then no vacancy is left behind. If the primary atom is of a different element from the replaced atoms, this mechanism of replacement collision is very efficient in disordering an ordered alloy.

## 7.15   Focusing Collisions

Since there are close-packed directions in a crystal, energy may be transferred efficiently or focused along such a direction following a primary knock-on event. This mechanism has been investigated theoretically by Liebfried and experimentally by Thompson and others. The mechanism can result in a large increase in the eventual distance between the vacancy and the interstitial since at higher energies the focusing collisions may transport matter as well as energy. Theoretical studies of the dynamics of collisions can be made by simulating the lattice atoms in a high-speed computer and perturbing the system, for example, by a primary knock-on atom. Figure 7.5 shows a number of possible atomic paths calculated in this dynamic way.

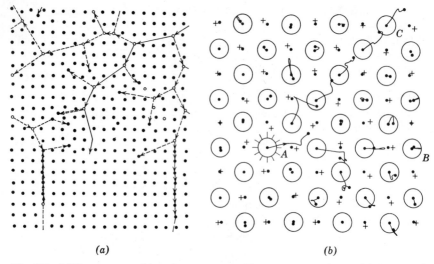

|   |   |
|---|---|
| (a) | (b) |

**Fig. 7.5** (*a*) Damage caused by a fast neutron incident upon a metal crystal (schematical). *A primary knock-on* (upper right corner) describes the path indicated by the full-drawn line, and causes in its way *secondary* and higher order *displacements*. Veritable *cascades* of *vacancies* (dotted circles) are formed, most branches ending finally in *interstitial atoms*. Focusing and defocusing collisions are indicated, whereas some atoms have received a large amount of extra vibrational energy (thermal spikes). (From J. Billington, *Sci. Amer*, **201**, 200, 1959) (*b*) Atomic orbits produced by incident particle transferring an energy of 40 eV to the atom at *A* in a direction 22½ above the horizontal axis. Large circles give the initial positions of the atoms in the plane of drawing, small dots of those in the plane below. Large dots give the final positions of the former, crosses those of the latter. A vacancy is left at *A*, an interstitial will probably be formed at *C*. (From J. B. Gibson, A. N. Goland, M. Milgram, G. H. Vineyard, *Phys. Rev.*, **120**, 1229, 1960)

Displacement, replacement, and focusing collisions are clearly seen in the figure.

### 7.16   Thermal Spikes

Equation 7.13 has shown us that an energy of the order of $10^5$ eV may be transferred to a primary knock-on atom of copper from an incident 1 MeV neutron. We have also estimated that the total number of displaced atoms should be of the order of $10^3$. Now let us assume that the energy of formation of a defect is, say 5 eV. Thus the energy stored in the lattice in the form of defects, assuming for the moment that none anneal out, will be $\simeq 10^3$ eV. The ratio

$$\frac{\text{stored energy}}{\text{transferred energy}} \simeq 10^{-1}$$

Thus some 90 per cent of the energy of the primary knock-on atom must have been dissipated in the form of heat. The path of the incident primary is thus one of increased temperature. It has been called a *thermal spike* with temperatures of the order of $1000°K$ being reached in times of $10^{-11}$ sec. The increased lattice vibration in such regions of, say, 1000 atoms results in defect and even dislocation production.

Much of the damage does not remain for long in the irradiated solid. Many of the Frenkel pairs recombine, especially if the vacancy-interstitial separation is not great. This has been discussed in Section 4.21. The calculation of damage remaining for different times and at different temperatures is, of course, a diffusion problem and forms a main topic of Chapter 4. We shall leave to subsequent chapters the description of physical property changes brought about by radiation damage.

### *Damage by Ionizing and other Radiations*

Energetic particles which carry electric charges are for the most part slowed down not by elastic collisions with the atomic nuclei of the bombarded solid, but by ionization. This means that the energy is transferred to the electrons of the solid by the Coulomb interaction with the charged particles. In a metal which has a high conductivity, ionization effects are quickly neutralized, but in an insulator or semiconductor they remain and constitute the most important kind of damage.

### 7.17 Irradiation by Heavy Charged Particles

Near the end of the flight of a charged particle through a solid, when it has been slowed down by ionization, it may still cause atomic displacement. We have seen in Table 7.2 the decreased efficiency in comparison with bombardment with neutrons.

We can show the importance of the ionization mechanism in dissipating the energy of a charged incident particle by an examination of the nature of the cross section. It can be shown by elementary physics that the energy $T$ transferred to an electron $-e$ of an atom during the passage nearby of a charged particle of charge $Ze$ and energy $E$ is given by

$$\frac{T}{E} = \frac{Z^2 e^4}{(4\pi\epsilon_0)^2 p^2} \frac{m}{m_e} \tag{7.14}$$

where $m$ and $m_e$ are the masses of particle and electron, respectively. The quantity $p$ is the impact parameter shown in Fig. 7.6a and b. This formula can be derived in a classical way by applying the well-known Coulomb law of

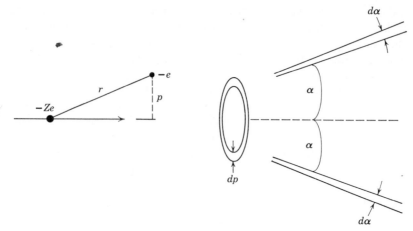

**Fig. 7.6**  A charged particle $-Ze$ being scattered by an electron $-e$. $p$ is the range of interaction or impact parameter.

attraction between charges.  The charged particle will give energy $T$ to the electron of the atom because of the force between them.  The differential cross section $d\sigma_I(E, T)$ for ionization is shown from Fig. 7.6 to be

$$d\sigma_I(E, T) = 2\pi p\, dp \tag{7.15}$$

and from (7.14)

$$d\sigma_I(E, T) = 2\pi p\, \frac{dp}{dT}\, dT$$

$$= \frac{\pi}{(4\pi\epsilon_0)^2}\, \frac{Z^2 e^4}{E}\, \frac{m}{m_e}\, \frac{dT}{T^2} \tag{7.16}$$

As the charged particles slows down to lower values of $E$ the cross section increases.  We can also see that there will be more interactions in which low energies are transferred because of the dependence of $d\sigma_I$ on $1/T^2$.

## 7.18  Stopping Power by Ionization

The *stopping power* is a measure of the loss of energy by the charged particle as it penetrates the bombarded solid.  If there are $N_e$ electrons per unit volume of target which are available for ionization, and if we recall that the cross section is the probability of an interaction taking place within a certain transferred energy range $T_1$ to $T_2$, then the loss of energy $-dE$ in a penetration distance $dx$ is given by

$$-dE = Ne \int_{T_1}^{T_2} T\, d\sigma_I(E, T)\, dx \tag{7.17}$$

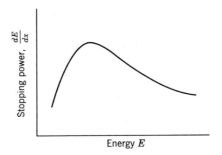

**Fig. 7.7**   Stopping power by ionization.

The stopping power $-dE/dx$ is plotted against $E$ in Fig. 7.7, with the main features of this discussion revealed. Two MeV deuterons have a stopping power in copper of about $1.4 \times 10^4$ MeV m$^{-1}$ and thus have a very short range of the order of $10^{-5}$ m.

### 7.19   Transfer of Energy to Atomic Nuclei (Rutherford Scattering)

Energetic charged particles can, of course, interact with the positively charged nuclei of target atoms to produce atomic displacements. This again is a Coulomb interaction, and the appropriate cross section $d\sigma_R(E, T)$ is similar in form to that for ionization. It is given in Equation 7.18.

$$d\sigma_R(E, T) = \frac{\pi z^2 Z^2 e^4}{(4\pi\epsilon_0)^2} \frac{1}{E} \frac{m}{M} \frac{dT}{T^2} \tag{7.18}$$

where $M$ is the mass of the atomic nucleus which carries a charge of $ze$. This is the famous Rutherford scattering formula, from which a first insight into the nature of nuclear dimensions was obtained.

We can compare the probability of ionization loss with the probability of loss by Rutherford scattering for a charged incident particle. From Equations 7.16 and 7.18 we have

$$R = \frac{\text{probability of Rutherford scattering}}{\text{probability of ionization}} = \frac{N}{N_e} \frac{d\sigma_R}{d\sigma_I}$$

where $N$ is the number of atoms and $N_e$ is the number of electrons per unit volume of target, respectively.

$$R \simeq \frac{Z^2}{z^2} \frac{m_e}{M}$$

$$\simeq 10^{-2} \text{ to } 10^{-3}$$

for many metals. The primary knock-on atom produced by Rutherford collision with the incident charged particle may, as in the case of neutrons (Section 7.13), subsequently displace other atoms in a cascade process.

## 7.20  Irradiation by Fast Electrons

Radiation damage by fast electrons has been much used in research since the damage produced is simple in nature. To date, few technological applications of the process have been encountered. The electron energies must be of the order of 1 MeV in order to displace atoms from their lattice positions. At these energies mathematical expressions for the energy and momentum of an impinging electron must be written in relativistic form. It is customary to quote the energy of the electron in electron volts, where $E$ is its kinetic energy ($\frac{1}{2}mv^2$), or its total energy minus its rest energy. The rest energy for an electron is $\simeq 0.5$ MeV. In relativistic form the momentum $p_e$ of an electron moving with velocity $v$ is given in most elementary physics texts:

$$p_e = \frac{mv}{\sqrt{1 - v^2/c^2}}$$

where $c$ is the speed of light.

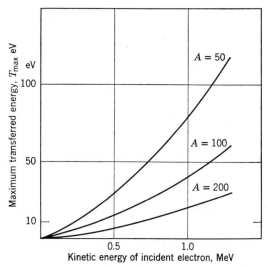

**Fig. 7.8**  Maximum energy transferred to atoms of atomic weight from incident electron. (After Liebfried)

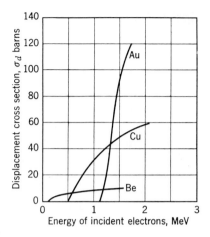

**Fig. 7.9** Displacement cross sections for irradiation of three elements by fast electrons. (After Holmes)

A little manipulation will show that

$$p_e{}^2c^2 = E(E + 2mc^2)$$

Now if the electron makes a head-on collision with a nucleus of mass $M$, which is much larger than the mass of the electron, then the maximum momentum transferred is $2p_e$. The maximum transferred energy $T_{max}$ will be $(2p_e)^2/2M$ and thus

$$T_{max} = \frac{2E}{Mc^2}(E + 2mc^2) \qquad (7.19)$$

Figure 7.8 shows a plot of the maximum energy transferred to atoms of atomic weight $A$.

If we again assume a threshold value of displacement energy of about 25 eV, then Fig. 7.8 shows that there is little likelihood of a displaced atom having enough energy to displace a neighboring atom. The damage is therefore a single Frenkel pair. Many of these may be closely spaced interstitial-vacancy combinations which will anneal out at low temperatures. This is discussed in Chapter 4.

The cross section formula for displacement of atoms by fast electrons is rather complicated and will not be quoted. Figure 7.9 shows displacement cross sections for three elements.

As in the case of bombardment by heavy charged particles, most of the energy of the incident electron radiation is lost by ionization. The range of penetration of electrons in the MeV energy range, for example, is only of the order of $10^{-4}$ m in metals.

## 7.21 Irradiation by Gamma Rays

Gamma rays, which are often produced in nuclear reactions, react with the electrons and nuclei of atoms in a number of ways. For gamma rays in the energy range most frequently encountered, say 0.5 to 3 MeV, one of these interactions is of major importance. Gamma rays have depths of penetration of the order of $10^{-1}$ m in many solids, and in their passage they may strip off electrons from the atoms of the solid. These are called *Compton electrons*. The Compton electrons have energies up to those of the gamma rays and may damage the material in the manner of high energy electrons. Clearly, two cross sections are involved in the displacement of a primary knock-on atom for this case. We have first the gamma-electron cross section and then the electron-atom cross section. The damage will be distributed throughout the solid if it is thicker than the gamma ray penetration depth. This contrasts with electron damage which, as we have discussed, is close to the surface. Figure 7.10 shows gamma ray displacement cross sections, again in copper for comparison. These are much less than for direct electron displacement, which is to be expected since two cross sections are involved.

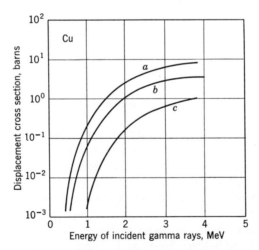

**Fig. 7.10** Gamma ray displacement cross sections for Compton mechanism in copper. The calculations are made for three displacement energies: (*a*) $T_d = 15$ eV; (*b*) $T_d = 25$ eV; (*c*) $T_d = 35$ eV. (From O. S. Oen and D. K. Holmes, Appl. Phys., **30**, 1289, 1959)

## 7.22 Damage by Fission Fragments and Introduction of Radiation Products

To conclude this chapter, we shall mention briefly two other kinds of radiation damage processes which are less elementary in nature than those already discussed. Solid elements and, in particular, metals that are transmuted by irradiation suffer lattice damage from the high energy transmutation products.

The best known example, of course, is the fission of the $U^{235}$ nucleus. The fission fragments carry energy of about 160 MeV and damage the neighboring lattice, each producing in excess of 30,000 Frenkel pairs. Thus

**Table 7.3** Some Isotopes which Transmute into Inert Gas Atoms

| Target Isotope | Reaction | Reaction Energy (MeV) | Threshold Energy (MeV) | Cross-Section in Barns | Gases Produced | Vol./unit vol. of Target for Dose of $10^{24}$ n · cm$^{-2}$ |
|---|---|---|---|---|---|---|
| $^6$Li | $(n, \alpha)$ | 4.70 | Slow | 950 | $2^4$He, $^3$He | $2.8 \cdot 10^6$ |
| $^9$Be | $(n, \alpha)$ | −0.64 | 0.71 | 0.050 | $2^4$He, $^3$H | $5.7 \cdot 10^2$ |
| $^9$Be | $(n, 2n)$ | −1.66 | 1.84 | 0.20 | $2^4$He | $2.0 \cdot 10^3$ |
| $^{10}$B | $(n, \alpha)$ | 2.26 | Slow | 3990 | $^4$He | $3.1 \cdot 10^7$ |
| U nat. | Fission | 180 | Slow | 4.2 | Xe, Kr | $3 \cdot 10$ |

From R. S. Barnes, "Atomic Displacement and Impurity Effects in Fissile Metals," Proc. Inter. School of Physics Enrico Fermi, *Radiation Damage in Solids*, Academic Press, New York, 1962, p. 860.

damage in uranium, plutonium, thorium, the control element boron, the moderator and canning element beryllium, and other materials is to be expected in reactor technology.

In addition, many of the products of the nuclear reactions are inert gases, and the presence and clustering of these gas bubbles within the metal cause major mechanical and other property changes. The mechanism of the clustering, which is of great importance, is discussed in Chapter 4. Table 7.3 shows some isotopes which transmute into inert gas atoms.

This chapter on radiation damage has been concerned with production of geometric defects in solid lattices. The presence of these defects causes changes in many physical properties of the solid. Further discussion of the changes in a particular physical property will appear in the related subsequent chapter.

## References

Damask, A. C., and G. J. Dienes, *Point Defects in Metals*, Gordon and Breach, New York, 1963.

*Radiation Damage in Solids*, Proceedings of the International School of Physics "Enrico Fermi," Academic Press, New York, 1962.

Van Bueren, H. G., *Imperfections in Crystals*, North-Holland, 1961.

## Exercises

1. Consider a row of atoms in a crystal of interatomic distance $d$. The radius of each atom is $R$ in a hard core approximation. Suppose that one of the atoms is struck by an incoming particle and itself collides with a nearest neighbor. Show by drawing that it is plausible to assume that the momentum is focused along the row of atoms if $R > d/2$, which is the focusing direction in a face-centered cubic crystal.

2. Calculate the mean number of atoms displaced by a 1 MeV neutron in gold and germanium.

3. Atoms of increasing atomic weights are bombarded by various types of radiation. Assuming a displacement energy of 25 eV, calculate the threshold radiation energies to complete the table.

| Type of Bombarding | Atomic Weight of Struck Atoms | | | |
|---|---|---|---|---|
| Particle | 10 | 20 | 100 | 200 |
| Neutrons, protons | | | | |
| Electrons, rays | | | | |
| α particles | | | | |
| Fission fragments of mass 100 | | | | |

# 8

# *Introductory Wave Mechanics*

The physical properties of solids that we have discussed in the previous chapters derive from the geometrical characteristics of the atomic packing. Before this treatment can be extended to cover the electrical properties of matter, an understanding must be reached of the nature of the charges that give rise to these properties. This will involve, in turn, a study of the nature of electrons, the electronic properties of atoms, and, finally, the behavior of electrons in the periodic lattice of the solids.

This preparatory material may seem at times to take us rather far from our real aim, the properties of solids. The electrical properties of solids cannot be adequately understood, however, without a knowledge of wave mechanics methods and their application to various problems, including, specifically, the physics of atoms.

## 8.1  The Particle Nature of Electrons

The electron was first clearly identified as an elementary particle by J. J. Thomson in 1897. His work on the deflection of a cathode ray beam in electric and magnetic fields showed that the constituents of the beam had a unique ratio of charge to mass, regardless of their source. This suggested the interpretation of the cathode ray beam in terms of a stream of elementary particles each of charge $e$ and mass $m$. The currently accepted values are $e = 1.6021 \times 10^{-19}$ coulomb and $m = 9.1090 \times 10^{-31}$ kg (at rest). Many properties of electrons can be described using nothing more than the assumption of a particle with a fixed charge and mass which obeys the laws of electrodynamics. The properties that can be so described are mostly those involving the interaction between electrons and electrostatic and electromagnetic fields, that is, the properties of electrons in free space. The treatment breaks down when the problem of electrons in matter is considered, and the necessary revisions to the theory are taken up later in this chapter.

The classical electrodynamics of charged particles is treated in the books on electricity but, because of the frequent use which must be made of it in the remaining part of this book, we wish to give a summary of the relations governing motion of a charge in electric and magnetic fields.

The force **F** on a charge $e$ situated in a field $\mathscr{E}$ is, by definition

$$\mathbf{F} = e\mathscr{E} \qquad (8.1)$$

The work $W$ done in moving a charge from point $A$ to point $B$ in an electrostatic field is

$$W_{AB} \int_A^B \mathscr{E} \, . \, ds \qquad (8.2)$$

and this is written in terms of the electrostatic potential $V$ as

$$W_{AB} = e(V_B - V_A) \qquad (8.3)$$

Equation 8.3 enables us to define commonly used units of work. If one *coulomb* of charge is moved through a potential difference of one *volt*, that is, if $V_B - V_A = 1$ volt, the amount of work done is one *joule*. The work done in moving an *electron* through a potential difference of one *volt* is one *electron-volt* (eV). Note that because the charge on an electron is a negative quantity, work is required to move the electron in the direction of decreasing electrostatic potential. From the value of the charge on the electron we thus have

$$1 \text{ eV} = 1.6021 \times 10^{-19} \text{ joule}$$

Following the definition of a scalar potential in Equation 8.3, we write the relation between field $\mathscr{E}$ and potential $V$ as

$$\mathscr{E} = - \left( \frac{\partial V}{\partial x} \mathbf{i} + \frac{\partial V}{\partial y} \mathbf{j} + \frac{\partial V}{\partial z} \mathbf{k} \right) \qquad (8.4)$$

where **i, j,** and **k** are unit vectors in the $x$, $y$, $z$ directions, respectively.

Equation 8.4 is often written

$$\mathscr{E} = -\operatorname{grad} V$$

The forces between moving charges are more complex than those already discussed. They are usually described in terms of a magnetic field of induction **B**. Consider a charge $e$ moving with the velocity **v** through a field **B**. The force **F** on the charge is then given in magnitude by

$$F = evB \sin \theta \qquad (8.5)$$

where $\theta$ is the angle between the directions of **v** and **B**. The force **F** may be written in terms of a vector product

$$\mathbf{F} = e(\mathbf{v} \times \mathbf{B}) \qquad (8.6)$$

In the special case where the particle $e$ is moving in a plane normal to the direction of **B**, the path will be circular with a radius $r$ determined by the equation expressing the balance between electromagnetic and inertial forces. This equation is

$$Bev = \frac{mv^2}{r}$$

that is,

$$r = \frac{mv}{Be} \tag{8.7}$$

We might note in passing that the time required for a complete circuit of the circular path is

$$t = \frac{2\pi r}{v} = \frac{2\pi m}{Be} \tag{8.8}$$

The time is thus independent of the velocity of the particle. This feature is fundamental to the design of the cyclotron, magnetron, and other particle accelerating machines. The principle will also be encountered later in the discussion of cyclotron resonance in solids.

It is of interest to consider the case of a sudden de-acceleration (or acceleration) of a charged particle. Suppose that at a certain time $t_0$ a moving charge is abruptly decelerated to rest within a very short time $\Delta t$. Prior to stopping, the charge was surrounded by a spherically uniform electrostatic field which moved with the charge. The information regarding the changed velocity of the charge will be propagated along the lines of force at the speed of electromagnetic interactions, that is, the speed of light. Now consider the circumstances at a time $t_1$ after the charge was stopped, as they are illustrated in Fig. 8.1. The point at which the particle was stopped is $A$. At a great distance (i.e., greater than $ct_1$) from the charge, the field lines have not yet received the information that the charge has stopped and so remain as a spherical distribution around the point $B$ that the particle would have reached at time $t_1$ had it not stopped. For distances smaller than $ct_1$ the field lines will be stationary and centered on $A$. Thus there must be a region of distortion $CD$ on each field line spreading out with velocity $c$, and this corresponds to a spherical pulse of electromagnetic energy of thickness $c\,\Delta t$. The conclusion is, therefore, that the effect of acceleration (positive or negative) on a charge is to cause it to radiate energy. Probably the best known example of this phenomenon is in X-ray tubes. Here the deceleration arises as a fast-moving electron strikes a target. Since the slowing down process is arbitrary, no distinct wavelengths are emitted, and the radiation spectrum is continuous. If sufficiently fast electrons (i.e., those that have been accelerated through some thousands of volts) are used, the resulting radiation lies in the X-ray region (Section 2.1).

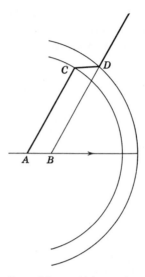

**Fig. 8.1**   The distortion of the lines of force which constitutes the pulse of electromagnetic energy emitted from an accelerated charge.

The foregoing recapitulation of elementary electrostatic and electromagnetic theory illustrates the *particle* properties of electrons. This model is completely adequate for most practical work on electron beams in tubes, gaseous discharges, etc. It is, however, inadequate for the discussion of many aspects of the behavior of electrons in atoms and solids. For this purpose we must give a description of the electron in terms of wave mechanics.

## 8.2   The Wave Nature of Electrons

Section 8.1 discusses the aspects of electron behavior that could be interpreted on the "charged billiard ball" model. Because other properties of electrons that cannot be treated by this model can be observed experimentally, the wave mechanics treatment that we are about to discuss was developed. Actually, the suggestion that we can picture electrons in terms of wave properties came from a converse proposal made in 1901–1905 by Planck and Einstein that electromagnetic radiation could be regarded (and in many cases had to be regarded) not as a smooth continuous wave but as a shower of discrete packets of energy, each given the name *quantum* or *photon*. The essential feature of this hypothesis is that the radiation can exchange energy with a system only in units of a definite size. Energy changes smaller than that corresponding to one quantum are not permitted. Planck proposed that the energy $E$ of a single quantum should be related linearly to the frequency $\nu$ of the radiation by the equation

$$E = h\nu \tag{8.9}$$

where $h$ is Planck's constant, of which the currently accepted value is $6.6256 \times 10^{-34}$ joule sec.

The proposal found almost immediate application and support in the photoelectric effect. This effect is discussed more fully in Chapter 11, and it is sufficient to say here that the evidence was, as Einstein pointed out, that an electron in a solid could gain energy from a monochromatic light beam only in definite amounts, and that this quantity of energy depended linearly on the frequency of the light.

The use of the alternative particle or wave models for the description of electromagnetic radiation is dictated by circumstance. Phenomena like reflection, refraction, interference, or diffraction can be treated in terms of wave properties of a continuous wave. On the other hand, in many problems such as those involving absorption and emission of radiation by atoms, the quantum or particle picture may be required.

It is instructive to calculate the number of photons in ordinary processes. Suppose a sodium vapor lamp emits one watt of radiation in the familiar yellow light of wavelength $5.9 \times 10^{-7}$ m. The energy of each quantum is given by Equation 8.9 and is $4 \times 10^{-19}$ joule. The number of photons emitted per second is consequently $2.5 \times 10^{18}$. In processes, such as reflection, that involve the behavior of a beam composed of such a large number of photons, it is not surprising that the radiation can be considered as continuous.

By 1924 the concept of quanta of energy had become sufficiently well established to prompt de Broglie to speculate that if electromagnetic radiation could be regarded as displaying either wave or particle characteristics, depending on the type of experiment, so might matter display a similar duality. Shortly after de Broglie made this proposal, experimental observation was made by Davisson and Germer and by G. P. Thomson of diffraction of an electron beam by a crystal. The concept was then placed on a firmer mathematical basis by Schroedinger in 1926, and it is the Schroedinger formulation that will be used in the following treatment.

According to de Broglie, the properties of a particle can be described by a wave that is defined to have a wavelength $\lambda$ given by

$$p = \frac{h}{\lambda} \tag{8.10}$$

where $p$ is the momentum of the particle. This proposal is obviously of immediate significance in cases where wavelike properties of electrons can be observed directly, as in electron diffraction. We now proceed, however, to make the assumption that the description of a particle in terms of a wave can be applied generally to all circumstances. The case of electron diffraction in which the diffraction angles can be calculated using the de Broglie wavelength alone has already been discussed in Section 2.7. We shall therefore proceed directly to the treatment of other problems in which the amplitude of the de Broglie wave is involved.

It is intended that the properties of the particle should be represented by those of the de Broglie wave, which we can assume to be represented generally by the wave function

$$\Psi = A \cos 2\pi\left(\frac{x}{\lambda} - \nu t\right) + B \sin 2\pi\left(\frac{x}{\lambda} - \nu t\right) \tag{8.11}$$

or, as it is more commonly written

$$\Psi = A \cos (\kappa x - \omega t) + B \sin (\kappa x - \omega t)$$

where $\kappa = 2\pi/\lambda$ and $\omega = 2\pi\nu$. The quantity $\Psi$ does not necessarily correspond to anything observable in the behavior of the particle. It is an invented concept and the way in which it is interpreted to give observable behavior will be given. $A$ and $B$ are constants, for the moment undetermined. $\kappa$ will be called the wave number of the wave (care must be taken to distinguish between $1/\lambda$, which is frequently termed the wave number, and the quantity $2\pi/\lambda$, which is, for convenience, being termed the wave number here) $2\pi/\lambda$ is sometimes called the propagation constant. The frequency of the wave is $\nu$ and $\omega$ is the angular frequency. We here assume that the de Broglie wave constitutes a quantum so that $\nu$ and $\omega$ are given in terms of the particle energy $E$ by

$$E = h\nu = \frac{h\omega}{2\pi} \quad \text{(sometimes written } \hbar\omega\text{)}$$

Now the wave number $\kappa$ and the angular frequency $\omega$ of the de Broglie wave must be related, because the momentum and energy of the particle are related. This is equivalent to a stipulation on the value of the velocity of the de Broglie wave. It actually emerges that the wave velocity of the de Broglie wave is not a particularly useful quantity but, on the other hand, it is instructive to calculate the group velocity. For any wave, the group velocity (the velocity at which amplitude modulation of the wave and hence information moves) is given by

$$v_g = \frac{d\nu}{d(1/\lambda)} = \frac{d\omega}{d\kappa} \tag{8.12}$$

Since (neglecting potential energy) the energy and momentum of a nonrelativistic free particle are related by

$$E = \frac{p^2}{2m}$$

we can write

$$\omega = \frac{2\pi E}{h} = \frac{\pi p^2}{mh}$$

Thus

$$\omega = \frac{h\kappa^2}{4\pi m}$$

and the group velocity is given by

$$v_g = \frac{h}{4\pi m} \cdot 2\kappa$$

$$= \frac{h\kappa}{2\pi m} = \frac{mv}{m} = v \tag{8.13}$$

Thus we have the fortunate result that the group velocity of the de Broglie waves, the velocity with which they transmit information, is the same as the velocity of the particle.

Only two problems remain. The first is the interpretation of the wave function $\Psi$ and the second is the application of the de Broglie wave principle to actual problems. The first problem is solved by a postulate formulated by Born that the square of the wave function $\Psi$ gives the probability density of observing particle properties. By this we mean that if we consider a small volume $dx\,dy\,dz$ in a region occupied by a particle,

$$|\Psi|^2\,dx\,dy\,dz = \text{probability of finding the particle}$$
$$\text{in the volume } dx\,dy\,dz \tag{8.14}$$

It remains only to find a way of evaluating the distribution of this function $\Psi$ within a region occupied by a particle so as to solve the problem of what the particle does in this particular environment. In other words, we should be able to find out what the particle, say an electron, does when it is placed in the field of a proton to form a hydrogen atom or in the field of an array of atoms in a solid. The quantity which specifies the environment of the electron is its potential energy $V$. Thus, since we want a solution for $\Psi$ that refers to a particular environment, we want a $\Psi$ which is specific to a certain value of $V$. In other words, we must construct an equation relating $\Psi$ and $V$. (Note that $V$ may be quite a complicated function of both space and time, e.g., the electron might be in an atom, subject to the static field of a nucleus and subject simultaneously to the time-dependent field of an approaching ion.)

Now we have an equation involving $V$ and the properties of the particle. It is

$$\text{Kinetic energy} + V = \text{total energy}$$

which we can write in terms of the momentum $p$

$$\frac{p^2}{2m} + V = E \tag{8.15}$$

or in terms of the wave constants

$$\frac{h^2\kappa^2}{8\pi^2 m} + V = \frac{h\omega}{2\pi} \tag{8.16}$$

If we can express $\kappa$ and $\omega$ in terms of $\Psi$ for substitution in Equation 8.16, we shall obtain the required relation between $\Psi$ and $V$. We can obtain values for $\kappa$ and $\omega$ in terms of $\Psi$ by differentiation of Equation 8.11

$$\frac{\partial \Psi}{\partial t} = \omega[A \sin(\kappa x - \omega t) - B \cos(\kappa x - \omega t)]$$

giving

$$\omega = \frac{1}{A \sin(\kappa x - \omega t) - B \cos(\kappa x - \omega t)} \cdot \frac{\partial \Psi}{\partial t}$$

Also

$$\frac{\partial \Psi}{\partial x} = \kappa[-A \sin(\kappa x - \omega t) + B \cos(\kappa x - \omega t)]$$

but we need $\kappa^2$, so try

$$\frac{\partial^2 \Psi}{\partial x^2} = \kappa^2[-A \cos(\kappa x - \omega t) - B \sin(\kappa x - \omega t)]$$

$$= -\kappa^2 \Psi$$

and

$$\kappa^2 = -\frac{1}{\Psi} \frac{\partial^2 \Psi}{\partial x^2}$$

We can now substitute for $\kappa^2$ and $\omega$ in Equation 8.16 to obtain

$$\frac{h^2}{8\pi^2 m}\left(-\frac{1}{\Psi} \frac{\partial^2 \Psi}{\partial x^2}\right) + V = \frac{h}{2\pi} \frac{1}{(A \sin(\kappa x - \omega t) - B \cos(\kappa x - \omega t)]} \frac{\partial \Psi}{\partial t}$$

This would be an equation wholly in $\Psi$ if we could express the function

$$A \sin(\kappa x - \omega t) - B \cos(\kappa x - \omega t)$$

in terms of $\Psi$. That is, can we write

$$A \sin(\kappa x - \omega t) - B \cos(\kappa x - \omega t)$$
$$= C[A \cos(\kappa x - \omega t) + B \sin(\kappa x - \omega t)]$$

where $C$ is some constant?

Clearly we can, if we have values for $A$, $B$, and $C$ as follows:

$$A = 1$$
$$B = i$$
$$C = -i$$

When we make these substitutions, the equation becomes

$$-\frac{h^2}{8\pi^2 m}\frac{\partial^2 \Psi}{\partial x^2} + V\Psi = \frac{ih}{2\pi}\frac{\partial \Psi}{\partial t} \tag{8.17}$$

This is the celebrated *time-dependent Schroedinger equation.* It has a solution which, in accordance with the foregoing values of $A$ and $B$, must be complex in form.

$$\Psi = \cos(\kappa x - \omega t) + i\sin(\kappa x - \omega t) \tag{8.18}$$

(We ignore, for the moment, the possibility of a constant multiplying the whole function $\Psi$.)

The principle of the wave mechanics method is therefore to specify the problem in terms of $V$, solve the Schroedinger equation using that particular value of $V$, obtain a solution for $\Psi$ as a function of space and time, and interpret that solution using Equation 8.14. Note that the type of solution given by this method differs from that found in classical mechanics. In classical mechanics the solution tells us that a particular particle will be at a particular point at a definite time and this deterministic solution has now been replaced by probabilities only. This is a characteristic feature of wave mechanics solutions and will be illustrated by specific examples later in this chapter.

If the environment of the electron happens to be static, so that $V$ is a function of space only, a simplification can be carried out. It will appear that the solution for $\Psi$ can be written in separable form, in terms of a function $\psi$ of $x$ only and a function $\varphi$ of $t$ only.

$$\Psi(x, t) = \psi(x)\varphi(t) \tag{8.19}$$

To show that this is so, substitute this form for $\Psi$ into Equation 8.17. We obtain

$$-\frac{h^2}{8\pi^2 m}\frac{\partial^2 \psi}{\partial x^2}\varphi + V\psi\varphi = \frac{ih}{2\pi}\psi\frac{\partial \varphi}{\partial t}$$

Divide by $\psi\,\varphi$

$$-\frac{1}{\psi}\left(\frac{h^2}{8\pi^2 m}\right)\frac{\partial^2 \psi}{\partial x^2} + V = \frac{ih}{2\pi}\frac{1}{\varphi}\frac{\partial \varphi}{\partial t} \tag{8.20}$$

Now the left-hand side is a function of $x$ only because of our assumption about $V$, and the right-hand side is a function of $t$ only. This situation is possible only if each side is equal to a constant $D$. Thus we can write

$$\frac{ih}{2\pi} \frac{1}{\varphi} \frac{\partial \varphi}{\partial t} = D$$

giving

$$\varphi = e^{-(2\pi i/h)Dt}$$

This is a simple oscillation in time, with frequency

$$\nu = \frac{D}{h}$$

But, because of the assumption represented by Equation 8.9, we have

$$\nu = \frac{E}{h}$$

whence

$$D = E$$

Thus we can write

$$\varphi(t) = e^{-(2\pi i/h)Et}$$

The left-hand side of Equation 8.20, which gives the space-dependent part of the wave function, must also be equal to $E$, so we have

$$-\frac{1}{\psi}\left(\frac{h^2}{8\pi^2 m}\right)\frac{\partial^2 \psi}{\partial x^2} + V = E$$

or

$$\frac{\partial^2 \psi}{\partial x^2} + \frac{8\pi^2 m}{h^2}(E - V)\psi = 0 \tag{8.21}$$

This is the *time-independent Schroedinger equation*, which, for a potential that does not vary with time, gives the space-dependent part of the wave function $\Psi$. The complete solution for such a static problem is then a space variation for the wave function $\psi$ multiplied by an oscillation in time at the frequency $E/h$, subject always to the interpretation that $\psi^2$ (or $|\Psi\Psi^*|$ where $\Psi^*$ is the complex conjugate of $\Psi$) at a point is a measure of the probability of observing a particle at that point. The whole solution can thus be regarded as a shimmering distribution of charge probability density of a certain shape. This nebulous solution contrasts with the sharp solutions of classical mechanics, whose definite predictions are replaced by probabilities.

As in classical oscillation theory, the type of solution will depend on the number of constraints enforced by the boundary conditions. Recall the case of a vibrating string where two constants (e.g., the coordinates of each fixed end) specify exactly the possible wavelengths of vibration. Similarly, it will be found that we can divide the solutions of the Schroedinger equation into two classes, *free* and *bound*. In the former the energy is unspecified and in the latter the energy (like the wavelengths of the vibrating violin string) is determined by the constants of the problem. Let us consider two simple problems illustrating, in turn, first a free solution and then a bound solution.

## 8.3   An Electron Meeting a Potential Discontinuity

Consider an electron free to move along the $x$ axis. Consider that in the regions on either side of $x = 0$ the electron would have a constant potential energy of $V_1 = 0$ for $x < 0$ (region 1) and $V = V_2$ for $x > 0$ (region 2). Let there be a discontinuous change of potential energy at $x = 0$. The diagram of potential energy with distance is given in Fig. 8.2. Let the total energy of the electron be $E$. This state of affairs is an idealization of circumstances encountered, for example, at the surface of a metal electrode, at the junction of two different metals, and in a number of other practical systems. The classical solution to this problem is simple if $E$ is larger than $V_2$, the particle can surmount the barrier to reach region 2. If $E$ is smaller than $V_2$, the particle must be reflected. As might be expected, the wave mechanics solution will show some other features.

The time-independent Schroedinger equation appropriate to region 1 can be written

$$\frac{\partial^2 \psi}{\partial x^2} + \frac{8\pi^2 m}{h^2} E\psi = 0$$

Let us refer to the constant $8\pi^2 mE/h^2$ by the symbol $\alpha^2$ to give

$$\frac{\partial^2 \psi}{\partial x^2} + \alpha^2 \psi = 0$$

This equation is a simple one to solve because it represents a simple harmonic variation of $\psi$ with $x$. Since the differential equation is insensitive to

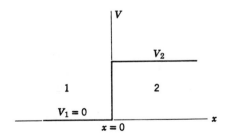

**Fig. 8.2**   A potential discontinuity.

the direction of propagation of such a wave, we must write the solution in the form

$$\psi = e^{i\alpha x} + Ae^{-\alpha x}$$

where the constant $A$ will have to be determined by the boundary conditions. The complete wave function is then

$$\Psi = (e^{i\alpha x} + Ae^{-i\alpha x})e^{-(2\pi i E/h)t}$$

In region 2 the Schroedinger equation can be written

$$\frac{\partial^2 \psi}{\partial x^2} + \frac{8\pi^2 m}{h^2}(E - V_2)\psi = 0$$

and, if we write $8\pi^2 m/h^2(E - V_2) = \beta^2$, we can write the solution

$$\Psi = Be^{i\beta x}e^{-(2\pi i E/h)t}$$

This solution is a traveling wave and the constant $B$ will be determined as $A$ was determined, by the boundary conditions. (There is no point in considering a term in $e^{-i\beta x}$ because there is no chance of encountering an electron approaching the barrier from the *opposite* side.) The boundary conditions from which $A$ and $B$ must be calculated can be shown to be:

$$\psi \text{ must be continuous at } x = 0$$
$$\partial\psi/\partial x \text{ must be continuous at } x = 0$$

Interesting features are apparent in the nature of the transmitted wave, that is, in the form of the solution in region 2. This form clearly depends on $\beta$ and so, in turn, on the relative values of $E$ and $V_2$. Let us consider two cases.

When $E > V_2$. In this case $\beta^2 > 0$, and the wave in region 2 is real. We thus have in region 1 a wave incident upon the boundary and a reflected wave. A wave is also transmitted through the boundary into region 2. This is illustrated in Fig. 8.3.

Each wave has an amplitude determined by the boundary conditions, leading to calculable probabilities for transmission and reflection. Note once again that this is in conflict with Newtonian mechanics which, if $E > V_2$, would predict uniform transmission across the potential step. That is, here the existence of the potential discontinuity automatically means there must be some reflected wave amplitude. This is to be expected in all wave transmission in discontinuous media, for example, at a discontinuity on a transmission line.

When $E < V_2$, $\beta^2 < 0$ and the solution has the form

$$\Psi = Be^{-\gamma x}e^{-(2\pi i E/h)t}$$

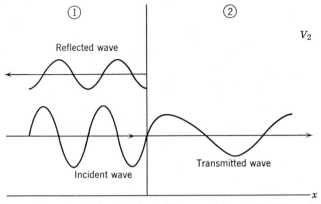

**Fig. 8.3** Electron waves incident on, reflected from, and transmitted through a potential discontinuity when $E > V_2$.

where

$$\gamma^2 = -\beta^2$$

Since the quantity $i$ in the exponent of the $x$ term has disappeared, this equation does *not* represent a traveling wave. It is an oscillation in *time* with an amplitude that depends on distance through the $e^{-\gamma x}$ term. It is, in fact, the so-called standing wave with an amplitude that decays exponentially from $x = 0$. The rate at which the amplitude decays depends on $\gamma$. The decay is steep if $E \ll V_2$ and less steep as $E$ is closer in value to $V_2$. This situation is illustrated in Fig. 8.4.

Let us extend this analysis to the interesting and important case where region 2 is followed by a third region, 3, where the potential $V_3$ is again zero. As we see in Fig. 8.5, we are dealing now with a potential barrier of width $d$.

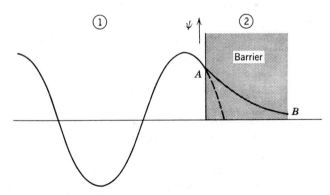

**Fig. 8.4** The stationary oscillation $AB$ behind a potential discontinuity when $E < V_2$.

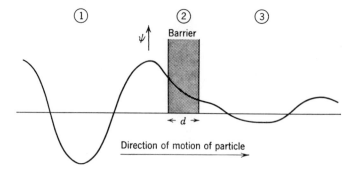

**Fig. 8.5**   Tunneling: the penetration of a particle wave through a barrier.

In region 3 the solution is

$$\Psi = Ce^{i\alpha x}e^{-(2\pi iE/h)t}$$

which is once again as in region 1 a traveling wave of maximum amplitude $C$. Continuity conditions across the second potential step determine $C$, and so $C$ depends on the value to which $Be^{-\gamma x}$ has decayed over the distance $d$.

Thus there exists a certain probability of transmission of the electron through the barrier, even though the energy of the electron $E$ is less than the potential step $V_2$. This is impossible in Newtonian mechanics. We can deduce the probability of transmission $T$, after taking all the continuity conditions into account, to be

$$T = \frac{\text{No. of electrons or particles penetrating the barrier}}{\text{No. of electrons or particles arriving at the barrier}}$$

$$= \frac{4}{4\cosh^2 \gamma d + \left(\dfrac{\gamma}{\alpha} - \dfrac{\alpha}{\gamma}\right)^2 \sinh^2 \gamma d}$$

This phenomenon by which an electron has a chance of appearing on the far side of a barrier with the same energy it had when incident on the barrier is called the *tunnel effect*. As will be seen later, it is fundamental to a discussion of electron behavior at intermetal contacts, electron emission from metal surfaces, and certain semiconductor devices.

We can visualize the magnitude of the tunnel effect by considering an electron of energy 5 eV incident on an insulating barrier of thickness 5 × $10^{-10}$ m between two metals when the barrier height is 6 eV. We find $\gamma$ to be 5 × $10^9$ and $T$ about 1.5 per cent.

Thus each electron stands a 1.5 per cent chance of penetrating the barrier, and so if $N$ electrons meet the barrier per second the number transmitted is

0.015$N$. The probability of transmission falls off very rapidly with barrier width $d$.

## 8.4   Electron in a Box

Let us now solve a bound electron problem. Consider an electron, free to move along the $x$ axis, as in Fig. 8.6, and confined between potential dis-continuities of infinite height at positions $x = 0$ and $x = a$.

The Schroedinger equation in the region $0 < x < a$ is

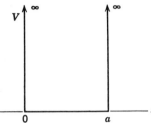

$$\frac{\partial^2 \psi}{\partial x^2} + \frac{8\pi^2 m}{h^2} E\psi = 0$$

The equation has to be solved subject to the conditions $\psi = 0$ at $x = 0$ and at $x = a$ be-cause the probability of observing an electron outside $0 < x < a$ is zero.

**Fig. 8.6**   A box defined by poten-tial discontinuities.

The space-dependent part of the solution is, once again, harmonic in form, and may be written

$$\psi = A \cos \alpha x + B \sin \alpha x$$

where, as before,

$$\alpha^2 = \frac{8\pi^2 m}{h^2} E$$

Inserting the boundary conditions into this trial solution we obtain

$$\text{at } x = 0, \qquad \psi = 0 = A$$
$$\text{and at } x = a, \qquad \psi = 0 = B \sin \alpha a$$

These conditions are met only if $\alpha a = n\pi$ where $n$ is integral, that is,

$$a\sqrt{8\pi^2 mE/h^2} = n\pi, \quad n = 1, 2, 3, \ldots$$

Thus solutions of the Schroedinger equation exist only if $E$ is confined to the magnitudes

$$E_n = \frac{n^2 h^2}{8ma^2}, \qquad n = 1, 2, 3, \ldots$$

We have thus demonstrated that the bound electron may only have certain energies or *energy levels*. The levels for this particular problem are shown in Fig. 8.7. This concept of energy levels in general plays a dominating role in the study of the electronic properties of matter, the essential feature being that the solution for $\Psi$ will exist only if the energy of the electron has one of a number of definite values. Note in passing that the mathematical solution is exactly analogous to the classical mechanics solution of the violin string problem, where only certain wavelengths are permitted.

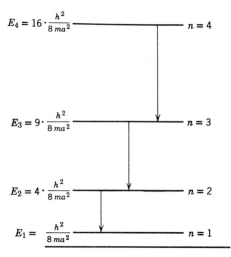

**Fig. 8.7**   The energy levels of a particle in a box.

Since the electron can exist only in certain energy levels, the energy that is emitted from or absorbed by the system can have only certain discrete values. This uniqueness of transition energy is one of the most striking features of atomic physics. It is also conveniently consistent with Planck's quantum postulate concerning radiation since we can imagine the quanta to correspond to the energy changes between levels.

The solution for $\psi$ is now completed by calculating the value of $B$. This is done by making the obvious assumption that the electron must be somewhere between $x = 0$ and $x = a$ so that

$$\int_0^a B^2 \sin^2 \alpha x \, dx = 1$$

which yields

$$B = \sqrt{2/a}$$

The final solution for $\psi$ is therefore

$$\psi = \sqrt{2/a} \sin \alpha x$$

Figure 8.8 illustrates the wave function $\psi$ and the probability $\psi^2$ as functions of $x$ for $n = 1, 2,$ and 3.

Remember that these graphs are to be interpreted as the spatial dependence of an oscillating function for which $\psi\psi^* \, dx \, dy \, dz$ gives the probability of finding the electron in $dx \, dy \, dz$.

The solution illustrated in Fig. 8.8 is in marked contrast to the classical picture of a particle trapped between perfectly reflecting walls, for instance,

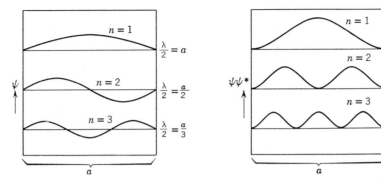

**Fig. 8.8** The wave functions and probability distributions for an electron in a box.

a billiard ball bouncing back and forth between the cushions. Here the probability of finding the ball is uniform along the path of the ball, since the velocity is constant between collisions with the cushion. The wave mechanical solution corresponding to the lowest energy state, that is, $n = 1$, departs most noticeably from the classical solution, being peaked midway between the reflecting walls. The wave functions corresponding to higher energy states tend to approximate more and more closely to the uniform classical solution. This is a common relation between wave mechanical and classical solutions.

## References

Cook, C. S., *Modern Atomic and Nuclear Physics*, Van Nostrand, Princeton, N. J., 1961.
Eisberg, R. M., *Fundamentals of Modern Physics*, John Wiley and Sons, New York, 1961.
Leighton, R. B., *Principles of Modern Physics*, McGraw-Hill Book Co., New York, 1959.
Merzbacher, E., *Quantum Mechanics*, John Wiley and Sons, New York, 1961.
Mott, N. F., and I. N. Sneddon, *Wave Mechanics and its Applications*, Clarendon Press, Oxford, 1948.
Sproull, R. L., *Modern Physics*, 2nd ed., John Wiley and Sons, New York, 1963.

## Exercises

1. An electron is accelerated through 500 volts. It enters a field of 0.5 webers m$^{-2}$ with an angle of 45° between its velocity vector and the field vector. What is the pitch and radius of the resulting helical path and what is the frequency of the rotational motion?

2. A sodium vapor lamp is sending out 1 watt of monochromatic radiation at a wavelength of 5893 A. Assuming radial symmetry calculate the number of photons falling on a surface of 1 square meter, set perpendicularly to the radiation at a distance of 1 m.

3. An X-ray photon has a wavelength of 1 A. Through what potential difference must an electron be accelerated in order that it can, on colliding with a target, generate such a photon? Assume that all the electron's energy is transferred to the photon.

4. Consider the electron discussed in Exercise 3. What would be its de Broglie wavelength after acceleration?

5. What is the wavelength associated with an $\alpha$ particle (He$^4$ nucleus) of kinetic energy 8 MeV?

6. An electron in a metal has an energy of 5 eV. What is its de Broglie wavelength?

7. An electron in a metal encounters a barrier layer of height 6 eV and thickness 5 A. If the electron's energy is 5 eV, what is the probability of tunneling through the barrier?

8. What is the Maxwell-Boltzmann probability of electrons going *over* the barrier (Exercise 7) by thermal excitation at room temperature?

9. Consider the one-dimensional case only and calculate the energy interval between the ground state and the first excited state for an electron contained within infinite potential barriers, (a) 5 A apart and (b) 1 cm apart. What would be the wavelength of the radiation produced by a transition between the first excited state and the ground state in each case?

10. A mass $M$ oscillates on a spring. $C$ is the spring constant and $x$ the displacement. Calculate the frequency of oscillation (classical). Compute the energies of the first two energy levels when (a) $M$ is the mass of the chlorine atom and $C \simeq 10^3$ joules m$^{-2}$, and (b) $M$ is a mass of $10^{-1}$ kg and $C \simeq 1$ joule m$^{-2}$. Substitute an expression for the potential energy in the time-independent Schroedinger equation and show that the first two wave functions for such an oscillator are

$$n = 0: \quad \psi_0 = 2^{1/4}\pi^{-1/4}b^{1/2}e^{-b^2x^2}$$

and

$$n = 1: \quad \psi_1 = 2^{5/4}\pi^{-1/4}b^{3/2}xe^{-b^2x^2}$$

where

$$b^2 = \frac{2\pi^2 M \sqrt{C}}{h} \nu$$

Sketch the wave functions.

11. Sketch $\psi$ for $n = 5$ for an electron confined between potential discontinuities of infinite height at $x = 0$ and $x = a$.

12. Show that a solution of Equation 8.17 for an electron traveling in a region of constant potential energy $V_0$ is given by

$$\psi = A \exp\left\{-2\pi i\left[\frac{E}{h}t - \frac{\sqrt{2m(E - V_0)}}{h}x\right]\right\}$$

$$+ B \exp\left\{-2\pi i\left[\frac{E}{h}t + \frac{\sqrt{2m(E - V_0)}}{h}x\right]\right\}$$

# 9

# Electronic Energy Levels in Atoms, Molecules, and Solids

The ultimate aim of this chapter is to describe the electronic energy levels available in a periodic atomic structure. We start by considering the levels in a single hydrogenlike atom. We go on to discuss the effects of bringing another atom into close proximity with the first. A periodic structure is then approximated by consideration of the levels in a line of equally spaced atoms. The chapter concludes with a qualitative description of the levels in some simple atomic structures.

## 9.1 The Wave Mechanics of the Hydrogen Atom

We suppose the existence of an infinitely massive, positively charged nucleus of charge $Ze$, where $Z$ is the atomic number and $e$ the charge on the electron. The single electron of hydrogen (when at a distance $r$ from the nucleus) moves with a potential energy $V(r)$ given by

$$V(r) = - \frac{Ze^2}{4\pi\epsilon_0 r} \quad \text{(mks units)} \tag{9.1}$$

These are the circumstances appropriate to a neutral hydrogen atom, a singly ionized helium atom, a doubly ionized lithium atom, and so on.

The time-independent Schroedinger equation can be written in three dimensions:

$$\left( \frac{\partial^2 \psi}{\partial x^2} + \frac{\partial^2 \psi}{\partial y^2} + \frac{\partial^2 \psi}{\partial z^2} \right) + \frac{8\pi^2 m}{h^2} (E - V)\psi = 0$$

or, more briefly,

$$\nabla^2 \psi + \frac{8\pi^2 m}{h^2} (E - V)\psi = 0 \tag{9.2}$$

**227**

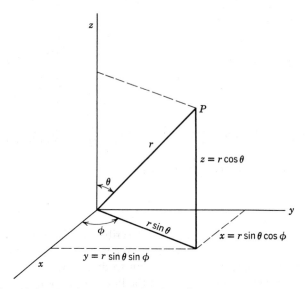

**Fig. 9.1**  The relation between rectangular Cartesian and spherical polar coordinates.

Substituting for the value of $V$ appropriate to the problem, from (9.1) we obtain

$$\nabla^2 \psi + \frac{8\pi^2 m}{h^2}\left(E + \frac{Ze^2}{4\pi\epsilon_0 r}\right)\psi = 0 \tag{9.3}$$

Equation 9.3 is not simple to solve, and we shall not attempt a complete solution. We shall discuss the circumstances under which a solution exists, for these will give us as much information as we need at the moment about the physical properties of the system.

Since $V$ is a simple function of $r$, Equation 9.3 is first expressed in polar coordinates, which are illustrated in Fig. 9.1, using the value for the operator $\nabla^2$ in spherical polar coordinates, namely,

$$\nabla^2 \equiv \frac{1}{r^2}\frac{\partial}{\partial r}\left(r^2 \frac{\partial}{\partial r}\right) + \frac{1}{r^2 \sin\theta}\frac{\partial}{\partial \theta}\left(\sin\theta \frac{\partial}{\partial \theta}\right) + \frac{1}{r^2 \sin^2\theta}\frac{\partial^2}{\partial \phi^2}$$

This gives

$$\frac{1}{r^2}\frac{\partial}{\partial r}\left(r^2 \frac{\partial \psi}{\partial r}\right) + \frac{1}{r^2 \sin\theta}\frac{\partial}{\partial \theta}\left(\sin\theta \frac{\partial \psi}{\partial \theta}\right)$$

$$+ \frac{1}{r^2 \sin^2\theta}\frac{\partial^2 \psi}{\partial \phi^2} + \frac{8\pi^2 m}{h^2}\left(E + \frac{Ze^2}{4\pi\epsilon_0 r}\right)\psi = 0 \tag{9.4}$$

We now make the assumption that the parts of the solution corresponding to the three coordinates $r$, $\theta$, and $\phi$ are independent, so that the solution of the equation can be written in the form

$$\psi = R(r)\Theta(\theta)\Phi(\phi) \qquad (9.5)$$

where $R$ is a function of $r$ alone, $\Theta$ of $\theta$ alone, and $\Phi$ of $\phi$ alone.

If we insert this form for $\psi$ in Equation 9.4 and divide through by $R\Theta\Phi$, the equation becomes

$$\left[\frac{1}{R}\frac{1}{r^2}\frac{\partial}{\partial r}\left(r^2\frac{dR}{dr}\right) + \frac{8\pi^2 m}{h^2}\left(E + \frac{Ze^2}{4\pi\epsilon_0 r}\right)\right]$$

$$+ \frac{1}{r^2}\left[\frac{1}{\Theta}\frac{1}{\sin\theta}\frac{\partial}{\partial\theta}\left(\sin\theta\frac{d\Theta}{d\theta}\right)\right] + \frac{1}{r^2\sin^2\theta}\left(\frac{1}{\Phi}\frac{d^2\Phi}{d\phi^2}\right) = 0 \quad (9.6)$$

The procedure has affected a convenient separation of the variables $R$, $\Theta$, and $\Phi$, and we can obtain a solution of (9.6) term by term. Consider the last term.

$$\frac{1}{\Phi}\frac{d^2\Phi}{d\phi^2}$$

It is, by definition, a function of $\phi$ only, and yet the equation shows that it is equal to a function of $r$ and $\theta$ only. To avoid this contradiction it must therefore be a function of none of $r$, $\theta$, or $\phi$, and so must be a constant. Let us call this constant $-m_l^2$.

Thus we can write

$$\frac{1}{\Phi}\frac{d^2\Phi}{d\phi^2} = -m_l^2$$

or

$$\frac{d^2\Phi}{d\phi^2} + m_l^2\Phi = 0$$

which has the solution

$$\Phi = \cos m_l\phi$$

This means that the spatial dependence of the wave function must have a wavelike form as it goes around the $\phi$ direction. For $\Phi$ to be unique, it should repeat for values of $\phi$ increasing by $2\pi$. Thus $m_l$ must be integral or

$$m_l = 0, \pm 1, \pm 2, \pm 3, \ldots \qquad (9.7)$$

The parameter $m_l$ is one of the so-called quantum numbers describing the hydrogen atom.

Equation 9.6 can now be rewritten

$$\left[\frac{1}{R}\frac{1}{r^2}\frac{\partial}{\partial r}\left(r^2\frac{dR}{dr}\right) + \frac{8\pi^2 m}{h^2}\left(E + \frac{2e^2}{4\pi\epsilon_0 r}\right)\right]$$

$$+ \frac{1}{r^2}\left[\frac{1}{\Theta}\frac{1}{\sin\theta}\frac{\partial}{\partial\theta}\left(\sin\theta\frac{d\Theta}{d\theta}\right) - \frac{m_l^2}{\sin^2\theta}\right] = 0 \quad (9.8)$$

and we have reduced the equation to one of two variables.

By the argument just used, the last term, being simultaneously a function of $r$ only and of $\theta$ only, must be a constant. Let us write this constant $-l(l+1)$. This constant gives a differential equation for $\Theta$ called the associated Legendre equation, whose solutions are functions called associated Legendre polynomials; these functions give the shape of the $\Theta$ function in much the same way as Bessel functions give the shape of the solution for a vibrating membrane such as a drum. The associated Legendre polynomials exist only if $l$ is integral and satisfies the condition

$$|m_l| \leqslant l$$

It is now possible to obtain the final part of the solution for $R$. It is convenient to change the variables, thus reducing the algebraic complexity of the $R$ function. Remembering that we wrote $-l(l+1)$ for the $\Theta$ function, if we also write

$$\frac{8\pi^2 mE}{h^2} = -a^2 \qquad b = \frac{\pi m Z e^2}{\epsilon_0 h^2 a}$$

$$x = ar \qquad X = rR,$$

then it is easy to verify that Equation 9.7 reduces to

$$\frac{d^2 X^2}{dx^2} + \left[ -1 - \frac{l(l+1)}{x^2} + \frac{2b}{x} \right] X = 0 \tag{9.9}$$

Without obtaining the complete solution to this equation, we can, by making some plausible assumptions about the nature of the solution, obtain several conditions with which the constants must comply. For instance, for very small values of $x$, Equation 9.9 implies a simple power law for $X$, that is,

$$X \propto x^n$$

Also, for very large $x$,

$$X \propto e^{-x}$$

Let us therefore assume that the solution of (9.9) for $X$ can be written in the form

$$X = A x^n e^{-x}$$

To see what conditions must be satisfied to permit this to be a solution, we substitute it back into Equation 9.9 and obtain

$$\left\{ \frac{1}{x^2} [n(n-1) - l(l+1)] + \frac{2}{x} (b-n) \right\} A x^n e^{-x} = 0 \tag{9.10}$$

Now if $A \neq 0$, Equation 9.10 will be satisfied for all values of $x$ only if the coefficients of $1/x^2$ and $1/x$ are separately zero. This gives

$$n = l + 1$$

and

$$b = n$$

It actually turns out that the other solutions are permitted, giving a final relationship between $n$ and $l$ of

$$l \leqslant n - 1 \qquad \text{where} \qquad n = 1, 2, 3, \ldots \tag{9.11}$$

The second condition, that is, $b = n$, can be rewritten

$$n = \frac{\pi Z e^2}{\epsilon_0 h^2 a}$$

or

$$E = - \frac{m e^4 Z^2}{8 \epsilon_0^2 h^2} \frac{1}{n^2} \tag{9.12}$$

The solution for $X$ in Equation 9.9 will exist only if this condition is met, and thus the energy of the atom is restricted to those values resulting from integral values of $n$. The number $n$ is known as the principal quantum number.

The atom will normally reside in the state with $n = 1$. The states of higher $n$ will be occupied only after the atom has been excited by the addition of energy from the outside. This excited state will decay after a very short time ($\sim 10^{-8}$ sec) with the emission of a quantum or series of quanta of electromagnetic energy until the atom is once again the the ground state.

The energy levels for the hydrogen atom are illustrated in Fig. 9.2. The actual energy values for the different levels are obtained from Equation 9.12. Level $E_1$ has the value 13.6 eV, which is thus the energy that would have to be supplied to remove the electron from a hydrogen atom. Such an atom minus its valence electron is called an *ion*, and the necessary energy is the *ionization* energy. It is obvious that $E_2$ (for $n = 2$) has a value one-fourth of the value of $E_1$. In a transition between $E_2$ and $E_1$, 10.2 eV of energy are emitted as a photon. The frequency of the photon is given by Equation 8.9, the value of $\nu$ being $9.7 \times 10^{14}$ sec$^{-1}$. This value corresponds to a wavelength of $3.1 \times 10^{-7}$ m, which places the spectrum line well into the ultraviolet. The reader may readily verify that the only transitions giving wavelengths in the visible region are those between the levels $n = 3$ and $n = 2$, $n = 4$ and $n = 2$, $n = 5$ and $n = 2$.

We must bear in mind at this point that we have not obtained a complete solution for the $R$ function, but only the conditions under which such a complete solution may exist. It is clear, however, that the $R$ function is the one specifying the size of the electron distribution just as the $\Theta$ function specifies its shape. The form of the $R$ functions are illustrated in Fig. 9.3 for $n = 1$ and $n = 2$.

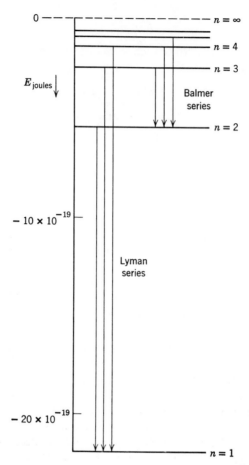

**Fig. 9.2**   The energy levels of atomic hydrogen.

It will be recalled that the probability of finding an electron at a particular position is proportional to $|\psi|^2$. To find the probability of an electron being a distance $r$ from the nucleus, the appropriate volume element replacing the familiar $dx\, dy\, dz$ volume element is a spherical shell of radius $r$ and thickness $dr$ that is of volume $4\pi r^2\, dr$, and so the charge distribution follows the function $|\psi|^2\, r^2$. This function is plotted as a function of $r$ in Fig. 9.4. The atom is thus seen to possess a kind of shell structure of a size that increases with the degree of excitation. The shape of the atom is spherically uniform only when $l = 0$. When $l \neq 0$ the $\Theta$ function multiplies the foregoing $R$ variations to give shape to the atom. The form of the $|\psi|^2$ function for various values of $n$, $l$, and $m$, is shown in Fig. 9.5.

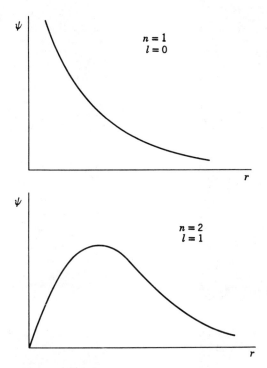

**Fig. 9.3** The radial part of the wave function for the ground state and one excited state of atomic hydrogen.

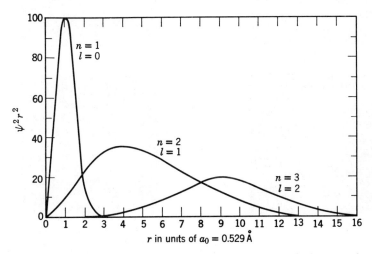

**Fig. 9.4** The probability density of the ground state and two excited states of atomic hydrogen showing the shell structure.

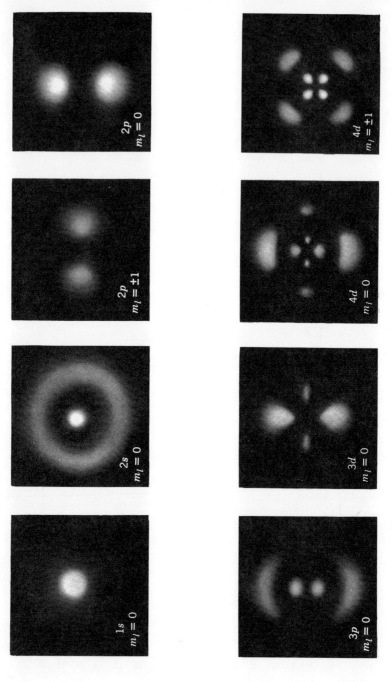

**Fig. 9.5** Diagrams of one plane of the electron probability density for various excited states of the hydrogen atom.

The actual value for the size of the charge distribution cannot easily be obtained from the preceding treatment. The calculation shows that the maximum charge distribution is at a distance of $0.53 \times 10^{-10}$ m from the nucleus for the ground state $n = 1, l = 0$, and at a distance of $2.1 \times 10^{-10}$ m for the excited state $n = 2, l = 1$. These are actually the same values given by an elementary treatment of the hydrogen problem first proposed by Bohr. The Bohr model, however, implies that the distribution is sharp, which is in contrast to the wave mechanical picture and to the implications of actual experimental findings.

## 9.2   The Significance of the Quantum Numbers *n*, *l*, and *m$_l$*

### The Quantum Number *n*

As we have just seen, the role of $n$ is simply to determine the over-all energy of the state and, in general terms, the radius of the electron distribution. As stated earlier, the hydrogen atom will normally exist in the ground state with $n = 1$ and the upper states will be occupied only after energy has been absorbed by the atom, and then only temporarily.

### The Quantum Number *l*

The significance of $l$ is found in the second term in Equation 9.9. Obviously, the quantity $l(l + 1)/x^2$ must be dimensionless. This implies that we can write

$$l(l + 1) = cx^2$$

where $c$ is a dimensionless constant. If we draw a crude analogy with the classical model of a point mass $m$ circulating around the nucleus with velocity $v$, the energy can be written

$$E = \tfrac{1}{2}mv^2$$

so that

$$l(l + 1) = c\,\frac{8\pi^2 m r^2}{h^2}\,\frac{1}{\frac{1}{2}mv^2} \quad \left(\text{from } x = ar: \quad \frac{8\pi^2 mE}{h^2} = -a^2\right)$$

or

$$l(l + 1)\,\frac{h^2}{4\pi^2} = c(mvr)^2 = cL^2$$

The quantity in parenthesis on the right-hand side is the angular momentum of the electron charge distribution. Although we have only indicated that there is a connection, through a simple number, between the angular momentum $L$ and the quantity $\sqrt{l(l+1)}(h/2\pi)$, a more rigorous treatment shows them to be actually equal.

This equality, then, is the significance of the quantum number $l$. Associated as it is with the shape of the electron charge distribution, $l$ is a measure of the angular momentum of the atom. It emerges that the angular momentum of the atomic state can often be a more important factor in the atom's behavior than the over-all energy state governed by $n$. Therefore it is common to specify the atomic state by a conventional symbol which is related to the $l$ value. States with $l = 0$ are designated *s-states*; with $l = 1$, *p-states*; with $l = 2$, *d-states*; with $l = 3$, *f-states*. A 3p-state, for example, is one in which $n = 3$ and $l = 1$.

### The Quantum Number $m_l$

It can be shown, although not by elementary means, that the quantity $m_l(h/2\pi)$ gives the value of the component of the orbital angular momentum, along the $z$ axis. This means that **L** may only be aligned at certain angles to the $z$ axis so that the $z$ component is an integral number times $h/2\pi$. There are, in fact, $2l + 1$ possible orientations of **L** with respect to the $z$ axis. Figure 9.6 illustrates such **L** orientations for $m_l$ values of up to $\pm 4$. The number of possible orientations is termed the *multiplicity* of the state.

It will be recalled that the solution in which $m_l$ appeared was associated with the $\phi$ coordinate, which describes the distribution around the $z$ axis. As long as the $z$ axis remains undefined, the states of differing $m_l$ are indistinguishable. If, however, such a direction is imposed on the atom from the outside in a manner that modifies the atomic behavior, the quantum number $m_l$ becomes significant. The normal method of doing this is to apply a magnetic field. For this reason $m_l$ is often called the *magnetic quantum*

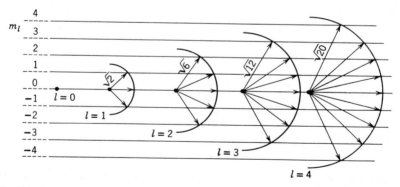

**Fig. 9.6** Space quantization: the possible orientations of the angular momentum vector with respect to an external field direction.

*number* and gives the possible orientations of the atomic angular momentum vector with respect to an external magnetic field. As we have seen, only certain orientations are allowed, so that there is, in fact, a "space quantization."

## 9.3 Intrinsic Spin

We must now consider a further quantum property of the atom which cannot be predicted by elementary wave mechanical theory. There are many instances where the theory we have considered so far predicts a single energy level, whereas actual observation shows that the level must be double. The familiar yellow double line in the spectrum of sodium is the consequence of transitions from such a double level. It was therefore found necessary to postulate the existence of another quantum number. This quantum number was attributed by Uhlenbeck and Goudsmit in 1925 to *spin* of the electron about its own axis. If we suppose the spin to be quantized with a total spin quantum number $s$, the value of $s$ may be obtained from the number of possible orientations of the spin angular momentum vector with respect to some fixed direction in the atom. This multiplicity must have value $2s + 1$ analogous to the $2l + 1$ multiplicity of the orbital angular momentum states. The multiplicity is observed to be 2, which gives

$$s = \tfrac{1}{2}$$

We therefore say that the electron has an intrinsic spin angular momentum of a value $L_s$ where

$$L_s = \sqrt{s(s + 1)}\,\frac{h}{2\pi}$$

In analogy with the definition of quantum number $m_l$, the $z$ component of spin angular momentum is $m_s(h/2\pi)$, where the quantum number $m_s = \pm\tfrac{1}{2}$ the two signs representing the two possible orientations with respect to some axis in the atom.

Subsequent to the suggestion of Uhlenbeck and Goudsmit, it was shown by Dirac in his theory of relativistic wave mechanics that the existence of electron spin could be predicted as a fundamental intrinsic property of the electron.

## 9.4 Summary of the Quantum Number Characteristics

We can summarize the predictions of the wave mechanical treatment of the hydrogen atom as a set of energy levels governed by the quantum numbers $n$, $l$, $m_l$, and $s$ with the following properties:

1. $n$ determines the state of excitation of the atom and can have any integral value. The ground state of the hydrogen atom has $n = 1$, and

$n = \infty$ corresponds to $E = 0$ and complete removal of the electron from the atom, that is, ionization.

2. $l$ determines the value of the orbital angular momentum in accordance with

$$L = \sqrt{l(l + 1)}\,\frac{h}{2\pi}$$

where $l$ can take any integral value between 0 and $n - 1$.

3. $m_l$ determines the possible orientations of the angular momentum with respect to an external magnetic field. Only orientations that make the component of the angular momentum along the field direction equal to $m_l(h/2\pi)$, where $m_l$ takes all integral values between $l$ and $-l$, are permitted.

4. $s$ gives the spin state of the electron. The value of $s$ is $\frac{1}{2}$, and the orientation of the spin angular momentum may be in one or other of two directions with respect to any significant reference direction such as an external magnetic field or the orbital angular momentum vector **L**.

Note that the energy of the atomic state on our simple wave mechanical model of the atom is determined only by $n$. This is a consequence of our assuming a strict coulomb potential between the nucleus and the electron. When this assumption breaks down either through the existence of electron spin, because of the presence of more than one electron in the atom or through the presence of an external magnetic or electric field, the energy levels are split according to the particular $l$, $m_l$, and $m_s$ values.

At this stage we have completed the description of the behavior of a single electron in an isolated atom. We must eventually extend the treatment to cover multielectron atoms, but that will be left until Chapter 10. In the meantime we shall continue the discussion of the properties of a single electron in situations which lead toward the solid state.

## 9.5    The Two Square Well Problem

Although we could start immediately with a discussion of the general solid, it is preferable to start with the simplest structure which shows the beginning of solid properties. This should enable the reader to have a clearer physical picture of the situation when we progress to the general case. The simplest structure to serve as an introduction to solids is the hydrogen ion molecule, which consists of one electron moving in the field of two adjacent protons.

Before considering the hydrogen ion molecule, however, it is instructive to investigate the solution of the Schroedinger equation for the simpler conditions in which an electron can occupy two one-dimensional square well

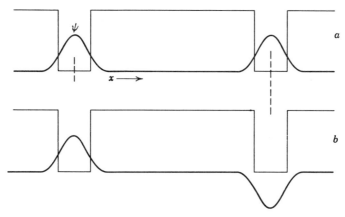

**Fig. 9.7** Symmetric and antisymmetric wave functions for the two square well problem. (After Sproull)

potentials, as shown in Fig. 9.7a. Since these are wells of finite depth, we do not have the strict harmonic functions found in Section 8.8 and we can represent the wave functions as shown in Fig. 9.7a. The only difference between the solutions for the infinitely deep well and for the well of finite depth which is significant for our purpose is that for the finite well the solutions do not go to zero at the boundaries of the well but extend for a distance on either side. There will be one part of the solution in each well, and, if the two wells are far enough apart, there is effectively no interaction between the two parts of the wave function. This is because each part of the solution has become sufficiently close to zero in the region between the wells that there is no problem of matching the two parts of the solution.

The significant feature of the two-well problem is that another solution of the Schroedinger equation is possible. This solution is shown in Fig. 9.7b, where the $\psi$ in one well is 180° out of phase with respect to the $\psi$ in the other well. Figure 9.7a shows the *symmetric* wave function and Fig. 9.7b the *antisymmetric*. There exists practically no difference in energy between the two $\psi$ configurations when the wells are far apart and essentially decoupled.

Suppose now that the distance between the wells decreases. Interaction between the two parts of the wave function becomes important, and difference in energy between the symmetric and antisymmetric states appear. The complete calculation of the energies for the symmetric and antisymmetric cases as a function of the distance between the wells is difficult, but it is possible to get some insight into the nature of the answer by considering the limiting case when the two wells come into contact. This condition is illustrated in Fig. 9.8a, in which it is seen that we are now dealing with one

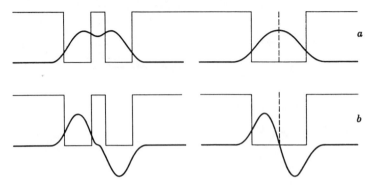

**Fig. 9.8** The symmetric and antisymmetric wave functions for the case in which the two wells are close and also for the limiting case. (After Sproull)

well twice as wide as the earlier ones. Figure 9.8a shows the symmetric wave function for the limiting case and Fig. 9.8b the antisymmetric wave function. It is now recognized that Fig. 9.8a illustrates a *ground state* wave function ($n = 1$) and Fig. 9.8b a *first excited* state wave function ($n = 2$) for the new well. In Section 8.4 we showed that for an infinitely deep well the energy was proportional to $n^2/(\text{width})^2$, and thus the ground state for a well of width $2a$ has an energy of only one quarter that for the ground state of width $a$. On the other hand, the first excited state for a well of width $2a$ has an energy equal to that of the ground state for a well of width $a$.

Although these figures are not exactly correct for a well of finite depth, it is now clear that two possibilities exist for the energy, depending on

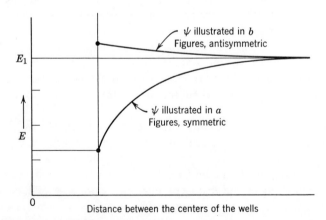

**Fig. 9.9** The variation of energy with distance apart of the wells for the symmetric and antisymmetric wave functions. (After Sproull)

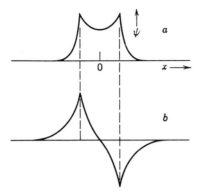

**Fig. 9.10** Symmetric and antisymmetric wave functions for the hydrogen molecule ion. (After Sproull)

whether the wave function is symmetric or antisymmetric. The energy versus distance plot is shown in Fig. 9.9 for the two cases.

## 9.6 The Hydrogen Ion Molecule

The foregoing argument can be repeated for an inverse square law of force in order to describe the conditions experienced by the electron in a hydrogen ion molecule. Here we can consider the wave functions appropriate to $s$ states and, as before, a distinction between symmetric and antisymmetric wave functions is possible, as shown in Fig. 9.10. The variation of state energy with distance apart of the two nuclei of the molecule is quite similar to the plot of Fig. 9.9 and is given in Fig. 9.11. In this case, however, we must

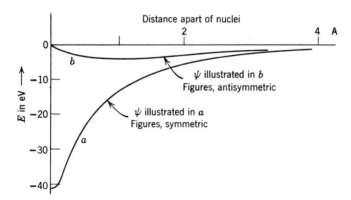

**Fig. 9.11** The variation of energy with distance between nuclei for the symmetric and antisymmetric wave functions for the hydrogen molecule ion. (After Sproull)

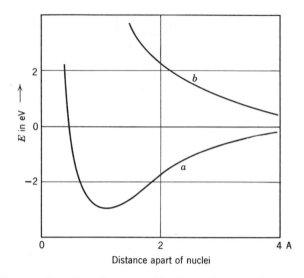

**Fig. 9.12**   The variation of total energy with distance between the two nuclei for the hydrogen molecule ion, *a* symmetric, *b* antisymmetric. (After Sproull)

add the energy of repulsion of the two protons in order to obtain the total energy of the system. This repulsion is proportional to the inverse square of the distance apart. Figure 9.12 is a graph showing the total energy with distance. Since an energy minimum gives stable equilibrium, the hydrogen molecule is stable only when the wave function for the electron is symmetric. The position of the minimum should give the equilibrium distance between the two protons and approximately does so.

## 9.7   The Case of More Than Two Nuclei

We can construct a picture of electron behavior in the solid state by extending the preceding argument to three or more nuclei. We find that the effect is to increase the number of wave functions available. The ground state wave function possibilities are illustrated in Fig. 9.13 for three nuclei, and Fig. 9.14 shows the corresponding energy versus distance plots.

It can thus be seen that if we have an electron moving in the field of $N$ nuclei, we shall have a subdivision of the ground state into $N$ separate levels. In pieces of solid matter of everyday experience, $N$ is very large; for instance, even a milligram of copper contains approximately $10^{19}$ atoms. Under these circumstances the subdivision of the energy range into $10^{19}$ separate levels becomes meaningless, and we talk instead of a *band* of allowed energies.

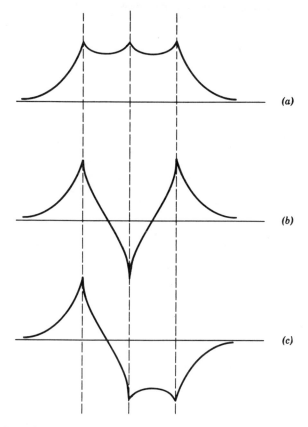

**Fig. 9.13**  Symmetric and antisymmetric wave functions for three nuclei.

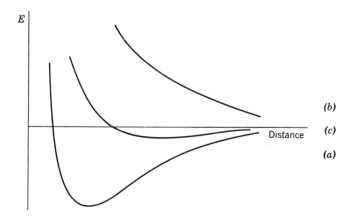

**Fig. 9.14**  The variation of total energy with distance apart of the nuclei for three nuclei.

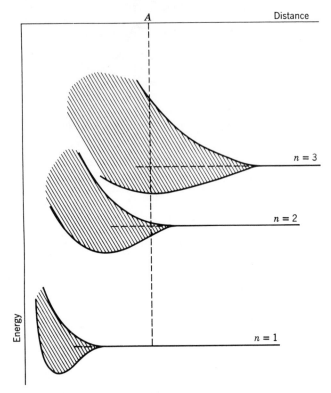

**Fig. 9.15**  The energy level diagram for solid hydrogen as a function of distance between the nuclei.

It is clear that the wave functions that correspond to excited states with $n = 2, 3$, etc., and which have a wider distribution in space than the ground state will be affected first by decreasing the distance between nuclei. The energy associated with the states of $n = 1, 2$, and 3 is plotted as a function of distance apart of the nuclei in Fig. 9.15. At any particular distance apart of the nuclei (e.g., at $A$) the inner levels are virtually unaffected by the presence of other nuclei, and the upper levels become bands, the width of which increases with energy.

In molecules or solids of multielectron atoms the number of filled levels depends on the number of electrons in a way that is discussed later. Thus there are electrons in both sharp levels and bands. Transitions between lower levels give rise to line spectra (as in X-ray spectra), whereas transitions between higher levels give band spectra (as in thermal radiation). The equilibrium spacing of the atoms in the molecule or solid is again determined by the minimizing of the whole energy of the nuclei and electron shells.

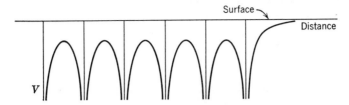

**Fig. 9.16** The potential energy of an electron in a periodic lattice.

## 9.8 The Motion of an Electron in a Periodic Lattice

As we saw in Chapter 1, atoms are usually arranged in solids in a periodic array. We will now study in greater detail the motion of an electron in the field arising from an array of nuclei. By an extension of the H atom treatment to a single electron in the field of an array of nuclei, we have shown that the sharp energy levels peculiar to isolated atoms are spread out into bands of available energy.

In view of the very great importance of this topic, we shall now extend the qualitative discussion of Section 9.7 and consider in greater detail the motion of an electron in the field of an array of nuclei. The actual potential energy of an electron in a linear array of positive nuclei must be as shown in Fig. 9.16. This array is a very complicated potential distribution, and for the sake of simplicity we must revert to the simple case in which we treat the nucleus as a rectangular potential well of finite depth. Initially we will discuss the one-dimensional case illustrated in Fig. 9.17. In this model, constructed by Kronig and Penny, the spacing is $a + b$, and the depth of the wells is greater than the energy of the electron.

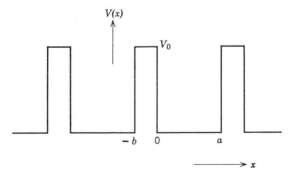

**Fig. 9.17** The potential distribution in a one-dimensional square well lattice.

The time-independent Schroedinger equation takes the form for the different regions

$$0 < x < a \qquad \frac{\partial^2 \psi}{\partial x^2} + \frac{8\pi^2 m}{h^2} E\psi = 0 \tag{9.13}$$

$$-b < x < 0 \qquad \frac{\partial^2 \psi}{\partial x^2} + \frac{8\pi^2 m}{h^2} (E - V_0)\psi = 0 \tag{9.14}$$

Let us write

$$\alpha^2 = \frac{8\pi^2 m}{h^2} E, \quad \text{and} \quad \beta^2 = \frac{8\pi^2 m}{h^2} (V_0 - E)$$

We have to find a solution that will be appropriate for both of these regions and that will satisfy boundary conditions at the potential barriers. The form chosen for the solution follows from a theorem by Bloch dealing with wave functions of particles moving in a periodic potential. Bloch showed that the solution must be periodic with the period of the lattice. The electron is therefore described by a wave with a certain wave number (momentum) $\kappa$ traveling through the crystal with an amplitude that is not constant but whose modulation is periodic. We can write this type of solution

$$\Psi = e^{i\kappa x}u(x) \tag{9.15}$$

where the first part represents the oscillating part of the wave and $u(x)$ represents the amplitude modulation. We now substitute the solution (9.15) in both (9.13) and (9.14). Hence, for

$$0 < x < a; \qquad \frac{d^2 u}{dx^2} + 2i\kappa \frac{du}{dx} - (\kappa^2 - \alpha^2)u = 0 \tag{9.16}$$

and

$$-b < x < 0; \qquad \frac{d^2 u}{dx^2} + 2i\kappa \frac{du}{dx} - (\kappa^2 + \beta^2)u = 0 \tag{9.17}$$

As may be readily verified by substitution, solutions for Equations 9.16 and 9.17 may be written

$$0 < x < a; \qquad u = Ae^{(-i\kappa+i\alpha)x} + Be^{(-i\kappa-i\alpha)x} \tag{9.18}$$

$$-b < x < 0; \qquad u = Ce^{(-i\kappa+\beta)x} + De^{(-i\kappa-\beta)x} \tag{9.19}$$

Equations 9.18 and 9.19 both represent two waves, one traveling in the positive $x$-direction and the other in the negative $x$-direction. All four waves are subject to the boundary conditions that both $\psi$ and $d\psi/dx$, that is, $u$ and $\partial u/\partial x$ must be continuous at $x = 0$ and $x = a$ and also that $u$ must be periodic in distance $a + b$.

From the boundary conditions, we can now obtain four equations that constitute the restrictions on the values of $A$, $B$, $C$, and $D$ so that Equations 9.13 and 9.14 will be solutions of the Schroedinger equation.

These four restriction equations, which will be more our concern than the actual solutions, are written accompanying the associated condition as follows:

For continuity of $u$ at $x = 0$,     $A + B = C + D$.

For continuity of $\partial u/\partial x$ at $x = 0$,

$$A(-i\kappa + i\alpha) + B(-i\kappa - i\alpha) = C(-i\kappa + \beta) + D(-i\kappa - \beta)$$

For periodicity of $u$,

$$Ae^{(-i\kappa+i\alpha)a} + Be^{(-i\kappa-i\alpha)a} = Ce^{(-i\kappa+\beta)(-b)} + De^{(-i\kappa-\beta)(-b)}$$

For periodicity of $\partial u/\partial x$,

$$A(-i\kappa + i\alpha)e^{(-i\kappa+i\alpha)a} + B(-i\kappa - i\alpha)e^{(-i\kappa-i\alpha)a}$$
$$= C(-i\kappa + \beta)e^{(-i\kappa+\beta)(-b)} + D(-i\kappa - \beta)e^{(-i\kappa-\beta)(-b)}$$

If these four condition equations are to be consistent, the determinant of the coefficients of $A$, $B$, $C$, and $D$ must be zero. This can be verified to give

$$\frac{\beta^2 - \alpha^2}{2\alpha\beta} \sinh \beta b \sin \alpha a + \cosh \beta b \cos \alpha a = \cos \kappa(a + b) \qquad (9.20)$$

Equation 9.20 is quite complicated, but a simplification is possible. Let us consider the possibility that $b$ should diminish while at the same time $V_0$ increases in such a way that the product $V_0 b$ remains finite. The model is thereby modified to one of a series of wells separated by infinitely thin potential barriers of which the $\lim_{\substack{V_0 \to \infty \\ b \to 0}} (V_0 b)$ represents the barrier strength. With this limit, Equation 9.20 becomes

$$\frac{1}{2\alpha} \frac{8\pi^2 m(V_0 b)}{h^2} \sin \alpha a + \cos \alpha a = \cos \kappa a \qquad (9.21)$$

and if we define $P$ by the equation

$$P = \frac{4\pi^2 ma(V_0 b)}{h^2}$$

then (9.21) reduces to

$$P \frac{\sin \alpha a}{\alpha a} + \cos \alpha a = \cos \kappa a \qquad (9.22)$$

The reader should remember that this equation is a condition of the existence of a solution for the electron wave function. It gives the values

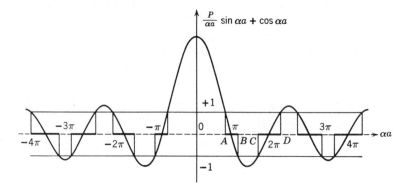

**Fig. 9.18** The function $P\dfrac{\sin \alpha a}{\alpha a} + \cos \alpha a$ plotted to show the region in which its value falls between $\pm 1$.

of $\alpha$ [the only variable in (9.22)] that permit a solution of the Schroedinger equation to exist. Now $\alpha$ is a function of the electron energy $E$, and thus once again the wave-mechanical solution restricts the energy to certain permitted values. The nature of the energy restriction depends on the value of $P$.

In equation 9.22 the left-hand side (on account of the right-hand side) can only have values between $\pm 1$. Figure 9.18 shows $P(\sin \alpha a/\alpha a) + \cos \alpha a$ plotted against $\alpha a$ with $P$ given the value $3\pi/2$. The allowed ranges of $\alpha a$ which permit a wave-mechanical solution to exist are marked by heavy lines, for example, between $A$ and $B$, $C$ and $D$. Thus, as has been suggested before, the motion of electrons in a periodic lattice is characterized by bands of allowed energy, with the band width increasing with the energy.

Let us discuss for a moment the effect of varying $P$. It will be remembered that $P$ is a measure of the potential barrier strength. If $P$ is large, the barriers are strong, and the electron, in the limit of $P$ infinitely large, can be considered to be confined to a single well. If, on the other hand, $P$ is small, the barrier strength is small, and the electron can, in the limit of $P$ equal to zero, range freely through the lattice. Between these two limits the energy band structure varies with the value of $P$, the variation being shown in Fig. 9.19. This graph shows the position of the points $A$, $B$, $C$, and $D$ on a vertical axis for any particular $P$ value.

At one extreme, when $P$ is at the right-hand side of the diagram, the situation corresponds to an electron in an infinitely deep well, and we see that the levels are sharp. These levels are easily calculated since if $P \to \infty$, $\sin \alpha a \to 0$. This is true when

$$\alpha a = n\pi$$

with $n$ an integer, or

$$E = \frac{n^2 h^2}{8ma^2}$$

which is the result previously obtained in Section 8.4.

On the other hand, when $P \to 0$ the situation corresponds to no barrier, and the electron can be considered to be free. Substitution of $P = 0$ in Equation 9.22 leads to

$$\cos \alpha a = \cos \kappa a$$

or

$$\alpha = \kappa$$

Thus

$$\frac{8\pi^2 mE}{h^2} = \kappa^2$$

If we replace the wave number $\kappa$ by the de Broglie value $2\pi/h$, where $p$ is the momentum, then

$$E = \frac{p^2}{2m}$$

which is, as expected, appropriate to a completely free particle (see Section 8.2). Here no energy level structure exists, and all energies are possible for

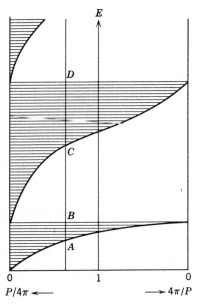

**Fig. 9.19** The dependence of energy band width on the value of $P$.

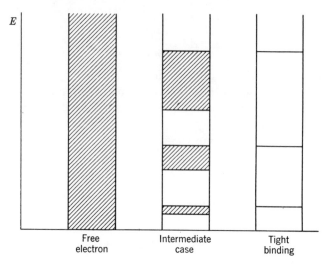

**Fig. 9.20**    Energy level structure for different degrees of binding.

the electron. The energy level diagrams for the cases of the tightly bound electron, the completely free electron, and the intermediate case are shown in Fig. 9.20.

The behavior of electrons in a solid will thus depend on the tightness of the binding, and in Chapter 10 we will consider various possibilities. We must in the meantime, however, continue the discussion of the possible energy values:

### 9.9  Brillouin Zones

#### In One Dimension

We have considered the motion of an electron along a one-dimensional periodic lattice. We have assumed the electron to travel with a momentum $p$, thus defining the de Broglie wave number $\kappa$. We have seen that, although the electron has been assumed to have arbitrary values of $\kappa$, its energy is nevertheless restricted to certain bands. It must be remembered that our intuitive notions about the relationship between energy and momentum hold for a free particle only. The electron we are considering is *not* truly free, and we must abandon preconceived ideas about its behavior. In fact, the whole set of properties of the electron in a periodic lattice will be derived from the energy-momentum relation which is the result of the present treatment.

Let us now consider the values of $\kappa$ at which the discontinuities in $E$ occur. They occur whenever $\cos \kappa a$ reaches its maximum value, that is, when

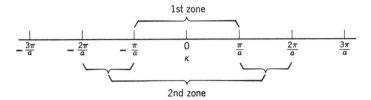

**Fig. 9.21** The first two Brillouin zones for a one-dimensional lattice.

$\cos \kappa a = \pm 1$ or when

$$\kappa = \frac{n\pi}{a} \qquad \text{where} \quad n = 1, 2, 3, \ldots \qquad (9.23)$$

At these values of $\kappa$ a small increase in electron momentum, that is, in $\kappa$, will make the energy of the electron jump discontinuously from the top of one allowed band to the bottom of the next. This situation is illustrated in Fig. 9.21. The region between the values of $\kappa$ where the first energy discontinuity takes place is called the *first Brillouin zone*. The region between the first and second values of $\kappa$ for which discontinuities occur is called the *second Brillouin zone*, and so on.

Within each zone the relationship between the energy $E$ and $\kappa$ is given by Equation 9.22, since it will be remembered that $\alpha$ is related to $E$. The solutions for $E$ as a function of $\kappa$, a so-called dispersion relationship, are quite complicated and the analysis will not be attempted. However, Fig. 9.22 shows graphically the energy-wave number relationship in which it will be

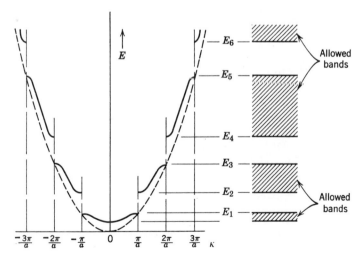

**Fig. 9.22** The relation between energy and wave number for a one-dimensional lattice.

seen that $E$ varies smoothly with $\kappa$ between the discontinuities at $\kappa$ values of $\pm\pi/a$, $\pm 2\pi/a$, etc. The dotted curve in Fig. 9.22 is the parabola

$$E = \frac{h^2}{8\pi^2 m}\kappa^2$$

which is the relation describing the behavior of a free electron. Note that this serves as an approximation of the behavior of the semibound electron, whereas the role of the periodic lattice is principally to introduce the perturbations that result in the energy discontinuities.

### In Two Dimensions

We shall now extend the discussions of the energy of an electron in a one-dimensional lattice to two- and three-dimensional periodic arrays. The treatment will be qualitative.

Let us first consider the motion of an electron in the field of a two-dimensional square lattice of characteristics similar to the previously considered linear lattice. The motion of the electron in two dimensions can now be described using a wave number $\kappa$, which, as before, is measured in the direction of propagation of the wave. This wave number $\kappa$ can be analyzed into components along the $x$ and $y$ axes, which are, respectively, $\kappa_x$ and $\kappa_y$.

To identify the first Brillouin zone, we note that along the $\kappa_x$ axis in Fig. 9.23 the values of $\pm\pi/a$ represent the limits of the zone. Similarly, along the $\kappa_y$ axis the values $\pm\pi/a$ also represent the limits of the zone. The first zone in two dimensions is therefore bounded along the axes by the points $A$, $B$, $C$, and $D$. The remainder of the boundary is less easy to evaluate, but it can be shown that, in general, just as the condition for an energy discontinuity in one dimension was

$$\kappa = \pm\frac{n\pi}{a} \tag{9.24}$$

so in two dimensions the condition reads

$$\kappa_x n_1 + \kappa_y n_2 = \frac{\pi}{a}(n_1{}^2 + n_2{}^2) \tag{9.25}$$

where $n_1$ and $n_2$ are integers corresponding to the single integer $n$ and referring to each one of the axes. To delineate the first zone, $n_1$ and $n_2$ are made equal in turn to $\pm 1$ or $0$. The equations of the lines bordering the first zone are therefore

$$n_1 = \pm 1, \qquad n_2 = 0, \qquad \text{giving} \quad \kappa_x = \pm\frac{\pi}{a}$$

and

$$n_1 = 0, \qquad n_2 = \pm 1, \qquad \text{giving} \quad \kappa_y = \pm\frac{\pi}{a}$$

The first Brillouin zone is thus a square passing through the points $A$, $B$, $C$, and $D$, as shown in Fig. 9.23.

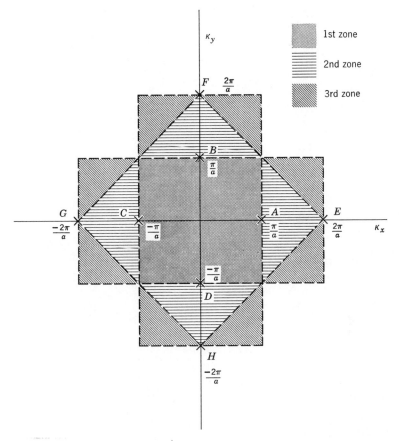

**Fig. 9.23** The first three Brillouin zones for a two-dimensional square lattice.

The second Brillouin zone must obviously pass through the points $E$, $F$, $G$, and $H$. The complete figure is obtained by taking $n_1$ and $n_2$ as the next integers in the series above those used for the first zone. These are $n_1 = \pm 1$ and $n_2 = \pm 1$. The equations of the second zone boundaries are therefore

$$n_1 = +1, \qquad n_2 = +1, \qquad \text{giving} \qquad \kappa_x + \kappa_y = \frac{2\pi}{a}$$

$$n_1 = -1, \qquad n_2 = +1, \qquad \text{giving} \qquad -\kappa_x + \kappa_y = \frac{2\pi}{a}$$

$$n_1 = +1, \qquad n_2 = -1, \qquad \text{giving} \qquad \kappa_x - \kappa_y = \frac{2\pi}{a}$$

$$n_1 = -1, \qquad n_2 = -1, \qquad \text{giving} \qquad -\kappa_x - \kappa_y = \frac{2\pi}{a}$$

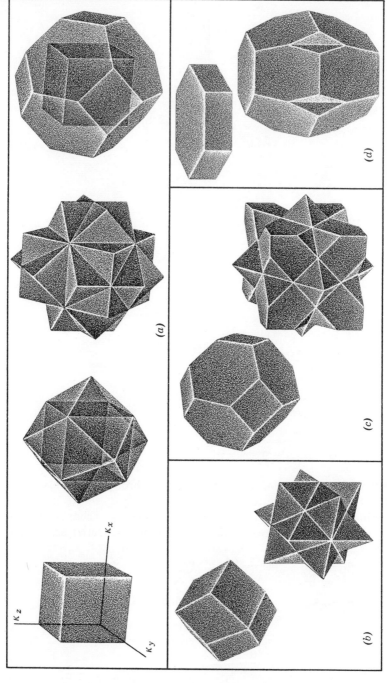

**Fig. 9.24** Three-dimensional Brillouin zones. (a) The first four zones for a simple cubic lattice. (b) The first two zones for a body-centered cubic lattice. (c) The first two zones for a face-centered cubic lattice. (d) The first two zones for a close-packed hexagonal lattice.

$\kappa_x$

$\kappa_z$

$\kappa_y$

(a)

(b)

(c)

(d)

254

These four equations describe a set of four lines at 45° to the $\kappa_x$ and $\kappa_y$ axes passing through $E$, $F$, $G$, and $H$. The second Brillouin zone is thus the region between the squares $ABCD$ and $EFGH$. The third Brillouin zone is defined giving $n_1$ and $n_2$ values of 0, $\pm 1$, and $\pm 2$. The reader can easily verify that its boundaries lie as shown in Fig. 9.23.

We must emphasize here that since the zone boundaries are measured in terms of $1/a$, they are a feature of the *lattice*. Their significance lies in the fact that although the electron is free to adopt almost any $\kappa$ value in direction and magnitude in two dimensions (subject to a restriction to be described in Section 9.11), the energy of the electron will make a discontinuous change as the $\kappa$ value crosses a zone boundary. Also from Fig. 9.22 we see that the functional dependence of the energy on the $\kappa$ value becomes most markedly different from the parabolic behavior of the free electron when the $\kappa$ value approaches a zone boundary. The full significance of this becomes clear later, when the acceleration properties are considered.

### In Three Dimensions

The form of the Brillouin zones in three dimensions is easily evaluated, using the generalized equation

$$\kappa_x n_1 + \kappa_y n_2 + \kappa_z n_3 = \frac{\pi}{a}(n_1{}^2 + n_2{}^2 + n_3{}^2) \tag{9.26}$$

The first zone for a simple cubic lattice is clearly a cube intersecting the $\kappa_x$, $\kappa_y$, and $\kappa_z$ axes at the points $\pi/a$. Just as in the triangular form of the second zone in two dimensions, the second zone in three dimensions is obtained by adding a pyramid to each face of the first zone cube, as illustrated in Fig. 9.24a.

The zone structure for lattices other than simple cubic can be determined by simple extensions of Equation 9.26, taking into account, for example, different lattice parameters in different directions. Figure 9.24 also illustrates some typical zone constructions.

We may notice in passing that the equations defining the boundaries of the Brillouin zones are identical with the interference conditions appropriate to Bragg reflection of a wave by the lattice. Such a condition obviously makes electron propagation through the lattice impossible and is consequently associated with the fact that the energy is undefined at the zone boundaries.

## 9.10   Constant Energy Curves and Surfaces

In one dimension the relation between energy and $\kappa$ value (or momentum) is simply the curve given in Fig. 9.22. In two dimensions, however, we have

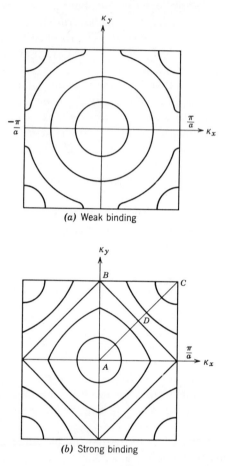

(a) Weak binding

(b) Strong binding

**Fig. 9.25** Equal energy contours in the first Brillouin zone of a two-dimensional square lattice. (a) Weak binding. (b) Strong binding.

an additional consideration. A line can be drawn in the $\kappa$ plane as a locus of all points of equal energy. For the *completely free electron* the form of this line is simple. Since all points of equal $\kappa$ value, that is, $\sqrt{\kappa_x^2 + \kappa_y^2}$ have the same energy, the curve is a *circle*. When, however, the electron is subject to a periodic potential and is therefore not completely free, we have seen that the $E$, $\kappa$ relation is no longer simply parabolic, and for this case the loci of points with equal energy are shown in Fig. 9.25 for the first Brillouin zone of a square lattice. Since points close to the origin correspond to electrons with small momentum, which suffer the least perturbation by the periodic lattice, the loci of equal energy will be circles near the center of the zone. For $\kappa$

values that reach further out into the zone, the effect of the periodic perturbations becomes of greater importance and the curves of equal energy deviate markedly from circular form. The degree to which these curves deviate from circular depends, of course, on the strength of the electron binding (i.e., on the $P$ value of Equation 9.22); the stronger the binding the closer to the origin will departure from the circular form be found and vice versa.

The treatment giving the complete relation between $E$ and $\kappa$ for two- and three-dimensional lattices cannot be given here, but one result is that, in the neighborhood of the corners of the zone, the curves of equal energy approximate to circles centered on the corners.

This result gives rise to a very important new feature. Refer again to Fig. 9.25 and consider first the change in energy along the direction $AB$. The energy must increase discontinuously as the zone boundary at $B$ is crossed. Now consider the energy increase in the direction $AC$. A continuous increase in $E$ with $\kappa$ will be found, reaching at $D$ the value corresponding to $B$. Now as the energy continues to increase from $D$, it may happen that the increase from $D$ to $C$ is greater than the discontinuous increase needed to cross the boundary at $B$. In other words, the electron energy at $C$, just within the first zone, is greater than the energy just past $B$ in the second zone. Here the *energy bands overlap*. This is often illustrated as in Fig. 9.26, where the energy is proportional to the vertical distance and different zones are shown by different hatching. Of course, zone overlap can only occur in two or three dimensional lattices. It might appear at first that such overlap is more likely for strongly bound than for weakly bound electrons since, as shown in Fig.

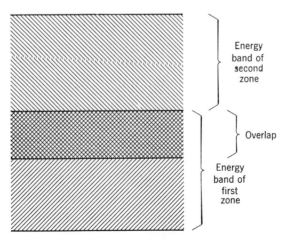

**Fig. 9.26** Overlapping energy bands.

9.25, the point $D$ which corresponds to the same energy as the point $B$ is further from the corner $C$ when the binding is stronger. We must not neglect the *size* of the energy discontinuity over the zone boundary at $B$, however. This discontinuity is greater for strong binding than for weak binding so that, over-all, energy band overlap is more likely for weak binding than for strong binding.

If we extend the treatment to three dimensions, the constant energy contours that we have been discussing in two dimensions become surfaces. The significance of these surface is, as in two dimensions, that if the $\kappa$ vector of the electron terminates anywhere on the surface, the energy of the electron will be the same. For the free electron, the shape of the surfaces is obvious— they are spheres, analogous to the circles seen at the center of the zones in Fig. 9.25. For the bound electron, however, the shapes are not simple and may become extremely complex. One of the simpler cases is illustrated in Fig. 10.17.

## 9.11   The Number of States in an Energy Band

In this chapter we have been concerned exclusively with the energies available to a single electron in various situations. We have said nothing about the total number of possibilities for an electron's $\kappa$ value. To calculate the number of different wave functions which can be possessed by an electron in a lattice, that is, the number of different states it can occupy, consider a simple linear lattice. Let there be $N$ atoms of spacing $a$ so that the total length of the array is

$$d = Na$$

Now the wave function $u$, which must be periodic in distances of $a$ or multiples of $a$, fits within a length $d$. This requires the wavelength of the wave function to satisfy such conditions as

$$\lambda = d$$

$$\lambda = \frac{d}{2}$$

$$\lambda = \frac{d}{3}, \text{etc.}$$

or, in general,

$$\lambda = \frac{d}{n}$$

The number of $\kappa$ values is therefore obtained from the condition

$$\frac{1}{\lambda} = \frac{n}{d} = \frac{n}{Nd} \qquad \text{where} \quad n = \pm 1, \pm 2, \pm 3, \ldots$$

the different signs referring to opposite directions of propagation.

If we consider the first Brillouin zone only, the maximum value of $\kappa$ is specified, and so the quantity we can calculate is the number of possible $\kappa$ values in the first zone. The maximum $\kappa$ value is given by

$$\kappa_{max} = \frac{\pi}{a}$$

that is,

$$\left(\frac{1}{\lambda}\right)_{max} = \frac{1}{2a}$$

whence

$$n_{max} = \frac{N}{2}$$

But each value of $n$ appears twice because of the $\pm$ sign, so that the total number of possible electron states in the first band is $N$. Note that this is consistent with the qualitative treatment given in Sections 9.4, 9.5, and 9.6, where we had two electron states for two wells or nuclei, three states for three centers, etc. Of course, in the kind of sample we can use in practice, $N$ is sufficiently large ($\sim 10^{26}$) that this enormous number of possible $\kappa$ values is, to all intents and purposes, a continuous distribution. The foregoing result has been obtained for a linear lattice but can be shown to hold also for two or three dimensions where $N$ is the total number of atoms involved. To avoid later confusion, it must be clearly noted at this stage that the previous calculation has given us the number of possible *wave functions* only. We have neglected spin throughout, and consequently, in terms of the Pauli Principle, the $N$ states can be occupied by $2N$ electrons.

## 9.12  Summary

The energy levels of an atom isolated in space are sharp. The influence of adjacent atoms is to spread out the levels into bands. The band spreading is least for inner levels, where the range of the electron wave functions is least. The band spreading is greatest for upper levels. Each band so formed is associated with one of the levels of the single atom and is described by the same nomenclature ($2s$, $3d$, etc.).

The momentum state of a particular electron will depend on circumstances and will be one of the $N$ states available in a single band. Given this value of

$\kappa$, the energy of the electron will be determined by the $E$, $\kappa$ relation (or vice versa, the momentum state will be similarly specified by the energy). As $\kappa$ increases through certain values, discontinuous changes in energy occur from the top of one band to the bottom of the next, provided the bands do not overlap. The $\kappa$ values defining the discontinuities are the limits of the Brillouin zones. Departures from the free electron approximation are most marked close to a Brillouin zone boundary, but up to such values $E$ depends on $\kappa^2$.

## Exercises

1. Ultraviolet light of wavelength 500 A falls on atomic hydrogen. With what velocity will an ejected electron leave the atom?

2. The electron in a hydrogen atom is in a state with $n = 3$. What is its energy? What are the possible values for its angular momentum? What is the wavelength of the photon emitted in a transition down to the state with $n = 1$?

3. According to the scheme of wave functions for the hydrogen atom,

$$\psi_{nlm}(r,\,\theta,\,\phi) = R_{nl}(r)\Theta_{lm}(\theta)\Phi_m(\phi) \qquad\qquad \text{(cf. Eq. 9.5)}$$

the 1s, 2s, and 2p wave functions are as follows:

$$1s: \qquad \psi_{100} = \frac{1}{\sqrt{\pi}}\left(\frac{Z}{a_0}\right)^{3/2} e^{-r/a_0}$$

$$2s: \qquad \psi_{200} = \frac{1}{4\sqrt{2\pi}}\left(\frac{Z}{a_0}\right)^{3/2} (2 - r/a_0)e^{-Zr/a_0}$$

$$\psi_{210} = \frac{1}{4\sqrt{2\pi}}\left(\frac{Z}{a_0}\right)^{3/2}\frac{r}{a_0}e^{-Zr/2a_0}\cos\theta$$

$$2p: \qquad \psi_{21\,\pm 1} = \frac{1}{8\sqrt{\pi}}\left(\frac{Z}{a_0}\right)^{3/2}\frac{r}{a_0}e^{-Zr/2a_0}\sin\theta\, e^{\pm i\phi}$$

where $a_0 = h^2\epsilon_0/\pi me^2 = 5.3 \times 10^{-11}$ $m$ and $Z = 1$ for hydrogen. Verify that these are solutions of the time-independent Schroedinger's equation (9.3). Compare the functions with Fig. 9.5.

4. Consider a two-dimensional square lattice of side 3 A. At what electron momentum values do the sides of the first Brillouin zone come? What is the energy of a free electron with this momentum?

5. Delineate boundaries of the fourth Brillouin zone for a two-dimensional square lattice.

6. Obtain the equations of the planes bounding the second Brillouin zone for a cubic lattice.

7. Obtain the equations of the planes bounding the first Brillouin zone for a close-packed hexagonal lattice.

# 10

# *The Distribution of Electrons in Atoms and Solids*

Chapter 9 is concerned with the behavior of a single electron in the electric fields of atoms and solids. We now turn our attention to actual atoms and solids that contain not one but many electrons. The differences we shall find arise because there are restrictions on how a number of electrons can occupy the available energies in a system. For our purpose the dominant feature is the way in which the electrons are distributed among the various energy levels, and this will be our first concern.

## 10.1 The Pauli Principle and the Fermi Distribution Function

Distribution functions describing how particles are arranged are of common occurrence in physics. They always arise when we are considering assemblies of large numbers of particles. When we deal with a system containing only a few particles, it is possible to describe the system item by item. For instance, we might say that on a particular billiard table there is one ball at a certain place with a certain velocity, another at another place with its velocity, and so on. In solids with $10^{28}$ particles per cubic meter, such detailed knowledge becomes meaningless and impossible to obtain. It is normally preferable to ask questions about *how many* particles are involved. For example, in considering a mass of gas we might ask how many particles, on the average, are contained in a certain volume, or how many in a certain volume have a particular energy, and so on. Such statistical information is just as useful for determining over-all assembly properties as detailed information would be if it were possible to obtain. The application of such statistical methods to gas kinetic theory is probably familiar to the reader in the form first enunciated by Boltzmann and Maxwell.

There exists, however, an essential difference between the distribution of energies among the atoms or molecules of a gas and the distribution of energies among the electrons of atoms or solids. In classical gas kinetic theory there is no restriction on the way in which the available energy can be shared among the molecules. The application of such a simple unrestricted distribution to the electrons in a solid leads, however, to quite obvious contradictions with experimental observation. One of the most striking of these concerns the heat capacity of metals. Gas kinetic theory would predict a contribution to the heat capacity of the metal from each of the mobile electrons of $\frac{1}{2}k$ for each degree of freedom, where $k$ is the Boltzmann constant. This large contribution is not observed. Many other examples of the failure of Maxwell-Boltzmann statistics when applied to electrons in solids could be cited.

The appropriate way of dealing with electrons evolved from a suggestion made by Pauli in 1925 concerning the distribution of energies among the electrons in an atom. The Pauli principle may be stated as follows: *In any particular system no more than two electrons may have the same set of quantum numbers n, l, and $m_l$, and these two electrons must have opposite spin.* In other words, no more than two electrons in a system can have a particular wave function.

On the basis of this new principle it is possible to work out, in a fashion analogous to gas kinetic theory, the way in which a large number of electrons in a system will be distributed among the available energies. The distribution, derived first by Fermi, will merely be quoted. The probability $F(E)$ for the occupation of a particular energy level is given by

$$F(E) = \frac{1}{e^{(E-E_F)/kT} + 1} \qquad (10.1)$$

Here $F(E)$ is called the *Fermi function*, $E$ is the energy of the level whose occupancy is being considered, $E_F$ is the *Fermi level* and is a constant for the particular system concerned.

Figure 10.1 shows the shape of the Fermi function at the temperature $T = 0°\text{K}$. The function $F(E)$ has the value unity for $E < E_F$ and zero for

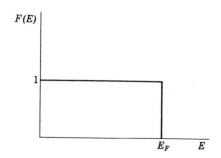

**Fig. 10.1**   The Fermi distribution function at $T = 0$.

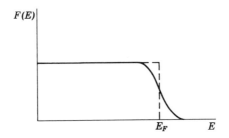

**Fig. 10.2**   The Fermi distribution function at a finite temperature.

$E > E_F$. Thus at $T = 0$, all levels with an energy less than $E_F$ will be completely filled and those above $E_F$ will be completely empty. For the special case in which the electrons have a continuous range of energy available to them, $E_F$ has the significance of being the maximum energy of filled states at $T = 0°$K. This will not be true where the electrons do not have a continuous energy range available, that is, if there are gaps in the energy spectrum. Such cases will be encountered later, when we discuss semiconductors. Furthermore, $E_F$ is the energy of the highest filled state only at $T = 0°$K; the nonzero temperature case will be described later. Unless we are dealing with a continuous electron energy distribution at $T = 0°$K, the quantity $E_F$ does not have an easily identifiable significance. It is merely a constant of the system which can be evaluated by methods to be discussed later. Notice, however, that at any finite temperature $F(E) = \frac{1}{2}$ for $E = E_F$.

Sometimes in the literature a temperature $T_F$ is defined by the relation

$$kT_F = E_F \qquad (10.2)$$

where $k$ is Boltzmann's constant. Temperature $T_F$ is called the Fermi temperature and is a constant of the system.

Figure 10.2 shows the Fermi function for a finite temperature. The curve differs from that of Fig. 10.1 in the smearing of the drop from value 1 to value 0. In actual fact, the extent of the smearing is very small except at very high temperatures. This can be seen by considering a specific point on the curve, say, $F(E) = 0.2$. The energy $E'$ for this value of $F(E)$ is easily seen to be given by

$$(E' - E_F) = 1.39 \, kT$$

Thus the extent of the smearing is of the order of $kT$, where the distribution as a whole has a dimension of $E_F$ (or $kT_F$). The smearing is therefore small in scale compared with the distribution as long at $T < T_F$.

The table of $T_F$ values (Table 10.3) shows that the condition $T \ll T_F$ holds for most materials at room temperature. Only by heating materials into the thousands of degrees does the smearing of the Fermi function become comparable with the scale of the distribution as a whole. We will observe later, however, that if we are considering the conditions very close to $E_F$, the very small degree of smearing even at room temperature can become very significant.

If, at a finite temperature, we consider the top of the distribution where we can write

$$E - E_F \gg kT$$

we may be able to ignore the constant of unity in the denominator and write

$$F(E) = e^{-(E - E_F)/kT}$$

This simplified form is identical with the Boltzmann distribution, which is valid for a classical gas. Thus at high temperatures the top of the Fermi distribution can be approximated by the classical statistics, and this can frequently simplify such calculations. We then refer to the "Boltzmann tail" of the distribution.

The Fermi function does not, by itself, give us the number of electrons which have a certain energy, for it gives us only the probability of occupation of an energy state by a single electron. To know the actual number of electrons with a given energy we must also know the number of states in the system which have the energy under consideration. Then by multiplying the number of states by the probability of occupation we get the actual number of electrons. If $N(E)$ is the number of electrons in a system that have energy $E$ and $Z(E)$ is the number of states at that energy, then

$$N(E)\,dE = Z(E)F(E)\,dE \tag{10.3}$$

$Z(E)$, of course, is a function of the system.

At this point we can see that the value of the Fermi energy $E_F$ can be obtained from the number of electrons in the system and on the distribution of states along the energy scale. For if, at $T = 0$, we start to create the system by adding electrons to the system one at a time, the lower states will be filled first, and the energy of the state into which any electron has to go will depend on the number of states at the lower energies and the extent to which they are already filled by electrons. If few states are available at each energy, the energy of the last electrons to be added will be greater than if many states are available. Thus if the state distribution function $Z(E)$ is known, the value of $E_F$ can be calculated for a certain total number of electrons. This calculation follows from the relation for $N$, the total number of electrons:

$$N = \int_0^{E_F} N(E)\,dE$$

$$= \int_0^{E_F} Z(E)F(E)\,dE \tag{10.4}$$

This relation would give the value of $E_F$ at absolute zero. For finite temperatures a similar calculation will yield the appropriate value of $E_F$, but the upper limit on the integral would then be $\infty$. A knowledge of $Z(E)$ is thus of fundamental importance, and this will now be discussed for several systems.

## 10.2   The Distribution of Electrons in Atoms

To calculate the number of states available in a single, isolated atom, recall the quantum numbers which were obtained for the hydrogen atom. The energy was determined by $n$ and, within each state thus defined, sub-states were defined, first by $l$, which could run from 0 to $n-1$, and second by $m_l$, which could run from $-l$ to $+l$. The theory, of course, said nothing about multielectron atoms, and indeed there exists no general exact solution for these cases. It is possible, however, to systematize the solution for the multielectron atom by using the quantum number notation for the states of the hydrogen atom. The analogy breaks down in several places when applied to multielectron atoms. We will, however, use it and begin by assuming that the energy of the state increases with increasing $n$.

If only two electrons may be given the same values of $n$, $l$, and $m_l$, the number of states at each energy level (i.e., $n$ value) must follow the scheme Tabulated in Table 10.1.

Let us now assume that the level density scheme in Table 10.1 can be applied to multielectron atoms. We shall discuss the energies of the various states, but first let us concentrate on the way in which the levels are filled up. For a particular multielectron atom the distribution of electrons among the various levels is now obtained by applying the Fermi function in that at

**Table 10.1**

| | | | | |
|---|---|---|---|---|
| $n = 1$ | $l = 0$ | $m_l = 0$ | | 2 states |
| $n = 2$ | $l = 0$ | $m_l = 0$ | 2 states | |
| | $l = 1$ | $m_l = -1$ | 2 states | 8 states |
| | | $m_l = 0$ | 2 states | |
| | | $m_l = 1$ | 2 states | |
| $n = 3$ | $l = 0$ | $m_l = 0$ | 2 states | |
| | $l = 1$ | $m_l = -1$ | 2 states | |
| | | $m_l = 0$ | 2 states | |
| | | $m_l = 1$ | 2 states | |
| | $l = 2$ | $m_l = -2$ | 2 states | 18 states |
| | | $m_l = -1$ | 2 states | |
| | | $m_l = 0$ | 2 states | |
| | | $m_l = 1$ | 2 states | |
| | | $m_l = 2$ | 2 states | |

$T = 0$ the lowest states will be filled up far enough to accommodate the electrons, and the higher states will be empty.

Let us take sodium as an example. Sodium has a nuclear charge of eleven times the electronic charge. Let us take a sodium nucleus and build up the atom by adding the outer electrons in turn. The first electron will fall into the lowest state, that is, $n = 1$, $l = 0$, $m_l = 0$. It will be a 1s electron. The next will do the same. The third electron is excluded from the 1s level by the Pauli principle; it therefore goes into the $n = 2$ shell. So does the next electron and so on until eight electrons are in the $n = 2$ shell. We have now accounted for ten electrons. We need to supply one more electron to complete the neutral sodium atom. It must go into the $n = 3$ shell, and it will be a 3s electron in its ground state. The result of this process is a sodium atom with two 1s electrons, two 2s electrons, six 2p electrons and one 3s electron. Let us now consider the energy levels occupied by these electrons.

The 1s electrons find themselves in the field of a nuclear charge of 11. Remembering Equation 9.12, we will see that the $n = 1$ shell of sodium is approximately 120 times as tightly bound as the $n = 1$ shell in the hydrogen atom. The electrons in the $n = 2$ shell have wave functions (as shown for the H atom in Fig. 9.4) which are mostly *outside* the wave functions of the $n = 1$ shell. Consequently, the positive nuclear charge is partially neutralized as far as the $n = 2$ electrons are concerned, and this is termed "screening." The $n = 2$ electrons therefore move in a field with an effective nuclear charge of approximately $Z = 9$. (The screening is not complete because of the spread of the wave function, and so the effective nuclear charge is a little over 9.) Consequently, this $n = 2$ level must be (because of Equation 9.12) approximately eighty times as tightly bound as the $n = 2$ level in atomic hydrogen.

The foregoing considerations lead to two conclusions. First, the inner shells of multielectron atoms are tightly bound, and second, the gaps between the inner energy levels are large. For example, $E_1$ for sodium is about $-1630$ eV and $E_2$ about $-270$ eV, and so the photon emitted in a transition between $n = 2$ and $n = 1$ in sodium has an energy of approximately 1360 eV, with a wavelength of about 8 A. This is in the X-ray region and, in general terms, transitions between the inner levels of multielectron atoms will give radiation in the X-ray region with a wavelength that decreases as the atomic number of the element increases.

X-ray spectroscopists have a nomenclature for the levels which runs

$n = 1$     K shell
$n = 2$     L shell
$n = 3$     M shell
$n = 4$     N shell
etc.

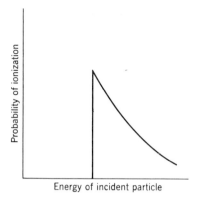

**Fig. 10.3** The probability that an energetic particle will ionize an atom from one particular shell.

Thus the X-rays emitted in the transitions between $n = 2$ and $n = 1$, $n = 3$ and $n = 1$, $n = 4$ and $n = 1$, etc., are known as the $K$ series, the transitions down to $n = 2$ as the $L$ series, and so on. Since the energy gaps between the various shells are dependent on $Z$, the atomic number, the X-ray spectrum is characteristic of the atom producing the X-rays. These characteristic X-rays are the basis of identification of elements by X-ray methods.

For transitions to take place between these normally filled levels of the atom, an electron must first be removed from an inner shell, thus allowing electrons from upper levels to fall into the lower state, emitting parts of the X-ray spectrum as they do so. Such ionization of the inner levels of an atom can be accomplished by bombarding the atom by a sufficiently energetic electron. The probability of such ionization of a particular shell is clearly zero if the energy of the bombarding electron is less than the energy of binding of the electron in the atom. If the energy of the bombarding electron is increased up to the required value, the probability of ionization rises abruptly, as shown in Fig. 10.3. Thereafter, further increase of the bombarding electron's energy will, even though there is sufficient energy for ionization, actually give a declining probability of ionization.

The preceding paragraphs have been concerned with the electrons in the inner levels. The single $3s$ electron in sodium is in a rather different position. Its wave functions are concentrated outside the $n = 1$ and $n = 2$ shell, giving screening to the extent that the effective nuclear charge is close to one. This electron is therefore, by comparison, very loosely bound at around 5 eV. This electron is responsible for the optical as opposed to the X-ray spectrum of the atom. It produces the optical spectrum by transitions between various excited levels above its $3s$ ground state, where a feature appears that is not found in the X-ray levels. The inner levels are bound so

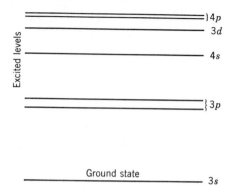

**Fig. 10.4**   The excited optical levels of atomic sodium (not accurately to scale).

tightly that they are relatively unaffected by differences in $l$ value. Thus all the $n = 2$ levels are approximately at the same energy. But the single outer electron experiences screening (and consequently binding), which depends very much on the detailed shape of the wave functions and consequently the excited levels are very dependent on the $l$ value of the state. The excited levels for the outer electron of sodium are shown in Fig. 10.4.

The influence of temperature on the sodium atom can be seen by applying the temperature dependence of $F(E)$ illustrated in Fig. 10.2. It is obvious that, in view of the discrete nature of the levels, the system is not going to be affected by temperature until the tail of the Fermi function reaches the next available level. Since the average thermal energy (measured by $kT$) at room temperature is about 0.025 eV, and the gap between the ground state in sodium and the first excited is about 2 eV, the probability of excitation of a sodium atom at room temperature is effectively zero. It takes a temperature of at least 1000°K to make $kT$ comparable with the energy gap and so to give appreciable excitation.

Thus, to summarize, the electronic system is completely condensed into the lowest states at all normal temperatures, and at higher temperatures the relative populations of the occupied levels can be calculated by use of the Fermi function. This is a satisfactory description of many of the physical and chemical properties of atoms.

The chemical properties, in particular, follow from the dependence of the binding between electron and nucleus on the quantum number state of the electron. In the case of sodium, discussed earlier, the binding of the outermost electron is weak, and it is therefore readily removed, permitting easy chemical reaction. All atoms that have this configuration will share this chemical property. Thus the *alkali metals*, lithium with one electron in $n = 2$, sodium with one electron in $n = 3$, potassium with one electron in $n = 4$, etc., will all be chemically reactive. If, on the other hand, an atom has its outermost shell just full, the nuclear binding is relatively strong. The structure is then such that there is little tendency from the atom to share electrons with other atoms. The resulting chemical inertness is characteristic of the *rare gases*, helium, neon, argon, etc. Any atom just short of having a complete shell will be chemically reactive. Thus the *halogens*, fluorine with seven electrons in $n = 2$, chlorine with seven electrons in $n = 3$, etc., will tend to share electrons by accepting one to form the stable structure of the closed shell. Electrons are readily shared by the halogens in chemical combination with the alkali metals. The *valence* of the elements arises naturally from this description as the number of electrons outside a closed shell or the number required to complete a closed shell. The valence of the alkali metals and halogens thus will be one, and for the elements that have a deficiency or excess of two electrons, such as magnesium, calcium, oxygen, etc., the valence is two. The tendency of some elements to form ions in gases or solution is again simply the same property. If an electron is easily removed, *positive ions* of unit charge are formed; if a closed shell can be completed by the addition of electrons, *negative ions* are readily formed.

We have seen in Table 10.1 that a simple scheme of allocating electrons in multielectron atoms to particular energy levels results from using the atomic hydrogen quantum number structure. The scheme is a good representation of the levels in elements at the beginning of the periodic table. Let us make a brief survey of the periodic table from this point of view.

In hydrogen and helium the $n = 1$ shell is occupied respectively by one and two 1s electrons. In lithium, beryllium, boron, carbon, nitrogen, oxygen, fluorine, and neon the $n = 2$ shell is occupied by 2s and 2p electrons up to a total of two and six, respectively. The $n = 3$ shell is occupied from sodium onward by adding first two 2s electrons and then six 2p electrons to give finally at argon eighteen electrons in the shell. At this stage we might expect the next electrons to be 3d, but this does not happen. The energies of this complicated structure containing a nucleus and nineteen electrons are such that the energy of the 4s state is then lower than that of the 3d state, and in potassium the outermost electron is in a 4s state, leaving ten 3d states empty. Thus these are two chemical periods of eight elements each when we would expect, on the basis of the quantum-number structure, one of eight and a second one of eighteen elements.

The structure of the elements just past potassium is important. Calcium adds a second 4s electron, leaving the 3d level still empty. Then from scandium onward the elements titanium, vanadium, chromium, manganese, iron, cobalt, nickel, and copper fill up the 3d shell until it is just full at copper. The partially filled 3d level is responsible for many of the striking properties of the so-called *transition elements*, in particular the high magnetic moment and ferromagnetic character of iron, cobalt, and nickel.

Other unfilled spaces in the quantum number structure exist and account for departures from a simple periodicity in the chemical properties. The most striking of these is in the *rare earth group*, in which the 4f shell is being filled while eleven electrons are occupying levels ranging from 5s to 6p. Such shielding of the 4f shell from the outside of the atom produces almost complete chemical indistinguishability of these elements, although other properties that arise from the 4f level, such as the magnetic moment, may be very different.

The evidence for the quantum number structure quoted previously is obtained from spectroscopic magnetic and other measurements and makes it possible to obtain the quantum number structure, even if a detailed theoretical treatment is impossible. The complete electronic structure of the elements is given in Table 10.2.

## 10.3   The Distribution Function for Free Electrons

In Section 10.2 we considered the distribution of electrons in a single atom. We now wish to extend this to a solid, but the procedure is not obvious. Our considerations of the binding energy of the various atomic shells suggests that for the inner shells we can ignore the spreading of the levels, which arises from the solid structure. We are left then with only the valence electron or electrons to consider. Their looser binding suggests that the Kronig-Penny treatment may be applicable. But the Kronig-Penny treatment given in Chapter 7 referred to a single electron. At this stage we want to consider the distribution among the available energies of a large number of electrons. It was demonstrated in Section 9.10 that the total number of electrons that could be accommodated within the first Brillouin zone was $2N$, where $N$ is the number of nuclei in the sample. For the application of Equation 10.3, however, we require not so much the total number of states available as the state density function $Z(E)$. Unfortunately, this is not easy to calculate for conditions treated in Sections 9.7 to 9.10. Because of this difficulty we shall perform a simpler calculation and then discuss its relevance to actual solids. The simplification consists of calculating the state density function for an assembly of completely free electrons, which we shall call an electron gas.

The potential function that defines a free electron in a solid is a rectangular well of the dimensions of the sample under consideration. Thus the problem of a free electron gas is just that of an electron in a box, considered in Section 8.4. There it was shown that a single electron confined in one direction to a space $a$ may have energy levels given by

$$E_n = \frac{n^2 h^2}{8ma^2} \tag{10.5}$$

**Table 10.2**  The Electronic Structure of Atoms

| Atomic Number | Element Symbol | K | L | | M | | | N | | | | Ionization Energy, eV | Atomic Radius, A |
|---|---|---|---|---|---|---|---|---|---|---|---|---|---|
| | | $1s$ | $2s$ | $2p$ | $3s$ | $3p$ | $3d$ | $4s$ | $4p$ | $4d$ | $4f$ | | |
| 1 | H | 1 | | | | | | | | | | 13.53 | 0.53 |
| 2 | He | 2 | | | | | | | | | | 24.47 | 0.30 |
| 3 | Li | 2 | 1 | | | | | | | | | 5.37 | 1.50 |
| 4 | Be | 2 | 2 | | | | | | | | | 9.28 | 1.19 |
| 5 | B | 2 | 2 | 1 | | | | | | | | 8.25 | 0.85 |
| 6 | C | 2 | 2 | 2 | | | | | | | | 11.20 | 0.66 |
| 7 | N | 2 | 2 | 3 | | | | | | | | 14.47 | 0.53 |
| 8 | O | 2 | 2 | 4 | | | | | | | | 13.55 | 0.45 |
| 9 | F | 2 | 2 | 5 | | | | | | | | 18.6 | 0.38 |
| 10 | Ne | 2 | 2 | 6 | | | | | | | | 21.47 | 0.32 |
| 11 | Na | 2 | 2 | 6 | 1 | | | | | | | 5.12 | 1.55 |
| 12 | Mg | 2 | 2 | 6 | 2 | | | | | | | 7.61 | 1.32 |
| 13 | Al | 2 | 2 | 6 | 2 | 1 | | | | | | 5.96 | 1.21 |
| 14 | Si | 2 | 2 | 6 | 2 | 2 | | | | | | 8.08 | 1.06 |
| 15 | P | 2 | 2 | 6 | 2 | 3 | | | | | | 11.11 | 0.92 |
| 16 | S | 2 | 2 | 6 | 2 | 4 | | | | | | 10.31 | 0.82 |
| 17 | Cl | 2 | 2 | 6 | 2 | 5 | | | | | | 12.96 | 0.75 |
| 18 | A | 2 | 2 | 6 | 2 | 6 | | | | | | 15.69 | 0.67 |
| 19 | K | 2 | 2 | 6 | 2 | 6 | — | 1 | | | | 4.32 | 2.20 |
| 20 | Ca | 2 | 2 | 6 | 2 | 6 | — | 2 | | | | 6.09 | 2.03 |
| 21 | Sc | 2 | 2 | 6 | 2 | 6 | 1 | 2 | | | | 6.7 | 1.80 |
| 22 | Ti | 2 | 2 | 6 | 2 | 6 | 2 | 2 | | | | 6.81 | 1.66 |
| 23 | V | 2 | 2 | 6 | 2 | 6 | 3 | 2 | | | | 6.76 | 1.52 |
| 24 | Cr | 2 | 2 | 6 | 2 | 6 | 5 | 1 | | | | 6.74 | 1.41 |
| 25 | Mn | 2 | 2 | 6 | 2 | 6 | 5 | 2 | | | | 7.40 | 1.31 |
| 26 | Fe | 2 | 2 | 6 | 2 | 6 | 6 | 2 | | | | 7.83 | 1.22 |
| 27 | Co | 2 | 2 | 6 | 2 | 6 | 7 | 2 | | | | 8.5 | 1.14 |
| 28 | Ni | 2 | 2 | 6 | 2 | 6 | 8 | 2 | | | | 7.61 | 1.07 |
| 29 | Cu | 2 | 2 | 6 | 2 | 6 | 10 | 1 | | | | 7.68 | 1.03 |
| 30 | Zn | 2 | 2 | 6 | 2 | 6 | 10 | 2 | | | | 9.36 | 0.97 |
| 31 | Ga | 2 | 2 | 6 | 2 | 6 | 10 | 2 | 1 | | | 5.97 | 1.13 |
| 32 | Ge | 2 | 2 | 6 | 2 | 6 | 10 | 2 | 2 | | | 8.09 | 1.06 |
| 33 | As | 2 | 2 | 6 | 2 | 6 | 10 | 2 | 3 | | | 10.5 | 1.01 |
| 34 | Se | 2 | 2 | 6 | 2 | 6 | 10 | 2 | 4 | | | 9.70 | 0.95 |

**Table 10.2** (*continued*)

| Atomic Number | Element Symbol | Number of Electrons N | | | | O | | | | | P | Ionization Energy, eV | Atomic, Radius A |
|---|---|---|---|---|---|---|---|---|---|---|---|---|---|
| | | 4s | 4p | 4d | 4f | 5s | 5p | 5d | 5f | 5g | 6s | | |
| 35 | Br | 2 | 2 | 6 | 2 | 6 | 10 | 2 | 5 | | | 11.30 | 0.90 |
| 36 | Kr | 2 | 2 | 6 | 2 | 6 | 10 | 2 | 6 | — | — | 13.94 | 0.86 |
| 37 | Rb | 2 | 6 | — | — | 1 | — | — | — | — | | 4.16 | |
| 38 | Sr | 2 | 6 | — | — | 2 | — | — | — | — | | 5.67 | |
| 39 | Y | 2 | 6 | 1 | — | 2 | | | | | | 6.5 | |
| 40 | Zr | 2 | 6 | 2 | — | 2 | | | | | | 6.92 | |
| 41 | Nb | 2 | 6 | 4 | — | 1 | | | | | | 6.8 | |
| 42 | Mo | 2 | 6 | 5 | — | 1 | | | | | | 7.06 | |
| 43 | Tc | 2 | 6 | 6 | — | 1 | | | | | | 7.1 | |
| 44 | Ru | 2 | 6 | 7 | — | 1 | | | | | | 7.7 | |
| 45 | Rh | 2 | 6 | 8 | — | 1 | | | | | | 7.7 | |
| 46 | Pd | 2 | 6 | 10 | — | — | | | | | | 8.3 | |
| 47 | Ag | 2 | 6 | 10 | — | 1 | | | | | | 7.54 | |
| 48 | Cd | 2 | 6 | 10 | — | 2 | | | | | | 8.96 | |
| 49 | In | 2 | 6 | 10 | — | 2 | 1 | | | | | 5.76 | |
| 50 | Sn | 2 | 6 | 10 | — | 2 | 2 | | | | | 7.30 | |
| 51 | Sb | 2 | 6 | 10 | — | 2 | 3 | | | | | 8.35 | |
| 52 | Te | 2 | 6 | 10 | — | 2 | 4 | | | | | 8.96 | |
| 53 | I | 2 | 6 | 10 | — | 2 | 5 | | | | | 10.44 | |
| 54 | Xe | 2 | 6 | 10 | — | 2 | 6 | | | | | 12.08 | |
| 55 | Cs | 2 | 6 | 10 | — | 2 | 6 | | | | 1 | 3.87 | |
| 56 | Ba | 2 | 6 | 10 | — | 2 | 6 | | | | 2 | 5.19 | |
| 57 | La | 2 | 6 | 10 | — | 2 | 6 | 1 | | | 2 | 5.59 | |
| 58 | Ce | 2 | 6 | 10 | 2 | 2 | 6 | — | | | 2 | 6.54 | |
| 59 | Pr | 2 | 6 | 10 | 3 | 2 | 6 | — | | | 2 | 5.8 | |
| 60 | Nd | 2 | 6 | 10 | 4 | 2 | 6 | — | | | 2 | 6.3 | |
| 61 | Pm | 2 | 6 | 10 | 5 | 2 | 6 | — | | | 2 | 6.3 | |
| 62 | Sm | 2 | 6 | 10 | 6 | 2 | 6 | — | | | 2 | 6.6 | |
| 63 | Eu | 2 | 6 | 10 | 7 | 2 | 6 | — | | | 2 | 5.64 | |
| 64 | Gd | 2 | 2 | 10 | 7 | 2 | 6 | 1 | | | 2 | 6.7 | |
| 65 | Tb | 2 | 6 | 10 | 8 | 2 | 6 | 1 | | | 2 | 6.7 | |
| 66 | Dy | 2 | 6 | 10 | 9 | 2 | 6 | 1 | | | 2 | 6.8 | |
| 67 | Ho | 2 | 6 | 10 | 10 | 2 | 6 | 1 | | | 2 | | |
| 68 | Er | 2 | 6 | 10 | 11 | 2 | 6 | 1 | | | 2 | | |
| 69 | Tm | 2 | 6 | 10 | 12 | 2 | 6 | 1 | | | 2 | | |

**Table 10.2** (*continued*)

| Atomic Number | Element Symbol | Number of Electrons | | | | | | | | | | Ionization Energy eV | Atomic Radius, A |
| | | O | | | | | P | | | Q | | | |
| | | 5p | 5d | 5f | 5g | 6s | 6p | 6d | 6f | 7s | 7p | | |
|---|---|---|---|---|---|---|---|---|---|---|---|---|---|
| 70 | Yb | 2 | 6 | 10 | 13 | 2 | 6 | 1 | | | 2 | 6.2 | |
| 71 | Lu | 2 | 6 | 10 | 14 | 2 | 6 | 1 | | | 2 | 5.0 | |
| 72 | Hf | 2 | 6 | 10 | 14 | 2 | 6 | 2 | — | — | 2 | 5.5 | |
| 73 | Ta | 6 | 3 | — | — | 2 | — | — | — | — | — | 6.0 | |
| 74 | W | 6 | 4 | | | 2 | | | | | | 8.1 | |
| 75 | Re | 6 | 5 | | | 2 | | | | | | 7.85 | |
| 76 | Os | 6 | 6 | | | 2 | | | | | | 8.7 | |
| 77 | Ir | 6 | 9 | | | 0 | | | | | | 9.2 | |
| 78 | Pt | 6 | 9 | | | 1 | | | | | | 8.9 | |
| 79 | Au | 6 | 10 | | | 1 | | | | | | 9.20 | |
| 80 | Hg | 6 | 10 | | | 2 | | | | | | 10.38 | |
| 81 | Tl | 6 | 10 | | | 2 | 1 | | | | | 6.07 | |
| 82 | Pb | 6 | 10 | | | 2 | 2 | | | | | 7.38 | |
| 83 | Bi | 6 | 10 | | | 2 | 3 | | | | | 8.0 | |
| 84 | Po | 6 | 10 | | | 2 | 4 | | | | | 7.25 | |
| 85 | At | 6 | 10 | | | 2 | 5 | | | | | 9.4 | |
| 86 | Rn | 6 | 10 | | | 2 | 6 | | | | | 10.69 | |
| 87 | Fr | 6 | 10 | | | 2 | 6 | | | 1 | | 4.0 | |
| 88 | Ra | 6 | 10 | | | 2 | 6 | | | 2 | | 5.25 | |
| 89 | Ac | 6 | 10 | | | 2 | 6 | 1 | | 2 | | | |
| 90 | Th | 6 | 10 | | | 2 | 6 | 2 | | 2 | | | 0.95 |
| 91 | Pa | 6 | 10 | | | 2 | 6 | 3 | | 2 | | 5.7 | 0.91 |
| 92 | U | 6 | 10 | | | 2 | 6 | 4 | | 2 | | 4.0 | 0.89 |
| 93 | Np | 6 | 10 | 5 | | 2 | 6 | — | | 2 | | | 0.88 |
| 94 | Pu | 6 | 10 | 5 | | 2 | 6 | 1 | | 2 | | | 0.86 |
| 95 | Am | 6 | 10 | 6 | | 2 | 6 | 1 | | 2 | | | 0.85 |
| 96 | Cm | 6 | 10 | 7 | | 2 | 6 | 1 | | 2 | | | |
| 97 | Bk | 6 | 10 | 8 | | 2 | 6 | 1 | | 2 | | | |
| 98 | Cf | 6 | 10 | 9 | | 2 | 6 | 1 | | 2 | | | |
| 99 | — | 6 | 10 | 10 | | 2 | 6 | 1 | | 2 | | | |
| 100 | — | 6 | 10 | 11 | | 2 | 6 | 1 | | 2 | | | |

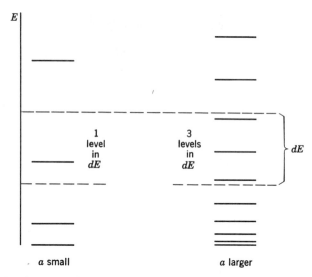

**Fig. 10.5**   The energy levels of an electron in a box as a function of box size.

It is clear that the spacing of the levels depends on $a$. If $a$ is small, the energies $E_n$ rise rapidly as $n$ increases and the spacing between the levels is large. If, on the other hand, $a$ is large, the spacing is small. This is shown in Fig. 10.5. It will emerge that when $a$ is of sample dimensions, say, cms, the number of levels becomes so enormous that it virtually constitutes a continuum.

Let us now calculate how many levels there are in a range of energies $dE$ at energy $E$. The result should be valid for three dimensions so that we write, without proof, the extended form of Equation 10.5 applicable to a cube of side $a$

$$E = \frac{h^2}{8ma^2} (n_x^2 + n_y^2 + n_z^2) \tag{10.6}$$

where $n_x$, $n_y$, and $n_z$ are integers. Thus states of the same energy can be constructed by various choices of the values for $n_x$, $n_y$, and $n_z$, and it is this multiplicity that provides a number of states all with the same energy, that is, a state density. We must calculate how many choices of these integers there are to give energies lying within a certain range of energy $dE$ at energy $E$.

To perform this calculation, construct a space of points represented by the values $n_x$, $n_y$, and $n_z$. In this space the radius from the origin to a point $(n_x, n_y, n_z)$ is given by $n$ where

$$n^2 = n_x^2 + n_y^2 + n_z^2 \tag{10.7}$$

Each point at this radius gives the same value of $E$, and so a volume element which is a spherical shell of thickness $dn$ at radius $n$ will give a measure of the number of states in the energy range $dE$ at $E$. The volume of the shell is clearly $4\pi n^2\, dn$, and since only positive values of $n_x$, $n_y$, and $n_z$ have any meaning, the number of states $Z(E)\, dE$ will be given by one-eighth of that volume. Thus

$$Z(E)\, dE = \tfrac{1}{2}\pi n^2\, dn \tag{10.8}$$

Using the value of $n$ from Equation 10.5, we obtain

$$dn = \frac{1}{2}\left(\frac{8ma^2}{h^2}\right)^{\frac{1}{2}} E^{-\frac{1}{2}}\, dE$$

Hence

$$Z(E)\, dE = \frac{1}{2}\,\pi\left(\frac{8ma^2}{h^2}\right) E \cdot \frac{1}{2}\left(\frac{8ma^2}{h^2}\right)^{\frac{1}{2}} E^{-\frac{1}{2}}\, dE$$

$$= \frac{\pi}{4}\left(\frac{8ma^2}{h^2}\right)^{\frac{3}{2}} E^{\frac{1}{2}}\, dE \tag{10.9}$$

It should be remembered that the Pauli exclusion principle permits two electrons in each state, so that the number of energy states which can be filled is

$$Z(E)\, dE = \frac{\pi}{2}\left(\frac{8ma^2}{h^2}\right)^{\frac{3}{2}} E^{\frac{1}{2}}\, dE \tag{10.10}$$

In terms of the volume $V$ available to the electrons ($= a^3$) this becomes

$$Z(E)\, dE = \frac{\pi}{2}\left(\frac{8m}{h^2}\right)^{\frac{3}{2}} VE^{\frac{1}{2}}\, dE \tag{10.11}$$

This simple parabolic function is illustrated in Fig. 10.6 and is used quite generally when any quasi-free particle situation is at hand.

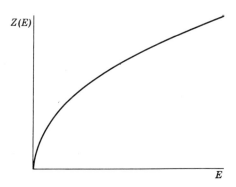

**Fig. 10.6**   The state density for a free electron gas.

The number of states $Z(E)\,dE$ in a volume of $10^{-6}$ m$^3$ lying below an energy of 1 eV will now be calculated.

$$\text{Number of states} = \int_0^E Z(E)\,dE = \frac{\pi}{2}\left(\frac{8m}{h^2}\right)^{3/2} V \int_0^E E^{1/2}\,dE$$

$$= \frac{\pi}{2}\left(\frac{8m}{h^2}\right)^{3/2} V \frac{2}{3} E^{3/2} = 4.6 \times 10^{21}$$

Thus, in spite of the exclusion principle, an enormous number of electrons can occupy a volume of $10^{-6}$ m$^3$ before the energy of the top level reaches 1 eV. These state numbers are high enough so that all the valence electrons in a metal can be accommodated without the Fermi energy rising above a few eV in all cases.

We should notice here that, although we do not require the result at the present moment, we can write Equation 10.11 in terms of momentum instead of energy. Replacing $E$ by $p^2/2m$ and $dE$ by $p\,dp/m$, we obtain for unit volume

$$Z(p)\,dp = \frac{8\pi}{h^3} p^2\,dp. \tag{10.11a}$$

This result will be used in the discussion of thermionic emission in Chapter 11.

The actual number of electrons $N(E)\,dE$ in a given energy range will now be obtained by multiplying the state density $Z(E)\,dE$ by the Fermi distribution function. Thus

$$N(E)\,dE = \frac{\pi}{2}\left(\frac{8m}{h^2}\right)^{3/2} V E^{1/2} \frac{dE}{e^{(E-E_F)/kT} + 1} \tag{10.12}$$

This distribution is shown in Fig. 10.7. At absolute zero the distribution is simple, all states up to the Fermi level will be filled and those above $E_F$ will be empty. At higher temperatures the typical tailing appears, the extent of this tailing being, of course, very small compared with the scale of the distribution until very high temperatures are reached.

Whenever the actual state density is known it is possible to calculate the Fermi level. The calculation is possible at any temperature, but is particularly simple at $T = 0°$K because of the simple numerical value of $F(E)$. At $T = 0$ for $N$ free electrons we have

$$N = \int_0^{E_F} N(E)\,dE$$

$$= \int_0^{E_F} \frac{\pi}{2}\left(\frac{8m}{h^2}\right)^{3/2} V E^{1/2} \frac{dE}{e^{(E-E_F)/kT} + 1}$$

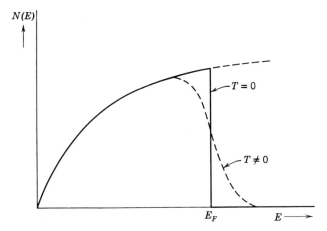

**Fig. 10.7** The population density for a free electron gas.

Remembering that at $T = 0$ the Fermi function has value unity, we easily perform the integration and find

$$E_F = \left(\frac{h^2}{2m}\right)\left(\frac{3N}{8\pi}\right)^{\frac{2}{3}}$$

(10.13)

if we now specify that $N$ is the number of electrons per unit volume.

This Fermi energy is a very important and useful quantity, because whenever we can use the free electron model, which is quite often, the value for $E_F$ obtained gives us (at $T = 0$) the energy at which the topmost electrons will be found.

For example, if we assume that the single-valence electron of sodium is completely free, we can calculate the Fermi energy for sodium. The number $N$ of atoms per unit volume is approximately $5 \times 10^{28}$ m$^{-3}$ giving a value for $E_F$ of $4.96 \times 10^{-19}$ joule or 3.1 eV. This energy relates only to the electrons considered to be free, that is, the valence electrons, and is consequently the energy difference between the bottom of the valence levels and the top of the distribution. Values for $E_F$ and $T_F$ for various materials are given in Table 10.3.

## 10.4  State Densities in Actual Solids

We are now ready to attempt the evaluation of the state densities, and ultimately the electron population, of actual multielectron atoms combined in a solid. We have given a generalized treatment of the energy levels of a single electron in a periodic potential, and this had as its two limiting cases

**Table 10.3**

| Material | Number of Free Electrons per m³ | $E_F$ eV | $T_F$ °K |
|----------|--------------------------------|----------|----------|
| Li | $4.6 \times 10^{28}$ | 4.72 | $5.5 \times 10^4$ |
| Na | 2.5 | 3.12 | 3.6 |
| K | 1.3 | 2.14 | 2.5 |
| Rb | 1.1 | 1.82 | 2.1 |
| Cs | 0.85 | 1.53 | 1.8 |
| Cu | 8.5 | 7.04 | 8.2 |
| Ag | 5.8 | 5.51 | 6.4 |
| Au | 5.9 | 5.54 | 6.4 |

the tightly bound electron with its sharp energy levels characteristic of an isolated atom and the free electron for which the binding is negligible and the energy level distribution virtually continuous. We have also considered how the electrons are packed into the available energy levels for the case where large numbers of electrons must be considered. Since there is no general solution to the final problem of actual multielectron atoms in actual solids, our task is to select, for each part of the electron structure, the appropriate model to serve as the best approximation.

The basis for such a choice lies in the binding experienced by the electrons. The electrons in the inner shells will experience strong binding from the nuclear charges, whereas the valence electrons will be less tightly bound. For the valence electrons it may be possible to use the free electron approximation.

Most of the considerations we shall now list have already been discussed, but it is helpful to summarize the whole discussion at this point. Let us consider the energy level distribution in $10^{-3}$ kg of sodium. There are approximately $10^{23}$ nuclei each of charge eleven times the electronic charge. The number of electrons is $11 \times 10^{23}$. Let us consider the first $10^{23}$ electrons and assume them distributed one each among the atoms. In the $n = 1$ shell each electron will experience a nuclear charge of eleven and will consequently be very tightly bound. From Equation 9.12 we saw that the binding energy was proportional to $Z^2$, and so the inner level electrons in sodium are approximately 120 times as tightly bound as the electron in hydrogen. Transitions into such levels would be well into the X-ray region of wavelength. The next $10^{23}$ electrons will go into the $n = 1$ shell. Again the wave functions will be those appropriate to the right-hand side of Fig. 9.20 and the energy levels will be sharp.

The $n = 1$ shell is now full and the next $10^{23}$ electrons must go into the $n = 2$ levels. Here they each experience a nuclear field that is diminished by

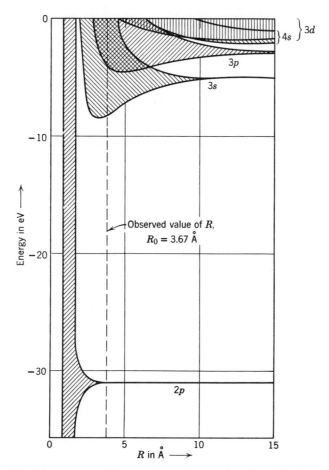

**Fig. 10.8** The energy level diagram for sodium as a function of lattice spacing.

the screening of the inner two electrons already added. However, the effective nuclear charge is approximately nine, which still constitutes very tight binding. The $n = 2$ level also is thus relatively sharp. As seven more electrons per atom are added, the $n = 2$ shell fills, each electron experiencing a nuclear charge of approximately nine and the level remaining sharp. The last $10^{23}$ electrons to be added must go into the $n = 3$ shell. Here each experiences an effective nuclear charge of approximately one, the binding is no longer tight, and the levels are spread into bands. The complete diagram of the energy levels as a function of lattice spacing is given in Fig. 10.8.

We still must consider the problem of the state density in the band. As we have already pointed out at the beginning of Section 10.3, it is not easy to calculate the state density throughout the whole first Brillouin zone for a bound electron. We have done so, however, for a free electron, and this result will be applicable to the bound case to the extent that the free electron approximation is valid. We have already considered this point in Section 9.9. The free electron approximation is good as long as we can consider the constant energy contours in Fig. 9.25 to be circular. This is the case at the bottom of the band, and so we can conclude that the state density function starts as a parabola at the bottom of the band.

Incidentally, we can write the equation of the parabola as in equation 10.11, because at this stage we are changing the origin of the energy scale. We have hitherto considered all energies in bound states as negative and based on $E = 0$ infinitely far from the system. Now, if we are going to apply the free electron theory, or slight modifications of it, to the valence electron or electrons in the solid, we shall regard them as a separate system and start the energy scale for the valence electrons at $E = 0$ at the bottom of the valence band. Thus the energy of an electron in the valence band, as, for example, the Fermi energy, will appear as a positive number even though it refers to a bound state.

Let us now consider the circumstances at the top of the band. Again referring to Fig. 9.25, it is clear from the geometry of the first Brillouin zone that the state density must decline to zero at the top of the band because the opportunities for a momentum vector to yield a particular energy diminish as the vector reaches into the corners of the zone. The actual state density function is associated with the form of the constant energy contours, and we have already seen in Fig. 9.25 that, near the corners of the zone, these contours become circles centered on the zone corners. This implies another parabolic function relating state density and energy, where the energy variable now is measured from the top of the band. Its equation would be

$$Z(E) = \text{constant } (E' - E)^{\frac{1}{2}} \tag{10.14}$$

if $E'$ is the energy at the top of the band.

For the two regions so far considered, the state distribution $Z(E)$ is drawn as a function of $E$ for the $n = 3$ electrons of sodium in Fig. 10.9.

The form of the $Z(E)$ curve for the region in the middle of the band cannot be obtained by a simple theoretical treatment. The characteristic feature is a cusp in the middle of the band, arising from a crowding of the states as the radius vector defining the $\kappa$ value approaches the sides of the first Brillouin zone (see Fig. 10.10). Experimental evidence from which the actual shape of bands in metals can be obtained is available and will be considered in Chapter 11.

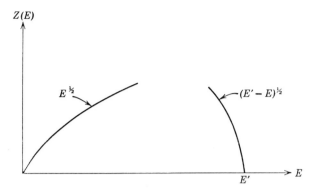

**Fig. 10.9**  The electronic state distribution at the top and bottom of a valence band in a solid.

Whatever the form of the state density within the band, however, we must remember that the total number of states in the band is given by the quantum number constitution of the band.  For example, in sodium the state is $3s$, giving two states per atom.  If a lump of sodium contains $N$ atoms, there will therefore be room for $2N$ electrons in the valence band.

Sodium has been chosen as an example of the circumstances most favorable to theoretical treatment.  The problem is more complicated for atoms with more than one electron per atom in the outer shell and the necessity of considering the occupation of the upper parts of the band involves such matters as the overlapping of the bands.  The resultant state density can be shown as in Fig. 10.11.  In the overlapping region the resulting state density is the sum of those in the two overlapping bands.  Further consideration will be given to such cases in Section 10.5.

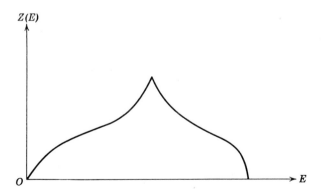

**Fig. 10.10**  The complete density function for a band.

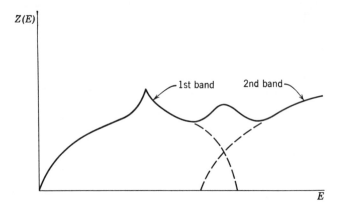

**Fig. 10.11**   Band shapes with overlapping bands.

## 10.5   Electron Population Density in Solids and the Fermi Surface

Section 10.4 was concerned only with state densities. We require electron population densities, however, and these will now be considered. Such electron densities will be determined by the number of levels in the bands and by the number of electrons that governs the extent to which the bands are filled.

The problem is simple for sodium. The band where the valence electron is found is a 3s band with, therefore, two places per atom. With one valence

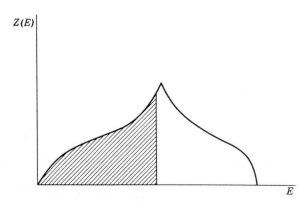

**Fig. 10.12**   The occupation of the valence band of a monovalent metal. The occupied region (at $T = 0°K$) is shaded.

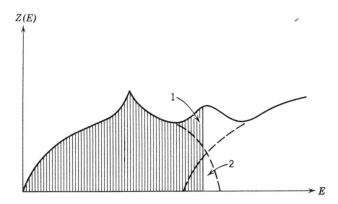

**Fig. 10.13**    The occupation of the valence bands of a divalent metal.

electron per atom the band is half full, as illustrated in Fig. 10.12. On the basis of this description, we might expect that in the element next up from sodium, magnesium, the 3s band would be just filled. In a way this is true, but the question of overlapping of the bands must be considered. The occupation would then be as illustrated in Fig. 10.13. On the assumption that the lower band would be just full in the absence of the upper, the extra occupied states at 1 must compensate exactly for those at 2 which will thus remain empty. The case of such occupied, overlapping bands is very important and will be found to account for very many metallic properties. The energy range between the first band and the value $E = 0$ is generally filled with an extremely complex mixture of overlapping bands. It can thus be regarded as a continuum of available energies right up to $E = 0$. Figure 10.14 summarizes the whole sodium structure.

One very important feature of the occupation of the available levels by electrons is the state of affairs at the surface of the distribution. We have been discussing the occupation in terms of energy only. It is constructive now to consider the occupation in momentum space. Consider, for the moment, a square lattice with constant energy contours as shown in Fig. 9.25. Remember that these constant energy contours give the momentum values appropriate to a certain energy in the various parts of the zone. Whatever the shape of these constant energy contours, one of them must be distinguished by being at the surface of the distribution. In other words, one energy contour must have the value $E_F$. At $T = 0°K$, therefore, this contour delineates the surface of the electron distribution. The three-dimensional situation leads to a surface instead of a linear contour. The surface is known as the Fermi surface.

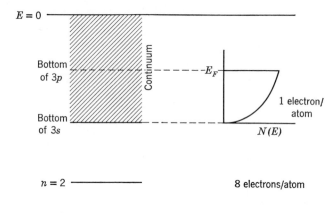

$E = 0$

Bottom of 3p

Bottom of 3s

Continuum

$-E_F$

1 electron/ atom

$N(E)$

$n = 2$ ———————  8 electrons/atom

$n = 1$ ———————  2 electrons/atom

Level  Occupation

**Fig. 10.14** The complete electron population distribution in metallic sodium at $T = 0°K$ (assuming a parabolic state density function for the valence electron).

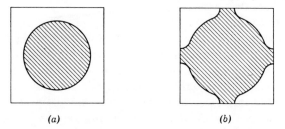

(a)  (b)

**Fig. 10.15** The Fermi surface in two dimensions for the case in which it (a) does not touch, (b) does touch, the first Brillouin zone boundary.

Clearly, for a free electron the two-dimensional contour is a circle and in three dimensions a sphere, known as the Fermi sphere. The Fermi surface for a monovalent metal may approximate a sphere which corresponds to the circular contour shown for the two-dimensional case in Fig. 10.15*a*, or it may show deviations, particularly if the occupied region touches the first Brillouin zone boundary as shown in Fig. 10.15*b*. The conditions illustrated in Fig. 10.15*a* may be found in the alkali metals, particularly in the case of sodium. Those illustrated in Fig. 10.15*b* are found in copper.

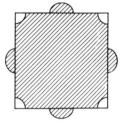

Band overlap can also be described in this way. After a situation like that illustrated in Fig. 10.15*b* has been passed, a stage can be reached at which any further electrons that must be added to complete the band may have to go into the second zone to result in an occupation diagram as illustrated in Fig. 10.16. Recent studies of complex materials such as tin have shown Fermi surfaces that penetrate not merely into the second Brillouin zone, but even into the third, fourth, and fifth zones. The Fermi surface is a very important

**Fig. 10.16** The Fermi surface in two dimensions for a divalent metal with overlapping bands.

feature in the electronic properties of solids, but further study—including the experimental techniques of delineating the surface—cannot be pursued here. Some aspects of the importance of the Fermi surface in relation to the Brillouin zones will be considered when conductivities are discussed in Chapter 12. One of the simpler Fermi surfaces is illustrated in Fig. 10.17.

**Fig. 10.17** The Fermi surface and the first Brillouin zone boundary for copper.

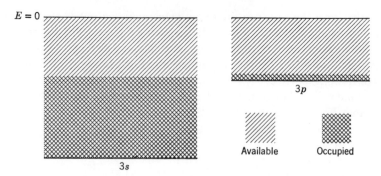

**Fig. 10.18**   The band structure for sodium.

## 10.6   Summary of the Energy Level Configurations for Typical Materials

Let us now summarize the results for some typical or important materials. The evidence leading to the structure to be described is usually a compound of pure theoretical calculation and of experimental results on a large range of phenomena. The theoretical treatment of the last two chapters is too elementary to allow electron distributions to be predicted, but it does serve as a basis for understanding.

### Sodium

Sodium has one 3s valence electron per atom. This state has two places per atom and hence the band is half filled. Actually, the 3p band does overlap the top of the 3s band, and this part of the band structure is shown in Fig. 10.18 (the bands are displaced laterally for clarity). Since the nuclear charge is so well shielded by the ten inner electrons, the valence electron is loosely bound and the free-electron treatment holds very well. Conditions similar to these are found in the other alkali metals, lithium with one 2s electron, potassium with one 4s electron, etc.

### Magnesium

Magnesium lies just above sodium in the Periodic Table and so has two 2s electrons. This would completely fill the 3s band but the overlapping by the 3p band prevents this. The energy level structure is shown in Fig. 10.19. Similar situations are found in beryllium with two electrons in 2s, calcium with two in 4s, etc.

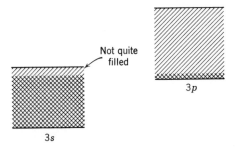

**Fig. 10.19**   The band structure in magnesium.

### Copper

Copper lies at the end of the series of elements in which the 3d band has been filling while the 4s levels are already wholly or partially occupied. In copper the 3d band is just full and there is one 4s electron. Since there is room for two electrons per atom in the 4s band it will be, as for the alkali metal potassium, half full. The next available state is a 4p, and in copper the 4p band completely overlaps the 4s. The 3d electrons are much more tightly bound than the 4s, since each experiences an effective nuclear charge of approximately 11, whereas the 4s experiences a charge of the order of 1 only. Consequently the 3d band is much narrower than the 4s. Figure 10.20 shows the copper electron diagram and it is similar to that for the other noble metals; silver with a 5s electron above a just completed 4d band and gold with a 6s electron above the 5d band.

### Iron

We have discussed copper in which the 3d band is full. The transition series of elements, in which this band is filling while the 4s is already occupied,

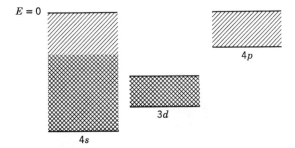

**Fig. 10.20**   The band structure for copper.

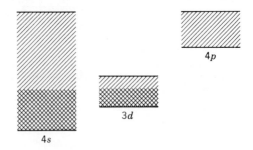

**Fig. 10.21**   The band structure in iron.

has chemical properties which are similar in many respects. Properties, however, such as ferromagnetism, which are dependent on the degree to which the $3d$ band is filled, are different for iron, nickel, and cobalt, where the band is nearly full, from those found in the elements of the series where the band is more empty. Figure 10.21 shows the iron energy band diagram.

### Diamond

A band theory treatment for diamond with its strongly directional C—C bands (see Section 1.6) is very difficult. The energy diagram is shown in Fig. 10.22, where it is seen that the lower band is completely filled, whereas the upper, which is separated from the lower by an energy gap, is completely empty.

### Silicon

Silicon has a type of covalent bond that is similar in nature to that of diamond. The energy diagram is thus like that shown in Fig. 10.22, with the

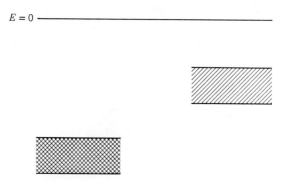

**Fig. 10.22**   The band structure for diamond.

highly significant difference that in silicon the energy gap between the bands is much narrower. In germanium the gap is still less (diamond 6 to 7 eV, silicon 1.1 eV, germanium 0.7 eV). The consequences of this band structure are discussed in Chapter 14.

## Exercises

1. Using the Fermi function, evaluate the temperature at which there is a 1 per cent probability that an electron in a solid will have an energy 0.5 eV above the Fermi energy of 5 eV.

2. Calculate the extent of the energy range between $F(E) = 0.9$ and $F(E) = 0.1$ at a temperature of 2000°K and express it as a fraction of $E_F$ which is 3 eV.

3. Assuming the electrons to be free, calculate the total number of states below $E = 5$ eV in a volume of $10^{-5}$ m³.

4. Assume that lithium has one electron per atom that can be considered free. Calculate the Fermi energy and the Fermi temperature for lithium.

5. Show that at $T = 0°$K the average kinetic energy of free electrons in a metal is $\frac{3}{5}E_F$. $(P_{av} = \int P\, dN / \int dN)$

6. Using the Boltzmann function, evaluate the number of H atoms excited to the state $n = 2$ in the atmosphere of the sun at a temperature of 6000°K as compared with the number in the ground state.

7. Calculate approximately the wavelength of copper K$\alpha$ radiation (i.e., arising from $n = 2 \rightarrow n = 1$) and the potential difference through which an electron must be accelerated in order to excite it.

8. Estimate the ionization energy in magnesium.

9. The sodium and chlorine ions in rock salt are 2.81 A apart. What is the magnitude of the electrostatic force between them?

# 11

# *Static Electron Properties of Metals*

In Chapters 11 and 12 we divide the electronic properties of metals roughly into two groups. The first group includes static electron properties and the other group involves conduction phenomena. The first group includes the various electron emission properties such as photoemission, thermionic emission, and field emission and properties such as contact potential. These properties can all be treated adequately for our present purpose if we consider only the energy level or distribution of energy levels from which the electrons have come. We consider only the over-all potential change of the electron without inquiring too closely into the detailed processes by which the transition has taken place. In general terms these phenomena occur as a consequence of the excitation of the metal by light photons, thermal energy, strong electric fields, etc. Here the free electron approximation is generally perfectly satisfactory; so almost all the work of Chapter 11 uses the free electron model with only incidental reference to the bound electron case.

In the second group of phenomena, the conduction effects considered in Chapter 12, we must be concerned with the detailed response of the electron to an external field and so must take into consideration the acceleration properties of the electron. In contrast to the first group, these conduction phenomena generally involve only a very slight perturbation of the electronic distribution.

## 11.1 Photoelectric Phenomena

The interaction between the electrons of a metal and light waves is an easily observed phenomenon. Charged electroscopes discharge more quickly if the collector plate is irradiated with ultraviolet light; the onset of spark discharges is facilitated if the electrodes are similarly treated; and there are many other similar effects. If the metal surface is placed in an evacuated enclosure and a second electrode sealed in with it as shown in Fig. 11.1, it

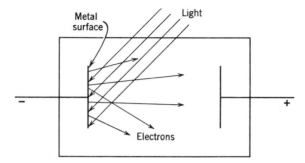

**Fig. 11.1**    The photoelectric effect.

can readily be found that the effect of the light is to cause the emission of charged particles from the surface; and from the sign of the potential required to collect the charges on the collector anode, it is clear that these must be electrons. This is called the *photoelectric effect*, and an apparatus such as that illustrated in Fig. 11.1 is called a *photoelectric cell*. The effect is not a big one, and with typical metal surfaces and light wavelengths and intensities, currents in the microamp range are observed. One of the most striking features is the dependence of the emitted current on the frequency and intensity of the incident light. It is found that the energy of the emitted electrons depends on the *frequency* of the light and not on its *intensity*. There exists also a minimum frequency below which no emission occurs. The part played by the light intensity is to influence the *number* of electrons emitted.

A simplified description of the phenomenon in terms of the models developed in Chapters 9 and 10 can be given. Consider a monovalent metal in which we can assume a state density function in the valence band giving an electron distribution illustrated in Fig. 11.2. To the extent that the free electron model is applicable, this function will be a parabola (e.g., for the alkali metals). Anyhow, there will be a continuous occupation of energy levels from the bottom of the valence band up to the Fermi level. As shown, this is at energy $E_F$ above the energy at the bottom of the valence band. There will then be a gap in the occupied energy spectrum between the Fermi level and the top of the energy scale at the value zero. This gap is usually called the *work function* and will be denoted by $\phi$.

Now consider the arrival of a photon at the metal surface. It is obvious that an electron at the top of the distribution will be able to absorb enough energy to escape from the metal, provided the photon has a sufficiently high frequency so that

$$h\nu \geqslant \phi \qquad (11.1)$$

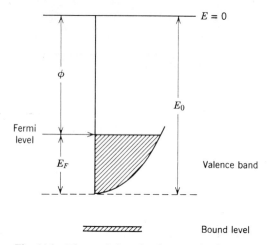

**Fig. 11.2**  The work function in a conducting solid.

This accounts immediately for the existence of a threshold frequency below which photoelectric emission is not possible. Typical values for $\phi$ and the corresponding threshold frequency are given in Table 11.1.

If $h\nu$ is greater than $\phi$, an electron which is initially at the top of the distribution in the solid will escape from the surface with an energy given by

$$\tfrac{1}{2}mv^2 = h\nu - \phi \tag{11.2}$$

If the electron has been taken from a point in the distribution below $E_F$, the energy with which it leaves the surface will be reduced. If the light frequency

**Table 11.1**  Photoelectric Constants

| Element | Work Function (eV) | Threshold Wavelength (A) |
|---------|--------------------|--------------------------|
| Li | 2.46 | 5040 |
| Na | 2.28 | 5430 |
| K | 2.25 | 5510 |
| Cs | 1.94 | 6390 |
| Mg | 3.70 | 3350 |
| Fe | 4.63 | 2680 |
| Cu | 4.48 | 2770 |
| Ag | 4.70 | 2640 |
| Zn | 4.27 | 2900 |
| Ge | 4.62 | 2680 |
| Si | 3.59 | 3450 |

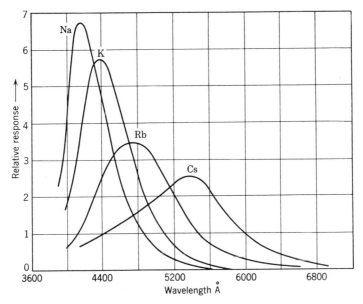

**Fig. 11.3** The spectral sensitivity of the photoelectric effect in the alkali metals.

is increased, the photons can excite electrons from points deeper and deeper in the valence band, giving increasing photoelectron yield up to the frequency at which $h\nu$ is greater than $\phi + E_F$ when no further increase is possible. After this point the yield will actually decline, although the photons have more than enough energy to cause excitation. This decline is related to a lessening probability of electron transition out of the original state, as illustrated in Fig. 10.3. The whole spectral sensitivity curves for the alkali metals are shown in Fig. 11.3.

Actually, the problem is not quite so simple as is suggested by the elementary energy balance conditions given earlier. It can be shown that the conditions of energy and momentum conservation make it impossible for a free electron in the interior of the material to receive energy in this way. Consequently, most of the emitted photoelectrons come from points very close to the surface where energy and momentum conservation is permitted. The effect is enhanced by the low penetrability of light into most solids and the inability of low energy electrons to escape from points deep in the solid. Thus altogether the photoemission is very sensitive to surface conditions as regards both magnitude of emitted current and threshold frequency. One consequence of this sensitivity is that although the measurement of the threshold frequency offers a very tempting possibility of measuring the work function $\phi$, such measurements must be made only with very careful attention to surface conditions if reliable results are to be obtained.

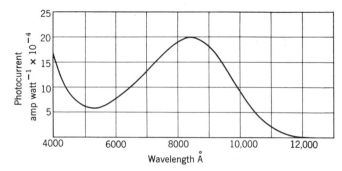

**Fig. 11.4** The spectral sensitivity of the photoelectric effect in the silver-oxygen-cesium photocathode.

One further factor of practical importance is the spectral response of the surface. This is seen from Fig. 11.3 to involve a peaked response. The position of this peak determines the uses for which the cathode may be employed. For example, many everyday applications require maximum sensitivity in the visible region, whereas special purposes may call for cathodes sensitive in the ultraviolet or infrared regions.

The manufacture of cathodes to meet specific requirements is something of an art, since the details of the physical mechanisms involved may not be clearly understood. The conditions to be filled include high quantum yield (number of photoelectrons produced per quantum of incident light) and low work function. Commercially manufactured cathodes are sometimes made of pure alkali metals (lithium, sodium, potassium, rubidium, or cesium) which have been "sensitized" by a glow discharge in hydrogen (which acts to produce hydrides at the emitting surface) inside the phototube. Sometimes composite cathodes are used. Among the more common of these is a silver-oxygen-cesium layer structure which has a response curve extending conveniently into the infrared, as illustrated in Fig. 11.4, and the antimony-cesium compound whose response curve is illustrated in Fig. 11.5. This last cathode has the amazing quantum yield of 20 per cent at the peak value, which is to be compared with the figures of $10^{-3}$ to $10^{-2}$ per cent for pure alkali metals. For a detailed study of materials and preparation methods for photoelectric emitters, reference should be made to the text by Zworykin listed in the Bibliography.

The actual collection of the photoelectrons by the anode is related to the geometry of the cell electrodes. A photoelectric cell is shown in Fig. 11.6. A fraction (*a*) of the photoelectrons will be emitted in such a direction as to strike the anode. When a positive potential is applied to the anode an additional fraction (*b*) will be attracted, and as the potential is increased

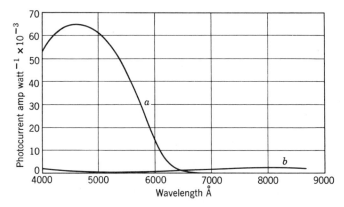

**Fig. 11.5** (*a*) The spectral sensitivity of the photoelectric effect in the antimony-cesium photocathode. (*b*) The curve of Fig. 11.4 for silver-oxygen-cesium redrawn on the same scale for comparison.

more and more electrons will contribute to the current. The increase will continue, however, only until all the emitted electrons are attracted to the anode, and thereafter a higher potential will not increase the current. The current-voltage relation is illustrated in Fig. 11.7. A phototube is normally operated in the saturation region, where it is insensitive to small changes in anode potential.

If a *negative* potential is applied to the anode, electrons will be retarded as they approach it. With a sufficiently high potential they may even be

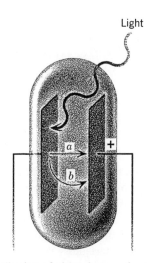

**Fig. 11.6** The collection of photoelectrons by a positive electrode.

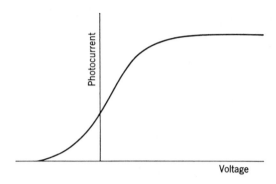

**Fig. 11.7**   The current-voltage characteristic for a typical phototube.

prevented from reaching the anode. The potential at which this happens depends on the energy with which the electron left the emitting surface. Clearly, therefore, the shape of the current curve in the negative potential region contains information about the number of electrons being emitted with a certain energy. Furthermore, with careful control over surface conditions and electrode geometry, this method has been used to obtain experimentally the distribution of state density in the valence band of the alkali metals.

One of the chief problems in interpreting such curves, even with favorable geometry, arises from the fact that in practice we are dealing not with a single electron, but with many electrons. Consequently, those electrons which are traveling after emission toward the collector constitute a "space charge" which reduces the accelerating potential experienced by an electron that has just left the emitting surface. This electron, in turn, influences the shape of the current-potential curve, giving, at any particular potential, lower currents than would otherwise be expected.

## 11.2   Transitions between Internal Energy Levels

The possibility exists that an electron may be excited into unoccupied energy levels by a light quantum or energetic incident electron *without leaving* the metal. Such a transition would normally be difficult to detect in view of the effectively unquantized structure of levels in the valence band. But if there is any preference for the electrons to come from a particular region of the valence energy band, the selective nature of the phenomenon might give it detectable characteristics. Apparently this is the case, for example, in copper, where excitation from the densely occupied 3*d* levels

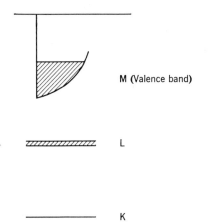

Fig. 11.8 The levels giving rise to the soft X-ray spectrum of sodium.

results in preferential absorption of blue wavelengths in the incident light, leading to the familiar red concentration in the reflected light.

Transitions between the inner tightly bound electron shells of an atom generally fall in the X-ray region. Such levels are usually sharp and un-affected by the proximity of neighboring atoms. Thus X-ray spectroscopy is generally unaffected by the physical state of the material. If we consider transitions involving the upper regions of the bound energy levels, however, then the X-ray spectrum is sensitive to the broadened nature of such levels found in solids. Consider the level diagram given in Fig. 11.8. The X-ray spectrum is excited by removing an electron from an inner shell of the atom. As electrons from the upper levels make transitions downward to fill the gap, quanta are emitted to constitute the X-radiation. If the *K* shell were ionized initially, the X-ray line corresponding to the L to K radiation will be relatively sharp, but the transitions from M (here the valence band) to L will cover a range of energies, depending on the point in the valence band from which the electron made its transition. The spectrum of this radiation, that is, the intensity at each frequency, will thus be a direct measure of the number of electrons at each level of the valence band. A slight correction to the shape is necessary because of possibly varying transition probabilities, but this is only a small effect and does not influence the character of the results. This *soft* X-ray spectrum should therefore be closely associated with the nature of the energy bands. Such spectra have been obtained by Skinner and are illustrated in Fig. 11.9. In this diagram *a* refers to a monovalent metal and should be compared with the band structure of Fig. 10.12, whereas *b* illustrates the case of a divalent metal for comparison with Fig. 10.13. Such experimental confirmation of the general results of

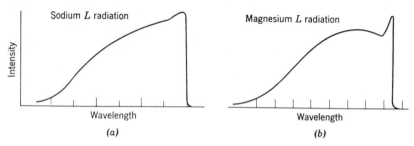

**Fig. 11.9** The soft X-ray band shapes for (*a*) a monovalent and (*b*) a divalent metal. (After Skinner)

band theory is very reassuring and enables measurements of quantities such as the energy width of an occupied band to be made in cases where the calculation from fundamental theory would be very difficult. Thus, for example, the valence band in aluminum is about 12 eV in width, in lithium is 4.2 eV, and in sodium is 3.0 eV.

### 11.3   Thermionic Emission

It was first observed by Edison that heating a wire filament in a vacuum caused an electrical current to pass between it and an electrode if an external voltage was applied to make the wire negative with respect to the electrode. No current is observed if the voltage is applied the other way. The current is interpreted as resulting from the emission of electrons from the wire and the phenomenon is called *thermionic emission*, which can be described by simple application of the free electron model. The Fermi function at temperature zero gives a sharp cutoff in the electron energy distribution at an energy $E_F$. At finite temperatures the tail in the distribution curve extends to higher values of energy $E$ and may, if the temperature is high enough, bridge the whole gap from $E = E_F$ to $E = 0$. When this happens some electrons are free to leave the surface and thermionic emission occurs. The condition allowing an individual electron to leave the surface is that its energy (measured from the bottom of the valence band in accordance with the ideas of section 10.5) must be at least equal to the value $E_0$ or $E_F + \phi$ (see Fig. 11.2). Although this condition is necessary, it is not sufficient because the electron must not only have enough energy but must be traveling in the right direction. If we take the $x$ direction perpendicular to the surface of the emitting solid, we can write an expression for $p_{x_0}$, the critical value of the electron's momentum in the $x$ direction, so that it *just* escapes from the surface.

Since

$$\frac{p_{x_0}^{2}}{2m} = E_F + \phi$$

$$p_{x_0} = \sqrt{2m(E_F + \phi)} \tag{11.3}$$

The actual thermionic current at a certain temperature will then be the product of the electronic charge and the number of electrons having a momentum in the $x$ direction greater than this critical value, which in unit time arrive at unit area of the surface. Let us suppose that the number of electrons per unit volume with values of momentum in the $x$ direction lying between $p_x$ and $p_x + dp_x$ is given by $N(p_x)\, dp_x$. Its value will now be calculated.

Since the velocity of arrival of an electron of momentum $p_x$ is given by $p_x/m$, the number arriving at unit area of the surface in unit time with a value of momentum greater than the critical value is given by

$$\int_{p_{x_0}}^{\infty} \frac{p_x}{m} N(p_x)\, dp_x$$

The thermionic current $j$ is thus

$$j = \frac{e}{m} \int_{p_{x_0}}^{\infty} p_x N(p_x)\, dp_x \tag{11.4}$$

Our task is now to calculate $N(p_x)$. It will be given by the product of the number of possible states of momentum $p_x$ and the probability than an electron is in each state.

The number of states in a certain momentum range $dp$ at momentum $p$ has already been obtained as Equation 8.11$a$. It was

$$Z(p)\, dp = \frac{8\pi}{h^3} p^2\, dp$$

This result refers to momentum values of $p$ in any direction, however, and we must be concerned with momenta in the $x$ direction specifically. We must therefore calculate the number of electrons that have a momentum lying in the range $dp_x$ at $p_x$ when the $p_y$ and $p_z$ values are unrestricted. It is illuminating to consider this problem in a geometrical fashion. Suppose we construct as in Fig. 11.10 a plot in "momentum space" in which each position represents a particular combination of the momentum components $p_x$, $p_y$, and $p_z$. A spherical shell of radius

$$p = p_x^2 + p_y^2 + p_z^2$$

and thickness $dp$ has been drawn. Each quantum state with momentum between $p$ and $p + dp$ lies in this shell. The fraction of states at momentum

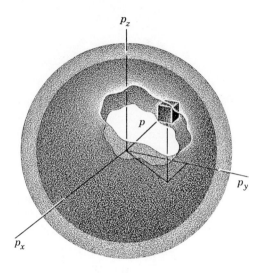

**Fig. 11.10**   To illustrate the calculation of the number of states within certain momentum ranges.  The volume element $dp_x\, dp_y\, dp_z$ is supposed to be contained in the thickness of the spherical shell between $p$ and $p + dp$.

$p$ which have a momentum lying in the interval $p_x$ to $p_x + dp_x$, $p_y$ to $p_y + dp_y$, $p_z$ to $p_z + dp_z$ is therefore given by the ratio of the volume $dp_x\, dp_y\, dp_z$ to that of the spherical shell of thickness $dp$ at radius $p$.  Thus

$$\text{fraction of states in } dp_x\, dp_y\, dp_z = \frac{dp_x\, dp_y\, dp_z}{4\pi p^2\, dp} \tag{11.5}$$

Therefore the actual number of states lying in the interval $dp_x\, dp_y\, dp_z$ is the product of the foregoing fraction with the total number of states in the momentum interval $dp$ at momentum $p$.  Thus

$$Z(p_x p_y p_z)\, dp_x\, dp_y\, dp_z = \frac{8\pi}{h^3}\, p^2\, dp\, \frac{dp_x\, dp_y\, dp_z}{4\pi p^2\, dp}$$

$$= \frac{2}{h^3}\, dp_x\, dp_y\, dp_z. \tag{11.6}$$

This is the number of states per cubic meter with momentum component in the $x$ direction lying between the values $p_x$ and $p_x + dp_x$ and similarly for $p_y$ and $p_z$.

The fraction of these states which is occupied by electrons is given by the Fermi function $F(E)$ of Equation 10.1.  That is,

$$F(E) = \frac{1}{e^{(E-E_F)/kT} + 1}$$

We thus come to the value of $N(p_x)\, dp_x$, which is

$$N(p_x)\, dp_x = \frac{2}{h^3}\, dp_x \int_{p_y=-\infty}^{\infty} \int_{p_z=-\infty}^{\infty} \frac{dp_y\, dp_z}{e^{(E-E_F)/kT} + 1} \qquad (11.7)$$

Since $\phi$ is of the order of a few electron volts, the quantity $E - E_F$ is much bigger than $kT$ ($k$ has a value of $8.6 \times 10^{-5}$ eV $^\circ K^{-1}$) even at temperatures in the thousands of degrees. We can therefore ignore the 1 in comparison with $e^{(E-E_F)/kT}$. Hence the Fermi function reduces to the Boltzmann function $e^{-(E-E_F)/kT}$.

On making this simplification and remembering that

$$E = \frac{1}{2m}\, (p_x{}^2 + p_y{}^2 + p_z{}^2)$$

Equation 11.7 becomes

$$N(p_x)\, dp_x = \frac{2}{h^3}\, dp_x e^{E_F/kT} e^{-p_x{}^2/2mkT} \int_{-\infty}^{\infty} e^{-p_y{}^2/2mkT}\, dp_y \int_{-\infty}^{\infty} e^{-p_z{}^2/2mkT}\, dp_z$$

The integrals have a standard form with value

$$\sqrt{2\pi mkT}$$

each. Thus, finally,

$$N(p_x)\, dp_x = \frac{4\pi mkT}{h^3}\, e^{E_F/kT} e^{-p_x{}^2/2mkT}\, dp_x \qquad (11.8)$$

When this value for $N(p_x)\, dp_x$ is substituted in (11.8),

$$j = \frac{e}{m} \int_{p_{x_0}}^{\infty} \frac{4\pi mkT}{h^3}\, e^{E_F/kT} e^{-p_x{}^2/2mkT} p_x\, dp_x$$

$$= \frac{4\pi mek^2}{h^3}\, T^2 e^{-\phi/kT} \qquad (11.9)$$

This equation is commonly written

$$= AT^2 e^{-\phi/kT}$$

where

$$A = \frac{4\pi mek^2}{h^3} = 120 \text{ amp cm}^{-2}\text{ deg}^{-2} \qquad (11.10)$$

This is the Richardson-Dushman equation. The equation gives only the total current density produced. There will, of course, be an energy distribution among the thermionic electrons arising from the part of the Boltzmann tail of the Fermi distribution that has reached out beyond a value of $E_0 = E_F + \phi$.

There are several auxiliary conditions that modify this result either theoretically or in practice. These conditions are now briefly discussed.

1. There is a certain probability that an electron approaching the metal surface will suffer reflection even though it has enough energy to escape. Consequently, this reflectivity slightly reduces the emitted current.

2. It has been assumed in the treatment that we are considering the passage of a single electron into a vacuum outside the metal. In practice the electrons emitted may, if not removed very quickly by a collector with a high positive potential, constitute a space charge which acts to decrease the current.

3. A large applied electric field can be arranged to remove space charge effects, but the field itself effectively reduces the values of $\phi$. This is discussed in Section 11.4.

4. The work function $\phi$ is often dependent on the crystal orientation relative to the emitting direction. In a polycrystalline material, therefore, an averaged value of $\phi$ is appropriate.

5. Just as was the case in photoelectric emission, the thermionic current is strongly dependent on surface conditions. Contamination—accidental or deliberate—may have a large effect on the $\phi$ value and because of the exponential function may greatly modify the thermionic current.

The choice of materials for the practical application of thermionic emission is dominated, as it was for photoelectric phenomena, by the necessity for a small value of $\phi$. One other consideration is necessary here which was not found in the previous case because the material must be stable at relatively high temperatures. It therefore must not be too volatile, and thus the alkali metals and compounds mentioned previously are not suitable. Materials combining adequate emissivity and low volatility include the alkali earth oxides (BaO, CaO and SrO) and adsorbed thin films of cesium, barium, thorium, or lanthanum on tungsten. In particular, thoriated tungsten is very frequently used. If emission at a very high filament temperature is desired, a pure tungsten filament may be used. Values for the thermionic constants of typical materials are given in Table 11.2. Further information regarding the

**Table 11.2**  Thermionic Constants

| Material | A (amp cm$^{-2}$ $^\circ$K$^{-2}$) | Work Function (eV) |
|---|---|---|
| W | ~75 | 4.5 |
| Ta | 60 | 4.1 |
| Thorium on tungsten | 4.0 | 2.7 |
| BaO | 0.1–60 | 1.4–1.5 |
| SrO | 100 | 2.2 |
| Thorium carbide | 100 | 3.2 |

practical application of thermoemissive materials may be found in the texts by Seeley, Ryder, and Egli listed in the bibliography. In practice, of course, the thermionic current must be generated and collected in some kind of evacuated system in a manner similar to that employed for photoelectric emission. Space charge characteristics similar in nature to those previously discussed are again found.

## 11.4   Field Emission and the Schottky Effect

### *Field Emission*

We can observe that it is possible to remove electrons from a metal surface by the action of an electric field alone, provided only that the field is strong enough. The phenomenon is called *field emission*. It is important in cases such as the onset of a spark discharge and is also the basis of the *field emission microscope*. This is a tool of importance in the study of solid surfaces and is described later.

The phenomenon can be described by the free electron model if we consider the total potential energy experienced by the electron. The free electron model treats the solid as a box with a potential energy which is constant inside the box and which rises discontinuously to zero at the boundaries of the material. This is illustrated in Fig. 11.11. (Note the inversion of the potential scale because electrons are conventionally negative.)

If a field is now applied, the potential, measured from zero at the surface of the solid at $x = 0$, can be considered to increase linearly with distance from $x = 0$. The total potential experienced by the electron is thus as illustrated in Fig. 11.12.

The top of the electron distribution can be considered to be at $A$ in Fig. 11.12. The free space potential is thus seen to take on the character of a

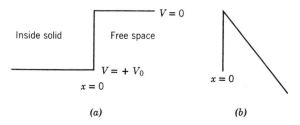

**Fig. 11.11**   (*a*) The potential distribution at the surface of an idealized solid in the absence of an external electric field. (*b*) The potential distribution outside a solid in the presence of an external electric field.

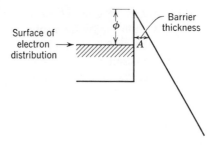

**Fig. 11.12**  The total potential at the surface of a solid in the presence of an external electric field.

*barrier* whose height depends on $\phi$ and whose width depends on the steepness of the rise of the potential curve, that is, on the field strength.  The behavior of an electron wave as it meets a rectangular potential barrier has already been discussed in Section 6.3 and a value for the transmission probability has been obtained.  The barrier involved in the present discussion is not rectangular but triangular, so the previous result is not applicable.  The result remains usable  however, to the extent that the transmission probability depends on the thickness of the barrier in an exponential fashion.  (The standing wave amplitude was proportional to $e^{-\gamma x}$ in Section 8.3.)  It is obvious from Fig.

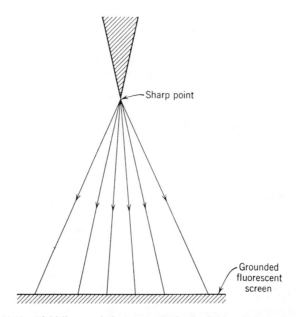

**Fig. 11.13**  Field lines and electron paths in the field emission microscope.

11.12 that the barrier thickness is inversely proportional to the electric field strength so that we may expect terms of the form

$$e^{-\text{constant/field}}$$

in the expression for the transmission current. The complete expression for the current (the Fowler-Nordheim equation) is similar in form to the Richardson-Dushman equation with the exception that in the former the field strength occupies the place of the temperature in the latter.

Very high field strengths are necessary to provide substantial emission through the foregoing mechanism. For a $\phi$ value of 3 eV, fields of the order of $10^9$ v m$^{-1}$ are necessary. Such fields are normally found only near very sharp points. The mechanism is thus of great importance, as stated earlier, in initiating spark breakdown between electrodes at high potentials. Unless the electrodes are atomically smooth, minor defects in the surface give field concentrations that lead to field enhanced emission of electrons. Field emission can be used to study surface detail in the *field emission microscope*. Consider a sharp point of metal to which is applied a high negative potential, as in Fig. 11.13. The field is made uniform around the point by a grounded enclosure. If the field is high enough and the point sharp enough, field emission of electrons takes place. Because of the approximately spherical geometry, the electrons are accelerated radially to strike a fluorescent screen. Since only radial movement is involved, the image on the fluorescent screen will represent the intensity with which electrons were given off in that particular direction, and can give a greatly magnified image of work function variations over the specimen point. Such a picture for a single crystal of tungsten is shown in Fig. 11.14. The dark spots correspond to points of high work function, and these can be correlated with specific directions in the crystal. This method has since been extended to use positive ions reflected from the surface instead of electrons for image production. This instrument is called an *ion emission microscope*. With it the magnification and resolution have been improved to the extent that it is now possible to "see" individual atoms in the solid surface.*

### The Schottky Effect

Another mechanism exists whereby electrostatic fields can influence the electron emission of solids. In the case of field emission, the presence of the field provided the possibility for tunneling without change of the actual value of the work function. Now if we consider a slightly more detailed model of the potential function near the surface of the metal, we shall find that the work function itself is changed by the external field. The refinement

* E. W. Muller, *J. Appl. Phys.* **28**, 1 (1957).

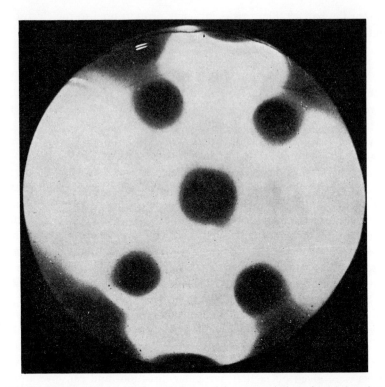

**Fig. 11.14**   A field emission microscope picture giving the variation of work function over a tungsten point.

which we wish to add to the potential function is the inclusion of the force on an electron outside the metal surface.  Any charge when placed near the surface of a conductor experiences a force arising from the polarization of the conducting material.  It can be simply shown that the force is equal to that which would be experienced if the conducting surface were replaced by a charge equal in magnitude but opposite in sign to the original charge at a point as far behind the surface as the original charge was in front of it.  In view of this feature the force is known as an "image" force.  To obtain the complete potential function for the electron at the surface of the metal, therefore, we must add in the contribution of the image force.  The potential for the image force must be

$$V_{\text{image}} = -\frac{1}{4\pi\epsilon_0}\frac{e}{4x} \tag{11.11}$$

where $x$ is the distance between the surface and the charge and $e$ is the value of the charge.  This potential is shown in Fig. 11.15.

Surface

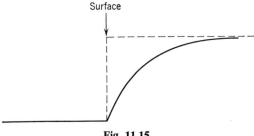

**Fig. 11.15**

Now if an external electric field $\mathscr{E}_x$ is applied, the potential experienced by the charge is the sum of the image potential and the applied potential. The total potential is shown in Fig. 11.16.

The most important feature of this result is that the work function in the field $\phi_F$ is smaller than that without the field. If the field is strong enough, it is clearly possible for $\phi_{F'}$ to vanish completely. When this happens the top of the electron distribution is free to leave the metal without the necessity for tunneling. This reduction in work function is known as the *Schottky effect*.

To obtain the actual value for the reduction in work function we write the total potential

$$V = -\frac{e}{16\pi\epsilon_0 x} - \mathscr{E}_x x \tag{11.12}$$

We require the maximum value of $V$. This is obtained by differentiating $V$ with respect to $x$ from which the value of $x$ ($= x_{\max}$) for which $V$ ($= V_{\max}$) is a maximum is easily shown to be

$$x_{\max} = \frac{1}{\sqrt{16\pi\epsilon_0}}\sqrt{\frac{e}{\mathscr{E}_x}} \tag{11.13}$$

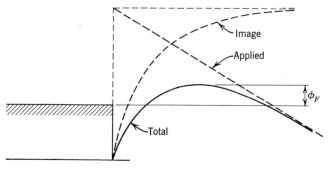

**Fig. 11.16** The total potential at the surface of an idealized metal including both image forces and an external electric field.

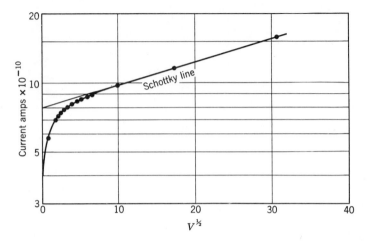

**Fig. 11.17**   The Schottky effect in tungsten.

and the actual value of $V$ at this value of $x$ is

$$V_{max} = -\frac{1}{\sqrt{4\pi\epsilon_0}}\sqrt{e\mathscr{E}_x}$$

The energy of an electron in this potential is

$$-\frac{1}{\sqrt{4\pi\epsilon_0}}e\sqrt{e\mathscr{E}_x}$$

and this represents a reduction in the work function. At a particular temperature, then, we can obtain the actual emitted current as a function of field by substitution of the modified value of $\phi$ into the Richardson-Dushman equation. We obtain

$$j = AT^2 e^{-\left(\phi - \frac{1}{\sqrt{4\pi\epsilon_0}}e\sqrt{e\mathscr{E}_x}\right)/kT} \tag{11.14}$$

This is normally represented by a graph of $\log j$ versus $\sqrt{\mathscr{E}_x}$ or $\sqrt{V}$ which gives a straight line known as the Schottky line and is illustrated in Fig. 11.17. Deviations occur at low $\mathscr{E}_x$ where small-scale influences on the value of $\phi$ itself might be expected to be important.

The effect on $\phi$ is not large ($\Delta\phi \simeq 1.2 \times 10^{-2}$ eV for $\mathscr{E}_x = 10^5$ v m$^{-1}$), but the effect on the emitted current can be appreciable. It is important, for example, for a diode rectifier at high voltages.

The mechanism of *quantum tunneling*, which was mathematically described in Section 8.3, has been used to account for the values of thermionic and field emission currents from metal surfaces. Later, in Section 14.14, we again discuss the mechanism in its application to semiconducting diodes.

## 11.5   Contact Potential

Consider two metals with different work functions $\phi_1$ and $\phi_2$ and allow them to become electrically connected. The state of affairs just after they have been brought into contact but before any electron transfer has taken place is illustrated in Fig. 11.18*a*.

If electron flow is possible, it will take place only from left to right since (at $T = 0$) there are no empty states below $E_F$. The electrons can lower the over-all energy of the system by flowing from metal 1 to metal 2, and they will continue to do so until the two Fermi levels are the same. The consequence of this flow is an excess of electrons in one metal and a deficiency in the other which can be observed as a potential difference between the two metals called a *contact potential*. The contact potential is commonly represented by a spacing between the "$V = 0$" levels as shown in Fig. 11.18*b*. The value of the contact potential is clearly the difference between the two work functions.

Contact potentials can be measured by making the two metals the opposite plates of a capacitor. If the plates are connected, the contact potential difference gives rise to charges on the electrodes. If now the distance between the plate is suddenly changed, a voltage pulse is produced in the connecting circuit because of the sudden change in capacitance. An external potential can be applied to the plates and adjusted so that with the distance between the plates in continuous oscillation the voltage pulse is reduced to zero. The applied potential must then just equal the contact potential which is thus

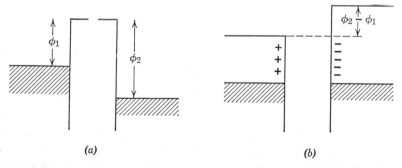

(a)                                            (b)

**Fig. 11.18**   The Fermi levels and potentials of two metals (*a*) Before electron transfer has taken place. (*b*) After electron transfer has generated the contact potential.

measured. Once the work function is known for one of the plates, the value of other unknown work functions can be easily obtained by substitution.

Contact potentials are important in practice if we wish to know to high precision a potential such as an accelerating potential between a cathode and an anode. The actual accelerating potential difference is that between their Fermi levels, which differs from that between the metal surfaces by an amount equal to the contact potential. Since contact potentials can be seen from Table 11.2 to often amount to 2 or 3 volts, this may be an important correction in precise work.

The concept of the lining up of the Fermi levels in two materials in contact will prove to be of the greatest importance in the semiconductor work described in Chapter 14, since most semiconductor applications involve junctions of one sort or another.

## 11.6   The Effect of Surface Conditions on the Work Function

Frequent reference has been made to the influence on the work function of surface conditions, particularly the presence of an adsorbed surface layer of foreign atoms. There are many different mechanisms whereby surface conditions can affect work functions, and many of these are used in the preparation of surfaces for photoemission and thermionic emission. Only one mechanism will be discussed here, but it will serve as an example of the type of phenomenon in question.

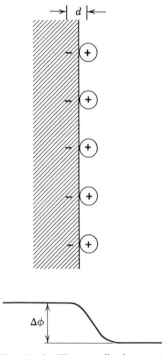

**Fig. 11.19**  The contribution to the work function of an adsorbed layer of atoms on the surface of a solid.

Consider an atom close to a metal surface. If that atom has an easily removable electron that can join the metal at a lower energy than it had in the atom, a positive ion will be formed. Electrostatic attraction between the negatively charged metal surface and the positive ion will cause it to adhere to the surface. If we now consider a complete monatomic layer covering the metal surface, we shall have a double sheet of charge, as illustrated in Fig. 11.19. This gives rise to no external field, but there is a field in the space between the two charge sheets. Thus, if we extract an electron from inside the metal, the amount of work we must do is reduced because of the assistance provided by this internal field in the surface layer. In other words, a mono-layer of electropositive atoms *reduces* the work function of the surface. This is the case for alkali atoms and alkali earth atoms adsorbed on metals like tungsten. On the other hand, a layer of negative ions will increase the work function, as, for example, with oxygen on tungsten.

To calculate the change in work function we must write down the field in the space between the double layer. It is

$$\mathscr{E} = \frac{\sigma}{\epsilon_0}$$

where $\sigma$ is the surface charge density. If the two charge sheets are separated by a distance $d$, the potential difference across the space will be

$$\Delta\phi = \frac{\sigma}{\epsilon_0} de$$

If the charge density $\sigma$ arises from $N$ ions per unit area each with charge $e$, we have finally

$$\Delta\phi = \frac{Ne^2d}{\epsilon_0}$$

For a monotomic layer, values of $\Delta\phi$ of about 1 eV can arise quite easily.

The foregoing is only one aspect of the effect of surface contamination on the work function. In spite of the technological importance of the topic, however, its great complexity precludes further discussion here.


## 11.7  The Heat Capacity of an Electron Gas

One further property remains to be described in the class of phenomena that depend, in general, only on the distribution of electrons among available energy levels. This is the heat capacity of electrons in a metal. It is not an important topic from the point of view of the everyday use of metals, but it becomes a dominant property at very low temperatures. It is also one of the properties whose treatment by classical methods gave strikingly wrong results and whose satisfactory description by wave mechanics was one of the early triumphs of the new theory.

To evaluate the heat capacity of the electrons in a metal we must first calculate their total energy as a function of temperature. If $N(E)\,dE$ is the number of conduction electrons per kilogram atomic weight having energies lying between $E$ and $E + dE$, we can write the total electron energy as

$$u = \int_0^\infty EN(E)\,dE \tag{11.15}$$

Just as in Section 11.3, we can write $N(E) \, dE$ in terms of the Fermi function and the state density function and then integrate. The electronic heat capacity $C_v$ per kilogram atomic weight at constant volume is then obtained as

$$C_v = \frac{\partial u}{\partial T} \tag{11.16}$$

The actual integration of (11.15) is rather complex and will not be given here. It is, in any case, possible to make an order-of-magnitude estimate of the heat capacity by an elementary argument. First of all it is clear that the heat capacity is going to be small. Only a very few conduction electrons at the top of the distribution, that is, near the Fermi level, will have empty states sufficiently close to them into which they can be thermally excited by normal temperatures. This contrasts with the classical view in which all particles in an assembly would be able to absorb energy and so contribute to the heat capacity.

At a temperature close to $T = 0$, consider an energy range between $E_F - kT$ and $E_F$. It is obvious from the graph of the Fermi function in Fig. 10.1 that the fraction of conduction electrons contained in this energy range is, ignoring tailing, $kT/E_F$. If all the conduction electrons behaved like gas molecules, the energy absorbed by the electrons per kilogram atomic weight in raising the temperature to $T$ would be of the order of $\mathscr{N}kT$, where $\mathscr{N}$ is the number of electrons per kilogram atomic weight. Since, however, it is only those electrons in the small energy range we are considering that can gain energy the value of $u$ is given by

$$u \simeq \mathscr{N}kT \left( \frac{kT}{E_F} \right) \tag{11.17}$$

Hence

$$C_v \simeq \mathscr{N}k \frac{kT}{E_F} \tag{11.18}$$

At normal temperatures $kT \ll E_F$, thus providing the expected small value of $C_v$. The value which is given by the complete theory differs from the value in (11.18) only by a constant and is

$$C_v = \left( \frac{\pi^2}{2} \right) \mathscr{N}k \left( \frac{kT}{E_F} \right) \tag{11.19}$$

This is commonly written

$$C_v = \gamma T \tag{11.20}$$

We shall see in Section 13.6 that the specific heat of a solid always contains a term that arises because of the thermal vibrations of the atomic lattice. At normal temperatures this lattice term dominates. However, at low temperatures the lattice specific heat varies as $T^3$, whereas from (11.20) the electronic specific heat obviously varies as $T$. Thus at very low temperatures ($\simeq 10°$K) the electronic specific heat can become an appreciable fraction of the total measured specific heat of the solid.

## Exercises

1. Calculate the photoelectric threshold for tungsten, which has a work function of 4.5 eV.

2. Light from a mercury vapor lamp passes through a filter to isolate the 5461 A line and falls on a cesium surface with an intensity of $10^{-2}$ watt m$^{-2}$. Assuming a quantum yield of $10^{-4}$, calculate the photocurrent produced. What retarding potential would have to be applied to the collector to reduce the current to zero?

3. Show that a photon cannot give up all its energy to an electron isolated in space. (The momentum of a photon is $E/c$ where $E$ is its energy and $c$ the velocity of light.)

4. What is the width in A of the $L$ radiation from sodium (Fig. 11.9)? Which electrons take part in the transition? Give a short description, attributing the transition to a hole in the valence band. In what way will the shape of the $k\beta$ ($3s \rightarrow 1s$) line differ from the $L$?

5. The quantum numbers $l$ and $s$ add to give the total angular momentum vector $j$. The figure shows the higher energy X-ray levels for the uranium atom and the allowed transitions. Give the quantum numbers $n$, $l$, and $j$ associated with

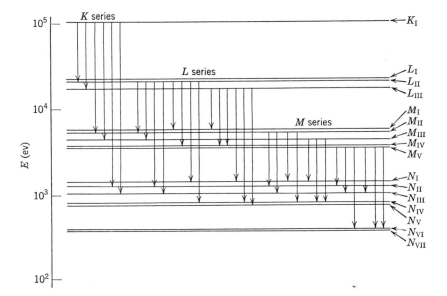

each level and confirm that the transition rules are $\Delta l = \pm 1$ and $\Delta j = 0, \pm 1$.

6. Calculate the thermionic current emitted by a tungsten ($\phi = 4.52$ V) filament 0.05 m long and $10^{-4}$ m in diameter which is at a temperature of 2000°K in no external field.

7. Repeat the calculation of Exercise 4 for the case in which an electric field at the surface of the filament is $5 \times 10^5$ volts m$^{-1}$ and state the amount by which the work function has been reduced.

8. Assume a thorium monolayer on a tungsten filament. The Th-Th distance is 5 A and the Th-W spacing 2 A. Each thorium ion carries a charge of $0.3 \times 10^{-19}$ coulomb. Estimate the reduction in the tungsten work function and the increased emission current for the filament of Exercise 6.

9. What is the contact potential between silver and tungsten?

10. A photocell (Fig. 11.6) has a copper collector ($\phi = 4.48$ V) and a barium emitter ($\phi = 2.10$ V). Draw an electron energy diagram when a negative cutoff voltage is applied to the cathode for light of wavelength 4000 A.

11. Calculate the heat capacity of the electron gas at room temperature in copper assuming 1 free electron per atom. Compare this with the value of $2.4 \times 10^4$ joule (kg mole)$^{-1}$ deg$^{-1}$ for the total heat capacity.

# 12

# *Electron Transport in Metals*

In Chapter 11 we were concerned with those properties of solids, and in particular of metals, which can be treated by using only the distribution of electrons in the energy bands. We gave only an elementary treatment which ignored the detailed mechanisms whereby the electrons were accelerated. We wish now to describe the properties of metals that depend in detail on the changes in electron velocity.

## 12.1 Electrical Conduction

It was known from the early days of experimenting with static electricity that certain materials possessed the property of conducting electric charge from point to point under the influence of an electric field.

In many instances it is found experimentally that the current density $j$ is proportional to the field $\mathscr{E}$ inside the conductor. If we specify that this observation is to be made under certain conditions (uniform temperature of conductor to avoid thermoelectric contributions to $\mathscr{E}$, freedom from external magnetic fields to avoid resistance contributions from bending of electron trajectories, etc.) we can write Ohm's law

$$j = \sigma \mathscr{E} \tag{12.1}$$

where $\sigma$ is the *conductivity* or the reciprocal of the *resistivity* $\rho$. The aim of any theory of conductivity must therefore be a prediction of Ohm's law in the cases where it is appropriate, and also the value of the resistivity of the material, that is, the resistance per unit length per unit cross-sectional area.

The ease with which materials conduct electricity varies widely, giving an empirical classification into good conductors (metals) whose resistivity is of the order of $10^{-7}$ ohm-m, "non" conductors (insulators) with resistivities of about the order of magnitude of $10^{13}$ ohm-m, and a group of materials with a

**Table 12.1**

| Element | Resistivity (ohm-m) | Temperature of Measurement |
|---------|---------------------|----------------------------|
| | Metals | |
| Ag | $1.6 \times 10^{-8}$ | 20°C |
| Al | $2.83 \times 10^{-8}$ | 20°C |
| Cu | $1.69 \times 10^{-8}$ | 20°C |
| Au | $2.44 \times 10^{-8}$ | 20°C |
| Fe | $8.85 \times 10^{-8}$ | 0°C |
| Hg | $95.8 \times 10^{-8}$ | 20°C |
| Ni | $7.24 \times 10^{-8}$ | 20°C |
| Na | $4.3 \times 10^{-8}$ | 0°C |
| | Semiconductors | |
| Ge | 0.47 | |
| Si | $3 \times 10^3$ | |
| In Sb | $\sim 2 \times 10^4$ | |
| | Insulators | |
| Mica | $9 \times 10^{14}$ | |
| Quartz | $3 \times 10^{14}$ | |
| Diamond | $10^{14}$ | |

wide range of intermediate resistivity values called semiconductors. Typical values of resistivities are given in Table 12.1.

The occurrence of this phenomenon of conductivity can be given an elementary description in terms of the band models we have been using. Consider a solid subject to an electric field. The electrons would like to move up the field direction, thereby gaining energy. However, the opportunity for any particular electron to gain energy is governed by whether or not there is an *available* and *empty* energy level at the new energy. If there is a level that can be occupied by the electron in its excited state, the electron will move under the influence of the field. If there is no available level, the electron cannot obtain energy from the field and so will not respond to it. The consequence of this argument is that, under the low energy kind of excitation involved in conductivity phenomena, the question of whether or not the material will conduct depends on whether or not the electrons at the *top* of the distribution can accept energy. If they can and do, they will leave spaces lower in the distribution into which electrons from deeper in the distribution can be excited, and so on. Thus the requirement of available states at the top of the distribution means that conductivity will occur only in an unfilled band, as in sodium (see Fig. 10.18), or in a filled band only if it

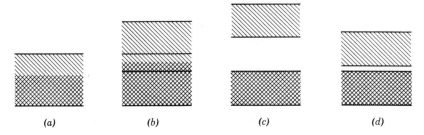

**Fig. 12.1** Electron occupation in various band configurations: (*a*) and (*b*) conductors; (*c*) insulator; and (*d*) semiconductor.

overlaps the next higher unoccupied band, as in magnesium (see Fig. 10.19). If a band is just filled, as, for example, in diamond (see Fig. 10.22), in general no response to a field will be possible. If, however, the energy gap between the filled band under discussion and the next higher unfilled band is not large, the possibility exists of excitation of electrons over the gap. This excitation could take place because of either thermal or field energy. In such a case conductivity would be observed, but its value would be a function of the degree of excitation between the two bands, that is, of the temperature or field. It will be seen in Chapter 14 that this is the situation in a semiconductor. The various possibilities are summarized in Fig. 12.1.

The response to an electric field can also be described in terms of the Fermi surface. In Fig. 12.2 the densely shaded sphere represents the Fermi surface in the absence of an external field. Electrons have velocities in all directions but no net current flows because the distribution is spherically symmetrical. Now consider the application of an electric field. On the

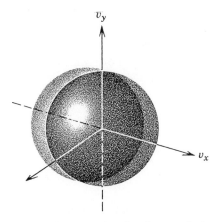

**Fig. 12.2** The displacement of the Fermi surface in a conductor carrying a current.

assumption that the electrons all acquire an average velocity $v_{\mathscr{g}}$ in the $-x$ direction in the field, the altered distribution will be shown as the displaced sphere in Fig. 12.2. The distribution is no longer symmetrical above $v_{\mathscr{g}} = 0$, and so net current flow will occur. Normally the energy supplied to electrons by a field is much smaller than the energy at the top of the distribution, and the displacement indicated in Fig. 12.2 is a greatly exaggerated representation of a small perturbation. Other mechanisms for conductivity exist, for example, in "insulators," but these will be considered later.

## 12.2    The Effective Mass of the Electron

To calculate the value of the conductivity it is necessary to consider the acceleration of an electron in the field applied to the material. One difference between the behavior of electrons bound in a solid and electrons in free space is immediately obvious. Electrons in free space are accelerated indefinitely by an applied field, but in a metal, even though we talk about "free" electrons, some process must be operative to restrict the current to the observed values. We shall discuss later the mechanism by which this limiting process works, but for the present it will suffice merely to say that the situation can be described by ascribing to the electron a time, $\tau$, called the relaxation time, during which it can be accelerated. At the end of time $\tau$ the electron is "scattered" into a new state, thereby losing all the momentum gained in the field direction. Clearly such an assumption constitutes a modification of the standard Krönig-Penney model treatment (Section 9.8). In that treatment an electron will remain in its particular momentum state indefinitely, that is, $\tau$ is infinite.

Consider now an electron in a conductor in an electric field $\mathscr{E}$. The electron will be accelerated by the field. It is not easy to see what value the acceleration should have on the basis of the treatment of the electron in a periodic lattice given in Chapter 9 because the motion of such an electron was shown not to obey the simple relations which hold for a free particle in classical mechanics. The classical mechanics energy-momentum relation for a free particle is simply

$$E = \frac{p^2}{2m} \tag{12.2}$$

and the acceleration $a$ of a charge $e$ in a field $\mathscr{E}$ is

$$a = \frac{e\mathscr{E}}{m} \tag{12.3}$$

For the electron in the periodic lattice, however, the energy-momentum relation turned out to be a most complicated function whose graph appeared in Fig. 9.22. This means that for this relation we no longer calculate velocities or accelerations from energy changes using the simple formulation of Newtonian mechanics.

To discuss this problem of the velocity of a particle in wave mechanics we refer to the statement in Section 8.2 that the *group velocity of the de Broglie waves is equal to the velocity of the particle which the wave is describing.* Let $\omega$ be the angular frequency of the de Broglie wave and $\kappa$ its wave number. Then the group velocity $v_g$ is $d\omega/d\kappa$. Thus for the electron

$$v = \frac{2\pi}{h}\frac{dE}{d\kappa} \tag{12.4}$$

This relation now provides a means of calculating the velocity of an electron in the band model and consequently the acceleration. The acceleration is simply

$$a = \frac{2\pi}{h}\frac{d}{dt}\left(\frac{dE}{d\kappa}\right)$$
$$= \frac{2\pi}{h}\frac{d^2E}{d\kappa^2}\frac{d\kappa}{dt} \tag{12.5}$$

Since we have the quantity $d^2E/d\kappa^2$ from the $E$, $\kappa$ relation, all we have to do now is to find the value of $d\kappa/dt$ under the influence of an applied field $\mathscr{E}$.

Consider an electron to be acted on by a field during a time $dt$. If the velocity of the electron is $v$, the distance traveled in $dt$ is $v\,dt$ so that

$$dE = e\mathscr{E}\cdot v\,dt$$
$$= e\mathscr{E}\frac{2\pi}{h}\frac{dE}{d\kappa}dt$$

That is,

$$\frac{d\kappa}{dt} = \frac{2\pi e\mathscr{E}}{h} \tag{12.6}$$

Combining Equations 12.5 and 12.6 gives us, finally, for the acceleration

$$a = \frac{4\pi^2 e\mathscr{E}}{h^2}\frac{d^2E}{d\kappa^2} \tag{12.7}$$

Now compare this result with Equation 12.3 for a free, classical particle. It is obvious that the two are identical in form if we define a new quantity.

$$m^* = \frac{h^2}{4\pi^2}\left(\frac{d^2E}{d\kappa^2}\right)^{-1} \tag{12.8}$$

so as to write in all cases

$$a = \frac{e\mathscr{E}}{m^*} \tag{12.9}$$

The quantity $m^*$ is called *the effective mass of the electron.* It serves to take into account the nonclassical properties of the electron in the periodic lattice and consequently to enable us always to use the simple form of the acceleration equation.

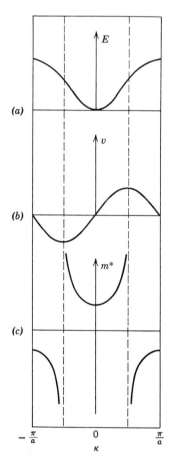

(a)

(b)

(c)

$-\dfrac{\pi}{a}$    0    $\dfrac{\pi}{a}$

$\kappa$

**Fig. 12.3** The $E, \kappa$ relation and effective mass in the first Brillouin zone of a linear lattice.

The graphs of $E$, $dE/d\kappa$, and $d^2E/d\kappa^2$ in the first Brillouin zone of a linear lattice are given in Fig. 12.3. These graphs illustrate some surprising properties of the electron. From a constant value at $\kappa = 0$, $m^*$ rises rapidly as the $\kappa$ value (and the momentum) of the electron increases. Then $m^*$ passes through a singularity and thereafter is clearly negative up to the top of the first zone. For a particular metal, of course, the actual behavior of the electrons will depend on the Fermi energy, that is, on how far out in the zone the electron distribution reaches. Some values of $m^*/m$ for particular metals are given in Table 12.2.

The values given in Table 12.2 can be understood in terms of the appropriate $E, \kappa$ relation. In Chapter 9 we did not write down an $E, \kappa$ relation explicitly but only drew the graph shown in Fig. 9.22. It is possible, however, to obtain an expression for $E$ as a function of $\kappa^*$ which shows that as the binding of electrons (i.e., the height $V_0$ of the potential barrier) increases, the steepness of the dependence of $E$ on $\kappa$ also increases. Consequently, metals like the transition metals, which have their Fermi energy falling in a tightly bound band like the $3d$ band, will show relatively high values of $dE/d\kappa$ and $d^2E/d\kappa^2$. These are represented by the very high values of $m^*/m$ for metals such as nickel and $\alpha$Fe. Lower values of $m^*/m$ arise for cases where the valence electrons are less tightly bound and are governed merely by the position of the Fermi energy in the $E, \kappa$ diagram.

It is worth taking some trouble to consider the physical basis of the somewhat surprising behavior represented by the $v$-$\kappa$ and $m^*$-$\kappa$ curves.

* A. H. Wilson, *The Theory of Metals,* Cambridge Univ. Press, Cambridge, 1953.

**Table 12.2**

| Metal | $m^*/m$ |
| --- | --- |
| Ni | 28 |
| Fe | 12 |
| Pd | 43 |
| Pt | 22 |
| Cu | 1.47 |
| Mb | 1.33 |
| Ti | 3.15 |
| Zr | 2.24 |
| Cr | 2.93 |
| Li | 1.53 |
| Na | 0.94 |
| K | 0.58 |
| Be | 1.62 |

For an electron near the middle of a zone having low energy, the de Broglie wavelength is large compared with the lattice spacing. This allows the wave to be propagated comparatively freely through the lattice. (This would also happen, of course, for a high energy particle in which the wavelength is much *less* than the lattice spacing.) However, in the intermediate range, where the de Broglie wavelength is of the same order as the lattice spacing, interference properties appear. Consider first the situation in which an electron has a $\kappa$ value that coincides with the value at the top of the first zone of a linear lattice, that is, using Equation 9.23,

$$\frac{1}{\lambda} = \frac{1}{2a} \tag{12.10}$$

As has already been pointed out, this condition corresponds to Bragg reflection of the electron waves. It is particularly easy to see this for the linear lattice because the double journey from one lattice site to the next and back again after reflection constitutes one wavelength retardation. The direct and reflected waves are therefore in phase; this condition is known as a "standing" wave and is characterized by the fact that its amplitude modulation is stationary in space, which gives us the $v = 0$ value at the top of the zone (remembering that it is the *group* velocity of the electron wave, i.e., the velocity of the amplitude modulation, which corresponds to the velocity of the electron). Now if we consider an electron with an energy in the upper part of the band, the wavelength of the de Broglie wave is greater than it was at the top of the band, and so the wave reflected from an adjacent lattice site is no longer exactly in phase with the direct wave. This results in an amplitude modulation which is not stationary and so corresponds to a finite velocity of the electron. However, it is a velocity which diminishes as the energy of the electron increases to make the wavelength closer to the "standing" wave value. This argument makes plausible the descending part of the $v$, $E$ curve in the upper part of the zone. Apparent violations of Newton's second law do not occur, because we are considering the response to the field of only part (the electron) of a compound system (the electron + the lattice).

The argument can be extended to cover the case of $m^*$ corresponding to a point of inflection on the $E$, $\kappa$ diagram. This value occurs at a wavelength that is twice as great as that at the top of the zone. The returning reflected wave is then exactly *out of phase* with the direct wave leading to the singularity represented by an infinite value of $m^*$.

We have by no means proved that the use of $m^*$ in the classical acceleration equation is justified. It turns out in practice, however, that it is an almost invariably satisfactory way of taking the electron-lattice interaction into account without the necessity for considering each problem in terms of the appropriate $E$, $\kappa$ relation. In this way we can almost always take a result which is valid on the free electron model and make it valid for the periodic potential by substituting $m^*$ for $m$. This is a great convenience. It must be noted carefully, however, that our simple treatment has used only a linear lattice. A real metal in three dimensions may be anisotropic, and the values of $m^*$ appropriate to the three coordinate directions may differ. An arbitrary direction for the electron momentum would then require a tensor representation for $m^*$.

The influence of the band structure on the electrical properties of solids will therefore be seen whenever the mass of the electron enters an equation. In this way even static properties like the heat capacity are influenced, because, as Equation 11.19 shows, the electronic heat capacity is inversely proportional to the Fermi energy, which is, in turn, inversely proportional to the electron mass. A similar situation holds for the paramagnetic properties of the electron gas and this is discussed in Chapter 15. The influence of the effective mass concept on properties like conduction is obvious and will be taken up in this chapter as the necessity arises.

## 12.3   The Value of the Conductivity

We are now in a position to evaluate the conductivity of a conductor that depends on electrons for the transport of charge. Assuming a value for the acceleration of an electron under the influence of a field $\mathscr{E}$ from Equation

12.9, we obtain for the velocity gained in time $\tau$ the value $v_{\mathscr{E}}$ where

$$v_{\mathscr{E}} = \frac{e\mathscr{E}}{m^*} \cdot \tau \tag{12.11}$$

Note that this velocity $v_{\mathscr{E}}$ constitutes a drift velocity along the field direction. It is superimposed on the ordinary random velocities of the electrons that make no contribution to the current.

The current $j$ is then the rate of flow of charge across unit area of the conductor perpendicular to the current flow; that is,

$$j = Nev_{\mathscr{E}} \tag{12.12}$$

where $N$ is the number of conduction electrons per unit volume. Thus

$$j = \frac{Ne^2\tau}{m^*} \mathscr{E} \tag{12.13}$$

We have now achieved our objective in obtaining Ohm's law, $j \propto \mathscr{E}$, as a consequence of the theory, and the conductivity is

$$\sigma = \frac{Ne^2\tau}{m^*} \tag{12.14}$$

It should be noted that $\tau$ will differ for electrons from different parts of the conduction band. However, Fig. 12.2 shows that the perturbed distribution due to the field can be constructed by rearranging only those electrons near the surface of the distribution. Thus even though all the electrons in the valence band contribute to the current, the value of $\tau$ appropriate to Equation 12.14 can be taken as that for the electrons near $E_F$. Using this condition we can define a mean free path $l$ for the electrons as

$$l = v_F\tau \tag{12.15}$$

where $v_F$ is the velocity of the electrons near the Fermi surface. The conductivity equation then becomes

$$q = \frac{Ne^2l}{m^*v_F} \tag{12.16}$$

At this stage the question arises regarding the value of $N$ to be used. On the free electron assumption this may be obvious as, for example, in sodium, where it would be fair to guess that the number of free electrons should be very close to one per atom. For more complicated atoms, however, the extent to which the band is filled becomes important because, as we shall see later, some of the electron distribution can be blocked from participation in the response to the electric field. In this case we cannot say immediately

**Table 12.3**

| Metal | $N_{eff}$ (electrons per atom) | $v_F$ (m sec$^{-1}$) | $\tau$ (sec) | $l$ (m) | $\sigma$ (ohm$^{-1}$ m$^{-1}$) |
|-------|-------------------------------|----------------------|--------------|---------|-------------------------------|
| Na | ~1 | $1.07 \times 10^6$ | $31 \sim 10^{-15}$ | $6.7 \times 10^{-8}$ | $2.09 \times 10^7$ |
| Cu | ~1 | $1.58 \times 10^6$ | $27 \times 10^{-15}$ | $8.4 \times 10^{-8}$ | $5.76 \times 10^7$ |
| Ag | ~1 | $1.40 \times 10^6$ | $41 \times 10^{-15}$ | $11.4 \times 10^{-8}$ | $6.12 \times 10^7$ |
| Au | ~1 | $1.40 \times 10^6$ | $29 \times 10^{-15}$ | $8.1 \times 10^{-8}$ | $4.37 \times 10^7$ |
| Ni | 0.6 | $1.34 \times 10^6$ | $10 \times 10^{-15}$ | $2.7 \times 10^{-8}$ | $1.36 \times 10^7$ |
| Fe | 0.2 | $0.91 \times 10^6$ | $24 \times 10^{-15}$ | $4.4 \times 10^{-8}$ | $1.01 \times 10^7$ |
| Pt | 0.6 | $1.23 \times 10^6$ | $9 \times 10^{-15}$ | $2.2 \times 10^{-8}$ | $0.92 \times 10^7$ |

what the number of conduction electrons should be and we talk about $N_{eff}$, the effective number of free electrons per atom. This number is the subject of either very detailed calculation or of measurement. Typical values of $N_{eff}$ $l$, $v_F$, and $\tau$ are given in Table 12.3.

The actual value of the conductivity is therefore governed by the quantities $N$, $m^*$, and $l$ (or $\tau$). The parameter $l$ plays the dominating role in determining the conductivity. No matter what value of $l$ is found, however, the value of $m^*$ will influence the conductivity. For instance, the high values of $m^*$ for the transition metals contribute to the low conductivity seen in Table 12.1, and the low $m^*$ values for the alkali metals and for metals like silver and copper contribute to high conductivity.

## 12.4  Sources of Resistance

In the band theory of Krönig and Penney there is no provision for any alteration of the electron state of energy and momentum. In fact, it has been proved by Bloch that, in an ideal, perfectly periodic lattice an electron would, in the absence of external influences, remain in its state of energy or momentum indefinitely. The existence of the finite relaxation time $\tau$ in a certain state which is necessary in the description of conductivity must therefore be the consequence of departure of the lattice from perfect periodicity. Such departures from perfection can be due to the following:

1. The vibration of lattice atoms by thermal agitation (see Chapter 13).
2. The presence of geometric or chemical defects such as vacancies, interstitial atoms, dislocations, grain boundaries, impurities, etc.
3. Surface or boundary effects such as exist in thin films.

The experimental variation of resistivity of a metal with temperature shows features which we can identify with particular types of imperfection.

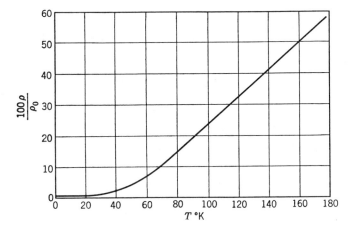

**Fig. 12.4** The temperature variation of the resistivity of copper. The resistivity is expressed as a fraction of that at 0°C. The curve is linear about a temperature of about 70°K, and the resistance is effectively constant at the residual value below about 15°K.

A curve for copper is shown in Fig. 12.4. The curve shows the presence of a temperature-dependent contribution to the resistance which is approximately linear with temperature. This temperature-dependent contribution we attribute to lattice vibrations. The curve also shows a constant contribution to the resistance at a temperature low enough for the lattice vibration contribution to be neglected. This latter resistance is called the *residual resistance* and is assumed to arise from the other classes of lattice imperfections.

At a temperature above about 20°K we must consider the presence of the two contributions simultaneously; that is, we must calculate the probability of scattering from one mechanism *or* the other. Since we can say that the scattering probability is proportional to $1/\tau$, we have

$$\frac{1}{\tau_{\text{total}}} = \frac{1}{\tau_R} + \frac{1}{\tau_T} \tag{12.17}$$

where $\tau_{\text{total}}$ is the effective relaxation time for the whole process, and $\tau_R$ and $\tau_T$ refer, respectively, to the relaxation time for scattering by defects and thermal vibrations. Thus we obtain for the total resistivity

$$\rho = \frac{m^*}{Ne^2}\left(\frac{1}{\tau_R} + \frac{1}{\tau_T}\right) \tag{12.18}$$

The presence of the two contributions can be seen in the resistivity of copper-nickel alloys shown in Fig. 12.5. Here the temperature-dependent resistance is added to the residual resistance, the residual resistance increasing as the copper lattice is progressively distorted by the addition of impurities.

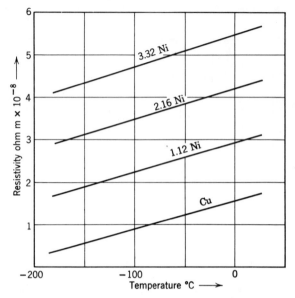

**Fig. 12.5** The resistivity of copper-nickel alloys showing the existence of the same temperature-dependent resistivity superimposed on varying amounts of residual resistance.

Finally, we should observe that the relaxation time $\tau$ which we have been discussing is related to the response time of the electron distribution. This response time can be defined if we consider the electron distribution to be in equilibrium just prior to the switching off of the field. When the field is switched off, the average drift velocity of the electrons will start to decay in a manner that can be assumed to be exponential, so that we can write

$$v_\mathscr{E} = v_{\mathscr{E}0}e^{-t/\tau} \tag{12.19}$$

as illustrated in Fig. 12.6.

Equation 12.19 depends on the scattering being isotropic so that an electron has an equal probability of meeting a scattering center in any direction. Relaxation times are very short, thus they affect only physical properties in which the electron distribution is very rapidly distorted.

## 12.5  The Lattice Vibration Contribution to the Resistivity

Experiment shows that the temperature variation of resistance is closely linear over a wide range of temperature. This linearity breaks down at low temperatures before the resistance falls to its residual value. The low temperature region is illustrated in Fig. 12.7. The linearity also breaks down

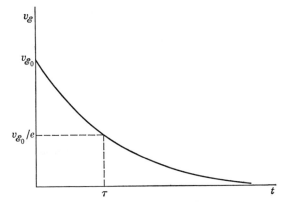

**Fig. 12.6** The relaxation of the average electron drift velocity.

at high temperatures, as illustrated in Fig. 12.8. These departures will be discussed later, but in the meantime we shall confine our attention to the middle temperature range.

Let us consider that the effect of temperature on a solid is to make each atom oscillate on the line between its neighbors. Suppose these oscillations

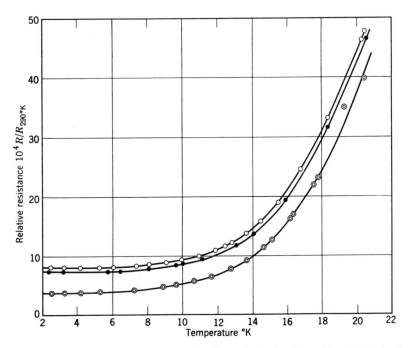

**Fig. 12.7** The resistance of three samples of sodium. (After MacDonald and Meldelssohn)

are harmonic. The differential equation for such an oscillation of one atom is

$$M\ddot{x} + Cx = 0 \tag{12.20}$$

where $M$ is the mass of the atom, $C$ is the restoring force for unit displacement, and $x$ is the displacement. The frequency $f$ of vibration is then given by

$$4\pi^2 f^2 = \frac{C}{M} \tag{12.21}$$

This frequency $f$ is used to define a temperature $\theta$ through the equation

$$hf = k\theta \tag{12.22}$$

where $k$ is Boltzmann constant. The quantity $\theta$ is called the *characteristic temperature* for the lattice because it depends specifically on the atomic masses and interatomic forces of the particular solid. Some characteristic temperatures are given in Table 13.1. It must be emphasized that this model

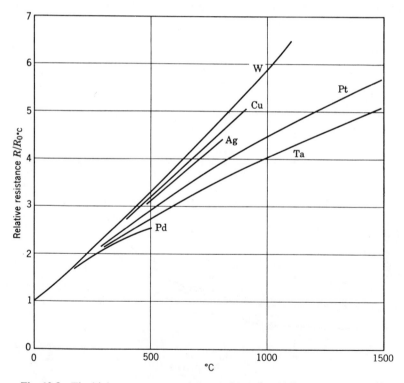

**Fig. 12.8**  The high-temperature resistance of metals. (After Mott and Jones)

of the vibrational properties of the solid is grossly oversimplified. It is much more likely that, instead of vibrating at one frequency, there should be a whole spectrum of frequencies. The single frequency model is due to Einstein and a frequency spectrum model is due to Debye. We will discuss the Debye model in Chapter 13. The divergence between the two is apparent only for $T < \theta$, and we are presently discussing the resistance at higher temperatures.

To return to the problem of electron scattering it can be shown rigorously that the probability that an electron will be scattered from a displaced atom is proportional to the square of the displacement. This is plausible because the probability of scattering should depend on the distortion of the potential seen by the electron. This distortion depends on the thermal energy of the displaced atom, which, in turn, is proportional to the square of the displacement. Hence the resistivity contribution should be proportional to the mean square displacement of the scattering atom. Other factors may enter, but we shall restrict ourselves to the simple calculation.

Let us assume

$$\rho \propto \overline{x^2} \tag{12.23}$$

Now we can calculate the value of $\overline{x^2}$ because it is the quantity that appears in calculating the potential energy of a body vibrating under elastic forces. In fact,

$$\tfrac{1}{2}c\overline{x^2} = \text{average potential energy in one cycle}$$
$$= \text{one-half maximum potential energy}$$
$$= \text{one-half total energy of vibration}$$

The last statement arises because in oscillation the energy is shared alternately between kinetic and potential forms, whereas the total is constant.

The law of equipartition of energy states that the total energy per degree of freedom per atom is $\tfrac{1}{2}kT$, so that, assuming a one-dimensional oscillation,

$$c\,\overline{x^2} = \tfrac{1}{2}kT$$

or

$$\overline{x^2} = \frac{1}{2}\frac{k}{cT} \tag{12.24}$$

Hence using Equations 12.24 and 12.22, it is easy to show that

$$\overline{x^2} = \frac{kh^2}{8\pi kM\Theta^2} \cdot T \tag{12.25}$$

and thus

$$\rho \propto \frac{T}{M\Theta^2} \tag{12.26}$$

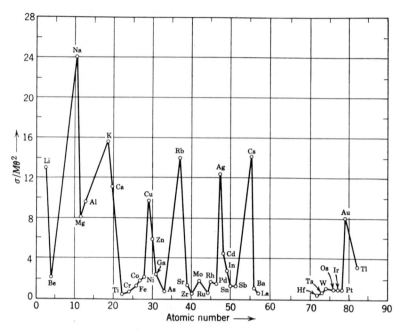

**Fig. 12.9** The variation of electron scattering by the lattice through the periodic table.

Equation 12.26 summarizes all the important aspects of the temperature-dependent scattering. It contains the result we wanted that, within a suitable temperature range (whose limits will be discussed shortly), the resistance is linearly dependent on the temperature. It also suggests that the mass and elasticity properties of the lattice are described by the $M\Theta^2$ term. Therefore, if we wish to isolate the factors *other* than the temperature that contribute to the absolute value of the conductivity of the metal, that is, those contained in the constant of the proportionality in Equation 12.26, the quantity we should discuss is $\rho M\Theta^2$ or $\sigma/M\Theta^2$. The other factors in question would be quantities such as the electron's momentum at the Fermi surface, the effective number of conduction electrons, and the actual value for the probability of scattering at any displaced atom.

The influence of these factors is illustrated in Fig. 12.9. This curve demonstrates, first, the high conductivity of the alkali metals and the copper, silver, gold group which arises from low scattering probability; second, it shows the much lower conductivity that is characteristic of the divalent metals, the reason for this probably being associated with the almost complete occupation of the first band. Nearly filled bands contribute very little to the conductivity because so much of the electron distribution is in contact with the zone boundary, as illustrated for a square lattice in Fig. 12.10*a*.

This situation cannot be perturbed much by an electric field since such a small fraction of the Fermi surface has adjacent and empty states that the electrons can occupy. These are conditions close to the completely filled band, which does not respond at all to the electric field. Even though the common divalent metals do show a certain degree of penetration of the Fermi surface into the second zone, as shown in Fig. 12.10*b*, considerable areas of the Fermi surface can still be blocked by Brillouin zone boundaries against perturbation by the field. Thus, although there are twice as many electrons per atom as in the monovalent metals, the value of $N_{eff}$ may be considerably less than one per atom. The electron distribution for a monovalent metal with its complete freedom to deform under an electric field is shown in Fig. 12.10*c* for comparison.

The last feature illustrated in Fig. 12.9 is the low conductivity exhibited by the transition metals. Here the reason is a high scattering probability. It is a general result of quantum mechanical scattering theory that scattering probabilities are proportional to the state density in the energy region to which the particle is scattered. In the transition elements the conduction is dominated by *s* electrons with an $m^*$ value not far from unity, whereas the electrons in the 3*d* band will contribute less to the conductivity because of their high $m^*$. Because of the high state density in the *d* band, however, the probability of scattering from the *s* band to the *d* band is high and the conductivity correspondingly low.

The deviations that arise at high and low temperatures are the consequence of breakdown of the assumptions regarding the frequency of the lattice vibrations. At low temperatures, that is, when $T < \Theta$ the assumption of a single frequency of lattice vibration becomes invalid. A more detailed treatment involving the actual spectrum of lattice vibration yields the result that the resistance should be proportional to the fifth power of the temperature.

At high temperatures the single frequency assumption is reasonably

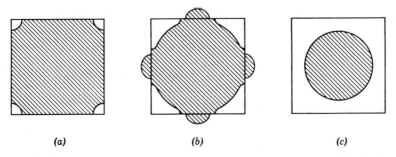

|     |     |     |
| :-: | :-: | :-: |
| (*a*) | (*b*) | (*c*) |

**Fig. 12.10** (*a*) The occupation of the first Brillouin zone in a case for which it is almost filled. (*b*) The complete occupation diagram for a divalent metal with band overlap. (*c*) The Fermi surface for a monovalent metal.

satisfactory, but the actual value of the appropriate frequency may be temperature dependent. This is because at temperatures of hundreds of degrees, thermal expansion reduces the magnitude of the atomic restoring forces. A lower frequency means a lower $\Theta$ and a resistivity greater than that expected on the basis of a simple proportionality with $T$. This is the case illustrated in Fig. 12.8. The figure also shows that in metals such as palladium, platinum, and tantalum the resistance lies *below* the linear variation with $T$. This is probably due to a change in the scattering probability with temperature. The scattering is of $s$ electrons into the $d$ band, but as the temperature rises the top of the electron distribution approaches the top of the $d$ band, where the state density is falling very sharply. This provides less opportunity for the higher energy electrons to be scattered, thus yielding a lower resistivity.

The value of the Debye $\Theta$ is also affected by external stress since the frequency of the atomic vibrations must be influenced by any extra contributions to the forces between the atoms. The resistivity of a material is therefore stress-dependent, a feature which forms the basis of strain gauge operation.

It may be mentioned in concluding the discussion of lattice scattering of electrons that a quantum description of the lattice vibrations is possible. Just as it was possible to construct a quantum picture for apparently continuous electromagnetic waves, so we can describe the lattice vibrations by quanta of sound waves. These are given the name *phonons*, and the problem of lattice scattering of electrons becomes one of electron-photon interactions. This interpretation becomes most significant at low temperatures. The nature and interactions of phonons are more fully discussed in Chapter 13.

## 12.6   The Residual Resistivity

It has been pointed out that the resistivity resulting from contributions other than the lattice vibrations can be studied at temperatures below about $10$–$15°K$ (see Fig. 12.7). The most important source of such a resistivity is impurity in the metal lattice. Provided the concentration of impurity atoms is not too high, the impurity resistivity turns out to be independent of temperature.

The value of $\rho_{impurity}$ is obviously dependent on the fraction of impurity atoms, and Fig. 12.5 shows how the contributions from $\rho_{impurity}$ rises with increasing concentration of nickel atoms in copper. Note that at these fractions of nickel, the added atoms can be regarded as an impurity in an otherwise pure matrix. The case where two components are present in more equal proportions to constitute an alloy will be considered later.

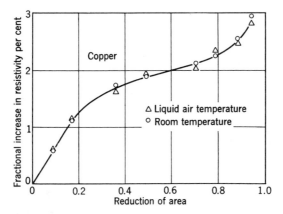

**Fig. 12.11** The increase in resistivity caused by cold work. The lattice distortion was effected by drawing the material through a die.

Yet another contribution to the residual resistance is provided by lattice defects. Unfortunately, currently the theory of scattering from such defects is far from satisfactory. In any case, the contribution to the resistivity from point defects or dislocations is small and is significant only for very pure materials at low temperatures. It becomes of practical importance at normal temperatures only after relatively severe working of the metal or after irradiation by high energy particles. Figure 12.11 shows resistivity changes brought about by lattice distortion.

The contributions from the various types of defect can be studied experimentally by creating a variety of defects in the lattice at a very low temperature. This is commonly done by irradiating the specimen at liquid hydrogen or liquid helium temperatures using a nuclear reactor or a particle accelerator. As the specimen is allowed to warm up gradually the excess resistivity disappears, frequently in sudden jumps at well-defined temperatures, as shown in Fig. 12.12. The temperatures at which the jumps take place are those at which certain types of defect become mobile and so anneal out. Since the activation energies for the movement of defects are known to some extent, it then becomes possible to identify each part of the excess resistivity with the various kinds of defect, interstitial-vacancy pairs, vacancies, etc.

## 12.7 The Resistivity of Alloys

In Section 12.6, mention was made of the resistance contribution to a pure solid from a second constituent. The additive was treated there as an

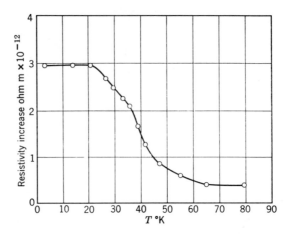

**Fig. 12.12** The annealing out of radiation-produced sources of resistance. The specimen was first irradiated at the low temperature. The experimental points were then obtained by pulse heating the specimen and holding it for 10-minute periods at successively higher temperatures; each 10-minute annealing was followed by a resistivity measurement at 4.2°K.

impurity. However, in a genuine alloy in which the constituents are present in more equal proportions, we must be concerned with the structure of the lattice as a whole rather than with the presence of a few impurity atoms in an otherwise perfect matrix.

Figure 12.13 shows typical behavior in copper-gold alloys. At each end of the curve there is a smooth increase in resistivity since this is the condition of a small amount of impurity distributed in an otherwise perfect lattice. The dashed curve represents the resistivity for disordered quenched alloys. However, annealed alloys can form the ordered structures $Cu_3Au$ and $CuAu$ and these have the minima of resistivity at the appropriate values of concentration.

## 12.8   High Frequency Conduction Effects

All standard books on electrodynamics show that alternating electric fields differ from static electric fields in that they do not penetrate uniformly through a conductor but decay in magnitude exponentially from the surface inward. The decay can be described by a *penetration depth*, which is the distance from the surface at which the field strength has been reduced by a factor of $1/e$. The penetration depth increases with increasing wavelength

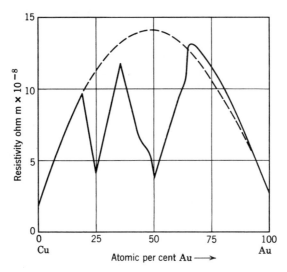

**Fig. 12.13** The resistivity of copper-gold alloys. The full line refers to annealed samples and the dashed line to quenched samples.

and also depends on the resistance of the material, being greater for poor conductivity materials. Typical values for copper are:

| Wavelength | 1 cm | 1 m | 100 m | 10 km |
|---|---|---|---|---|
| Penetration depth | $2.4 \times 10^{-4}$ cm | 0.024 mm | 0.24 mm | 2.4 mm |

The electromagnetic theory from which these values are calculated is valid only in the region $T > \tau$, where $T$ is the period of the alternating electric field and $\tau$ is again the relaxation time of the electron distribution. At frequencies of alternating electric field which are high enough to correspond to the optical region, a typical penetration depth for metals is about 200 A. A mathematical theory appropriate to the optical region is developed in Chapter 17.

## 12.9   Electrical Conduction in Thin Films

We mentioned in Chapter 3 some of the nucleation characteristics of thin films. These films, which may be only a few atomic layers in thickness, have electrical resistivities which vary somewhat from specimen to specimen. The resistivity is always higher than in the bulk material. Three effects may contribute to the increased resistance.

1. The structure of the films is more disordered than in the bulk material. Smaller grains with higher dislocation and defect concentrations are typical. This condition is often reduced by annealing.

2. In the vacuum evaporation and cathode sputtering methods of producing thin films, the film may not be homogeneous in thickness. In the noble metals "islands" of greater thickness than the connecting portions are often produced.

3. Very thin films with thickness comparable to the mean free path of the electrons have a residual resistance which rapidly increases with decreasing thickness. The increase is caused by nonspecular electron scattering at the film surfaces.

It is difficult to produce a simple theory for the last effect. Most attempts are empirical in nature. A number of relations between resistivity and thickness have been produced. The following, which is due to Wilkinson and Weale, is perhaps the simplest:

$$\rho_F = \rho_B\left(1 + \frac{4L_T}{\pi t}\right) \tag{12.27}$$

where $\rho_F$ and $\rho_B$ are the resistivities of the film of thickness $t(\text{A})$ and the bulk material, respectively, and $L_T$ is the mean free path of the conduction electrons. Comparison between theory and experiment is made in Fig. 12.14.

The choice of film material depends on its use in an electrical circuit. Gold, copper, and aluminum films are used as connection leads and terminals

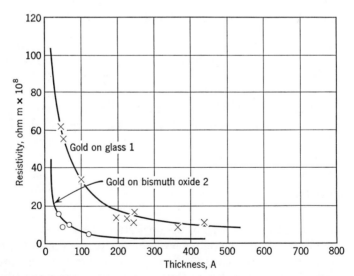

**Fig. 12.14**   Resistivity of gold films as a function of thickness. The solid line 1 is Equation 12.27 with $L_T = 970$ A.

in networks.  They may also be used for capacitor plates with film dielectrics such as SiO, $MgF_2$, and $Ta_2O_5$.  Resistor films are made from carbon, nichrome, tin oxide, and other materials.  The industrial use of these film circuits is widespread and steadily increasing.

## 12.10   Cyclotron Resonance

One important type of experiment in which high frequency radiation is absorbed is called *cyclotron resonance*.  The technique is well known for ions in free space but has only recently been studied for electrons in solids.

Consider a charge $e$ to move with velocity $\mathbf{v}$ in a plane perpendicular to a field of magnetic induction $\mathbf{B}$.  The path is circular with a radius $r$ given by the equilibrium condition

$$Bev = \frac{mv^2}{r}$$

or

$$r = \frac{mv}{Be} \tag{12.28}$$

The time for the circuit is

$$T = \frac{2\pi r}{v}$$

or

$$T = \frac{2\pi m}{Be} \tag{12.29}$$

Notice that the time is independent of $r$, a feature on which the operation of the nonrelativistic cyclotron accelerator is based.  If energy is supplied in the form of an alternating field of the correct frequency, energy will be absorbed by the charge regardless of the radius of the path.

In the solid state the phenomenon is particularly important.  The frequency at which absorption will take place is given by an equation like 12.29, but for such an application we must use the effective mass $m^*$.  Thus the resonant frequency $\nu$ is

$$\nu = \frac{Be}{2\pi m^*} \tag{12.30}$$

This phenomenon is therefore suitable for making a direct measurement of effective mass.  If a single crystal specimen is used, the effective mass tensor for the various crystal axes can be determined by using different orientations of $\mathbf{B}$.  To observe the cyclotron resonance absorption signal it is necessary that the electron be able to traverse a significant fraction of the whole circular path before being scattered. This normally restricts the observation of the effect to very pure materials at liquid helium temperatures. A simple calculation will show that, for typical values of $m^*$, magnetic inductions of the order of webers per square meter require frequencies in the tens of thousands of megacycles. If both electrons and holes are present in a specimen, they will both resonate, and two separate resonance frequencies will be observed.

The measurement of $m^*$ gives, of course, the value of $dE/d\kappa$ at the top of the electron distribution. By using varying orientations of orbit for a single crystal specimen, the shape of the whole constant energy surface for a material may be evaluated.


## 12.11   The Conduction of Heat by Electrons

In metals, electrons are the principal carriers of heat energy. They do this by being excited by energetic scattering centers (usually atoms) and carrying the extra energy to another scattering center in a cooler part of the metal. The heat conductivity will obviously behave like the electrical conductivity.

Let us consider a metal across which a thermal gradient is established. We require an expression for the thermal conductance between two planes spaced apart a distance of one electronic mean free path. Since the heat is carried by the free electrons, this problem is directly analogous to that of the thermal conductivity of a gas, and the standard texts give an expression for the conductivity $K$:

$$K = \tfrac{1}{3}Cv\lambda \qquad (12.31)$$

where $C$ is the heat capacity of the gas, $v$ is the average velocity of the gas molecules, and $\lambda$ is the mean free path. If we apply this result directly to our case of a free electron gas we must use the electron heat capacity (Equation 11.19) for $C$, $v_F$, the Fermi velocity, for $v$ (since only electrons near the surface of the distribution are affected by scattering processes), and the electronic mean free path $l$ of electrons near the Fermi energy. With these substitutions we obtain an expression for the thermal conductivity due to electrons in metals, namely,

$$K = \frac{\pi^2}{3} \frac{\mathcal{N} k^2 l T}{m^* v_F} \qquad (12.32)$$

In metals the thermal conductivity due to electrons is much larger than the lattice conductivity due to the vibrational motion of the ions (which will be considered later) and accounts for the familiar high thermal conductivity of metals. Typical values are given in Table 12.4.

**Table 12.4**

| Element | Thermal Conductivity at Room Temperature [watts $m^{-2}(°Km)^{-1}$] |
|---|---|
| Al | 208 |
| Ag | 421 |
| Au | 295 |
| Cu | 384 |
| Fe | 67 |
| Hg | 6.3 |
| Mg | 157 |
| Na | 134 |
| Pb | 35 |
| Pt | 69 |
| Ge | 59 |
| Si | 84 |
| Stainless Steel | 123 |
| Monel | 125 |
| Constantan | 220 |
| Brass | 87 |

The temperature dependence of $K$ is not obvious. Certainly it contains a simple $T$ term, but we must not forget that the electronic mean free path is also a function of temperature. Insofar as $\rho \propto T$, $l$ will be proportional to $l/T$ and the thermal conductivity should be independent of temperature. At lower temperatures, however, the balance breaks down. The complete curve is shown in Fig. 12.15. The conductivity, of course, has to go to zero at very low temperatures because $l$ becomes constant and the $T$ term remains.

From Equation 12.14, which gave the electrical conductivity, and from (12.32), which gave the thermal conductivity, we can find the ratio of the two, namely,

$$\frac{K}{\sigma} = \frac{\pi^2}{3}\left(\frac{k}{e}\right)^2 T \tag{12.33}$$

This linear dependence of $\kappa/\sigma$ on $T$ is known as the *law of Wiedemann and Franz*. The constant multiplying number is called the *Lorenz number L*, that is,

$$L = \frac{\pi^2}{3}\left(\frac{k}{e}\right)^2$$

$$= 2.45 \times 10^{-8} \text{ watt ohm deg}^{-2} \tag{12.34}$$

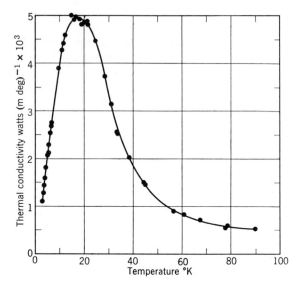

**Fig. 12.15**   The temperature variation of thermal conductivity in copper.

In the region in which $\rho \propto T$, that is, for $T > \Theta$, the value of $\kappa/\sigma T$ should be a constant for all conductors. Values of the Lorenz number obtained from various metals are given in Table 12.5.

Although the electronic contribution to the heat conductivity in metals is by far the larger, we must not forget that the lattice, too, conducts heat. The relative magnitudes of the two mechanisms in different materials are discussed in Section 13.8.

**Table 12.5**

| Element | Lorentz Number (watt ohm deg$^{-2}$) |
|---------|-----------------------|
| Al | $2.23 \times 10^{-8}$ |
| Ag | $2.37 \times 10^{-8}$ |
| Cu | $2.33 \times 10^{-8}$ |
| Fe | $2.47 \times 10^{-8}$ |
| Pb | $2.56 \times 10^{-8}$ |
| Pt | $2.60 \times 10^{-8}$ |

## 12.12   Thermal Electricity

The thermoelectric effect is a phenomenon related to the thermal conductivity of electrons in that it too is a consequence of the drift of electrons under a thermal gradient. There are two aspects to thermoelectric phenomena. The first is the Seebeck effect in which a temperature difference between the two junctions of two dissimilar materials gives rise to an emf in the circuit. The second is the Peltier effect in which, if a current is circulated in a circuit consisting of two dissimilar materials, heat is liberated at one junction and absorbed at the other.

It is possible to give a qualitative explanation of these thermoelectric effects with reference to the electronic band structure in the materials of the junction. Although the effects are greater in semiconductors than in metals, we will refer for simplicity to the contact between two metals. In Section 11.5 it was shown that the lining up of the Fermi levels resulted in a contact potential being established. Figure 12.16$a$ shows two junctions at the same temperature $T_1$. A potential $V_1$ is present. If in Fig. 12.16$b$ junction 2 is raised to temperature $T_2$, then a different potential $V_2$ is established at junction 2. If the junctions are formed by joining the ends of two metal wired, a current will flow in the circuit so formed as long as the difference in temperature is maintained. Clearly the voltage will depend on the variation of Fermi level with temperature in the two materials. We have seen in Section 10.3 that the Fermi level depends on the temperature and on the density of energy states. In metals the dependence of $E_F$ on $T$ is not great and small Peltier and Seebeck coefficients are encountered. The greater sensitivity to temperature of the state densities in semiconductors (see Chapter 14) gives coefficients which make the commercial use of such materials attractive as solid state refrigerators.

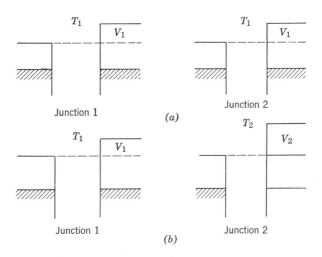

**Fig. 12.16**  Production of thermal emf between junctions at different temperatures.

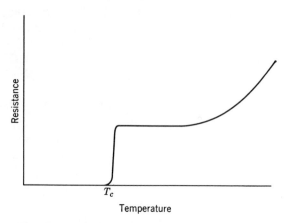

**Fig. 12.17**   The form of the superconducting transition.

## 12.13   Superconductivity

We have stated earlier that if the temperature of a metal is lowered, the resistance diminishes until, at temperatures below about $10$–$15°K$, it levels out at the residual value. This is true of many of the metals we have been discussing, the alkali metals, the transition elements, and metals like copper, silver, and gold. It was discovered by Kammerlingh Onnes in 1911, however, that a totally new phenomenon can be observed at temperatures in the liquid helium range. It appeared that at a certain temperature and within a very narrow temperature range the resistance of many metals could become zero, as illustrated in Fig. 12.17. The name *superconductivity* was given to the phenomenon.

The absence of resistance in superconducting metals and alloys is a transport property and might well be discussed in this chapter. However, it will appear later that related magnetic effects are technologically more important, and hence a separate chapter on superconductivity follows the one on magnetism.

## References

Mott, N. F., and H. Jones, *The Theory of the Properties of Metals and Alloys*, Dover, New York, 1958.

# Exercises

1. Calculate the velocity of the conduction electrons at the Fermi surface for some of the metals listed in Table 10.3.

2. The resistivity of a piece of silver at room temperature is $1.6 \times 10^{-8}$ ohm m. The effective number of conduction electrons is 0.9 per atom and the Fermi energy is 5.5 eV. Estimate the mean free path of the conduction electrons. Calculate the electronic relaxation time and the electronic drift velocity in a field of 100 V m$^{-1}$. The density of silver is $1.05 \times 10^4$ kg m$^{-3}$. $(m^*/m \simeq 1)$.

3. Cyclotron resonance has been observed in lead at a frequency of 8900 MHz and a field of 0.24 webers m$^{-2}$. What result does this give for the effective mass of electrons in lead?

4. Using the data of Exercise 2 estimate the *thermal* conductivity of the silver specimen.

5. Estimate the residual resistivities of the Cu–Ni alloys of Fig. 12.5 with the use of Fig. 12.4. Is the impurity scattering independent of temperature? (Matthiessen's rule).

6. Estimate from Fig. 12.5 and Equation 12.27 the resistivity of a copper film of thickness $10^{-6}$ m (a) at 300°K and (b) at 100°K.

# 13

# *Lattice Vibrations in Solids*

This chapter deals with the thermal motion of atoms in a crystal. We have already seen in Chapter 4 that such motion gives rise to diffusion of atoms and defects through the lattice, with many associated metallurgical and chemical effects. We have also seen that other physical properties, such as electrical conductivity, are modified by thermal agitation of the atoms.

We begin by inventing a simple model of a crystal. The model is a regular array of atoms connected by springs which simulate the atomic bonds.

## 13.1 The Hydrogen Molecule Harmonic Oscillator

Let us first consider the simplest of all molecules, the hydrogen molecule, approximated by two atoms and a connecting spring, as in Fig. 13.1*a*. The total energy for the singlet state (antiparallel spins) is reproduced from Section 9.6 and shown in Fig. 13.1*b*.

If the atoms oscillate along the line connecting them, then the electron clouds adjust very rapidly to the changing internuclear distance. Electron effects may be neglected in consideration of the atomic movements. For *small amplitudes of oscillation*, vibration of the atoms is *harmonic*, and elementary *classical* analysis shows that the natural frequency $v$ of oscillation is given by

$$v = \frac{1}{2\pi}\sqrt{\frac{2K}{M}} \tag{13.1}$$

where $M$ is the mass of the hydrogen atom and $K$ is the spring constant. The factor 2 in this formula arises because of the atoms at both ends of the spring.

## 13.2 The Hydrogen Molecule Anharmonic Oscillator

In Section 13.1 we have stated the classical harmonic frequency of vibration of the hydrogen molecule. The energy can have any value from zero on up,

(a)

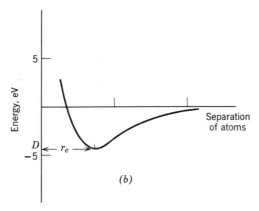

(b)

**Fig. 13.1** (a) The hydrogen molecule model. (b) The total energy versus interatomic distance for the singlet state of the hydrogen molecule.

depending on the amplitude of vibration. For many properties the assumption of a harmonic force versus distance relation between atoms gives results in good agreement with experimental data. It is, however, obvious from inspection of Fig. 13.1b around the region of the minimum, that the potential energy rises more steeply on the compression side of the minimum. Thus, for a physical property which involves appreciable vibration of the atom around the minimum, the harmonic assumption must be inadequate. We will see later (Fig. 13.6) that the specific heat at high temperatures is such a property.

In this section we will first select a potential versus distance function which fits the curve of Fig. 13.1b around the region of the minimum. A suitable potential has been suggested by Morse, that is.,

$$V(r) = D[e^{-2a(r-r_e)} - 2e^{-a(r-r_e)}] \tag{13.2}$$

where $r$ is the internuclear separation, $r_e$ is the equilibrium distance (0.74A), and $a$ is an adjustable parameter (1.93 A in this case). $D$ is the minimum energy value ($-4.72$ eV) and is equal to $k/a^2$.

Now let us insert this potential in the Schroedinger equation and obtain the allowed energy values. As in all quantum solutions these will be discrete allowed values. The energies $\epsilon_n$ are given by

$$\epsilon_n = h\nu(n + \tfrac{1}{2})\left[1 + \frac{h\nu(n + \tfrac{1}{2})}{4D}\right] \tag{13.3}$$

where $h$ is Planck's constant and $n = 0, 1, 2, \ldots$.

The asymmetry of the potential energy of Fig. 13.1*b* around the minimum gives rise to the second term in the square bracket. It is called the *anharmonic* term. The anharmonic term is not large except at large values of $n$, that is, at high temperatures, where higher modes of oscillation of the atoms are thermally excited. In metals, the energy values are not appreciably affected below $n \simeq 10$.

At zero temperature $n = 0$. If we neglect the anharmonic term, which is then negligible, it is seen that the energy of this quantum oscillator is not zero as in the classical calculation but has the value $\tfrac{1}{2}h\nu$. Thus even at the absolute zero of temperature atoms have *zero point energy* $\tfrac{1}{2}h\nu$. It is, in fact, a fundamental postulate of quantum theory that specific location of atoms is always associated with a spread in momentum value and the associated increase in energy.

The frequency of the anharmonic oscillator is identical with that of the classical oscillator given by Equation 13.1. Substitution of appropriate values for hydrogen in (13.1) gives

$$\nu \simeq 13 \times 10^{13} \text{ Hz}$$

### 13.3   The Coupled Harmonic Oscillator

In a real crystal the oscillators are coupled together, since each atom can be regarded as connected by strong springs to its nearest neighbors and by weaker springs to its next nearest neighbors. We can add coupling to the hydrogen molecule model in an elementary way (see Fig. 13.2). By neglecting the small anharmonic terms, the Schroedinger equation gives the allowed energy values for such an oscillator as

$$\epsilon_n = h\nu(m + \tfrac{1}{2}) + h\sqrt{3}\nu(n + \tfrac{1}{2}) \tag{13.4}$$

where $m = 0, 1, 2, \ldots$ and $n = 0, 1, 2, \ldots$. Here

$$\nu = \frac{1}{2\pi}\sqrt{\frac{K}{M}}$$

Classical analysis of the coupled harmonic oscillator gives, of course, all values of energy but again agrees with quantum analysis in giving the two frequencies of oscillation, $(1/2\pi)\sqrt{k/M}$ and $(\sqrt{3}/2\pi)\sqrt{k/M}$.

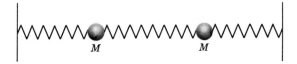

**Fig. 13.2** The coupled harmonic oscillator model of the hydrogen molecule.


## 13.4 The Probability Distribution

The Schroedinger equation gives the probability of finding an atom at a particular displacement. It will be recalled that this is given by the square of the wave function. In Fig. 13.3 we have plotted the relative probability of finding the atoms against their average displacement for a value of $m = 5$. The classical probability is also shown in Fig. 13.3. In the classical case the maximum value of the average displacement is a definite quantity and the atoms cannot be found outside this value. Within their allowed range of displacement, the atoms spend most of their time near the endpoints of motion, where their directions are reversed. Thus the classical probability peaks before the sharp cutoff end values. The differences between the quantum and classical probabilities become small for the higher quantum number modes of oscillation ($m$ greater). Similar features were found in Section 8.4, where we analyzed allowed electron energies.

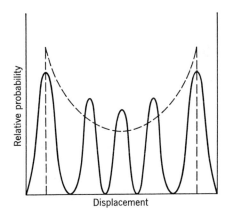

**Fig. 13.3** The relative probability of finding the atoms of the coupled oscillator of Fig. 13.2 at various displacements. Solid line represents quantum calculation for $m = 5$; dashed line represents classical calculation.

### 13.5   A One-Dimensional Array of Identical Atoms

We now extend the calculation to a one-dimensional chain of atoms of mass $M$ coupled $a$ apart by springs of equal strength. If we write Newton's second law of motion we can obtain a set of classical solutions for the displacement. These are of the mathematical form of running waves. Again, by analogy with the electron problem (Section 8.4) this result is anticipated.

The solutions are of the form

$$x_n = e^{-i(2\pi vt - \kappa na)} \tag{13.5}$$

where $k$, the wave number, equals $2\pi/\lambda$ and $\lambda$, the wavelength, is the distance along the chain at which the value of $x_n$, the displacement, repeats. A definite frequency $v$ of the waves corresponds to each wave number, the relationship being

$$v = \frac{1}{\pi}\sqrt{\frac{K}{M}} \sin \frac{\pi a}{\lambda}$$

$$= v_{\max} \sin \left(\frac{a\kappa}{2}\right) \tag{13.6}$$

This relation is plotted in Fig. 13.4a. The positive values of $\kappa$ correspond to waves propagated in one direction; the negative values represent waves

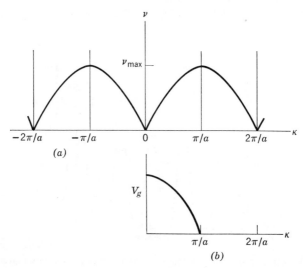

**Fig. 13.4**  (a) Frequency versus wave number for a one-dimensional chain of atoms. (b) Group velocity versus wave number.

going in the opposite direction. The frequency is seen to be a periodic function of $\kappa$ with the first Brillouin zone, defined by the region

$$-\frac{\pi}{a} \leqslant \kappa \leqslant \frac{\pi}{a} \tag{13.7}$$

The group velocity $v_g$ ($= \partial\omega/\partial\kappa$ from Equation 8.12) is graphed in Fig. 13.4$b$. The velocity is constant for small wave number or long wavelength, when it represents the velocity of sound. As the wave number increases the velocity falls in value, a phenomenon known as *dispersion*, and reached the value zero when the wavelength is just twice the lattice spacing. For the chain of atoms there is thus an upper frequency limit $\nu_{max}$ for propagation.

Between the limits of lowest frequency, when the wavelength is twice the length of the chain, and the highest frequency, when the wavelength is twice the lattice spacing, there exists a spectrum of *normal modes* of *oscillation*. Each normal mode is called a *phonon* by analogy with the optical *photon*. As can be seen by inspection of Equation 13.3, the energy of a phonon is given by $(n + \frac{1}{2})h\nu$. Phonons of frequency up to about $10^5$ Hz are simply called *sound waves*, whereas those in the frequency range $10^5$ to about $10^9$ Hz are frequently designated *ultrasonics*. Phonons of frequency greater than about $10^{11}$ Hz contribute significantly to the *thermal energy* in a crystal.

## 13.6  The Debye Phonon Distribution

In a solid three-dimensional crystal of $N$ atoms there are $3N$ phonons, one longitudinal and two transverse for each atom. The number of phonons in a crystal of significant size is thus enormous and it is quite impossible to identify each one. Once again we work with a density of states function $Z(\nu)$. This is specifically the number of phonons or normal modes for which the frequency lies between $\nu$ and $\nu + d\nu$.

Debye regarded a solid crystal not as a lattice of atoms but as a solid continuum. The crystal rings so that the lowest frequency corresponds to a wavelength twice the crystal dimension. The highest or cutoff frequency is characteristic of the type of material. The shortest wavelength must obviously be of the order of a lattice spacing. The Debye cutoff frequency $\nu_{max}$ is defined as

$$\nu_{max} = \frac{k\Theta}{h} \tag{13.8}$$

where $\Theta$ is called the *Debye temperature*. Debye temperatures are listed for several solids in Table 13.1 and for metals in Table 12.4.

**Table 13.1**    Debye Temperatures

| Solid | Θ | Solid | Θ |
|-------|------|------------|-------|
| A | 93°K | Ge | 290°K |
| H para | 116 | Ti | 428 |
| D ortho | 106 | C (diamond) | 1860 |
| Be | 1160 | NaCl | 281 |
| Si | 636 | CaF | 474 |

Debye's suggestion for the form of the density of states function is

$$Z(\nu) = \frac{9N\nu^2}{\nu_{max}^3}$$

In other words, the number of phonons $Z(\nu)$ per frequency interval is proportional to $\nu^2$ up to the cutoff frequency. For many solids the cutoff frequency is of the order of $10^{12}$ to $10^{13}$ Hz. Figure 13.5 shows the Debye frequency spectrum $Z(\nu)$ plotted for lithium with a Debye temperature Θ of 360°K. An experimentally determined spectrum is also shown for comparison. As can be seen, the simple Debye spectrum is only a first approximation to the spectrum in real crystals. Debye's theory is, however, markedly successful in predicting the temperature dependence of several lattice properties.

## 13.7   The Specific Heat of a Crystal

With our present knowledge of the energy of a normal mode of oscillation, or *phonon*, and using Debye's suggested distribution of frequencies, we should

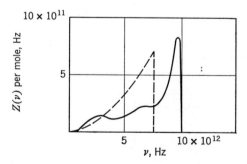

**Fig. 13.5**  Debye frequency spectrum for lithium ($\theta = 360°K$). Solid line represents calculated spectrum from experimental data; dashed line represents Debye frequency spectrum.

now be able to calculate the total thermal energy in a crystal at a particular temperature.

From classical statistical mechanics the average energy $\langle\epsilon\rangle$ of a harmonic oscillator is

$$\langle\epsilon\rangle = \frac{\sum\limits_0^\infty \epsilon e^{-\epsilon/kT}\, d\epsilon}{\sum\limits_0^\infty e^{-\epsilon/kT}} \tag{13.10}$$

We have already met this Boltzmann distribution in one form or another throughout the text. By neglecting the zero point energy term, the possible quantum energy levels are given by

$$\epsilon = nh\nu$$

Consider now the sum

$$S = \sum_0^\infty e^{-\epsilon/kT}$$

$$\simeq (1 - e^{-h\nu/kT})^{-1}$$

If we differentiate the integral $S$ with respect to $1/kT$, we obtain

$$\partial S \Big/ \partial\left(\frac{1}{kT}\right) = -\sum_{n=0}^{n=\infty} nh\nu e^{-nh\nu/kT} \tag{13.11}$$

$$= -\frac{h\nu e^{-h\nu/kT}}{(1 - e^{-h\nu/kT})^2} \tag{13.12}$$

Note that expression (13.11) really appears in (13.10). Using this new (13.12), we obtain for the average energy of each phonon or vibrational mode

$$\langle\epsilon\rangle = \frac{h\nu}{(e^{h\nu/kT} - 1)} \tag{13.13}$$

We can now calculate the total energy $U$ in a crystal at temperature $T$. To obtain each term of the total we multiply the average energy of each phonon by the number of phonons per frequency interval. Summing all such terms then gives the total energy $U$ per mole

$$U = \left(1 + \frac{kT}{D}\right)\int_0^\infty \frac{h\nu}{e^{h\nu/kT} - 1}\, Z(\nu)\, d\nu + \frac{1}{2}\int_0^\infty h\nu Z(\nu)\, d\nu \tag{13.14}$$

The last integral is, of course, the zero point energy. We have put in the anharmonic factor $(1 + kT/D)$ once again to make the mathematical description more realistic.

The definition of specific heat $C_V$ at constant volume is as follows:

$$C_V = \left(\frac{\partial Q}{\partial T}\right)_V = \frac{\partial U}{\partial T} \qquad (13.15)$$

where $\partial Q$ is the transferred heat at constant volume and no external work is done. It follows from (13.14) that the specific heat per mole is given by

$$C_V = \left(1 + \frac{kT}{D}\right) \int_0^\infty k\left(\frac{h\nu}{kT}\right)^2 \frac{e^{h\nu/kT}}{(e^{h\nu/kT} - 1)^2} Z(\nu)\, d\nu \qquad (13.16)$$

For comparison with experiment we substitute the Debye distribution for $Z(\nu)$ and mathematically compute the integrals. These are given in many tables. A graph of $U$ and $C_V$ as a function of temperature for lithium is shown in Fig. 13.6a and b. There is very close agreement with experiment.

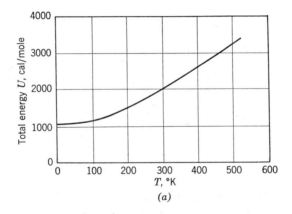

(a)

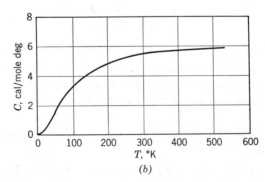

(b)

**Fig. 13.6** (a) Total energy $U$ versus temperature $T$ for lithium. (b) Specific heat $C$ versus temperature $T$ for lithium.

At high temperatures the value of $C_V$ from Equation 13.16 takes the simple form

$$C_V \simeq 3N_0 k\left(1 + \frac{kT}{D}\right) \quad \text{per mole} \tag{13.17}$$

where $N_0$ is Avogadro's number.

The slow rise of specific heat with temperature, above the value $3N_0 k$ (5.958 cal/mole °K) predicted by Dulong and Petit, is thus due to anharmonicity.

At low temperatures, say below one-hundredth of the melting temperature, the integral for $C_V$ also takes a simple form. Then

$$C_V \simeq 234 N_0 k\left(\frac{T}{\Theta}\right)^3 \quad \text{per mole} \tag{13.18}$$

This is the famous Debye $T^3$ law.

## 13.8  Experimental Determination of the Phonon Distribution

The phonon spectrum in a solid is not readily accessible to experimental determination. Recently, however, a rather direct measurement using inelastic scattering of neutrons has become possible. Phonon energies of, say, 0.01 eV are comparable to the energies of thermal neutrons in the nuclear reactor. This is not so for X-rays, which have energies of about $10^3$ eV. For both X-rays and neutrons the momenta are comparable with those of phonons.

Let us suppose that a neutron of momentum $h\kappa/2\pi$ impinges on a solid crystal. If the collision is inelastic, the neutron loses or gains energy and momentum. The energy loss excites one or many phonons in the crystal. If $h\kappa_0'/2\pi$ is the momentum of the scattered neutron after inelastic collision and $hC/2\pi$ is the momentum of the crystal as a whole, then conservation of momentum gives

$$\frac{h\kappa_0}{2\pi} = \frac{h\kappa_0'}{2\pi} + \frac{hC}{2\pi} \pm \frac{h\kappa}{2\pi}$$

The last term, $\pm h\kappa/2\pi$, is the momentum of the phonon created ($+$) or absorbed ($-$) in the process. Obviously, this equation can be written

$$\kappa_0 = \kappa_0' + C + \kappa \tag{13.19}$$

Phonon absorption and creation are illustrated in Fig. 13.7.

Since the energy of a neutron of wave number $\kappa$ is given by $h\kappa^2/2\pi^2$, conservation of energy gives

$$\frac{h^2\kappa_0^2}{2\pi^2} = \frac{h^2\kappa_0'^2}{2\pi^2} \pm h\nu_\kappa \tag{13.20}$$

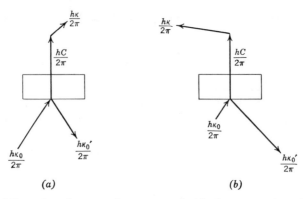

**Fig. 13.7** (a) Scattering of neutron from a crystal with phonon creation. (b) Scattering with phonon absorption. The momenta values of the neutron, crystal, and phonon are shown.

where $h\nu_\kappa$ is the energy of the phonon created ($+$) or absorbed ($-$). In the neutron inelastic scattering experiment it is thus necessary to find (a) the change in neutron wavelength on scattering which will give $h\nu_\kappa$; and (b) the corresponding scattering direction which gives $\kappa_0 - \kappa_0'$. Brockhouse and others have determined the frequency spectrum of a number of solids by these means. The frequency spectrum for sodium is shown in Fig. 13.8. A number of singularities occur showing preferred modes of oscillation characteristic of the atomic structure.

## 13.9   Thermal Conductivity

### In Metals

In metals the transport of heat is by electrons. We have already discussed this topic in Section 12.10 and have noted the relationship between *thermal* and *electrical* conductivity in metals. A good conductor like silver has an electrical conductivity which is $10^{24}$ times higher than a poor conductor like quartz. However, their thermal conductivities differ by a factor of only $10^3$. Obviously, some process other than conduction by electrons transports heat in nonmetals. This other mechanism is conduction of heat by phonons. Figure 13.9 shows the dependence of the electrical and thermal conductivities on the number of free electrons in different solids. The thermal conductivity, although affected by the drop in electron numbers, is maintained in non-metals by phonon conduction.

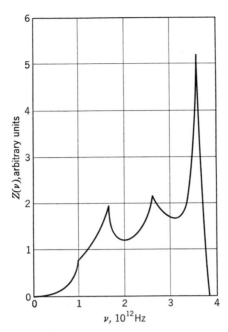

**Fig. 13.8** Frequency spectrum of sodium. (Redrawn from A. E. Dixon, A. D. B. Woods, and B. N. Brockhouse, *Proc. Phys. Soc.*, **81**, 973, 1963)

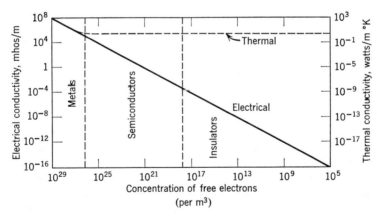

**Fig. 13.9** Full line represents electrical conductivity versus concentration of free electrons. Dashed line represents thermal conductivity versus concentration of free electrons. (After Sproull, *Scientific American*, December, 1962)

### In Nonmetals

Thermal conductivity by phonons is proportional to the number of phonons present. It must also be proportional to the speed of the phonons. This is the speed of sound, which is about $10^5$ m s$^{-1}$ and varies little with temperature. Also, like the electrical conductivity, phonon conductivity is proportional to the mean free path. This is the distance the phonon travels before being scattered and changing direction.

Summarizing in mathematical form, we can write

$$K = \tfrac{1}{3} \sum_i \sum_j C_{ij} v \Lambda_{ij} \tag{13.21}$$

where $K$ is the conductivity, $C$ the specific heat, $v$ the velocity of sound, and $\Lambda$ the mean free path. The subscript $j$ refers to a specific direction of polarization of a phonon. The summation over $i$ must be made over the whole frequency spectrum. This means that for each scattering process and for a particular direction the product of the energy of each phonon in the spectrum (affecting $C_{ij}$) and its mean free path (affecting $\Lambda_{ij}$) must be computed. The theory is difficult and will not be given quantitatively.

The principal mechanisms of phonon scattering are the following:

1. Phonon-phonon interactions.
2. Scattering at imperfections in the crystal.
3. Scattering by the boundaries of the crystal.

If we write $1/K_U$, $1/K_I$, and $1/K_B$ for the thermal resistivities due to these scattering processes, respectively, the resultant thermal resistivity $1/K$ can be generally regarded as the sum:

$$\frac{1}{K} = \frac{1}{K_U} + \frac{1}{K_I} + \frac{1}{K_B} \tag{13.22}$$

Although the number of phonons increases as the temperature rises, the phonons themselves, with a rising population, shorten the mean free path. Each time an atom is displaced from its equilibrium position by the passage of a phonon, another phonon, encountering the displaced atom, is scattered.

At low temperatures crystals such as rock salt have thermal conductivities several hundred times higher than at room temperature. The increase in mean free path on lowering the temperature is greater than the reduction in the number of phonons. Figure 13.10 shows the increase in phonon mean free path with decrease in temperature in sapphire.

Eventually a temperature is reached in most crystals when the mean free path is restricted by impurity or defect scattering. The presence of heavy

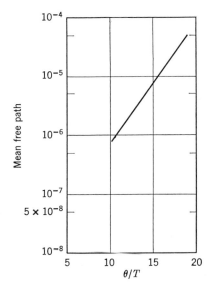

**Fig. 13.10** Increase in phonon mean free path with decrease in temperature in sapphire ($\theta = 980°K$). (After Berman, Simon, and Wilks, *Nature*, **168**, 277, 1951)

atom impurities in a solid is particularly effective in reducing the thermal conductivity, since in addition to increasing the scattering, the heavy atoms reduce the velocity of sound. Thus, in the manufacture of thermoelectric materials, metal compounds may be used with a heavy atom such as tellurium present. The metal atoms provide the necessary electrons for fair electrical conductivity and the tellurium atoms reduce the phonon transport. By these means high temperature differences may be maintained between the hot and cold junctions of the thermoelectric generator.

For very pure crystals at low temperatures ($\simeq 10°K$) the path length may become comparable to the dimensions of the crystal. Then the phonons are reflected back into the crystal by the bounding faces. If this condition prevails, the thermal conductivity must drop sharply below such temperatures, since the number of phonons decreases rapidly with temperature. Figure 13.11 shows these phenomena in crystals which differ in perfection and in size.

## 13.10 The Gruneisen Relation

Three important physical properties of a solid are linked together in the Gruneisen relation: $\alpha$, the coefficient of thermal expansion, $C_V$, the specific

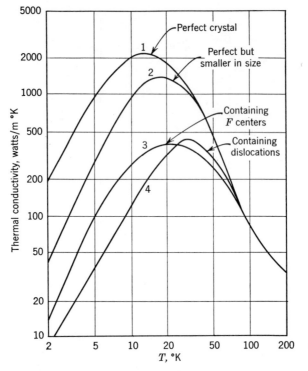

**Fig. 13.11** Thermal conductivity of insulator crystals at different temperatures. 1. Reasonably perfect crystal. 2. Reasonably perfect but smaller in size than 1. 3. Containing *F* centers. 4. Containing dislocations. (After Sproull)

heat at constant volume, and $\chi$ the compressibility. On the basis of a simple model of a solid similar to the one we have used, Gruneisen predicted that for a solid of volume $V_0$ the parameter $\gamma$ should be independent of temperature, where

$$\gamma = \frac{\alpha V_0}{C_V \chi} \tag{13.23}$$

For this to be true the thermal expansion coefficient must be proportional to the specific heat and have the same temperature dependence. For many substances this is found experimentally. The magnitude of $\gamma$ is approximately 2 in most cases.

We will illustrate the physical basis of the Gruneisen relation by again referring to a spring model of a solid. Here we simplify by working with $N$ oscillators of identical frequency $\nu$ each having an equilibrium energy $\epsilon$.

### The Compressibility of the Oscillator Model

The compressibility $\chi$ of a solid is defined

$$\chi = -\left(\frac{V - V_0}{V_0}\right)\frac{1}{p} \qquad (13.24)$$

where the difference in volume $(V - V_0)$ is produced by the applied pressure $p$. At absolute zero the work done to compress the solid is

$$-\int_{V_0}^{V} p\, dV = \frac{1}{\chi}\int_{V_0}^{V}\left(\frac{V - V_0}{V_0}\right) dV$$

$$= \frac{1}{2}\frac{(V - V_0)^2}{\chi V_0} \qquad (13.25)$$

On the other hand, if there are $N$ atoms and the increase in energy of each above equilibrium is $(\epsilon - \epsilon_0)$, then the work done is also $N(\epsilon - \epsilon_0)$. Using Taylor's theorem we can obtain a good approximation for this quantity:

$$N(\epsilon - \epsilon_0) = N(V - V_0)\left(\frac{\partial \epsilon}{\partial V}\right)_{V=V_0} + \tfrac{1}{2}N(V - V_0)^2\left(\frac{\partial^2 \epsilon}{\partial V^2}\right)_{V=V_0} + \cdots \qquad (13.26)$$

Here we have assumed $V_0$ to be the equilibrium volume, that is, the volume at which the crystal energy is a minimum. If this is so, then the first term on the right hand side of 13.26 is zero, and using (13.25) we obtain the following expression for the compressibility:

$$\frac{1}{\chi} = NV_0\left(\frac{\partial^2 \epsilon}{\partial V^2}\right)_{V=V_0} \qquad (13.27)$$

### Elementary Thermodynamics of the Oscillator Model

Suppose $\bar{n}$ is the mean quantum number for all of the $N$ oscillators. Then we can write

$$\bar{n}h\nu = 3kT \qquad (13.28)$$

The internal energy $U$ is given approximately by

$$U = N(\epsilon + \bar{n}h\nu)$$

For a small change in volume $dV$ we have

$$dU = N(d\epsilon + \bar{n}h\, d\nu + h\nu\, d\bar{n})$$

The term $h\nu\, d\bar{n}$ represents the heat $dQ$ flowing into the oscillator systems.

Thus

$$dU - dQ = N(d\epsilon + \bar{n}h\,d\nu)$$

But from the first law of thermodynamics the term $dU - dQ$ is the external work which is zero for a solid in equilibrium. Hence

$$N\left(\frac{d\epsilon}{dV} + n\frac{h\,d\nu}{dV}\right) = 0$$

and substituting for $\bar{n}$, from Equation 13.28 we get

$$N\left[\frac{d\epsilon}{dV} + 3kT\frac{d}{dt}\left(\frac{d\nu}{\nu}\right)\right] = 0$$

or

$$N\left[\frac{d\epsilon}{dV} + 3kT\frac{d}{dV}(\ln\nu)\right] = 0 \tag{13.29}$$

This equation will be used to obtain the Gruneisen relation.

### The Gruneisen Relation for the Oscillator Model

We must now include the thermal expansion $\alpha$ and the specific heat $C_V$. These are defined for our model by

$$\alpha = \left(\frac{V - V_0}{V_0}\right)\frac{1}{dT} \tag{13.30}$$

and

$$C_V = \frac{3NkT}{dT} \tag{13.31}$$

To link the quantities together we expand $d\epsilon/dV$ as before

$$\frac{d\epsilon}{dV} = \left(\frac{d\epsilon}{dV}\right)_{V=V_0} + (V - V_0)\left(\frac{d^2\epsilon}{dV^2}\right)_{V=V_0}$$

and since the first term on the right hand side is zero,

$$\frac{d\epsilon}{dV} = (V - V_0)\left(\frac{\partial^2\epsilon}{\partial V^2}\right)_{V=V_0}$$

Examination of Equations 13.27, 13.29, and 13.32 show that

$$\left(\frac{V - V_0}{V_0}\right) = -3NkT\chi\,d\left(\frac{\ln\nu}{dV}\right)$$

Finally,

$$\left(\frac{V - V_0}{V_0}\right)\frac{1}{dT} = \frac{3NkT}{dT}\chi\frac{d(\ln\nu)}{d(\ln V)}$$

or

$$\alpha = -C_V \chi \frac{d(\ln \nu)}{d(\ln V)} \frac{1}{V_0}$$

The Gruneisen parameter $\gamma$ is thus given by

$$\gamma = \frac{\alpha V_0}{C_V \chi} = \frac{d(\ln \nu)}{d(\ln V)} \tag{13.33}$$

To calculate $\gamma$ exactly we would need a detailed knowledge of the vibration spectrum. Although we know from the work of Debye that a better model of a solid is one in which a spectrum of frequencies exists, nevertheless at

**Table 13.2** Approximate Specific Volumes, Compressibilities, Expansion Coefficients, and Specific Heats of Metals (The Gruneisen constant is calculated.)

| Metal | $V_0$ (m³/kg) | $\chi$ (m²/n) | $\alpha$ (/deg K) | $C_V$ (joule/kg.deg) | $\gamma$ $\dfrac{\alpha V_0}{\chi C_V}$ |
|---|---|---|---|---|---|
| Na | $105 \times 10^{-5}$ | $15.8 \times 10^{-11}$ | $216 \times 10^{-6}$ | $14 \times 10^2$ | 1.0 |
| Cu | 11 | 0.75 | 49 | 3.9 | 1.9 |
| Ni | 11 | 0.54 | 38 | 4.6 | 1.7 |
| As | 17 | 4.5 | 16 | 3.3 | 0.18 |
| Pb | 9.1 | 2.3 | 86 | 1.4 | 2.4 |

temperatures above about 50°K this simple model, of $N$ oscillators at a fixed frequency $\nu$, agrees well with experimental data on real solids.

Table 13.2 gives values of the Gruneisen constant for a number of metals and also lists the compressibilities, thermal expansion coefficients, and specific heats.

## References

Brillouin, L., *Wave Propagation in Periodic Structures*, Dover, New York, 1953.

## Exercises

1. Work out the thermodynamic relation for the difference in the specific heats,

$$C_p - C_V = -T \left(\frac{\partial V}{\partial T}\right)^2 \left(\frac{\partial p}{\partial V}\right)_T$$

Show also that

$$C_p - C_V = \alpha_v^2 \frac{TV}{\chi}$$

where $\alpha_V$ is the volume coefficient of thermal expansion and $\chi$ is the compressibility.

From the values in Table 13.2 calculate $C_p - C_V$ for sodium and copper.

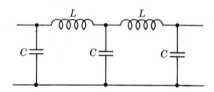

2. Confirm that the upper cutoff frequency for the low-pass filter shown is given by

$$\omega_0 = \sqrt{\frac{2}{LC}}$$

and the low-frequency phase shift $\theta$ per period is

$$\theta = \omega\sqrt{2C}$$

In a one-dimensional chain of atoms of spacing $a$ (as in Fig. 13.2) the wave velocity $v_a$ is

$$v_a = \frac{\omega a}{\theta}$$

Deduce the cutoff frequency.

For a metal in which the spacing is 3 A and the velocity of sound is $5 \times 10^3$ m sec$^{-1}$ calculate the phonon cutoff frequency. What is the energy (in eV) of such a phonon? Calculate the Debye temperature.

3. A one-dimensional chain of atoms (as in Fig. 13.2) is formed with alternate atoms of mass $M$ and $m$ where $M > m$. The spring constant is $K$ and the repeat distance is $a$ (twice the interatomic spacing). Show that the dispersion formula corresponding to (13.6) for this case is

$$\nu = \frac{1}{2\pi}\sqrt{\frac{K}{Mm}}\,(M + m \pm \sqrt{M^2 + m^2 + 2Mm\cos a\kappa})^{\frac{1}{2}}$$

where the *plus* sign gives *optical* modes of oscillation for $\pi/a \leq \kappa \leq 2\pi/a$ and the *negative* sign gives *acoustic* modes for $0 \leq \kappa \leq \pi/a$. Plot the dispersion curve for $M = 2m$ (i.e., $\nu$ versus $\kappa$). Give the frequencies at the limits of the forbidden range.

4. Give in detail the mathematical reasoning between Equations 13.16 and 13.17 and also between (13.16) and (13.18).

5. Two single crystals of KCl have the following characteristics:

| Thickness | Temperature at Which Thermal Conductivity is a Maximum |
|---|---|
| $25 \times 10^{-4}$ m | 7°K |
| $75 \times 10^{-4}$ m | 5.5°K |

If the specific heat of KCl at 4°K is 420 joules °K$^{-1}$ m$^{-3}$ and the thermal conductivity is 4200 watts m$^{-1}$ estimate the velocity of sound in KCl.

# 14

# *Semiconductors*

In Chapter 12 we saw how the electrons in metals carry current when influenced by an electric field, the resistivity for any particular metal being caused by imperfections in the metal lattice. In semiconductors the situation is quite different. Unlike that for metals, the *number* of conducting electrons in semiconductors varies with temperature and field, giving rise to conductivities whose dependence on temperature and field is quite characteristic. The numbers of current carriers in useful semiconductors at room temperature are such that the conductivities have values between those of metals and insulators.

The crystalline structure of the best known semiconductors, silicon and germanium, has been described in Chapter 1. This structure, the diamond cubic, is characterized by bonds between the atoms in which the neighboring atoms share electrons. Certain of these bonds in the pure material must be broken before electrons are released to carry current. The agency that breaks the bond is usually thermal agitation. At zero temperature, therefore, a pure semiconductor will have no broken bonds and will have the electrical characteristics of an insulator. We begin this chapter by reminding the reader of the nature of the band structure in semiconductors and then go on to make calculations of the number of charge carriers which are in the conduction band at a certain temperature (i.e., taking part in conduction) and the variation in that number with temperature and voltage.

## 14.1 The Band Structure of Intrinsic Semiconductors

An intrinsic semiconductor is one in which the degree of conduction is a property of the pure crystal. Chapter 10 gave a description of the band structure of diamond and pointed out that in silicon and germanium the nature of the bands were similar, with the highly significant difference that

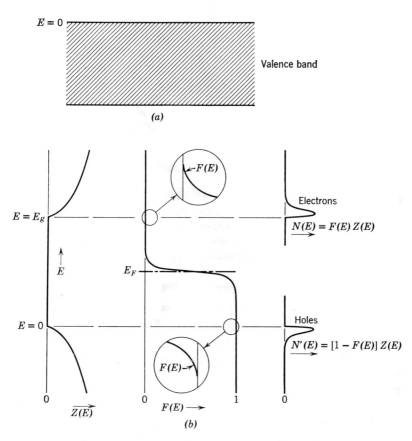

$E = E_g$ ———————————— Conduction band

$E = 0$

Valence band

*(a)*

$-F(E)$

Electrons

$E = E_g$

$N(E) = F(E) \, Z(E)$

$E$

$E_F$

$E = 0$

Holes

$N'(E) = [1 - F(E)] \, Z(E)$

$F(E)$

$0$

$\overrightarrow{Z(E)}$

$0$

$F(E) \longrightarrow$

$1$

$0$

*(b)*

**Fig. 14.1** (*a*) The valence and conduction bands in an intrinsic semiconductor at $T = 0°K$. (*b*) The density of states $Z(E)$, the Fermi function $F(E)$, and densities of electrons $N(E)$ and holes $N'(E)$ at a temperature above zero. (After Sproull)

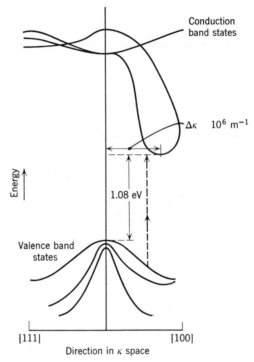

**Fig. 14.1** (*c*) Sections through Brillouin zone in $\kappa$ space for silicon. (From H. Brooks, *Advances in Electronics and Electron Physics*, Vol. 7, 1955)

the energy gap between the valence and conduction band was much narrower than in diamond.

Until recently the theory of simple semiconductors assumed a parabolic relationship between $E$ and $\kappa$, with the effective mass of the electron differing from that of the free electron to take account of the effect of the lattice. The surface of constant energy was a sphere. These relationships have already been developed. Now, with increased knowledge of the properties of semiconductors, it is possible to specify $E$ versus $\kappa$ curves for different directions in a particular semiconductor. Figure 14.1*a* gives the energy band scheme and electron densities for a simple semiconductor by the older theory. This is adequate to demonstrate the techniques of making simple calculations of distributions of electrons and carrier densities and will be so used in the next sections.

Because of the necessity for both *energy* and *momentum conservation* in electron-photon and electron-phonon collisions the energy data alone are inadequate to calculate specific properties of a semiconductor. Figure 14.1*c* gives sections through the Brillouin zone in momentum space for silicon.

The parabolic $E$ versus $\kappa$ curve has been replaced by a complicated set of curves having minima at $\kappa = 0$ and at $\kappa = 0$. The constant energy curves are no longer a single sphere but a set of ellipsoids. We will use the additional information of Fig. 14.1c in our discussion of photon absorption in Section 14.7.

## 14.2  The Number of Electrons in the Conduction Band

In an intrinsic semiconductor like germanium the energy gap is narrow enough so that at room temperature appreciable electrons may be thermally excited from the valence band across the gap into the conduction band. Some quantum states in the valence band which were filled at $0°K$ are thus emptied.

We saw in Equation 12.8 that the effective mass $m^*$ of the electron is given by the curvature of the $E$ versus $\kappa$ surface

$$m^* = \frac{h^2}{4\pi^2}\left(\frac{d^2E}{d\kappa^2}\right)^{-1} \tag{14.1}$$

We have also seen that, because of the dependence of $E$ on $\kappa$, our simple model of band structure makes $m^*$ positive near the bottom of a band and negative near the top. The empty electron states near the top of the valence band will be associated with negative electron masses. Thus in conduction the empty electron states are equivalent to positive particles with positive effective masses.* For this reason the empty quantum state is called a *positive hole* or simply a *hole*. Our first task is to calculate the number of electrons in the conduction band and hence free to migrate through the crystal. The number of holes also free to migrate will follow as a direct consequence of the electron calculations.

As outlined in Chapter 10, we must calculate the density of states function $Z(E)$ and the Fermi function $F(E)$. The product of these two functions will then give us $N(E)$, the actual number of electrons of a given energy $E$ in the conduction band. A plot of $F(E)$ and $N(E)$ is also made in Fig. 14.1b. An expression for $Z(E)$ has been already derived in Equation 10.11. At the bottom of the conduction band where $E = E_g$ and making the quadratic approximation for the surface heat a band edge minimum, the expression is, for unit volume

$$Z(E)\, dE = \frac{\pi}{2}\left(\frac{8m^*}{h^2}\right)^{3/2}(E - E_g)^{1/2}\, dE \tag{14.2}$$

where $m^*$ is the effective mass of the electron.

* For a full description of the equivalence, see R. A. Smith, *Semiconductors*, Cambridge Univ. Press, 1957.

We shall now find the Fermi level $E_F$ at a temperature $T$ that is above zero. A hole in the valence band is produced for each electron that is thermally excited into the conduction band. This implies that the probability of finding an electron at the energy value $E_g$ is equal to that of finding a hole at the energy value $E = 0$. Thus

$$F(E_g) = 1 - F(0) \qquad (14.3)$$

We now insert the total expression for the Fermi function given in Equation 10.1. This gives

$$\frac{1}{e^{(E_g - E_F)/kT} + 1} = 1 - \frac{1}{E^{-E_F/kT} + 1} = \frac{e^{-E_F/kT}}{e^{-E_F/kT} + 1}$$

$$e^{-E_F/kT} + 1 = e^{-E_F/kT}[e^{(E_g - E_F)/kT} + 1]$$

$$1 = e^{(E_g - 2E_F)/kT}$$

that is,

$$E_F = \frac{E_g}{2} \qquad (14.4)$$

This expression is strictly true only if the effective mass of the electron $m_e^*$ is equal to the effective mass of the hole $m_p^*$. Thus in an intrinsic semiconductor the Fermi level lies midway between the top of the valence bond and the bottom of the conduction band. Hence in a pure crystal the number of electrons in the conduction band (or holes in the valence band) is proportional to $e^{-E_g/2kT}$ and increases exponentially with temperature.

We can now complete the calculation of the number $N_n$ of electrons in the conduction band. It is convenient to introduce an "effective density of states in the conduction band," which we will designate $Z_c$. This quantity is defined by writing $N_n$, the total number of electrons per unit volume in the conduction band, as the product of $Z_c$ and the Fermi function *evaluated at the bottom of the band.* That is,

$$Z_c F(E_g) = \int_{E_g}^{\infty} N(E)\, dE = \int_{E_g}^{\infty} Z(E) F(E)\, dE \qquad (14.5)$$

Since $E_g - E_F$ is greater than a few times $kT$, we can write

$$F(E_g) = \frac{1}{e^{(E_g - E_F)/kT} + 1} \simeq e^{-(E_g - E_F)/kT} \qquad (14.6)$$

Thus

$$Z_c e^{-(E_g - E_F)/kT} = \int_{E_g}^{\infty} Z(E) F(E)\, dE$$

$$= \int_{E_g}^{\infty} \frac{\pi}{2}\left(\frac{8m^*}{h^2}\right)^{3/2} (E - E_g)^{1/2} e^{-(E - E_F)/kT}\, dE \qquad (14.7)$$

Equation 14.7 uses the substitutions given in (14.2) and (14.6). The integration gives the expression for $Z_c$, namely,

$$Z_c = 2\left(\frac{2\pi m^* kT}{h^2}\right)^{3/2}$$

that is,

$$Z_c = 4.83 \times 10^{21} T^{3/2} \tag{14.8}$$

The total number of electrons per cubic meter in the conduction band, that is, $N_n$, is thus given by

$$N_n = 4.83 \times 10^{21} \, T^{3/2} F(E_g) \tag{14.9}$$

and the total number of holes per cubic meter in the valence band, that is, $N_p$, is given by

$$N_p = 4.83 \times 10^{21} \, T^{3/2} [1 - F(0)] \tag{14.10}$$
$$= N_n \text{ for an intrinsic semiconductor}$$

For an intrinsic semiconductor with an energy gap of 1 eV, the value of the Fermi function at room temperature is approximately $e^{-20}$. Thus the number of electrons in the conduction band, that is, $N_n$, is given by

$$N_n = 4.83 \times 10^{21} \times 300^{3/2} \, e^{-20} = 10^{17} \text{ m}^{-3}$$

Since the number of atoms per cubic meter may be of the order $10^{28}$, only a very small fraction of the valence electrons are excited into the conduction band.

## 14.3   Conduction by Electrons and Holes

If an electric field is applied to the intrinsic semiconductor in the $x$ direction, the electrons receive energy and there is a drift velocity of electrons in the $-x$ direction superimposed on their random thermal motion. This means that a positive current flows in the $+x$ direction. The field also imposes a drift velocity in the $+x$ direction on the random movement of the holes. Thus positive charge is also carried by the holes in the $+x$ direction. Based on the definition of the drift velocity given in Section 12.3, the mobility $\mu$ can be defined as the drift velocity per unit electric field. In an ideal intrinsic semiconductor the mobility is determined by scattering of the electrons (and holes) by lattice vibrations. At low enough temperatures, however, where the "mean free path" of the electrons becomes long, scattering by impurity atoms and defects sets a limit to the mobility attained. The successful use of semiconductors had to await the development of the zone-refining technique (see Section 3.11) before sufficiently high purities were attainable to give useful values of mobilities.

The total conductivity $\sigma$ by electrons and holes in an intrinsic semi-conductor is then given by

$$\sigma = N_n e\mu_n + N_p\, e\mu_p \tag{14.11}$$

where $\mu_n$ and $\mu_p$ are the mobilities of electrons and holes, respectively, and $e$ is the electron charge. Finally, by combining Equations 14.9 and 14.10 with Equation 14.11, we obtain

$$\sigma = 4.83 \times 10^{21} T^{3/2} e(\mu_n + \mu_p) e^{-E_g/2kT} \tag{14.12}$$

The temperature dependence of conductivity in an intrinsic semiconductor is dominated by the exponential term, the $T^{3/2}$ factor varying relatively slowly by comparison. Thus in the intrinsic range, a plot of log $\sigma$ against $1/T$ will be linear, the slope of the line giving the value of $E_g/2k$ or, in effect, the energy gap in the semiconductor.

In germanium at temperatures above about 150°C, most of the electrons in the conduction band are excited from the valence band in the manner outlined. This is the intrinsic semiconductor region. At lower temperatures, impurities in the germanium contribute in a major way to the supply of electrons and holes. This process is called *impurity* or *extrinsic semiconduction*.


## 14.4   The Band Structure of Extrinsic Semiconductors

The conductivity of a semiconductor may be increased by several powers of ten by the addition of a fraction of one atomic per cent of certain chemical impurities. If we take germanium or silicon as our typical semiconducting elements, the chemical impurities (or dopants) which are commercially used are either from Group V or Group III of the periodic table. Let us consider in some detail the effect of adding elements such as phosphorus, arsenic, or antimony to germanium. An arsenic atom contains five valence electrons, and if it occupies a normal germanium lattice site, only four of its valence electrons will form electron-pair bonds with the neighboring Ge atoms. Thus four positive charges of the $As^{5+}$ core are compensated by the bonding electrons of the four germanium neighbors leaving only one positive charge to bind the extra electron. The field of the positive charge in which the electron moves is further weakened because the surrounding medium is germanium which is polarized with a dielectric constant of $\epsilon_r = 16$ (see Chapter 17). The charge cloud of the fifth arsenic electron is therefore extended around the impurity center. The electron may be easily removed from the impurity and can migrate as a conduction electron. For this reason impurities like arsenic act as *donors* of electrons.

As may be seen from Equation 9.1, the energy required to remove an electron from the field of a proton is inversely proportional to the square of the dielectric constant of the medium in which the electron moves. Thus since the ionization energy of hydrogen is 13.5 eV, the ionization energy of the arsenic atom in the germanium medium will be approximately 13.5 $m^*/\epsilon_r^2$. Ionization energies of impurities phosphorous, arsenic, and antimony in germanium should be taken as about 0.01 eV.

An essentially similar argument can be carried through for a substitutional impurity from Group III. Typical impurities are boron, aluminum, gallium, or indium. Such an impurity has one too few electrons to complete the covalent bands. The charge cloud of the vacant state or *hole* is extended, and the calculation of the binding energy of the hole to the impurity or *acceptor* site is similar to the calculation of the binding energy of the electron to the donor. These energies are also approximately 0.01 eV for boron, aluminum, gallium, and indium in germanium. Germanium containing donor impurities is referred to as *n-type* ("negative" conductivity), germanium containing acceptor impurities is called *p-type* ("positive" conductivity), and semiconductors in which the conduction electrons or holes are supplied by impurities are called *extrinsic*.

Out next task is to calculate the Fermi level just as we did for the intrinsic semiconductor. Before doing so it is important to emphasize a fundamental difference between the wave functions of electrons in the conduction band and those in *donor* levels. We saw in Chapter 10 that the wave functions of

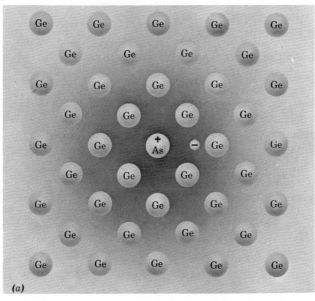

(a)

**Fig. 14.2** Substitution of an arsenic atom for a germanium atom. The charge cloud of the extra arsenic electron is extended around the impurity site. (After Spenke)

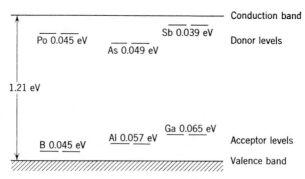

**Fig. 14.3** Energy levels of some impurity states in silicon. The levels are drawn as short dashes near the particular impurity to signify the localized nature of an electron in this energy level. The donor and acceptor energy values are measured from the conduction and valence band edges, respectively.

the conduction band are of the form of propagating waves, and the probability of finding the electron in a certain location is distributed over all the lattice cells. The wave function of the donor level, on the other hand, is concentrated around the donor site in a localized cloud. Similar considerations apply to holes. Figure 14.2 shows an arsenic donor in the germanium lattice, and Fig. 14.3 shows the energy levels of impurity states in silicon. The donor levels are localized to signify the localized nature of the electron and hole energy levels around the impurity.

## 14.5  Ionization of Donor and Acceptor Levels in Extrinsic Semiconductors

In Section 14.2 we calculated the number of electrons in the conduction band in an intrinsic semiconductor. The calculation began with an estimate of the Fermi level. In Fig. 14.4 we show the valence, conduction, and donor levels in *n*-type germanium. The donor level is $E_g - 0.01$ in the figure. From Equation 14.9 the number of electrons $N_n$ in the conduction band is given by

$$N_n = 4.83 \times 10^{21} T^{3/2} e^{-(E_g - E_F)/kT} \tag{14.13}$$

If there are $N_d$ donor atoms per cubic meter, the number of vacant donor states is

$$N_d[1 - F(E_g - 0.01)] = N_d[1 - e^{-(E_g - 0.01 - E_F)/kT}] \tag{14.14}$$

To simplify the calculation, let us assume $T = 300°K$ and $N_d = 5 \times 10^{22}$ m$^{-3}$.

If all the donors are ionized, the number of electrons in the conduction band is obviously equal to $N_d$, and from Equation 14.14 $e^{-(E_g - 0.01 - E_F)/kT}$ is

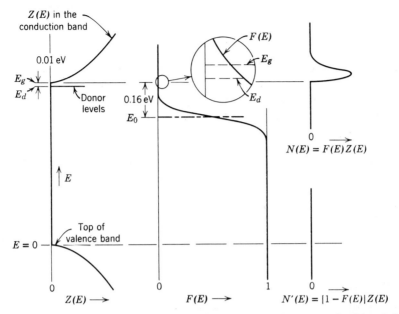

**Fig. 14.4** The density of states $Z(E)$, and Fermi function $F(E)$, and the densities of electrons $N(E)$ and holes $N'(E)$ in $n$-type germanium. (After Sproull)

much less than unity. Let us begin by making this assumption. Obviously, from Equations 14.12 and 14.13

$$4.83 \times 10^{21}(300)^{3/2}e^{-(E_g-E_F)/1.38\times10^{-23}\times300} = 5 \times 10^{22} \qquad (14.15)$$

This gives $E_g - E_F = 0.16$ eV. The number of electrons from the valence band (or holes in the valence band) is given by Equation 14.9. It is

$$4.83 \times 10^{21} \cdot 300^{3/2}e^{-(0.72-0.16)/300\times1.38\times10^{-23}} \simeq 10^{16} \qquad (14.16)$$

This number is much less than the number of electrons in the conduction band which come from the donor levels, and thus the assumption used in the calculation of $E_F$ is justified.

The quantity $e^{-(E_g-0.01-E_F)/kT}$ is negligible if $E_F$ lies more than a few $kT$ below $E_g$. This is the condition for complete ionization of the donors. In such a condition electrons are the "majority" carriers, "holes" are the minority carriers and the conductivity $\sigma$ is given simply by

$$\sigma = N_d\,e\mu_n \qquad (14.17)$$

The Fermi level thus lies below the donor level but above the value $E_g/2$ associated with intrinsic semiconduction. From the development of Equation 14.4 we see that the Fermi level is closer to $E_g$ if $N_d$ is larger or if $T$ is lower.

If only acceptors are present in $p$-type material, the Fermi level lies below the value $E_g/2$. The acceptors are ionized at room temperature, and the calculation of $\sigma$ is similar to that for $n$-type material. Holes are then the "majority" carriers.

The manner in which the Fermi level depends on the dopants present may be qualitatively illustrated by a consideration of the consequences of charge conservation. Any crystal in which electrical charges are free to move will have an electrically neutral interior since any excess charge resides on the surface. If $N_d$, $N_a$, $E_d$, and $E_a$ are, respectively, the numbers per unit volume and energy level values of donors and acceptors, then we can express for the number of negative and positive carriers in the interior of the crystal as follows.

*Negative*

Number of electrons in the conduction band $= 4.83 \times 10^{21} T^{3/2} e^{-(E_g - E_F)/kT}$

$$\text{Number of acceptor ions} = \frac{N_a}{1 + e^{(E_a - E_F)/kT}}$$

*Positive*

Number of holes in the valence band $= 4.83 \times 10^{21} T^{3/2} e^{-E_F/kT}$

$$\text{Number of donor ions} = \frac{N_d}{1 + e^{(E_F - E_d)/kT}}$$

The position of the Fermi level may be calculated by equating the number of positive and negative carriers. The calculation can be simplified if, as is often the case, the crystal contains a negligible number of either donor or acceptor states.

Let us now consider a practical example: $n$-type germanium at a temperature of above 200°K. The dopant level will modify the factors $N_n$ and $\mu_n$, which contribute to the conductivity.

### The Factor $N_n$ or $N_p$

At high doping levels, say, $N_d$ equal to $10^{24}$ per cubic meter, the effect of intrinsic semiconduction is negligible since so many carriers are provided by the donors. At low doping levels, say, $N_d$ equal to $10^{20}$ per cubic meter, intrinsic semiconduction will become important at temperatures above about 350°K.

### The Factor $\mu_n$ or $\mu_p$

The mobility of the carriers is decreased by scattering. This may be by phonons or by impurities and defects. Figure 14.5 shows the variation of

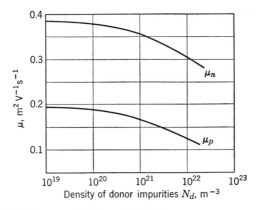

**Fig. 14.5** Electron and hole mobilities in $n$-type germanum at 300°K.

$\mu_n$ and $\mu_p$ in $n$-type germanium with doping level at a temperature of 300°K. Phonon scattering, which, of course, increases with temperature as discussed in Chapter 12, is significant at low doping levels and higher temperatures.

Figure 14.6 shows the variation with temperature of the conductivity of $n$-type germanium for low and high doping levels. The features we have discussed are apparent in the graph.

Table 14.1 gives some room temperature properties for a few common semiconductors.

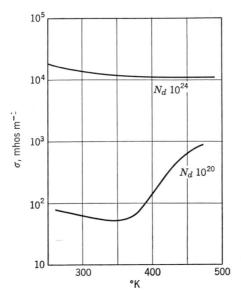

**Fig. 14.6** Conductivity of $n$-type germanium.

**Table 14.1**    Physical Properties of Semiconductors at 300°K*

| Material | Band Gap (eV) | Electron Mobility (m² volt⁻¹ s⁻¹) | Hole Mobility (m² volt⁻¹ s⁻¹) | Dielectric Constant, $\epsilon_r$ |
|---|---|---|---|---|
| Si | 1.15 | 1.9 | 0.48 | 11.8 |
| Ge | 0.65 | 3.8 | 1.8 | 16.0 |
| GaAS | 1.35 | 8.5 | 0.40 | 13.5 |
| GaSb | 0.69 | 4.0 | 0.65 | 15.2 |
| InSb | 0.17 | 70.0 | 1.0 | 16.8 |
| SiC | 3.0 | 0.06 | 0.008 | 10.2 |
| PbS | 0.37 | 0.80 | 1.0 | 17.9 |
| ZnO | 3.2 | 0.19 | | 8.5 |
| CdS | 2.4 | 0.20 | | 5.9 |
| HgTe | 0.2 | 2.2 | 0.16 | |

* Values from W. C. Dunlop, *Encyclopedia of Physics*, Reinhold Pub. Co., New York, 1966.

## 14.6    Hall Effect

It is possible to determine the density and type of charge carrier in metals and semiconductors by measuring the *Hall effect*. We will discuss the experiment in terms of an *n*-type semiconducting material or a metal where the charge carriers are also electrons. In Fig. 14.7 a rectangular slab of material is subjected to a *horizontal electric* and *vertical* magnetic field. The applied electric field $\mathscr{E}_x$ is in the $+x$ direction, and thus the flow of electrons is in the $-x$ direction. In the presence of the magnetic field of magnetic induction **B**, each electron is subject to a Lorentz force **F** given by

$$\mathbf{F} = e\mathbf{v} \times \mathbf{B} \qquad (14.18)$$

where **v** is the drift velocity of the electron. In the presence of the electric field $\mathscr{E}_x$ the conducting electrons have a small drift velocity $\Delta\mathbf{v}$ superimposed on their otherwise random motion. The magnitude of $\Delta\mathbf{v}$ is given by

$$\Delta v = \mu\mathscr{E}_x \qquad (14.19)$$

which follows from the definition of mobility $\mu$. Thus the Lorentz force **F** is in the $-y$ direction and is of magnitude

$$F_y = -eB\,\Delta v = -eB\mathscr{E}_x\mu \qquad (14.20)$$

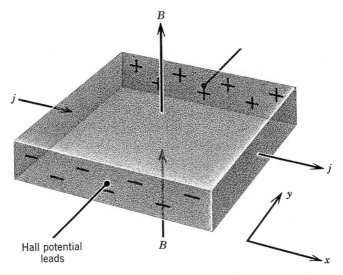

**Fig. 14.7** Hall effect in an *n*-type semiconductor or metal.

The electrons are deflected toward the $-y$ face of the slab (toward the reader) and produce a positive charge on the back face and a negative charge on the front face. Thus a potential difference, called the *Hall potential*, is built up between these faces; this voltage may be measured at the leads. If $\mathscr{E}_y$ is the transverse field (= voltage/slab width), the transverse force $-e\mathscr{E}_y$ on each electron must just balance the Lorentz force. Hence

$$\mathscr{E}_y = B\mathscr{E}_x\mu \tag{14.21}$$

The *Hall coefficient R* is defined by

$$R = \frac{\mathscr{E}_y}{Bj} \tag{14.22}$$

where $j = \sigma\mathscr{E}_x$ is the current density in amperes per square meter in the $x$ direction. We may measure $R$ experimentally. Since $\sigma = Ne\mu_n$ where $N$ is the number of charge carriers, it follows also that

$$R = -\frac{1}{eN} \tag{14.23}$$

Thus if the charge carriers are electrons, the Hall coefficient is negative and an experimental determination of $R$ gives the density of conducting electrons. The polarity of the voltage measured across the Hall potential bands is reversed if the charge carriers are holes, and again the density of carriers may be determined.

## 14.7   Production, Recombination, and Trapping of Electrons and Holes

### *Production*

We have seen in our discussion thus far that the production of charge carriers in semiconductors at a fixed temperature is by thermal excitation. In intrinsic semiconductors, electron excitation takes place from the valence into the conduction band. In extrinsic semiconductors electrons are excited into the conduction band from impurity states or out of the valence band into impurity states.

Another mode of excitation of electrons into the conduction band is by direct illumination with electromagnetic radiation. Such a process is, of course, the important one in photodevices. Two carriers, an electron and a hole, are produced by the incident photon. In the process there must be both energy and momentum conservation. A simple energy diagram like Fig. 14.1*a* is inadequate to describe the process. We will refer to the energy-momentum diagram 14.1*c* for the specific case of silicon. The lowest energy conduction band states (at the top of the diagram) lie at some distance from the origin of the Brillouin zone in the [100] direction, that is, the lowest energy corresponds to a nonzero value of momentum. The highest energy states of the valence band are those of zero momentum.

In order that momentum be conserved, the photon must impart momentum to the electron-hole pair of a value corresponding to $\Delta\kappa$ in the diagram, which is of the order of $10^6$ m$^{-1}$. The energy of such a photon is greater than the minimum energy between the bands of 1.08 eV. Hence in order that a photon be absorbed and produce an electron-hole pair, its energy must be well above $E_g$, the gap width. A permitted transition is shown by the dashed line in the figure.

Thus charge carrier densities are increased by thermal and photon excitation. Many semiconductor devices also operate by injection of *minority* carriers from regions of neighboring crystal of opposite semiconductor type. It is important to consider the mechanisms by which majority and minority carriers are reduced in number. For equilibrium densities of carriers these reduction processes maintain a balance with excitation. For devices where the number of carriers is not in equilibrium (such as the *p-n* junction), the reduction processes are especially important. We shall distinguish between the process of *recombination*, which is the permanent removal of a carrier, and *trapping*, which involves the temporary removal of a carrier to a localized level.

## Recombination

When an electron is separated from a hole it may be reunited with the permanent loss of the carrier by (*a*) direct recombination or (*b*) recombination through a *recombination center*, which are both illustrated in Fig. 14.8.

In direct recombination the electron drops from the conduction band into the valence band with energy emission in the form of a photon. Direct recombination is the major process in some compound semiconductors such as GaAs. It is, however, of negligible probability in Si and Ge because the electron energy and momentum relationships (Fig. 14.1*c*) for these materials are such that conservation of both cannot be achieved in the process.

Recombination in Ge and Si is *indirect*, by which the electron drops first to a *recombination center* with the release of energy in the form of phonons. The electron may then be thermally assisted out of the potential well of the recombination center to fall to an unoccupied state in the valence band, with the further release of phonon energy. Obviously, the last step could be described as that of a hole moving into the recombination center.

The state of ionization of the recombination center is obviously of fundamental importance in its role of annihilating the electron and hole. We have already seen that the state of ionization is dependent on how close the localized level is to the edges of the conduction and valence bands. The potential well associated with a center which is close to a band edge is shallower than that of a center whose energy level is near the middle of the gap. For this reason an electron can be more easily excited from the center. On the other hand, the potential well associated with a localized level close to a band edge is broader than that of a midgap level and is more efficient in

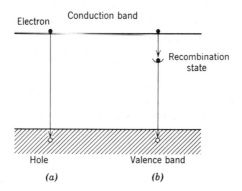

**Fig. 14.8** (*a*) Direct recombination of electron and hole with the emission of a photon. (*b*) Electron first trapped in recombination state before recombining with hole.

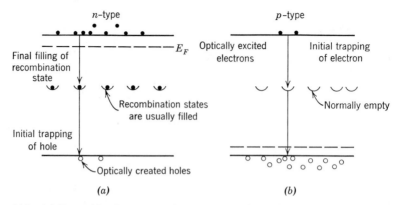

**Fig. 14.9**   (*a*) Recombination process in *n*-type material.  (*b*) Recombination process in *p*-type material.

trapping electrons over greater lattice distances.  In Fig. 14.9 we show indirect recombination in *n*-type and *p*-type material.

In strongly *n*-type material the Fermi level is close to the conduction band, and traps at lower energies will be nearly filled by electrons.  These traps or recombination states then have electrons available to recombine with or trap holes.  If an electron-hole pair is first formed, the hole may be trapped in this way.  The lifetime of the hole is nearly inversely proportional to the density of trapping centers.  When the hole is trapped, the trap that has lost an electron in the process then becomes a localized state into which a migrating electron can fall to complete the annihilation of the original electron-hole pair.

In strongly *p*-type material the Fermi level is near the valence band, and traps are normally empty of electrons.  When an electron-hole pair is produced, electrons fall into the traps.  Once trapped, the electron recombines with one of the many available holes in a very short time to complete the annihilation of the original electron-hole pair.

In the vast majority of cases, injected electrons and holes in excess of the equilibrium density are held in localized states *prior to recombination*. Even in pure semiconductors crystal imperfections are usually present in sufficient number to act as localized trapping states for electrons and holes. The surface of the device contains many imperfections and is of very great importance in this way.

### Trapping

Often the probability of an electron transition between a localized state and the conduction band is higher than the transition probability between the

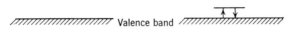

**Fig. 14.10** (*a*) Trapping and emission of an electron at a localized trap. (*b*) Trapping and emission of a hole at a localized trap.

localized state and the valence band. The localized state then acts as an *electron trap*. The opposite probability criterion applies to a hole trap. The electron and hole are then more likely to be emitted back into the conduction and valence bands, respectively, from their localized trapping states.

Figure 14.10 shows the trapping and re-emission of electrons and holes from localized traps. It is obvious that the "nearness" of the trap to the edge of the conduction or valence band governs the efficiency of the trapping process and decides whether electron or hole trapping will be the more probable.

## 14.8 Carrier Lifetimes

The depth of a trap or recombination center defines the probability of an electron or hole being excited out of the trap. The spatial extent of the wave functions associated with the trap defines the probability of an electron or hole being trapped. Thus the number of electrons and holes taking part in conduction at any moment will depend on the relative probabilities of trapping, recombination, and transition between levels.

Suppose that we start with a semiconductor having an equilibrium concentration of electrons in the conduction band. Suppose that the probability of electron transition from the conduction band into a recombination center is $P_{CR}$ and that the density of unfilled recombination centers is $S_R$. The reader will remember that when an electron enters a recombination state it is soon lost. Now imagine that an *extra* $n_0$ electrons per unit volume are injected into the conduction band at time $t = 0$. The rate of decay of the excess carriers will be proportional to the chance of transition $P_{CR}S_R$ and to the number of electrons in the conduction band. Mathematically

$$\frac{dn}{dt} = -nP_{CR}S_R \tag{14.24}$$

This, of course, assumes that $S_R \gg n_0$ or that the unfilled localized states can easily accommodate the extra electrons. Then for $S_R$ constant

$$n = n_0 \exp\left(-\frac{t}{\tau_n}\right) \qquad (14.25)$$

where $\tau_n$ is the *electron lifetime* and is equal to $(P_{CR}S_R)^{-1}$.

The concept of *carrier lifetime* is of great importance in semiconducting devices. We are most often interested in *minority carrier* lifetimes, for example, in the lifetimes of holes in *n*-type material or of electrons in *p*-type material. Lifetimes may vary, according to the nature of the device, from nanoseconds in the case of some electronic applications to hours in the case of phosphorescent materials.

### 14.9  Surface Trapping and Recombination

In many semiconductor applications, recombination centers and traps are more numerous on the surface than throughout the bulk of the material. Suppose that the thickness of the device is, say, $10^{-4}$ m and the surface area is, say, $10^{-6}$ m². Assuming a donor concentration of $10^{20}$ m⁻³, there would be of the order of $10^{10}$ donors in the bulk material. The surface would contain of the order of $10^{13}$ lattice sites. Thus, in our example, only one surface site in one thousand need act as a trap to make the surface contribution comparable to the trapping at bulk impurity sites. In fabrication of semiconductor devices, the utmost care is taken to reduce as much as possible the number of defect traps at the surface.

### 14.10  Radiation Effects in Semiconductors

Measurements of minority carrier lifetimes, conductivity, and Hall coefficients are extremely sensitive indicators of radiation damage in semiconductors. Table 14.2 shows the result of irradiation by fast neutrons of a number of semiconducting materials.

**Table 14.2**

| | |
|------|---------------------|
| Ge   | Becomes *p*-type    |
| Si   | Becomes intrinsic   |
| GaSb | Becomes *p*-type    |
| InAs | Becomes *n*-type    |

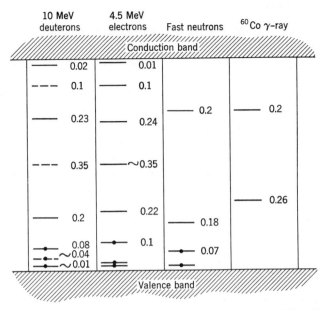

Fig. 14.11 Irradiation-produced defect energy levels in germanium. (After Crawford)

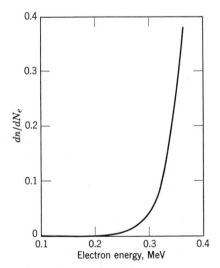

Fig. 14.12 The (number of carriers removed by displacement per cubic meter)/(number of bombarding electrons per square meter), that is, $dn/dN_e$ as a function of the energy of the bombarding electrons in indium antimonide. (From F. H. Eisen and P. W. Bickel, *Phys. Rev.*, **115**, 345, 1959)

The radiation produces defects in the irradiated material. The vacancies and interstitials produced have been assumed, in models of the defect state, to act as acceptor and donor levels, respectively. Several models of the behavior of defects exist, however, in the literature, and a multiplicity of levels has been detected in the irradiated material. Figure 14.11 shows some defect energy states which have been detected in Ge irradiated by various kinds of incident high energy particles.

It is quite obvious from the experimental work that the electrical changes in semiconductors on irradiation are a result of atom displacement. Figure 14.12 shows the change in conductivity of a sample of indium antimonide on bombardment with a constant dose of electrons of varying energies. Analysis of the curve shows that two threshold energies of 240 and 285 eV are involved, corresponding to displacement of indium and antimony atoms, respectively.

## 14.11    Rectifying Action of Metal-Semiconducting Junctions

Metal-semiconductor junction devices have been used for many years in the form of copper oxide and selenium rectifiers. Such rectifiers are not now, however, of great technological importance compared to *p-n* and other junction devices. It is nevertheless convenient to discuss metal-semiconducting junctions because of the simplicity of some of the mechanisms involved.

The theory we will present is qualitatively true of only some of the metal semiconductor rectifiers and fails to account for the detailed behavior of the rectifying action of metal-germanium or metal-silicon rectifiers particularly. When a metal and a semiconductor are brought into contact, a potential barrier arises, (*a*) because of the difference in thermionic work function of semiconductor and metal or (*b*) from the existence of localized electron states on the surface of the semiconductor. We shall now discuss the nature of the first possibility for the case of a metal *n*-type semiconductor contact. We start with a qualitative discussion, and later, when we discuss junction diodes, we shall apply the equations for carrier densities that we have already developed. Figure 14.13*a* shows the energy level diagrams of a metal and *n*-type semiconductor *before* contact is made between them. The *work function for the metal is* $\phi_M$ and is the energy required to remove an electron from the metal. The *work function* $\phi_S$ *for the semiconductor* can be regarded as the sum of two parts, namely, the *internal work function* $\phi_I$, which is the energy difference between the Fermi level and the bottom of the conduction band, and the *external work function* $\phi_E$, which is the energy required to remove a free electron. Figure 14.13*a* refers to the case when $\phi_M > \phi_S$.

Figure 14.13*b* shows the redistribution of the energy levels after the metal and semiconductor have been brought into contact. Electrons occupying

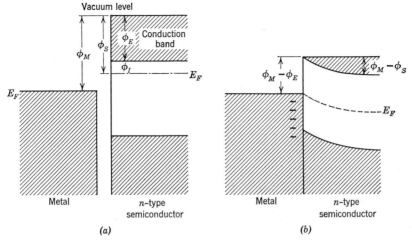

**Fig. 14.13** Electron energy bands in a metal and $n$-type semiconductor when $\phi_M > \phi_S$. (*a*) Before contact of metal and semiconductor. (*b*) After contact of metal and semiconductor.

levels in the conduction band of the semiconductor have escaped to the metal. As discussed in Chapter 11, *equilibrium is reached when the Fermi level of both metal and semiconductor is at the same energy value.* The surface of the metal has received electrons, whereas a thin region of the semiconductor near the surface is depleted of electrons. The metal surface is thus negatively charged with respect to the surface of the semiconductor. The electrons that have escaped from the $n$-type semiconductor into the metal ultimately come from donors near the surface of the semiconductor. This transfer produces a layer in the semiconductor close to the surface which is depleted of electrons. This layer, devoid of free carriers, is an insulating region often called the *barrier layer.* Viewed from the metal side, the height of the barrier between metal and semiconductor $V_{M_s}$ in volts obviously is given by

$$eV_M = \phi_M - \phi_E \qquad (14.26)$$

Electrons do continue to cross this barrier from both sides, but in equilibrium the numbers are equal and no net current flows, as expected.

Suppose now that an electric potential $V$ is applied to the system in a direction such that in Fig. 14.14$a$ the semiconductor is positive. The energy levels in the semiconductor are *lowered* with respect to the metal. The barrier for electron flow from the semiconductor is now *increased to* $V_{S_M}$ where

$$eV_{S_M} = \phi_M - \phi_S + eV \qquad (14.27)$$

while the barrier height for electron flow from metal to semiconductor remains at the value $eV_{M_s}$. The electron flow from semiconductor to metal is

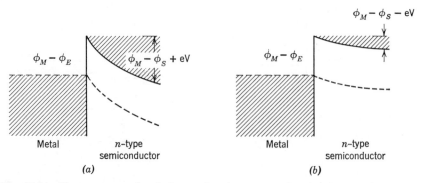

**Fig. 14.14** Electron energy bands in metal and $n$-type semiconductor when in contact. Again, $\phi_M > \phi_S$. (*a*) When a positive voltage $V$ is applied to the semiconductor, that is, reverse bias. (*b*) When a positive voltage $V$ is applied to the metal, that is, forward bias.

consequently reduced from the equilibrium case, and the junction is said to be operating under *reverse bias.*

If the applied voltage $V$ is in the opposite direction such that the negative pole of the battery is connected to the semiconductor, the junction operates under *forward bias.* As is seen in Fig. 14.14*b*, the barrier height for electron flow from semiconductor to metal is reduced to the value $V_{S_M}$ where

$$eV_{S_M} = \phi_M - \phi_S - eV \tag{14.28}$$

and the flow of electrons increased. It should be emphasized that when $\phi_M > \phi_S$, electron flow in both directions is *opposed* by a potential barrier, the height of the barrier being different when viewed from metal or semiconductor. It is this difference in height that gives rise to the rectifier action.

Now let us suppose that the work function of the metal is less than that of the $n$-type semiconductor, that is, $\phi_M < \phi_S$. Figures 14.15*a* and *b*, respectively, show the energy level diagrams before and after contact is made. Here electrons flow from the metal into the semiconductor, which makes the metal surface positive and the semiconductor surface negative. The negative surface charge depresses the bottom of the conduction band near the contact surface of the semiconductor.

The application of an electrical voltage to the $n$-type semiconductor-metal combination is shown in Fig. 14.16*a* and *b*, the metal being negatively and positively biased, respectively. The method of constructing Fig. 14.16 is similar to that used in Fig. 14.14, and the complete explanation need not be repeated. There is, however, one important difference between the two figures. *No potential barrier* to electron flow is presented in Fig. 14.16. The magnitude of the current is completely dependent therefore on the voltage applied and is described by Ohm's law. The contact between the metal and $n$-type semiconductor is thus *rectifying* if $\phi_M > \phi_S$ and *ohmic* if $\phi_M < \phi_S$.

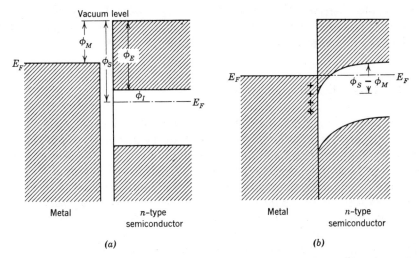

**Fig. 14.15** Electron energy bands in a metal and *n*-type semiconductor when $\phi_M < \phi_S$. (*a*) Before contact of metal and semiconductor. (*b*) After contact of metal and semiconductor.

Let us complete our consideration of contact between metals and semiconductors by briefly discussing the situation for *p*-type semiconducting material. The situations are exactly reversed. When $\phi_M > \phi_S$ and contact is made between the metal and a *p*-type semiconductor, positive charge is left at the semiconductor surface and negative at the metal. Holes are the majority carriers in the *p*-type material and *holes* can flow *uphill* on an electron energy diagram just as *electrons* flow *downhill*. Raising or lowering the energy levels on the right-hand side by applying a voltage in either direction does not change the condition that for current flow by holes there exists

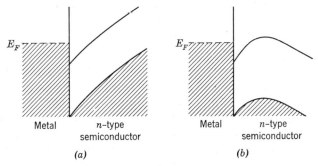

**Fig. 14.16** Electron energy bands in metal and *n*-type semiconductor when in contact. $\phi_M < \phi_S$. (*a*) When a positive voltage is applied to the semiconductor. (*b*) When a positive voltage is applied to the metal.

no potential barrier. The contact is therefore *ohmic*. Finally, if $\phi_M < \phi_S$ a barrier potential is presented to current flow by holes, and the contact will rectify if connected to an applied voltage.

## 14.12    Fabrication of a *p-n* Junction

The fabrication of junctions between *p* and *n*-type materials, which have become of great technical importance, will now be described. A *p-n* junction is, in a sense, an *internal* boundary within a single crystal. On one side donors and on the other side acceptors are in excess. Ordinarily, the transition is not completely sharp and the width over which the conductor changes from *n*-type to *p*-type is a most important parameter. Double junctions such as a *p-n-p* arrangement can be formed where the *n*-type material between the regions of *p*-type (called the *base* region) can now be narrower than 1 mil. The following are the three common fabrication processes:

1. Alloying.
2. Diffusion, which gives better control and makes narrower base regions possible.
3. Growth of epitaxial films.

*The Alloying Technique.*    As an illustration of the alloying technique we shall briefly describe the principles of fabrication of a germanium *p-n* junction.

This technique starts with the production of a single crystal of *n*-type or *p*-type material. Initial production of bulk germanium is always followed by zone refining (see Chapter 3). Since the distribution coefficients of the usual impurities in germanium differ markedly from unity, these impurities move easily to the ends of the ingots under zone melting. Zone melting is also employed to make the distribution of donor (or acceptor) uniform along the length of the ingot (zone leveling). The donor element may be introduced into the molten germanium in a number of ways.

Single crystals of the *n*-type germanium are often produced by the same equipment as used in zone refining. A carbon-coated quartz boat is charged with an oriented single-crystal seed, a slice of germanium alloy containing the measured amount of dopant, and a polycrystalline ingot of germanium. The molten zone may be passed along the ingot several times to melt in the dopant and level the impurity distribution. The zone is then taken back to just melt a part of the seed. A slow traverse of the zone will then allow growth of a single crystal with the seed orientation continued along the whole length of the ingot. Several other techniques of single crystal preparation are in common use. The crystal is usually oriented so that the axis lies in the

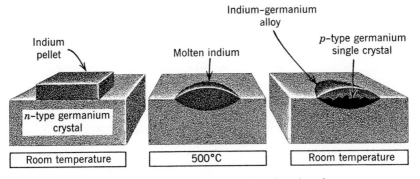

**Fig. 14.17** The preparation of an alloyed *p-n* junction.

[111] direction. The diameter of the crystal with the horizontal boat technique may be as large as 1 inch. In a technique in which the germanium ingot is vertical, with the molten zone held only by surface tension (floating zone) and thus eliminating contact with a containing vessel, the diameter of the single crystal grown will not be greater than about 2 cm.

After solidification, the *n*-type single crystal (or *p*-type) ingots are sliced into wafers about 20 mils thick, often parallel to the (111) planes. Because of "flat" penetration the (111) planes provide good faces for alloying in germanium and silicon. Since *p-n* or *p-n-p* devices are quite small (say 0.02 in square) a great number may be fabricated from a single ingot. Great care and special techniques are used in surface preparation procedures since surface imperfections can act as traps and recombination centers (Section 14.7).

With *n*-type germanium an acceptor layer has to be introduced to make a *p-n* junction. A small piece of, say, indium can be placed on one side of the wafer, as in Fig. 14.17. Two pieces of indium, alloyed into each face of a wafer, would make a *p-n-p* transistor. The combination is heated to a temperature above that of the eutectic alloy formed between the indium and the germanium. By reference to Fig. 3.10, one can see that for a combination of aluminum and silicon the eutectic temperature would be about 580°C. In general, alloying and diffusion temperatures are higher for greater band gap, for example, Si compared to Ge. As the system of In and Ge forms a eutectic, the Ge is dissolved in the In. On cooling the Ge seeds on the parent crystal.

The wafer is then allowed to cool and the alloy close to the *n*-type material recrystallizes. The regrown material is, of course, In-doped and *p*-type, and a *p-n* junction exists between the recrystallized region and the original *n*-type germanium. Figure 14.18 shows the final form of a *p-n-p* transistor produced by the alloying technique, with appropriate dimensions marked on the diagram.

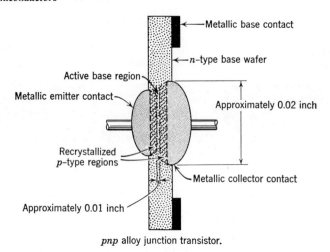

pnp alloy junction transistor.

**Fig. 14.18** *pnp* alloy junction transistor.

*The Diffusion Technique of Junction Formation.* Greater control of the junction dimension can be obtained by the diffusion technique. This means that base regions in transistors can be made narrower with resulting advantage for high frequency operation. We will discuss this technique with reference to the production of a *p-n* junction rectifier. *P*-type silicon single crystals are first prepared by a technique similar to that used in the production of *n*-type germanium. The wafers are sliced and stacked in a furnace. Starting with *p*-type silicon we must introduce into a region of the crystal a donor impurity in order to prepare a *p-n* junction. Frequently, a donor impurity such as phosphorus is carried in the gaseous phase to the surface of the *p*-type wafers. The phosphorus diffuses into the silicon at a rate determined by the temperature of the furnace and the annealing time. Appropriate diffusion constants which fit the simplified diffusion equation (4.3) have been measured at various temperatures for a number of donor impurities in silicon. These are shown in Fig. 14.19.

*Growth of Epitaxial Crystal Layers.* We have discussed the principles of the growth of epitaxial films produced on a heated substrate by deposition from the vapor phase (Section 3.10). This technique offers some very special advantages in the future commercial fabrication of *p-n* junctions and transistors. Epitaxial film techniques using $GeI_2$, $SiI_2$, and also the chlorides in the vapor phase have been investigated a great deal. When these iodides or chlorides cool they decompose into $GeI_4$ and $SiI_4$ with the deposition of Ge and Si, respectively. If this deposition takes place on heated single crystal seeds, then epitaxial layers are built up. In one technique, iodine, a

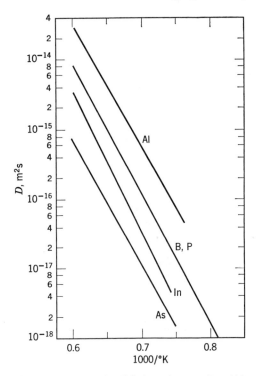

**Fig. 14.19** Diffusion constants, simplified to fit equation 413 versus temperature for various elements in silicon. (After Levine)

silicon source, and a seed crystal are placed in a furnace with the silicon source at about $1400°K$ and the seed at $1200°K$. The iodine vapor reacts with the source crystal releasing silicon vapor which diffuses to the seed where the vapor then separates, allowing Si to seed on the substrate. Doped source materials may be used to build, for example, an $n$-type layer on a $p$-type seed. Multiple junctions may also be fabricated.

## 14.13  Rectifying Action of a *p-n* Junction

Let us now consider the rectifying action of a *p-n* junction. Figure 14.20 shows the energy diagram of a junction in equilibrium. Since the density of electrons is greater in the $n$-type material, electrons diffuse across into the $p$-type region, where they recombine with free holes. The $p$-side thus becomes progressively negatively charged with respect to the $n$-side, and the barrier so formed ultimately stops further diffusion. The region over which the

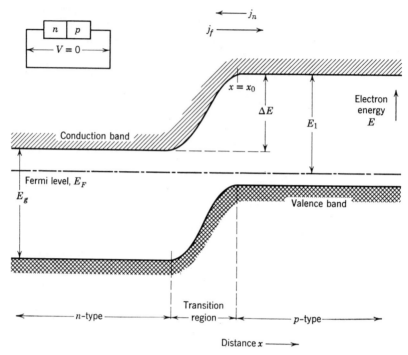

**Fig. 14.20**   Electron energy diagram of a *p-n* junction in equilibrium. When the applied voltage is zero, no net current flows. (After Sproull)

barrier is formed is called the *space charge* or *transition region*. Once more the Fermi levels on both sides of the transition are aligned.

Considering at first only the electron currents, we see that the current $j_n$ to the left at the point $x = x_0$ in the diagram is proportional to the number of electrons in the conduction band of the *p*-type region, that is, to $e^{-E_1/kT}$, where $E_1$ is equal to $E_g - E_F$ on the *p*-side. This small number of thermally excited electrons flow "downhill" into the *n*-type region from a layer near the junction. At the same time, the current to the right at $x = x_0$ consists of electrons that have climbed the barrier from the *n*-side. The number of electrons in the conduction band on the *n*-side of the junction is proportional to $e^{-(E_g-E_F)/kT}$ on the *n*-side. Not all of these electrons can climb the barrier, and the fraction able to do so is $e^{-\Delta E/kT}$. The current $j_f$ is thus proportional to $e^{-(E_g-E_F)/kT} e^{-\Delta E/kT}$. Since $E_1 = E_g - E_F + \Delta E$, then $j_f$ is proportional to $e^{-E_1/kT}$ and is equal in magnitude to $j_n$, which is the expected condition at equilibrium.

Let us now suppose that an external voltage $V$ is applied to the junction so that the *p*-type region is made more negative with respect to the *n*-type region. This is called *reverse bias*, and the energy diagram is shown in Fig. 14.21*a*. The barrier height has been *increases* from $\Delta E$ to $\Delta E + eV$, and very few electrons can climb the hill from the *n*-type region to the *p*-type region, which makes the current $j_f$ very small. The current $j_n$, however, is very little different from the equilibrium value under reverse bias since the rate of arrival at the bottom of the hill is essentially that of arrival at the top. The values of the currents are now $j_f = j_n e^{-eV/kT}$ with $V < 0$ and $j_n$. The net current of electrons to the right is thus

$$j = j_f - j_n = j_n(e^{eV/kT} - 1) \tag{14.29}$$

If $eV$ is more negative than about $-4\,kT$, the current is constant at the saturation value $j_n$.

*Forward bias* is shown in Fig. 14.21*b*. Equation 14.29 also applies with, of course, the difference that $V$ in this case is positive. The forward current $j_f$ is increased above its equilibrium value by a factor $e^{eV/kT}$. A net current of electrons to the right results from the increased concentration on the *n*-side. Note that we have assumed that the electrons in excess of the equilibrium value do not recombine in the transition region but travel into the *p*-type material.

It may be shown easily that an expression similar to Equation 14.29 accounts for the current due to the flow of holes. If, therefore, $j$ is the total current due to electrons and holes and $j_0$ is the saturation value of this current, the equation relating current and voltage for a *p-n* junction is

$$j = j_0(e^{eV/kT} - 1) \tag{14.30}$$

This equation accounts very well for the rectifying behavior of a *p-n* junction and is plotted in Fig. 14.22.

Before we leave the discussion of the *p-n* junction, let us speculate for a moment on the subsequent behavior of the electrons and holes after they have actually crossed the transition region. Equation 14.30 gives us the current that arises because of these carriers, but obviously such a current cannot be maintained were there not a sink for the electrons and holes to fall into beyond the transition region. The process of recombination provides such a sink. The penetration of minority carriers (e.g., electrons into the *p*-type) into regions in excess of their equilibrium density is called *current injection* of minority carriers. Such penetration could arise in two ways. It could arise because of conduction beyond the transition region owing to the driving electric field set up by the voltage $V$. This is not the case since the field on both sides is "short circuited" by the large density of majority carriers. Beyond the junction the penetration is actually a consequence of diffusion. A concentration gradient must exist. With forward bias, for example, the

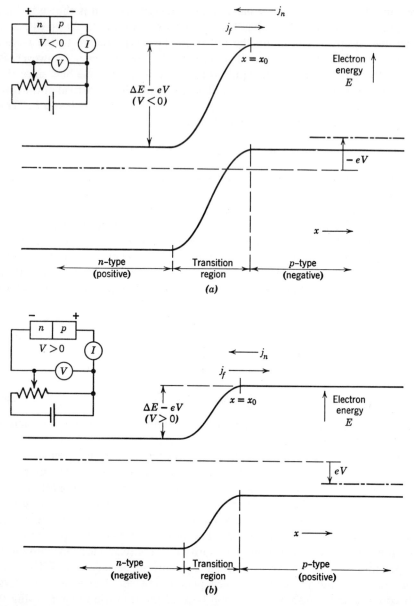

**Fig. 14.21** (*a*) A *p-n* junction with *reverse* bias.  Electron currents only are shown.  (*b*) A *p-n* junction with *forward* bias.  (After Sproull)

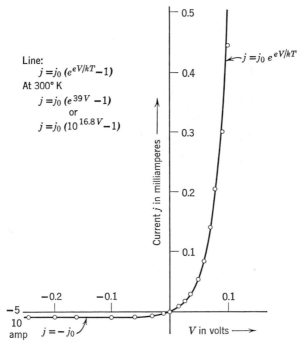

Line:
$$j = j_0 (e^{eV/kT} - 1)$$
At 300° K
$$j = j_0 (e^{39V} - 1)$$
or
$$j = j_0 (10^{16.8V} - 1)$$

**Fig. 14.22** Current voltage relationship for a *p-n* junction. (After Sproull)

concentration of electrons at the *p*-side of the junction, that is, $N_n{}^p$, is in excess of the equilibrium value $N_n^{\text{equ}}$. In fact,

$$N_n{}^p = N^{\text{equ}} e^{-eV/kT} \qquad \text{at} \quad x = x_0 \qquad (14.31)$$

The concentration of electrons $N_n$ at any point $x$ falls from the value $N_n{}^p$ to $N_n^{\text{equ}}$ as the distance from $x = x_0$ increases. The excess concentration of electrons at any point $x$ is related to the distance by the equation

$$N_n - N_n^{\text{equ}} = N_n^{\text{equ}}(e^{eV/kT} - 1)e^{-(x-x_0)/L_n} \qquad (14.32)$$

Here $L_n$ is the *diffusion length* for electrons and gives the distance from $x = x_0$ at which recombination has reduced the electron density by a factor of $1/e$. Equation 14.32 is plotted in Fig. 14.23. A reduction in $L_n$ will obviously increase the concentration gradient of electrons. From our former discussion of diffusion in Chapter 4 it follows that the diffusion current will be increased. Thus trapping and recombination processes that tend to reduce the lifetime and diffusion length of electrons beyond the junction will result in increased forward current at low voltages.

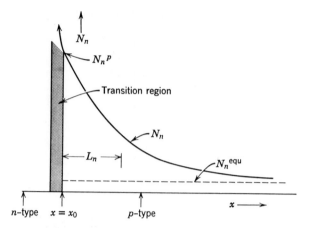

**Fig. 14.23**   The concentration $N_n$ of electrons on the $p$ side of a forward biased $p$-$n$ junction plotted as a function of the distance $x$ from the junction.   (After Sproull)

## 14.14   Semiconductor Devices

Many semiconductor devices exist in modern technology, and their number is increasing at a very rapid rate.   We will conclude this chapter by giving a brief discussion of the physical principles on which some of these devices depend.   Description of the circuits in which they are used is inappropriate to this text and will not be treated.

### The Junction Transistor: Minority Carrier Transport

The semiconductor device of greatest commercial importance is the *junction transistor*.   This consists of two $p$-$n$ junctions within a single crystal. Transistors may be used for amplification of electrical signals and for many of the other electronic applications of thermionic tubes.   Their small size and increasing reliability make them ideal for electronic miniaturization.

The principle of operation of the junction transistor will be illustrated with reference to the $n$-$p$-$n$ junction.   As with the $p$-$n$ junction diode, the characteristic property is the fact that voltages are taken up in the space charge layer and the effect of the electric field exerted on the carriers responsible for the current is negligible.   The only means of barrier transfer across the junction, at least for small voltages, is by diffusion.   Figure 14.24 shows an $n$-$p$-$n$ transistor wired so that the *left n-p* junction, called the *emitter*, is *forward biased*, and the right junction, called the *collector*, is reverse biased. The actual dimensions of the transistor are small, typical sizes being about 0.020 inch square section with the $p$-type region or *base* about 0.001 inch or less in thickness.   In operation, charge is transferred from the low impedance

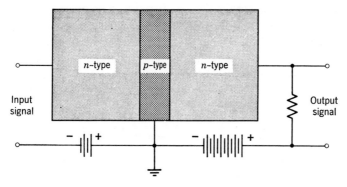

**Fig. 14.24** An *n-p-n* junction with the left *n-p* junction forward biased and the right *p-n* junction reverse biased.

input circuit to the high impedance output circuit, thus resulting in power gain.

Figure 14.25 shows the energy-level diagram for an *n-p-n* transistor biased as in Fig. 14.24. Consider first the emitter junction. The input signal voltage is applied across the junction. The height of the potential hill varies according to the input signal, and the current varies according to Equation 14.29. In practice, the donor concentration is made much higher than the acceptor concentration in the base, and thus almost all the emitter current is a current

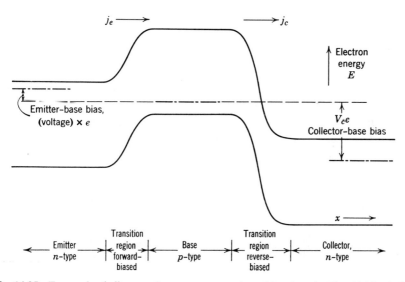

**Fig. 14.25** Energy level diagram for an *n-p-n* transistor biased as in Fig. 14.24. Only electronic currents are shown. (After Sproull)

of electrons to the right with very few holes to the left. The base is made very thin, less in thickness than the diffusion length $L_n$, and thus almost all electrons entering the base from the emitter diffuse across the thin base to the collector. Once across the collector junction these electrons are accelerated by the reverse bias to the collecting electrode. The collector current $j_c$ is only slightly less in value than the emitter current. Figure 14.26 shows the

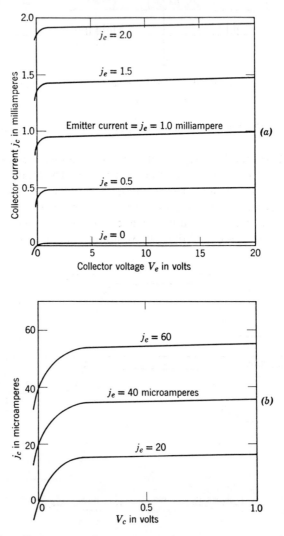

**Fig. 14.26**  The collector current in an *n-p-n* transistor plotted as a function of collector voltage for various emitter currents. (After Shockley, Sparks, and Teal)

collector current $j_c$ plotted as a function of collector voltage $V_c$. An analogy exists between the junction transistor and the negative grid triode electronic tube. The emitter and collector act like the cathode and plate of the triode, respectively. The applied voltage between emitter and base has an effect similar to the applied voltage between cathode and grid in the triode. The base current, like the grid, is small. The capacitances between emitter and base and between base and collector limit the frequency response of the transistor. The emitter-base and base-collector impedances are such that power gains of 50 db are common.

### Varactor Diodes

Let us examine in a little more detail the distribution of charges across a *p-n* junction. On the *p*-side, holes are the majority carriers and they diffuse across the junction into the *n*-side, where electrons are in the majority. Electrons from the *n*-side also diffuse across the junction. The resulting field depletes a layer of carriers of either type at the junction. In the absence of charge carriers in this *depletion* or *space charge* layer, the charge distribution will be negative on the *p*-side, due to the negative acceptor ions, and positive on the *n*-side, due to the positive donor ions. Figure 14.27*a* shows the *p-n* junction after diffusion and recombination have occurred in the junction region. The charge distribution is also given and the boundaries of the space charge layer shown. Figures 14.27*b* and *c* show the charge carriers and potential diagrams under conditions of forward and reverse bias, respectively. As discussed before, the potential barrier is higher under reverse bias.

Under reverse bias the field tends to pull the carrier electrons and holes away from the barrier and thus widen the depletion or space charge layer. The arrows in Fig. 14.27*b* and *c* give the directions of the electrical forces on the majority carriers. The width $W$ of the depletion layer is thus dependent on the applied reverse voltage $V$. In fact, the relationship is quite simple and for an abrupt junction $W$ varies as $(V_J - V)^{\frac{1}{2}}$ where $V_J$ is the *p-n* junction potential corresponding to the equilibrium case.

The *p-n* junction has an associated capacitance since it consists of a depleted negatively charged *p*-region adjacent to a depleted positively charged *n*-region. The magnitude of the capacitance $C$ which is given by $dQ/dV$ varies with the width of the depletion layer $W$, and physically a small change in voltage essentially adds or subtracts charge at the edge of the depletion region. Here

$$C \simeq \frac{\epsilon_0 \epsilon_r}{W} \tag{14.33}$$

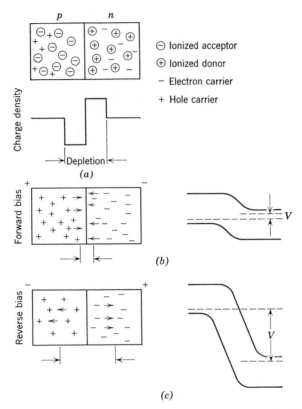

**Fig. 14.27** (*a*) Ionized donors and acceptors in *p-n* junction at equilibrium. The charge density is also shown. (*b*) Carriers under forward bias. Potential diagram. (*c*) Carriers under reverse bias. Potential diagram.

where $\epsilon_r$ is the relative permittivity (dielectric constant) and $\epsilon_0$ is the permittivity of vacuum ($8.85 \times 10^{-12}$ fm$^{-1}$). Thus for

$$W \simeq 10^{-6} \text{ m}$$

then

$$C \simeq 150 \ \mu\text{f m}^{-2}$$

Since the capacitance depends on the applied voltage in a nonlinear way, we have the interesting possibility of a device with its reactance controlled by the voltage. *P-n* junctions doped to give low capacitance and low resistance with this variable reactance junction characteristic are called *varactor* diodes. Varactor diodes are important because of their use in low-noise microwave amplifiers. The cutoff frequencies can be as high as 100 GHz.

### Avalanche Diodes

We have just seen that the reverse bias is supported across the depletion layer in a *p-n* junction. If the reverse bias is increased sufficiently, "breakdown" can occur. The doping may, in fact, be regulated so that breakdown will occur at a chosen voltage, which in Si can lie between 7 and 1000 volts. Figure 14.28 shows the reverse characteristic of a *p-n* junction with the breakdown reverse voltage marked.

Breakdown is described by an avalanche carrier generation process. An electron in the conduction band is accelerated by the field across the depletion layer. Suppose that the electron collides with an atom and has sufficient energy to break the valence bond, thus releasing another electron and creating an electron-hole pair. We now have three carriers present. If the released electron gains enough energy to itself create another electron-hole pair, then there will be continuous carrier multiplication, or the *avalanche effect*. Holes also contribute to the avalanche multiplication process. In silicon the pair production energy is 2.3 eV.

The depletion layer width $W$ varies approximately as $(N_d)^{-\frac{1}{2}}$ for an abrupt junction where $N_d$ is the donor or acceptor concentration here assumed equal. In order to control the breakdown voltage, careful preparation of the junction is required, and for this purpose the diffusion technique (Section 14.12) is generally used. Breakdown occurs in silicon for fields across the depletion layer of magnitude $2 \times 10^7$ volts m$^{-1}$. This corresponds to an applied voltage of 20 volts across a depletion layer of $10^{-6}$ m. The dopant concentration $N_d$ for such a junction would have to be about $10^{23}$ m$^{-3}$.

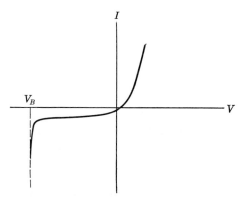

**Fig. 14.28**   Breakdown at reverse voltage $V_B$ in a *p-n* junction.

### Tunnel Diodes

We have already seen that increasing the doping concentration can produce a very narrow depletion layer in a *p-n* junction. There is then a non-negligible probability of *quantum tunneling* across the depletion layer. For *W* less than about 100 A the chance of avalanche processes, on the other hand, is much reduced since the probability of electron-hole generation over such thin regions is low.

In Section 8.3 we discussed quantum tunneling and quoted an expression for the probability of particle transmission through a potential barrier. With a depletion layer of 50 A in a germanium junction doped to $N_a$ equal to $10^{25}$ m$^{-3}$, the tunneling probability works out to be of the order of $10^{-4}$. To calculate the currents tunneling across the barrier it is necessary to know the currents approaching the depletion layer. We can assume that the electrons from the donor ions can travel small distances such as 50 A without loss by recombination. Let us assume then that the electrons from close to the barrier attack the barrier at thermal energies and velocity $v_T$. Then

$$m^* v_T{}^2 \simeq kT$$

and at room temperature after substitution of the appropriate values this gives

$$v_T \simeq 10^5 \text{ m s}^{-1}$$

The current density approaching the barrier will then be approximately $eN_d v_T$ and of the order of $10^{11}$ amp m$^{-2}$. With the just mentioned tunneling probability, the transmitted currents will therefore be of the order of $10^7$ amp m$^{-2}$.

For tunneling to occur the electrons must occupy energy states facing available empty states (holes) on the other side of the barrier. This is always possible at strong negative bias as is shown in Fig. 14.29. It may be possible at forward bias with high concentrations of donors and acceptors. Figure 14.29 shows the energy levels at three values of forward bias. The Fermi levels are aligned at zero bias and no current will flow. At a higher forward bias, unfilled valence and acceptor states (on left) are placed opposite filled conduction and donor states (on right) and tunneling current can flow. At increased forward bias the filled states come opposite the band gap and tunneling current ceases. Figure 14.30 shows a tunnel diode characteristic curve which results from the relative positions of the energy bands at various bias voltages.

The negative resistance section of the tunnel diode's current-voltage characteristic can be utilized in an amplifier or bistable switching circuit. The rate of tunneling changes at the speed of the change in energy levels,

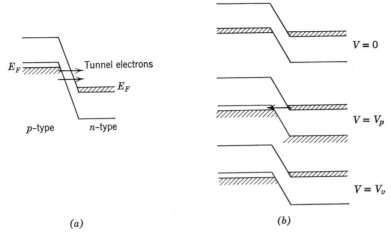

$V = 0$

$E_F$ Tunnel electrons

$E_F$

*p*-type   *n*-type

$V = V_p$

$V = V_v$

(*a*)                    (*b*)

**Fig. 14.29** (*a*) Tunneling at negative bias. Electrons from valence band states tunnel to empty conducting band states. (*b*) Only at a value of forward bias voltage around $V_p$ is tunneling possible.

giving the diode very high frequency characteristics. The cutoff frequencies can be above 10 GHz in an oscillator circuit or about a factor of 1000 higher than is normally possible with transistor devices which operate by diffusing charge carriers.

### Thermoelectric Devices

Let us suppose that an *ohmic* contact is made between an *n*-type semiconductor and a metal. We have already discussed the necessary conditions

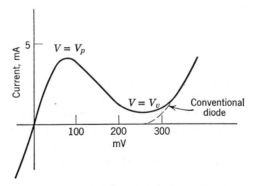

**Fig. 14.30** Germanium tunnel diode characteristic at forward and reverse bias. The peak and valley values of the bias voltages correspond to the band positions of Fig. 14.29.

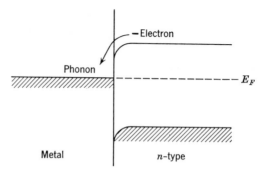

**Fig. 14.31**   Thermoelectric effect at *n*-type metal junction.

which apply to this situation. In Fig. 14.31 we again show the bands and Fermi levels.

The diagram shows an electron passing from the semiconductor to the metal. Its energy is lowered and the difference is converted into phonons. Heat is given off in the process. Conversely, heat must be supplied to establish the energy distribution of the electrons if the current is reversed and electrons pass from the metal to the semiconductor. The energy absorbed or given off per electron in passage across the ohmic junction may be an appreciable fraction of the band gap $E_g$. This gives rise to much greater Seebeck coefficients than are found in metal thermocouples. These coefficients, which measure the voltage produced for a certain imposed temperature change, may be of the order of 500 $\mu V\,^{\circ}K^{-1}$. The Seebeck coefficient is greater for materials of large $E_g$. Moreover, clearly, materials of low *phonon* (heat) conductivity are best if large temperature differences are to be established. Largely because of this factor, compound semiconductors such as bismuth telluride have so far offered the greatest potential as thermoelectric devices.

### Hall Devices

As a final example of the many uses of semiconducting devices in commercial practice, we will briefly describe the use of the Hall effect in semiconductors as a means of measuring quantities such as the magnitude of a magnetic field and the power in watts supplied to an electrical circuit. We recall that the Hall field $\mathscr{E}_y$ across a crystal is given as the product of the applied electric field $\mathscr{E}_x$, the magnetic induction $B$, and the mobility $\mu$, that is,

$$\mathscr{E}_y = -B\mathscr{E}_x\mu$$

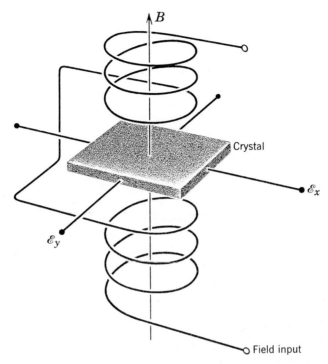

**Fig. 14.32** Gaussmeter and wattmeter applications of the Hall effect apparatus.

Figure 14.32 shows a circuit in which this effect can be employed for various practical measurements. If, for example, the value of $B$ is to be measured in a *gaussmeter* application, $\mathscr{E}_x$ is supplied from a battery source and $\mathscr{E}_y$ read on a meter gives the value of $B$. In another application as a *wattmeter*, the voltage drop in the electrical circuit is applied across a field coil giving rise to $B$, and the current of the circuit, or a known portion thereof, is passed through the Hall crystal. The product, which is proportional to the power consumed in the circuit, is then given by the Hall voltage across the crystal.

## References

Le Croissette, D., *Transistors*, Prentice-Hall, Englewood Cliff, N. J., 1963.
Levine, S. L., *Principles of Solid State Microelectronics*, Holt, Rinehart and Winston, New York, 1963.

## Exercises

1. Calculate the intrinsic conductivity $\sigma$ at 300°K for germanium from the following data:

$$E_g = 0.72 \text{ eV}$$
$$\mu_n = 0.39 \text{ m}^2 \text{ V}^{-1} \text{ sec}^{-1}$$
$$\mu_p = 0.19 \text{ m}^2 \text{ V}^{-1} \text{ sec}^{-1}$$

Calculate also the dependence of conductivity on temperature about room temperature. Express the answer in mhos per m°K.

2. Calculate the position of the Fermi level $E_F$ and the conductivity at 300°K for a germanium crystal containing $5 \times 10^{22}$ arsenic atoms per cubic meter.

3. Calculate the position of the Fermi level and the conductivity at 300°K for a germanium crystal containing $10^{22}$ gallium atoms per cubic meter.

4. Calculate the position of the Fermi level and the conductivity at 300°K for a germanium crystal containing $5 \times 10^{22}$ arsenic atoms per cubic meter and $10^{22}$ gallium atoms per cubic meter.

5. The resistivity of a doped silicon crystal is $9.27 \times 10^{-3}$ ohm-m and the Hall coefficient is $3.84 \times 10^{-4}$ m$^3$ coulomb$^{-1}$. Assuming that conduction is by a single type of charge carrier, calculate the density and mobility of the carrier.

6. Calculate the Hall voltage across the width of a semiconducting specimen from the following data:

Specimen dimensions: width 0.1 m, thickness 0.01 m. Field, applied perpendicular to both width and length has $B = 0.6$ weber m$^{-2}$.
Current flowing lengthwise = 10 mA.
Hall coefficient = $3.84 \times 10^{-4}$ m$^3$ coulomb$^{-1}$.

7. The saturation current of a *p-n* junction is $10^{-6}$ amp. For a temperature of 300°K, plot current versus voltage from Equation 14.26 for a voltage range of $-5$ to $+0.5$ volt. Also plot on log-log paper.

8. Calculate the applied voltage for current across a *p-n* junction of 1 mA. Use the data:

| | |
|---|---|
| Temperature | = 300°K |
| Conductivity on $n$ side | = 500 mhos m$^{-1}$ |
| Conductivity on $p$ side | = 2000 mhos m$^{-1}$ |
| Junction area | = $10^{-6}$ m$^2$ |
| Saturation current | = $10^{-6}$ amp |

9. A cadmium sulfide photodetector crystal is irradiated over a receiving area of $4 \times 10^{-6}$ m$^2$ by light of wavelength $0.4 \times 10^{-6}$ m and intensity 20 watts m$^{-2}$.
   (a) If the energy gap of cadmium sulfate is 2.4 eV, confirm that electron-hole pairs will be generated.
   (b) Assuming each quantum generates an electron-hole pair, calculate the number of pairs generated per second.

(c) The increase in the density of electrons is given by the product (number of electrons produced per second) × (lifetime of the electron carriers). Calculate the increase in conductivity for an electron lifetime of $10^{-3}$ sec and an electron mobility of $10^{-2}$ m$^2$ V$^{-1}$ sec.

10. Figure 14.27 shows the charge density $\rho(x)$ and distribution in an abrupt alloy *p-n* junction. Suppose that the depletion layer extends from $x = x_1$ to $x = x_2$ with $x = x_0$ at the midpoint. The varying potential $V(x)$ (in volts) across the depletion layer is related to the charge density $\rho(x)$ which also varies with $x$. The relation is Poisson's equation

$$\frac{d^2V(x)}{dx^2} = -\frac{\rho(x)}{\epsilon_r \epsilon_0} \quad \text{(mks units)}$$

(a) First show that the hole density $p$ and electron density $n$ in the junction region are given by

$$p = p_p \exp\left[\frac{-eV(x)}{kT}\right]$$

and

$$n = n_n \exp -e\left[\frac{V_J + V - V(x)}{kT}\right]$$

where $p_p$ is the hole density at $x < x_1$, $n_n$ is the electron density at $x > x_2$, and $V_J$ is the equilibrium barrier height.

(b) If $V_1(x)$ is the solution of Poisson's equation in the region $x_1 \leqslant x \leqslant x_0$ and $V_2(x)$ is the solution in the region $x_0 \leqslant x \leqslant x_2$, then by applying the conditions at $x = x_0$,

$$V_1(x) = V_2(x) \quad \text{and} \quad \frac{dV_1(x)}{dx} = \frac{dV_2(x)}{dx}$$

obtain the relations

$$V_1(x) = \frac{eN_a}{2\epsilon_r\epsilon_0}(x - x_1)^2$$

where $N_a$ is the acceptor density.
Also

$$V_2(x) = (V_J + V) - \frac{eN_d}{2\epsilon_r\epsilon_0}(x_2 - x)^2$$

where $N_d$ is the donor density.

11. Obtain the Einstein relation (in a manner similar to that used for Equation 4.15)

$$D = \frac{kT}{e}\mu$$

where $\mu$ is the mobility and $D$ the diffusion constant for minority charge carriers in a semiconductor.

(a) Show that the diffusion current of electrons into the $p$ side of a *p-n* junction is

$$J_n = \frac{eD_nN_n{}^p}{L_n}(e^{eV/kT} - 1)e^{-(x-x_0)/L_n}$$

where $L_n$, the diffusion length, is related to the minority carrier lifetime $\tau_n$ by

$$L_n = \sqrt{D_n \tau_n}$$

(b) Write down an expression for the diffusion current of holes into the $n$ side.

(c) Show that the saturation current $J_s$ at $x = x_0$ is

$$J_s = \frac{e D_n N_n{}^p}{L_p} + \frac{e D_p N_p{}^n}{L_n}$$

(d) From the data of Table 14.1 calculate the saturation current densities for $p$-$n$ junctions in both Ge and Si where the donor and acceptor densities are $10^{22}$ m$^{-3}$ and the minority carrier lifetimes are $10^{-6}$ sec.

# 15

# *Magnetism*

In the past, solids were classified according to the *magnitude* of their magnetic properties into three groups: *diamagnetic*, *paramagnetic*, and *ferromagnetic*. Now, with many new magnetic materials in use, it is more meaningful to classify solids in terms of both the *magnitude* of their magnetic properties and the *temperature dependence* of these properties. Then eleven groups actually exist. In Section 15.1 we shall introduce the quantity *magnetic susceptibility*. This is the quantity that best characterizes the magnetic property of the atom and relates it to the macroscopic magnetic property of the solid. We will construct a table summarizing the different types of magnetic behavior in terms of susceptibility. The susceptibility relates three fundamental parameters, **B**, **H**, and $\mu$, whose nature we will discuss first.

### The Magnetic Induction or Flux Density B

A magnetic field of induction **B** exerts a force **dF** on an element *dl* of wire carrying a current **I** when the wire is placed in the field. The force is given by

$$\mathbf{dF} = \mathbf{I} \times \mathbf{B}\, dl \tag{15.1}$$

**B** is expressed in weber $m^{-2}$, **dF** in newtons, **I** in amps, and *dl* in meters. Forde **dF** is perpendicular to **I** and **B** and is in the direction in which a right-handed screw advances when **I** is rotated to coincide with **B**.

### The Magnetic Field Intensity H

The intensity **H** is defined so that the line integral of **H** along a closed curve is equal to the total current enclosed. That is,

$$\oint \mathbf{H} \cdot dl = I \tag{15.2}$$

Thus **H** is expressed in amp $m^{-1}$. The relationship between **B** and **H** is

$$\mathbf{B} = \mu_0 \mu_r \mathbf{H} \tag{15.3}$$

where $\mu_0$ is the *permeability of free space* and equals $4\pi \times 10^{-7}$ weber m$^{-1}$ amp$^{-1}$, and $\mu_r$ is the *relative permeability of the medium* in which **B** exists and is a pure number equal to unity for a vacuum.

Note that Equation 15.3 implies a unique relationship between **B** and **H**.

### The Magnetic Dipole Moment μ

A magnetic dipole moment **μ**, which arises in ways that we will discuss, produces a magnetic field which at large distances is identical with that produced by a current loop. The moment **μ** is defined in terms of a planar loop of area $A$ carrying a current $I$ by the relation

$$\mathbf{\mu} = \mathbf{n}IA \qquad (15.4)$$

Here **n** is a unit vector in a direction normal to the loop.

In a solid the *total magnetic dipole moment per unit volume* is referred to as **M**.

## 15.1 Magnetic Susceptibility

We shall now discuss the relationship between **B**, **H**, and **M**. Suppose in Fig. 15.1 that a cylinder of material whose relative permeability is $\mu_r$ is placed in a magnetic field **H**. The magnetic induction **B** in the cylinder is given by Equation 15.3.

Now suppose that a small cylinder of length $dl$ and cross section $dA$ is cut from the original cylinder. The magnetic induction inside the cylinder will change. It is possible, however, to conceive of a current, flowing around the cylinder walls, being introduced to keep the magnetic induction inside the cavity the same as it was before the material was removed.

Let us first calculate the magnitude of this current. The value of $\mu_r$ inside the cavity is unity. Thus if the subscript $c$ refers to "inside the cavity," then in magnitudes

$$B_c = B$$

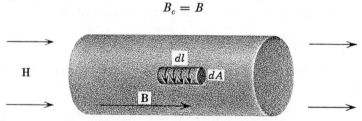

**Fig. 15.1**  A cylinder of material of relative permeability $\mu_r$ in a magnetic field **H**. When a small cylinder of the material is removed, the magnetic induction inside the cavity falls and a current must be conceived to pass around the cavity walls to restore the induction inside to its former value. This current is shown by the circular arrows.

**Table 15.1**

| Type | Magnitude of Susceptibility | Temperature Dependence | Examples |
|---|---|---|---|
| Diamagnetic | Small, negative | Independent | Organic materials, light elements |
| | Intermediate, negative | Varies with field and temperature below 20°K (not discussed in text) | Alkali earths Bismuth |
| | Large, negative | Exists only below critical temperatures (see Section 16.1) | Superconducting metals |
| Paramagnetic | Small, positive | Independent (see Section 15.6) | Alkali metals Transition metals |
| | Large, positive | $\chi = \dfrac{C}{T - \theta}$ | Rare earths |
| Antiferromagnetic | Small, positive | When $T > T_N$; $$\chi = \frac{C}{T + \theta}$$ When $T < T_N$; $\chi \propto T$ (see Section 15.14) | Salts of transition elements |
| Ferromagnetic | Very large, positive | $T > T_c$; $\chi = \dfrac{C}{T - \theta}$ $T < T_c$; (see Section 15.8) | Some transition and rare earth metals |
| Ferrimagnetic | Very large, positive | $T > T_N$; $\chi = \dfrac{C}{T \pm \theta}$ $T < T_N$ (see Section 15.15) | Ferrites |

that is,

$$\mu_0 H_c = \mu_0 \mu_r H \tag{15.5}$$

and hence

$$H_c - H = (\mu_r - 1)H$$

This increase in field $H_c - H$ inside the cavity can be produced by a current, according to Equation 15.2, of magnitude $I$ where

$$I = (\mu_r - 1)H \, dl \tag{15.6}$$

Now, using Equation 15.4, we deduce that the material that was removed from the cavity must have been contributing a magnetic dipole moment **μ** whose magnitude is given by

$$\mu = (\mu_r - 1)H \, dl \, dA$$

The magnetic dipole moment per unit volume $M$ is thus related to $H$ by

$$M = (\mu_r - 1)H = \chi H \tag{15.7}$$

where $\chi$ is called the *magnetic susceptibility*.

We shall now complete this section by classifying solids according to the magnitude and temperature dependence of magnetic susceptibility.

In Table 15.1 $T_c$, the critical temperature, $C$, the Curie constant, and $\theta$, the Curie temperature, are all characteristic of the material considered.

Technologically, the most important of the materials classified in Table 15.1 are the ferromagnetics and the ferrimagnetics. These have remanent magnetism even in the absence of a magnetic field. In fact, as we shall discuss later, the *value* of $M$ in these materials remains essentially constant and only the *direction* of the magnetization varies. Since most electronic devices using these materials operate in changing magnetic fields, we must, at a later point in this chapter, discuss the *dynamics* of change of magnetization. At present, however, in order to establish the *nature* of the magnetic susceptibility we shall discuss magnetic character with reference to *static* fields only.

*Magnetic Properties in Static Magnetic Fields*

## 15.2    Orbital Diamagnetism

An external magnetic field induces in all atoms and ions a diamagnetic moment equivalent to a negative susceptibility. This is often masked, however, by the permanent moments and positive susceptibility associated with the other classes of magnetism.

We will derive the magnetic susceptibility for a special case. Figure 15.2 shows an electron of charge $-e$ describing a circular orbit of radius $r$ around a proton. The angular frequency of the electron is $\omega_0$. From Equation 15.4 the magnitude of the orbital magnetic dipole moment $\mu$ is given by

$$\mu = IA$$

$$= -\frac{e\omega_0}{2\pi} \pi r^2$$

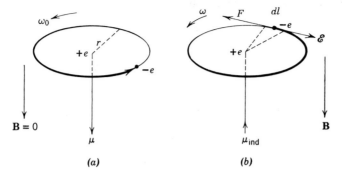

*(a)*          *(b)*

**Fig. 15.2** A simplified atom consisting of an electron circling a proton. The angular velocity $\omega_0$ in the absence of a magnetic field is increased to $\omega$ when **B** is applied. The increase in angular velocity is associated with an induced magnetic moment $\mu_{ind}$ which is opposite in direction to **B** and thus is diamagnetic in character.

that is,

$$\mu = -\tfrac{1}{2}er^2\omega_0 \tag{15.8}$$

Suppose now that the magnetic induction is increased from zero in Fig. 15.2*a* to a value *B* in Fig. 15.2*b*. As the flux $\phi$ is increasing, by Lenz's law an *electric field* $\mathscr{E}$ is set up in the circular orbit such that

$$\oint \mathscr{E}\, dl = -\frac{d\phi}{dt} \tag{15.9}$$

where *dl* is an increment of the circular path of the electron. The electric field induces a current in the orbit, and the magnetic field associated with this current is in such a direction that it counteracts the increase $d\phi$. This is the meaning of the negative sign in Equation 15.9.

Solving (15.9) for the complete orbit gives

$$\mathscr{E} = -\frac{1}{2\pi r}\cdot\frac{d\phi}{dt}$$

Since

$$B = \frac{\phi}{\pi r^2}$$

then

$$\mathscr{E} = -\frac{r}{2}\cdot\frac{dB}{dt} \tag{15.10}$$

While $\mathscr{E}$ is present, that is, while *B* is changing, the electron will be subject to a force *F* of magnitude $-e\mathscr{E}$ which increases its angular momentum.

The increase in angular momentum $mr^2 \, d\omega$ is given by

$$mr^2 \, d\omega = Fr \, dt$$

$$= -e\mathscr{E}r \, dt$$

$$= \frac{er}{2} \cdot dB$$

The new angular frequency of the electron in the presence of the magnetic induction $B$ is obtained from the last equation by integration.

$$m \int_{\omega_0}^{\omega} d\omega = \frac{e}{2} \int_0^B dB$$

Thus

$$\omega = \omega_0 + \frac{e}{2m} \cdot B \tag{15.11}$$

The electron will retain this new frequency as long as **B** does not change. The term $e/2m \cdot B$ is called the *Larmor frequency*.

The change in frequency $e/2m \cdot B$ gives rise by Equation 15.8 to a change in orbital magnetic dipole moment. The moment induced by $B$ is thus given by

$$\mu_{\text{ind}} = (-\tfrac{1}{2}er^2)\left(\frac{e}{2m} B\right) = -\frac{e^2 r^2}{4m} \cdot B \tag{15.12}$$

The direction of this induced moment is opposite to that of **B**.

An expression for the diamagnetic susceptibility can now be obtained from the definition of Equation 15.7. The term $r^2$ can be identified as the mean square radius of the projection of the orbit on a plane perpendicular to **B**. For an atom containing $Z$ electrons where the distribution of charge is spherically symmetrical and of average radius $\bar{r}$,

$$\bar{r}^2 = x^2 + y^2 + z^2 = \tfrac{2}{3}r^2$$

Thus when the foregoing treatment is extended to a solid containing $N$ atoms per unit volume, each with $Z$ electrons, we obtain for the diamagnetic susceptibility $\chi$, defined as the induced magnetic dipole moment per cubic meter in amp per meter,

$$\chi = -NZ \frac{e^2}{6m} \bar{r}^2(\mu_0 \mu_r) \tag{15.13}$$

Suppose $\bar{r}^2 \simeq 10^{-20} \, m^2$, $N \simeq 10^{28}$, $Z = 10$, then $\chi \simeq 10^{-5}$. Table 15.2 gives the measured values of susceptibility of the elements. Diamagnetic susceptibilities are preceded by a negative sign.

Clearly, the electrons associated with the largest values of $\chi$, that is, the outer electrons in the atom, make the major contribution to the diamagnetic susceptibility. Diamagnetism is a characteristic of all matter. We have just developed a *classical* expression for the susceptibility, but the *quantum* expression is similar. From previously developed ideas on the spread of the wave functions it is possible to make estimates of the magnitude of $\bar{r}^2$ and thus calculate values of $\chi$ which are in reasonable agreement with experimental values.

## 15.3   Paramagnetism

Paramagnetism, and other types of magnetism associated with positive susceptibility, occur because many atoms have a permanent magnetic moment which outweighs the diamagnetic effect.

Permanent magnetic moments are the sum of these three components: (*a*) the *orbital* magnetic dipole moment of the electrons, (*b*) the *spin* magnetic dipole moment of the electrons, and (*c*) the *nuclear* spin magnetic moment.

### The Orbital Magnetic Dipole Moment

In Fig. 15.2*a* we envisaged a single electron moving in orbit around a proton. The orbital magnetic dipole moment $\mu$ of the single electron was given by Equation 15.8.

The orbital angular momentum of the electron is, of course, $mr^2\omega$. If we call this quantity $L$, then

$$\mu = -\frac{e}{2m} L \tag{15.14}$$

We have seen in section 9.2 that orbital momenta are expressed in units of $h/2\pi$ and that

$$L = \sqrt{l(l+1)} \frac{h}{2\pi} \tag{15.15}$$

Thus

$$\mu = \left(-\frac{e}{2m}\frac{h}{2\pi}\right)\sqrt{l(l+1)} \tag{15.16}$$

The quantity $[(-e/2m)(h/2\pi)]$ is called the *Bohr magneton* $\beta$ and is of magnitude $9.27 \times 10^{-24}$ amp m². 

Also in Section 9.2 we saw that the orientation of the electron orbital momentum with respect to a magnetic field is limited so that the components of $\mathbf{L}$ in the field direction take the integral values $l, (l-1) \cdots -l$ when expressed in units of $h/2\pi$.

Thus as $s$ electron for which $l$ is zero can have no orbital magnetic moment. A single $p$ electron for which $l$ is unity can have a moment. If, however, in a

**Table 15.2**    Magnetic Susceptibility of the Elements*

| | | $\chi$ Magnetic Moment m$^{-3}$ (amp m$^{-1}$) | | | | $\chi$ Magnetic Moment m$^{-3}$ (amp m$^{-1}$) |
|---|---|---|---|---|---|---|
| 1 | H | $-0.0022 \times 10^{-6}$ | | 24 | Cr | $+313.2 \times 10^{-6}$ |
| 2 | He | $-0.0011$ | | 25 | Mn | $+871.2$ |
| 3 | Li | $+13.73$ | | 26 | Fe | Ferro |
| 4 | Be | $-23.19$ | | 27 | Co | Ferro |
| 5 | B | $-18.22$ | | 28 | Ni | Ferro |
| 6 | C | $-12.56$ | | 29 | Cu | $-9.632$ |
| 7 | N | $-0.0067$ | | 30 | Zn | $-15.65$ |
| 8 | O | $+1.936$ | | 31 | Ga | $-25.96$ |
| 9 | F | | | 32 | Ge | $-70.81$ |
| 10 | Ne | $-0.0038$ | | 33 | As | $-5.283$ |
| 11 | Na | $+8.483$ | | 34 | Se | $-19.14$ |
| 12 | Mg | $+11.78$ | | 35 | Br | $-0.0337$ |
| 13 | Al | $+20.74$ | | 36 | Kr | $-0.0161$ |
| 14 | Si | $-4.066$ | | 37 | Rb | $+3.829$ |
| 15 | P | $-21.10$ | | 38 | Sr | $+34.31$ |
| 16 | S | $-12.57$ | | 39 | Y | $+114.1$† |
| 17 | Cl | $-0.0231$ | | 40 | Zr | $+109.1$ |
| 18 | A | $-0.0110$ | | 41 | Nb | $+226.0$ |
| 19 | K | $+5.749$ | | 42 | Mo | $+118.9$ |
| 20 | Ca | $+19.44$ | | 43 | Tc | $+364.9$ |
| 21 | Sc | $+263.4$ | | 44 | Ru | $+66.07$ |
| 22 | Ti | $+180.6$ | | 45 | Rh | $+168.1$ |
| 23 | V | $+374.9$ | | 46 | Pd | $+805.5$ |

* Converted using molecular weights from *Handbook of Chemistry and Physics*, 46th ed., The Chemical Rubber Co., Cleveland, Ohio, 1965.

† Converted from *Proc. Phys. Soc.*, **85**, 963, 1965.

multielectron atom, all three $p$ states corresponding to $m_l = 1$, $m_l = 0$, and $m_l = -1$ in the $L$ shell are filled by electrons, the total magnetic moment of the $p$ electrons would again be zero. In general, we can only expect a resultant orbital magnetic moment from electrons in incompletely filled shells. The elements that have filled electron shell configurations consequently have small magnetic moments and are often diamagnetic. As we shall see later, a magnetic moment is associated with the *spin* of an electron. However, in atoms with filled shell atoms these electrons are "paired off" with electrons of oppositely directed spins, and the resultant magnetic moment is again zero. Conduction electrons give rise to small paramagnetic moments and we will calculate the magnitude later.

**Table 15.2** (continued)

| | | $\chi$ Magnetic Moment m$^{-3}$ (amp m$^{-1}$) | | | $\chi$ Magnetic Moment m$^{-3}$ (amp m$^{-1}$) |
|---|---|---|---|---|---|
| 47 | Ag | $-23.85 \times 10^{-6}$ | 72 | Hf | $+70.17$ |
| 48 | Cd | $-19.15$ | 73 | Ta | $+177.5 \times 10^{-6}$ |
| 49 | In | $-51.13$ | 74 | W | $+78.03$ |
| 50 | Sn | $+2.399$ | 75 | Re | $+93.66$ |
| 51 | Sb | $-68.37$ | 76 | Os | $+14.70$ |
| 52 | Te | $-24.31$ | 77 | Ir | $+37.53$ |
| 53 | I | $-21.65$ | 78 | Pt | $+279.0$ |
| 54 | Xe | $-0.0247$ | 79 | Au | $-34.51$ |
| 55 | Cs | $+5.151$ | 80 | Hg | $-20.52$ |
| 56 | Ba | $+6.597$ | 81 | Tl | $-37.09$ |
| 57 | La | $+65.97$ | 82 | Pb | $-15.82$ |
| 58 | Ce | $+3137.5$ | 83 | Bi | $-164.2$ |
| 59 | Pr | $+3030.2$ | 84 | Po | |
| 60 | Nd | $+3383.2$ | 85 | At | |
| 61 | Pm | | 86 | Rn | |
| 62 | Sm | $+1171.5$ | 87 | Fr | |
| 63 | Eu | $+14740$ | 88 | Ra | |
| 64 | Gd | $+479500$ | 89 | Ac | |
| 65 | Tb | $+95500$ | 90 | Th | $+83.64$ |
| 66 | Dy | $+68320$ | 91 | Pa | |
| 67 | Ho | | 92 | U | $+411.3$ |
| 68 | Er | $+30500$ | 93 | Np | |
| 69 | Tu | $+17700$ | 94 | Pu | $+603.1$ |
| 70 | Yb | $+126.2$ | 95 | Am | $+604.7$ |
| 71 | Lu | | | | |

The transition elements with $Z$ equal to 21 to 28, 39 to 45, 58 to 70, and 89 to 92 have incomplete shells, and the *free atoms* of these elements have permanent magnetic moments. Two groups with elements of large magnetic moment are the *iron-group* elements with incomplete $3d$ subshells and the *lanthanide-group* elements with incomplete $4f$ subshells.

Suppose now that the atoms are grouped together in a solid. The magnetic properties of the solid are then very dependent on the degree to which the incomplete subshells are electrostatically "screened" from the magnetic and electric fields of neighboring atoms. Thus the measured paramagnetic magnetic moment for these elements will depend on the environment of the magnetic atoms. The $3d$ wave functions of the iron group are not well screened, giving rise to a large magnetic moment.

## 15.4   The Spin Magnetic Dipole Moment

As discussed in Section 9.3, the electron has, in addition to an orbital angular momentum $L$, an intrinsic spin angular momentum $L_s$. This momentum can be written

$$L_s = \sqrt{s(s+1)}\,\frac{h}{2\pi} \tag{15.17}$$

where $s = \frac{1}{2}$. We might expect to be able to write an expression for the spin magnetic moment $\mu_s$ which is analogous to that for orbital magnetic moment $\mu$. In fact, experiment shows that we must write

$$\mu_s = g_s\,\sqrt{s(s+1)}\,\beta \tag{15.18}$$

where $g_s$ is called the *Landé splitting factor* and has for pure electron spin a value of almost exactly 2.

The reason for the necessary introduction of the $g_s$ factor in electron spin theory is the interactions that exist between spin and orbital momenta. These interactions, commonly called the *coupling* in the system, are complicated. They become more complicated in multielectron atoms. We will not discuss the question in detail. Let us merely summarize the results of theory in the current nomenclature. The *total angular momentum* quantum number for an atom arises because of spin, orbital, and the coupling terms. It is called $J$. The total angular momentum $M_J$ is then

$$M_J = \sqrt{J(J+1)}\,\frac{h}{2\pi} \tag{15.19}$$

and we write $\mu_J$, the total angular magnetic moment, in the form

$$\mu_J = g_J\,\sqrt{J(J+1)}\,\beta \tag{15.20}$$

where all the coupling complexity is accommodated in the quantity $g_J$. We must have recourse to experiment to form an idea of what type of momentum term is most important in a particular system. Since $g_J = 1$ for orbital momenta only, and $g_J = 2$ for spin momenta, experimental values of the Landé factor close to 2 indicate that the magnetic moments are largely of a spin nature and the orbital momenta are quenched. This is the case in the first transition elements, where interaction between the lattice atoms prevents reorientation of the orbital dipole moments.

## 15.5 Nuclear Spin Magnetic Dipole Moment

The angular momentum associated with *nuclear* spin is also expressed in units of $h/2\pi$. The magnetic moment is in units of $[(-e/2m)(h/2\pi)]$. The mass of the nucleus, however, is of the order of one thousand times that of the electron. Hence the magnetic dipole moment associated with nuclear spin, a quantity called the *nuclear magneton*, is of the order of $10^{-3}$ Bohr magneton.

## 15.6 Calculation of Susceptibility. Electron Spin

Thus far we have merely discussed the nature of the permanent moments that are associated with an atom. To compute the susceptibility we must make a calculation of the numbers of magnetic dipole moments which line up parallel to an applied magnetic field. The magnitude of the susceptibility will be determined by the fractional number of magnetic dipole moments which line up in this way.

Let us carry out the calculation for a simple system in which the magnetic dipole moments are due to pure electron spin and assume that they do not interact with one another. Let us further assume that the spin quantum number $s = \frac{1}{2}$ so that there are just two possible orientations of the magnetic moment with respect to the external field, one parallel to the magnetic field and the other antiparallel. In this system the $g_J$ factor is, of course, simply equivalent to $g_s$ and has the value 2

Now the energy of a magnetic moment in the presence of a magnetic field of induction $B$ is given by the vector dot product of these quantities Thus an energy difference exists between spin magnetic dipole moments parallel and antiparallel to the field, the magnitude of the energy difference being $2\beta B$. If *no interaction exists between neighboring spin moments*, the permeability is that of free space $\mu_0$. The two spin energy levels are thus $+\mu_0\beta H$ and $-\mu_0\beta H$. This is summarized in Fig. 15.3. Let us suppose that in unit volume of the paramagnetic material there is a total of $N$ atoms and the spin moments of $N_1$ atoms are parallel to the field and $N_2$ spin moments are antiparallel. The populations in both of the two energy levels are given by Boltzmann statistics. These populations are

$$\frac{N_1}{N} = \frac{e^{\mu_0\beta H/kT}}{e^{\mu_0\beta H/kT} + e^{-\mu_0\beta H/kT}} \tag{15.21}$$

and

$$\frac{N_2}{N} = \frac{e^{-\mu_0\beta H/kT}}{e^{\mu_0\beta H/kT} + e^{-\mu_0\beta H/kT}} \tag{15.22}$$

Also, $N = N_1 + N_2$, and the total magnetic moment per unit volume $M$ is given by

$$M = (N_1 - N_2)\beta$$

Thus

$$M = N\beta \frac{e^{\mu_0\beta H/kT} - e^{-\mu_0\beta H/kT}}{e^{\mu_0\beta H/kT} + e^{-\mu_0\beta H/kT}} \qquad (15.23)$$

This may be written more concisely as

$$M = N\beta \tanh \frac{\mu_0\beta H}{kT} \qquad (15.24)$$

We have performed this simplified calculation in order to illustrate the manner in which population of energy levels is related to susceptibility. The treatment is restricted to materials in which $s = \frac{1}{2}$, that is, ions such as $Ti^{3+}$, $V^{4+}$, and $Cu^{2+}$. For more complicated cases where $s$ is greater than $\frac{1}{2}$ and orbital moments are included, the form of the mathematical analysis is similar to the simple case just given. Naturally, the summation must be made over more energy levels. We have already remarked that the total angular momentum quantum number $J$ includes the interactions between spin and orbital momenta. The full expression for the magnetic moment $M$ per unit volume for a system with $s$ greater than $\frac{1}{2}$ and including orbital moments will therefore include $J$.

$$M = \mu_0 N g J\beta \left[ \frac{2J+1}{2J} \coth \left( \frac{2J+1}{2J} \right) x - \frac{1}{2J} \coth \frac{x}{2J} \right] \qquad (15.25)$$

where

$$x = \frac{\mu_0 g J\beta H}{kT}$$

Figure 15.4 shows experimental measurements of magnetic moments of the chromium, iron, and gadolinium ions for various field temperature ratios. Equation 15.25, shown by the full lines in the figure, is a good representation

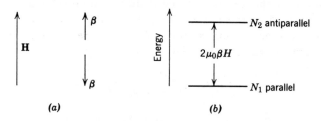

(a)                                        (b)

**Fig. 15.3**   In the presence of a magnetic field **H** the two spin moments will align parallel and antiparallel to the field as in (a). The energy difference of the two configurations is shown in (b).

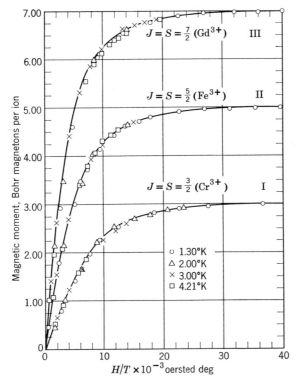

**Fig. 15.4**  The magnetic moment versus $H/T$ for specimens of:  I, potassium chromium alum;  II, ferric ammonium alum;  and III, gadolinium sulfate octohydrate.  (After Henry)

of the experimental results.  In these substances quenching of the orbital momenta is virtually complete.  We will examine the nature of the function given in Equation 15.25 for two regions of $x$.

## When $\mu_0 gJ\beta H \ll kT$

This is the normal circumstance since even in a strong field of magnetic induction $\mu_0 H = 1$ weber m$^{-2}$, the value of $\mu_0 \beta H \simeq 9 \times 10^{-24}$ joule, whereas at room temperature $kT \simeq 4 \times 10^{-21}$ joule.  Under these circumstances, the quantity in the brackets of Equation 15.25 tends to the value $[(J + 1)/3J]x$.  Then

$$\chi = \frac{M}{H} = Ng^2\mu_0{}^2 J(J + 1)\frac{\beta^2}{3kT} \tag{15.26}$$

$$= \frac{C}{T} \tag{15.27}$$

This reciprocal dependence of $x$ on $T$ is called *Curie's law*. The Curie constant $C$ is characteristic of the material. There is no solid element with unpaired $d$ or $f$ electrons in which magnetic moment interaction between neighboring atoms does not complicate this theory. In a sufficiently dilute alloy, however, of, say, one-tenth per cent of iron in aluminium, the unpaired electrons are far enough apart to reduce the interaction, and Equation 15.26 gives good values for the paramagnetic susceptibility. Agreement with the Curie law is also found for dilute solutions of the rare earths. In measurements of most paramagnetic salts and, in particular, the rare earth themselves, however, the graph of $\chi$ versus the reciprocal temperature does not pass through the origin and the law is therefore modified to read

$$\chi = \frac{C}{T - \theta} \tag{15.28}$$

where $\theta$ is also characteristic of the paramagnetic substance.

Let us estimate the order of magnitude of the paramagnetic susceptibility of solids at room temperature. In mks units,

$$N \simeq 10^{28} \qquad \beta \simeq 10^{-23} \qquad k \simeq 10^{-23}$$

and thus for $T \simeq 10^2$ the order of magnitude of $\chi$ is $10^{-3}$. Table 15.2 shows measured susceptibility values for the elements.

### When $\mu_0 g J \beta H \gg kT$

This condition will apply only in the presence of strong fields at low temperatures. Then the quantity within the bracket in Equation 15.25 tends to 1. The susceptibility $\chi$ tends to the saturation value $\mu_0 N g \beta H$. This implies that every dipole moment of the material is lined up parallel to the magnetic field. Figure 15.4 shows that the condition can be achieved experimentally.

In the section discussing nuclear spin magnetic dipole moment, we noted that the nuclear magneton was of order $10^{-3}\beta$. Since the susceptibility $\chi$ depends on $\beta^2$, we would expect the susceptibility of a nuclear paramagnetic system to be smaller by a factor of $10^{-6}$ than that of an electronic paramagnetic system. This is experimentally found to be the case. It should also be recalled at this point that diamagnetic susceptibilities are of the order $10^{-5}$ m$^{-3}$. Thus in a system of permanent spin magnetic dipole moments the positive paramagnetic susceptibility will mask the diamagnetic and nuclear terms.

## 15.7 Pauli Paramagnetism of Electrons at the Fermi Surface

In the alkali and noble metals the spin moments due to the electrons are balanced in the absence of a magnetic field even though each atom has a nonzero spin moment. We have seen that if a field $H$ is applied, then the energy of those electrons with spin parallel to the field is lowered by $\mu_0\beta H$. Conversely, the energy of the electrons with spins antiparallel to the field is raised by $\mu_0\beta H$. Electrons of antiparallel spin can then contribute to a lowering of the total energy of the system by spilling over into unfilled energy levels of the parallel electrons. This continues until there is a common Fermi level for both parallel and antiparallel electrons. Now more electrons have spins parallel to the field than antiparallel, giving rise to a positive Pauli paramagnetic susceptibility.

Figure 15.5$a$ shows the instantaneously raised and lowered levels of the electrons corresponding to antiparallel and parallel spins. Figure 15.5$b$ shows the redistribution of the electrons in available levels which lowers the total energy and leaves more electrons with spin parallel to the field than antiparallel.

The temperature dependence of the paramagnetic susceptibility of electrons at the Fermi surface is determined by two opposing factors. First, raising the temperature decreases the ordering or disorients the spins and hence decreases the susceptibility. Second, raising the temperature allows more electrons to be thermally excited into states of parallel spin and leads to an increase in the susceptibility.

In the alkali and noble metals these two effects essentially balance and the paramagnetic susceptibility for these materials is independent of temperature. The temperature dependence in the nonmagnetic transition elements can go either way.

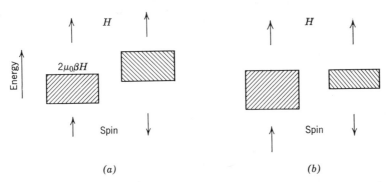

**Fig. 15.5** ($a$) Filled energy levels on application of magnetic field. ($b$) Redistribution of electrons giving rise to paramagnetism.

## 15.8 Ferromagnetism

The magnetic behavior of the three elements—iron, cobalt, and nickel—at the end of the first transition series is quite unique. Let us recall the magnetic characteristics of these elements and of the many ferromagnetic alloys which exist.

Ferromagnetic solids have very high values of susceptibility which are both field and temperature dependent. Above a certain temperature $\theta$, which is characteristic of the particular substance, the temperature dependence of the susceptibility is similar to that of many paramagnetic solids, that is,

$$\chi = \frac{C}{T - \theta} \tag{15.28}$$

At lower temperatures the dependence of *magnetization M* and the magnetic induction $B$ on field strength $H$ is shown by the familiar hysteresis curve of Fig. 15.6. The shape of the curve is dependent on the preparation and treatment of the ferromagnetic specimen. The value of $M$ at high fields, corresponding to induction $B_S$, that is, the saturation magnetization $M_S$, depends only on the constitution and purity of the specimen. If the ratio of $M_S$ at a particular temperature to the value at $0°K$ is plotted against the ratio of the temperature to the temperature $\theta$ at which ferromagnetism disappears, the plot of these reduced parameters is common for all ferromagnetic materials. This is shown in Fig. 15.7 for iron, cobalt, and nickel. These are

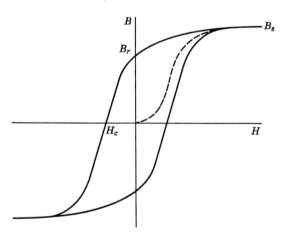

**Fig. 15.6** The hysteretic behavior of magnetic induction versus field strength for a ferromagnetic solid. The dashed curve gives the initial behavior of an unmagnetized specimen.

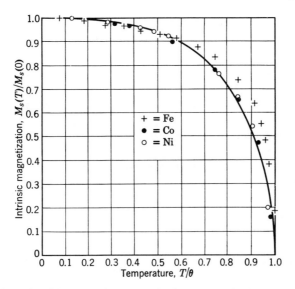

**Fig. 15.7** The ratio of the saturation magnetization at a particular temperature $T$ to that at $0°K$ plotted against the ratio of the particular temperature $T$ to that at which ferromagnetism disappears $\theta$, for the metals iron, cobalt, and nickel. The solid line shows the theoretical curve from Equation 15.38 with $J = \frac{1}{2}$.

some of the unique magnetic properties of ferromagnetic materials which a theory must attempt to explain.

In Section 15.6 on paramagnetic materials we saw that it was possible, at low temperatures and with strong magnetic fields, to produce saturation values of $M$. In ferromagnetic materials saturation magnetization is possible at ordinary temperatures and with small or zero fields. Pierre Weiss in 1907 invented a concept to account for this behavior. He postulated the existence of an internal "molecular" field $H_E$ which is proportional to the magnetization $M$. Thus

$$H_E = \lambda M \qquad (15.29)$$

where $\lambda$ is the *Weiss field constant*.

Weiss supposed this internal field to be the result of the *cooperative interaction of neighboring dipoles*. Let us now make a quick estimate of the magnitude of the interaction necessary to account for experimental values. In Fig. 15.6 the value of $B_r$ at $H = 0$ for a typical ferromagnetic material is about 1 weber m$^{-2}$. Thus $M_r \simeq B_r/\mu_0 \simeq 10^6$ ampere m$^{-1}$. In most solids there are about $10^{29}$ atomic dipole moments per cubic meter, each of moment $\beta$, which is of magnitude $10^{-23}$ ampere m$^2$. Thus to obtain the measured value of $M_r$, the interaction must be such that *all the magnetic dipoles are aligned parallel* in the ferromagnetic material.

## 15.9  The Classical Molecular Field Theory of Ferromagnetism

Pierre Weiss was unable to explain the origin of the internal molecular field which exists in ferromagnetic materials. His assumption, Equation 15.29, can, however, be used to develop a phenomenological theory that describes many of the experimental features. We shall reproduce this theory since it is illuminating in this connection and also in the theory of ferrimagnetic crystals.

In the presence of an applied external magnetic field each dipole in a ferromagnetic material is subject to a total field of $H + \lambda M$. Let us again use the simplified model of Section 15.6 in which $N$ spins per cubic meter line up parallel or antiparallel to the applied magnetic field. We simply replace $H$ in Equation 15.25 by the new total field $H + \lambda M$. Thus

$$M = Ng\beta J[B(x)] \tag{15.30}$$

where $[B(x)]$ is the Brillouin function

$$\left[ \frac{2J+1}{2J} \coth \left( \frac{2J+1}{2J} \right) x - \frac{1}{2J} \coth \frac{x}{2J} \right]$$

and $x$ in this case is

$$\frac{\mu_0 g J \beta}{kT} (H + \lambda M) \tag{15.31}$$

### The Spontaneous Magnetization Region

Now, following the suggestion of Weiss that the ferromagnetic material is magnetized to saturation at zero or very low fields, let us obtain first a theoretical expression for the spontaneous magnetization. To do this we set the external field $H = 0$. Then from Equation 15.31 we have

$$x = \frac{\mu_0 g J \beta \lambda}{kT} M(T) \tag{15.32}$$

where we have written $M(T)$ instead of $M$ to emphasize the temperature dependence. Then if

$$M(0) = Ng J \beta \tag{15.33}$$

we have

$$\frac{M(T)}{M(0)} = \frac{kTx}{N\lambda g^2 \beta^2 J^2} \tag{15.34}$$

Also from Equation 15.30 we have

$$\frac{M(T)}{M(0)} = [B_J(x)] \tag{15.35}$$

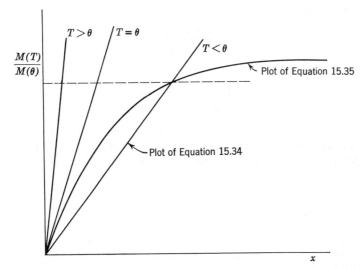

**Fig. 15.8** The graphical solution of the simultaneous Equations 15.34 and 15.35. The point of intersection shows that intrinsic magnetization exists even in the absence of a field. This magnetization vanishes at $T > \theta$, since no crossing point of the curve is then possible.

Before we attempt the simultaneous solution of these last two equations for $M(T)/M(0)$, note that $[B_J(x)] \rightarrow 1$ as $x \rightarrow \infty$, that is, as $T \rightarrow 0$. Thus $M(0)$ is the maximum value of the magnetization and would occur if the temperature were reduced to zero.

Now we can obtain the simultaneous solution of Equations 15.34 and 15.35 by plotting both functions for $M(T)/M(0)$ against $x$. These are shown in Fig. 15.8. Below a critical temperature $T = \theta°$K, where the straight line is tangential to the Brillouin function at the origin, there are two intersections of the curves. The intersection at $x = 0$ is an unstable situation, and the higher intersection corresponds to a spontaneous magnetization.

*Thus below a certain temperature there can exist in a ferromagnetic solid a magnetization within the material even in the absence of a magnetic field.*

At or above the critical temperature, called the Curie temperature, the only intersection is at $M(T)/M(0) = 0$, which means that the spontaneous magnetization vanishes.

A little more algebra gives the ratio $M(T)/M(0)$ as a function of $T/\theta$. For $x \rightarrow 0$ $[B_J(x)]$ is given by

$$[B_J(x)] \simeq \left(\frac{J+1}{3J}\right) x + \left( \quad \right) x^3 \tag{15.36}$$

so that the slope of the tangent is $(J + 1)/3$. Also, the slope of the line of Equation 15.34 at $T = \theta$ is given by $k\theta/N\lambda g^2\beta^2 J^2$. If we now equate these two slopes, we get

$$\theta = \frac{Ng^2\beta^2 J(J+1)\lambda}{3k} \tag{15.37}$$

and employing Equation 15.34, finally,

$$\frac{M(T)}{M(0)} = \frac{J+1}{3J}\left(\frac{T}{\theta}\right) \tag{15.38}$$

This equation is plotted as the full line in Fig. 15.7 for the value $J = \frac{1}{2}$. The agreement suggests that the magnetization comes from spin moments rather than from the orbital moments and that the appropriate value for $g$ is 2.

### The Paramagnetic Region

Above the Curie point the spontaneous magnetization is zero. We saw at small values of $x$ (i.e., high temperature) that

$$[B_J(x)] \simeq \left[\frac{J+1}{3J}\right]x \tag{15.39}$$

If we now substitute (15.39) in the original equation, we get

$$M = \frac{Ng\beta J(J+1)}{3J}x \tag{15.40}$$

where $x$ is now given by

$$\frac{\mu_0 J g\beta}{kT}(H + \lambda M)$$

Solving for $M/H$, we obtain

$$\chi = \frac{M}{H} = \frac{C}{T - \theta} \tag{15.41}$$

where

$$C = \frac{\mu_0 Ng^2\beta^2 J(J+1)}{3k} \tag{15.42}$$

and

$$\theta = \frac{\lambda\mu_0 Ng^2\beta^2 J(J+1)}{3k} = \lambda C \tag{15.43}$$

Equation 15.41 is just the Curie-Weiss law (Section 15.6) that accounts for the temperature behavior of the susceptibility of many paramagnetic materials. It also gives excellent agreement with data for ferromagnetic substances above the Curie point, with the small disagreement that the Curie point defined from the spontaneous magnetization theory differs by a few degrees from the experimental value found for the paramagnetic region.

We have observed that the Weiss or classical theory has successfully accounted for spontaneous magnetization and the temperature dependence of magnetization in ferromagnetic materials. It has, however, said nothing about the actual nature of the molecular field. We shall now discuss the modern interpretation of the field.

## 15.10 The Internal Field: Exchange Interaction

Ideas on the fundamental nature of the internal field were first formulated by Heisenberg, Slater, and Stoner, subsequent to the introduction of the concept by Weiss, and they are not yet satisfactory.

From equation 15.43 we find that the magnetic induction of the Weiss internal field is of the order of $10^3$ webers$^{-2}$. This value is about one thousand times as large as we would obtain on the assumption that the internal field is due to the *magnetic* interaction of the atomic dipoles. But electrostatic coulomb repulsion between two electrons is many orders of magnitude greater than the magnetic force between them that arises because of their spin magnetic moments. The source of the very large spin interaction found in ferromagnetic materials must therefore be sought in a spin-dependent electrostatic interaction. Quantum mechanics provides such an interaction—called the *exchange interaction.*

The quantum theory of ferromagnetism has not yet been developed to a point permitting calculation of actual measurable values. A central feature of the most modern theories is the assumption of a short-range electron-electron interaction that is localized between adjacent atoms and aligns neighboring spin moments.

The older band theory of exchange, developed by Slater and Stoner, is undoubtedly incorrect in detail. It is, nevertheless, of sufficient interest to warrant a short discussion. We will use the element iron as a specific example.

In Fig. 10.21 we showed the band structure of iron with the narrow, partially filled $3d$ band and a broad, overlapping $4s$. In Fig. 15.9$a$ we again show the $3d$ band, this time separating the band into partial bands of positive and negative spin, each capable of holding five electrons. We will neglect the effect of the $4s$ band since this is not of major importance to the discussion. If the exchange interaction were not present, three of the six $3d$ electrons in iron would have spin $+\frac{1}{2}$ and three $-\frac{1}{2}$. Naturally, without a preponderance of spin of one direction, the iron atom would have no spin magnetic moment. The exchange interaction causes the effect shown in Fig. 15.9$b$. In solid iron the total energy is lowered by making the maximum number of spins parallel. Thus five electrons go into $+\frac{1}{2}$ spin partial band and one in the $-\frac{1}{2}$ spin partial band. The Fermi energy is increased since the states now occupied

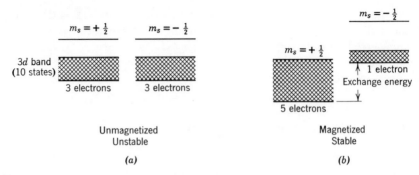

**Fig. 15.9** The partially filled 3d bands of iron shown with (a) three electrons in each band giving the unmagnetized state, and (b) with five electrons in one band and one electron in the other giving the magnetized state. The latter is stable for iron since the exchange energy lowers the total energy more than the Fermi energy raises it.

at the top of the $+\frac{1}{2}$ band are of greater energy than those vacated near the middle of the $-\frac{1}{2}$ band. The exchange energy, however, lowers the whole $+\frac{1}{2}$ band, and in iron this is the more important term. The magnetized state of Fig. 15.9b is therefore the one of lower total energy and thus the stable one.

If the outer unfilled band in a metal is much broader than we have pictured for iron, the magnetized state of Fig. 15.9b would be unstable. This is so because filling the $+\frac{1}{2}$ spin band, if it were very broad, would mean adding many electrons near the top of the band. These electrons would, of necessity, be of higher energy. The increase in the Fermi energy term would then be greater than the decrease by the exchange energy.

A criterion for the appearance of ferromagnetism is therefore the width of the 3d band. Figure 15.10 shows the energy of magnetization—that is, the difference in energy between the magnetized and unmagnetized states— plotted as a function of the ratio of the interatomic spacings to the calculated

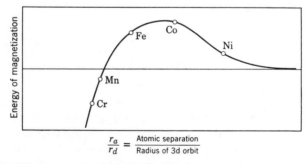

**Fig. 15.10** The energy of magnetization plotted as a function of the ratio of interatomic spacing to the radius of the 3d orbit. The magnetized state is stable for the elements iron, cobalt, and nickel.

radius of the 3*d* orbit. When the separation of the atoms is great, there is a small reduction of energy by the exchange effect. On the other hand, when the ratio becomes small, the 3*d* band is broadened, and the Fermi energy term makes the magnetized state the unstable one. The magnitudes of band width and atomic spacing favor magnetization in the solids—iron, cobalt, and nickel. If the interatomic distance in a metal is altered by compound or alloy formation, the process might cause a metal that is not ferromagnetic to become so. In the Heusler alloys, which consist of aluminum, copper, and manganese, the effective interatomic distance for manganese is increased. The energy of magnetization if Fig. 15.10 is now positive, and the alloy is ferromagnetic within a certain composition range.

### 15.11  Domains

To explain the fact that actual pieces of ferromagnetic materials are normally found in the demagnetized state, Weiss made his second postulate. He assumed the existence of small domains within which the ferromagnetic material is magnetized to saturation. The *direction of magnetization*, however, varies from domain to domain, and thus the *net macroscopic magnetization* may have values between zero and the saturation value. Section 15.11 contains further discussion of the second Weiss postulate.

Direct evidence of domain structure is obtained from powder patterns. In this technique a drop of a colloidal suspension of finely divided ferromagnetic powder is allowed to spread over a prepared surface of the ferromagnetic material under investigation. The colloidal particles collect along the domain boundaries where strong magnetic fields exist. Photographs can then be made of the powder pattern. Figure 15.11 shows such a pattern on a silicon-iron crystal.

Domain structure occurs in order to minimize the total energy of the ferromagnetic solid. The total energy comprises the sum of the *exchange energy*, the *anisotropy energy*, and the *magnetic energy*.

### *Anisotropy Energy*

It is found experimentally that the relationship between the magnetizing field *H* and the magnetization *M* in a single ferromagnetic crystal depends on the direction of magnetization in the crystal. Figure 15.12 shows magnetization curves for iron with the applied field directed along different crystallographic directions. It is evident that very much greater fields are required to produce magnetic saturation in the [111] direction than need be applied in the [100] direction. The difference in magnetic energy to produce saturation in an

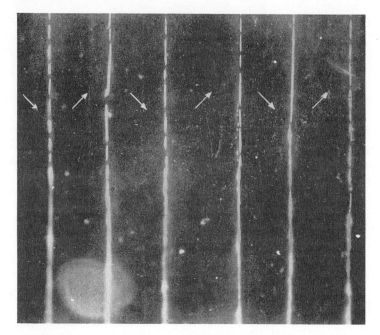

**Fig. 15.11** Domain walls in silicon-iron crystal. The arrows indicate the direction of magnetization. (After Williams, Bozorth, and Shockley)

easy and hard direction is called the *anisotropy energy*. Magnetization of a crystal in a certain direction always produces changes in atomic spacing in that direction. This is called *magnetostriction*. Thus the basis of anisotropy energy lies in the work done against elastic forces by the magnetostrictive forces.

### The Magnetic Energy

The magnetic energy can be calculated if we recall from Section 15.6 that the energy of a magnetic dipole $\mu$ antiparallel to magnetic induction $B$ is given by the product of these quantities. Thus, if the magnetization is $M$ and the induction $B$, the magnetic energy is $MB$ with dimensions (amp m$^{-1}$) (weber m$^{-2}$) $\simeq 10^6$ joule m$^{-3}$. In the transition elements the anisotropy energy is generally about $10^4$ times smaller than the exchange energy.

Let us suppose that in Fig. 15.13$a$ the exchange energy has established a single domain in a specimen of ferromagnetic material. The magnetic energy can be reduced by dividing the specimen into two domains, as in Fig. 15.13$b$. In the example, the magnetic energy is roughly halved. The subdivision continues until the reduction in magnetic energy is less than the increase in

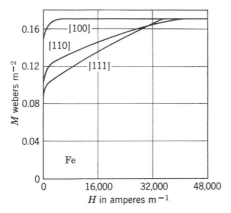

**Fig. 15.12** Magnetization curves for a single crystal of iron.

energy to form another domain, and its boundary, called a *Bloch* wall. The energy to form a wall arises because across each wall the directions of the magnetic moments (of neighboring atoms) gradually rotate from the direction in one domain to the direction in the other. Easy directions in, say, iron are 90° apart and the anisotropy energy tends to make the Bloch wall very thin in order to reduce to a minimum the number of neighboring magnetic moments pointing in a hard crystallographic direction. In contrast, the exchange energy tends to keep neighboring moments as parallel as possible and so tends to make the wall as thick as possible. The compromise makes the Bloch wall in iron about 100 A thick and gives it an associated energy of about $10^{-3}$ joule m$^{-2}$.

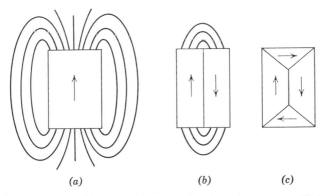

**Fig. 15.13** In ($a$) the exchange energy has established a single domain. In ($b$) the magnetic energy, which is roughly proportional to the spatial extension of the field, has been halved. In ($c$) the magnetic energy has been reduced to zero by the domains of closure.

## 15.12   Magnetization of a Ferromagnetic Specimen

When a magnetic field is applied to a ferromagnetic material, the domain walls move so that the domains which are favorably oriented with respect to the field grow at the expense of domains less favorably oriented. Eventually the magnetic directions of the few remaining domains rotate toward that of the applied field.

We gave in Fig. 15.6 a representation of a $B$, $H$ hysteresis loop. Starting with a virgin specimen, $B$ varies reversibly with $H$ for small fields. In this region the *initial permeability* is defined in the same way as the permeability of a paramagnetic material, $B = \mu_0\mu_r H$. In this region the Bloch walls move reversibly under small fields. As the applied field $H$ is increased, $B$ increases more rapidly and a *differential permeability* is defined as $1 + dM/dH$. The differential permeability increases at first with $H$. In this region Bloch walls move irreversibly through the material as orientation favored domains grow at the expense of those less favored. As $B$ approaches its saturation value $B_s$, the differential permeability falls to unity and the moments of the favored domains rotate partially toward the field direction. If the applied field is now reduced, the rotation of the moments away from the field takes place almost reversibly in contrast to the region of Bloch wall movement, which is quite irreversible. At zero applied field $B_r$, the *remanent induction*, remains and a reverse field $-H_c$, the *coercive force*, must be applied to reduce the induction to zero.

Thus the magnetic behavior of ferromagnetic materials is determined largely by the ease with which Bloch walls move through the crystals. The coercive force and the hysteretic characteristics are measures of the restriction to wall movement by impeding obstacles.

In *magnetically hard* materials these obstacles may be impurities or stress or grain boundaries. *Magnetically soft materials* with low values of $H_c$ and high permeability, on the other hand, should be highly purified, well annealed, correctly oriented for easy magnetization, and should be treated to remove other types of imperfection that would impede the movement of the Bloch walls.

The coercive force varies over wide limits in ferromagnetic materials. For *permanent magnet materials* the coercive force should be high, whereas material used in transformers and in applications where the magnetic induction is rapidly varied should have low values of coercive force but high values of maximum permeability.

Table 15.3 shows some data on permanent magnet and high permeability materials.

**Table 15.3** Data for Permanent Magnet and Soft Magnetic Materials

| | Permanent Magnet Materials Made from Powder | | |
|---|---|---|---|
| | $B_r$ (weber m$^{-2}$) | $H_c$ (amp m$^{-1}$) | |
| Cobalt ferrite | 0.4 | 40,000 | |
| Iron-cobalt | 0.92 | 80,000 | |
| Iron-cobalt ferrite | 0.60 | 130,000 | |
| | Permanent Magnet Materials Made from Alloys | | |
| Alnico 11 | 0.73 | 47,000 | |
| Alnico V | 1.27 | 54,000 | |
| Ticonal XX | 1.18 | 10,900 | |
| Carbon steel | 1.0 | 4,000 | |
| Cobalt steel | 1.0 | 20,000 | |
| Platinax 11 | 0.64 | 400,000 | |
| | High permeability materials | | |
| | $\mu_r$(max) | $B_s$ (weber m$^{-2}$) | $H_c$ (amp m$^{-1}$) |
| Iron, commercial | 6,000 | 2.16 | 80 |
| Iron, pure | 350,000 | 2.16 | 0.9 |
| 4% Si-Fe | 6,500 | 2.01 | 40 |
| Mumetal | 100,000 | 0.75 | 4 |
| Supermalloy | $10^6$ | 0.80 | 0.34 |

## 15.13 Antiferromagnetism and Ferrimagnetism

To complete our discussion of the different kinds of magnetic behavior found with static fields in solid materials, we have yet to deal with the classes exhibiting *antiferromagnetism* and *ferrimagnetism*.

In Section 15.10 it was pointed out that the origin of the internal field in ferromagnetic materials was due to the exchange interaction that lined up neighboring spin moments in the solid. In some compounds of the transition metals the spacing of the magnetic ions is such that the exchange interaction is negative. Below a critical temperature, called the Néel temperature $T_N$, this can lead in certain structures to antiparallel alignment of electron spins in neighboring atoms. In the *antiferromagnetic* class, Néel first envisaged the spins to be balanced so that the net moment of the material was zero. The term is now used to include materials with triangular, spiral, or canted spin arrangements with a *small* net magnetic moment. In the *ferrimagnetic* class the spins are unbalanced and a *considerable* net magnetic moment is present. Figure 15.14 shows the spin arrangements characteristic of ferromagnetism, antiferromagnetism (spins balanced), and ferrimagnetism, the temperature in each case being below the critical temperature for spin disordering.

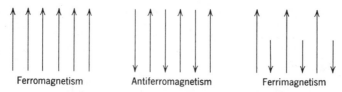

Ferromagnetism        Antiferromagnetism        Ferrimagnetism

**Fig. 15.14**  Spin arrangements in ferromagnetic, antiferromagnetic, and ferrimagnetic materials.

Let us consider in an antiferromagnetic material that the structure consists of two interpenetrating sublattices $A$ and $B$ in which all nearest neighbors of an $A$ ion lie on $B$ sites.  The body-centered cubic structure is an example and for simplicity we shall use it.  Figure 15.15 shows a unit cell with the spin directions of the ions marked by arrows.

## 15.14   Molecular Field Theory of Antiferromagnetism

Following a procedure similar to that used to describe the internal field in ferromagnetic materials, we introduce an expression $H_{IA}$ for the internal field acting on an atom of an antiferromagnetic material which lies on an $A$ site.  If $\lambda_{AA}$ is the internal field constant for the $A$-$A$ interaction and $\lambda_{AB}$ is the constant for the $A$-$B$ interaction, then

$$H_{IA} = -\lambda_{AA}M_A - \lambda_{AB}M_B \qquad (15.44)$$

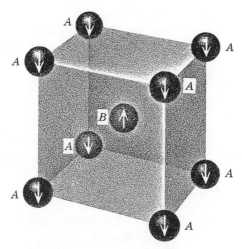

**Fig. 15.15**  Body-centered unit cell with the spins of the $A$ atoms oppositely directed to those of the $B$ atoms.

In this expression $M_A$ and $M_B$ are the magnetizations of the $A$ and $B$ sublattices, respectively. Similarly, we can write an expression for the internal field acting on a $B$ atom, $H_{IB}$,

$$H_{IB} = -\lambda_{BB}M_B - \lambda_{BA}M_A \tag{15.45}$$

In the presence of an external field $H$ the fields $H_A$ and $H_B$ on an $A$ and $B$ atom, respectively, are

$$H_A = H - \lambda_{AA}M_A - \lambda_{AB}M_B \tag{15.46}$$

and

$$H_B = H - \lambda_{BB}M_B - \lambda_{BA}M_A \tag{15.47}$$

At this point we write expressions for the magnetizations of the $A$ and $B$ lattices. These expressions are derived in a manner similar to that used to derive Equation 15.30 for the ferromagnetic case. Since the antiferromagnetic coupling is due to spin, we can replace $J$ in the Brillouin function by the total spin quantum number $S$. The magnetization of the $A$ sublattice $M_A$ is thus given by

$$M_A = \tfrac{1}{2}Ng\beta S[B(x_A)] \tag{15.48}$$

where

$$x = \frac{\mu_0 Sg\beta H_A}{kT} \tag{15.49}$$

and

$$[B(x_A)] = \frac{2S+1}{2S}\coth\frac{2S+1}{2S}x_A - \frac{1}{2S}\coth\frac{x_A}{2S} \tag{15.50}$$

The expression for $M_B$, the magnetization of the $B$ sublattice, is similar in form. A spontaneous magnetization of the $A$ and $B$ sublattices exists at fields $H = 0$. There is no antiferromagnetic ordering above the Néel temperature $T_N$. We will first consider the magnetic behavior above this temperature.

### Antiferromagnetic Susceptibility above the Néel Temperature

The analysis will be similar in form to that given for ferromagnetic material above the Curie temperature. We shall consider the $A$ sublattice in detail and assume the results for the $B$ sublattice by analogy.

The Brillouin function is again replaced by the first term

$$B(x_A) \simeq \left(\frac{S+1}{3S}\right)x_A$$

Equation 15.48 then becomes

$$M_A = \frac{\mu_0 Ng^2\beta^2 S(S+1)H_A}{6kT}$$

Also

$$H_A = H - \lambda_{AA}M_A - \lambda_{AB}M_B$$

In this region of no antiferromagnetic interaction, the applied field $H$ and the magnetizations $M_A$ and $M_B$ must be parallel. Hence

$$M_A = \frac{\mu_0 N g^2 \beta^2 S(S+1)}{6kT}(H - \lambda_{AA}M_A - \lambda_{AB}M_B) \qquad (15.51)$$

Similarly,

$$M_B = \frac{\mu_0 N g^2 \beta^2 S(S+1)}{6kT}(H - \lambda_{BB}M_B - \lambda_{BA}M_A) \qquad (15.52)$$

In a lattice where the same type of atoms occupy the $A$ and $B$ sites

$$\lambda_{AA} = \lambda_{BB} = \lambda_{ii}$$

and

$$\lambda_{AB} = \lambda_{BA} = \lambda_{ij}$$

Although this is not necessarily always the case, we shall complete the analysis making this assumption. The magnetization of the whole lattice is the sum of $M_A$ and $M_B$. Hence

$$M = M_A + M_B = \mu_0 N g^2 \beta^2 \frac{S(S+1)}{6kT}[2H - M(\lambda_{ii} + \lambda_{ij})] \quad (15.53)$$

The susceptibility $\chi$ is given by

$$\chi = \frac{M}{H} = \frac{C}{T + \theta} \qquad (15.54)$$

where

$$C = \frac{\mu_0 N g^2 \beta^2 S(S+1)}{3k} \qquad (15.55)$$

and

$$\theta = \tfrac{1}{2}C(\lambda_{ii} + \lambda_{ij}) \qquad (15.56)$$

In the structure shown in Fig. 15.15 the field interaction parameter $\lambda_{AB} > \lambda_{AA}$, and in general $\lambda_{ij} > \lambda_{ii}$. Thus whether $\lambda_{ii}$ is positive or negative the value of $\theta$ will be positive. The magnetic behavior of an antiferromagnetic solid is therefore paramagnetic at high temperatures with the temperature dependence given by Equation 15.54.

### The Néel Temperature

We have now given a molecular field theory of antiferromagnetism which explains the high temperature behavior and shows how the spontaneous magnetization arises at lower temperatures. The spontaneous magnetization below the Néel temperature of both sublattices is equal. This enables us to predict the Néel temperature. At $H = 0$, from Equation 15.51 we have

$$M_A = \frac{C}{2T}(-\lambda_{ii}M_A - \lambda_{ij}M_B)$$

and

$$M_B = \frac{C}{2T}(-\lambda_{ij}M_A - \lambda_{ii}M_B)$$

If these are equal at $T_N$, then it may be simply shown

$$T_N = \tfrac{1}{2}C(\lambda_{ij} - \lambda_{ii}) \tag{15.57}$$

This is an entirely reasonable result since we would expect the Néel temperature to be higher for strong *A-B* type interactions and weak *A-A* type interactions.

**Table 15.4**

|  | $T_N °K$ |  | $T_N °K$ |
| --- | --- | --- | --- |
| MnO | 122 | MnS | 165 |
| FeO | 198 | MnTe | 307 |
| CoO | 291 | MnSe | 160 |
| NiO | 523 | $MnF_2$ | 72 |

The metal chromium has the body-centered structure of Fig. 15.15 with the spin directions as marked. However, the simple theory just given does not account well for the magnetic behavior of chromium and is, in fact, successful only for ionic compounds of the transition metals. These form the largest group of antiferromagnetic materials. Often in these compounds an oxygen

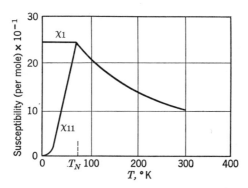

**Fig. 15.16** Susceptibility versus temperature for $MnF_2$. (H. Bizette and B. Tsai, *Compt. rend.*, **238**, 1575, 1954)

ion lies between the transition metal ions. The oxygen ion, which is para-magnetic, can apparently couple the two metallic ions so that their spins are antiparallel. Sulfur, tellurium, selenium, and fluorine ions can also act in this role. Some antiferromagnetic compounds with their Néel transition tempera-tures are given in Table 15.4.

Figure 15.16 shows the temperature dependence of susceptibility of $MnF_2$ with the Néel temperature dividing the regions of spontaneous magnetization and paramagnetic behavior.

## 15.15   Ferrimagnestism

Ferrimagnetism is the term given to the magnetic behavior of certain materials in which spontaneous magnetization arises below a certain tempera-ture, the net magnetization resulting from a nonparallel arrangement of coupled magnetic dipoles. It was first found in crystals with the spinel structure shown in Fig. 15.17. The chemical formula is $XY_2Z_4$ in which X is a divalent negative ion, Z is mostly the divalent oxygen ion $O^{2-}$, and Y is $Fe^{3+}$. In the *garnets*, whose chemical formula is $P_3Q_2R_3O_{12}$, the negative ions Q occupy octahedral or *a* sites in a cubic structure and the R negative

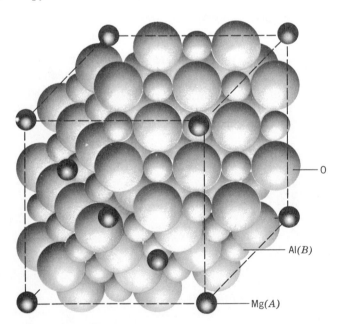

**Fig. 15.17**   The spinel structure of $MgAl_2O_4$.  *A* and *B* sites are occupied by Mg and Al, respectively.  (After Azaroff)

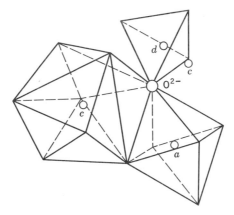

**Fig. 15.18** *a, b,* and *c* sites nearest to a certain oxygen ion in the garnet structure. Other oxygen ions are located at the vertices of the polyhedra. (After M. A. Gilleo and S. Geller, *Phys. Rev.*, **110,** 73, 1958)

ions occupy tetrahedral or *d* sites. The other metal ion P is surrounded by eight oxygen ions on *c* sites. Figure 15.18 shows the *a, b,* and *c* sites that are closest to a given oxygen ion.

The best known ferrimagnetic garnet is $Y_3Fe_2Fe_3O_{12}$, commonly called YIG. The magnetic ions are on *a* and *d* sites. The arrangement and the position of the magnetic ions relative to the oxygen ions are quire similar to the *A* and *B* positions in the spinels (see Fig. 15.17). Again the interaction of the magnetic ions by way of the oxygen ions, a process called superexchange, gives rise to large magnetic moments. The rare earth garnets have one of the trivalent rare earth ions in place of $Y_3$. Although the garnets have three sublattices, the magnetic behavior is described quite well by a phenomenological molecular field theory developed for the spinel structure of two sublattices. The results of this theory will be briefly discussed.

### 15.16  Molecular Field Theory of Ferrimagnetism

The molecular fields for a ferrimagnet are identical in form to those given for an antiferromagnetic material (Equation 15.53). Now, however, $\lambda_{AA} \neq \lambda_{BB}$ and $M_A \neq M_B$. Generally $\lambda_{AB}$ is much larger than $\lambda_{AA}$ or $\lambda_{BB}$. If the subscript *i* indicates ions with a spin quantum number $S_i$ and there are $N_i$ of those per unit volume, then, as in previous results, we have

$$M_A = \sum_i \mu_0 N_i g_i \beta S_i [B_{S_i}(x_A)]  \tag{15.58}$$

A similar expression exists for $M_B$.

Again, a paramagnetic region exists above the Néel temperature and the temperature dependence of susceptibility is also given by

$$\chi = \frac{C}{T + \theta}$$

### 15.17   The Value of the Magnetization in the Spinels and Garnets

Equation 15.58 enables us to calculate the magnetic moment of ions on $A$ sites. The net magnetic moment is, of course, given by the difference of $A$ and $B$ moments, etc.

In magnetite, which has the chemical formula $FeO \cdot Fe_2O_3$ and the spinel structure, we can attribute 5 Bohr magnetons to $Fe^{3+}$ and 4 Bohr magnetons to $Fe^{2+}$. Half of the $Fe^{3+}$ ions are in $A$ sites and the $Fe^{2+}$ and remaining $Fe^{3+}$ ions are in $B$ sites. Thus per "molecule" of $A$ and $B$ sites, the $A$ site moment is $5\beta$ and the $B$ site moment is $5\beta + 4\beta = 9\beta$. Therefore, the net moment per molecule should be $9\beta - 5\beta = 4\beta$, which is in agreement with experiment. Slight departures from theory are found experimentally for the spinels. These are usually attributed to values of $g$ which differ slightly from the spin value 2.

In the YIG garnet the molecular field arises solely from $Fe^{3+}$ with a moment of $5\beta$. There are three $Fe^{3+}$ ions on $d$ sites for every two $Fe^{3+}$ ions on $a$ sites. The magnetic moment at $0°K$ should therefore be $15 - 10 = 5\beta$ per "molecule", which is also in good agreement with experiment. In cases where the agreement is not as good the experimental value invariably lies between the theoretical values for spin-orbital coupling and pure spin.

From a technological point of view, the spinels and garnets are important because of their very high resistivities in addition to their magnetic properties. Commercial spinels or ferrites like Ferrox cube 3 have resistivities in excess of silicon-iron or permalloy by a factor of at least $10^6$. This high resistivity greatly reduces the eddy current losses and gives the spinels and garnets enormous potential in high frequency circuits.

### *Magnetic Properties in Alternating Fields*

Thus far we have described the magnetic behavior of materials with reference to static or nonvarying magnetic fields. We shall now discuss very briefly the types of resonance that can occur with alternating fields.

### 15.18   Electronic and Nuclear Spin Resonance

We saw in Section 15.6 that the magnetic sublevels in an atom, character-ized by the value of single electron spin, are separated by an energy difference

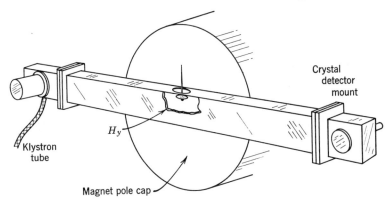

**Fig. 15.19** Apparatus to measure spin resonance in solids.

of $2\mu_0\beta H$. In general, the energy difference is $g\mu_0\beta H$. Let us now suppose that electromagnetic radiation is supplied to a paramagnetic crystal at a frequency $\nu$ such that the following condition is fulfilled:

$$h\nu = g\mu_0\beta H \qquad (15.59)$$

Here transitions between the magnetic sublevels are induced and energy is absorbed from the radiation source.

Figure 15.19 shows a simplified experimental setup to carry out studies of this nature. A static magnetic field $H_y$ is applied in the direction indicated. The field $H_x$ varies at the frequency $\nu$, and the absorption of high frequency energy is measured in an associated circuit. Obviously, either the magnitude of the static field $H_y$ or the frequency $\nu$ may be varied to satisfy the resonance condition given by Equation 15.59, which gives for *electrons*

$$\nu(Mc) = 3.52 \times 10^{-2}H \ (H \text{ in amp m}^{-1}) \qquad (15.60)$$

and for *protons*

$$\nu(kc) = 5.35 \times 10^{-2}H \ (H \text{ in amps}^{-1}) \qquad (15.61)$$

In most materials the measured magnetic moment is not due solely to electron spin but is modified by spin-orbital coupling. The appropriate Landé $g$ factor indicates the degree of coupling in each case. Measured $g$ factors have been obtained from resonance techniques applied to each of the cases we have discussed: paramagnetism in transition metals, paramagnetism in Fermi electrons, ferromagnetism, antiferromagnetism, and ferrimagnetism. We have also seen that the saturation magnetization in each case gives the appropriate value for $\mu_0 gJ$. Thus from combined measurements we can calculate $J$ and deduce appropriate values for $L$ and $S$ to fit trial models of the coupling.

## 15.19 Magnetic Storage Devices

To conclude this chapter we shall briefly mention the application of ferrimagnetic materials and thin films of magnetic alloys to the manufacture of storage devices in computer technology. Many circuits of great sophistication now use these and other materials.

A necessary property of a storage device is that it remain stable in two configurations. The passage of a magnetizing current pulse through a primary winding on a core of the material leaves a remanent magnetic flux $B_r$ in the core (see Fig. 15.6). The direction of the remanent magnetization depends on the direction of the current pulse. The core must hold this remanent flux indefinitely without further power consumption. It can then function as a repository for information in a binary code. Let us suppose that $-\phi_r$ represents "zero" and $+\phi_r$ represents "one".

This stored information must be readily accessible and identifiable. To achieve this the core is fitted with a secondary winding of, say, $n$ turns. The integrated voltage pulse appearing at the secondary terminals during a flux change from $\phi_1$ to $\phi_2$ is then $n(\phi_2 - \phi_1)$. To read out the stored information, let us suppose that a negative current pulse is passed through the primary. If the duration of the pulse is sufficiently long to bring the ferrite core flux to $-\phi_s$, the voltage on the secondary for a remanent flux of $+\phi_r$ will be $n(\phi_r + \phi_s)$. If, on the other hand, the remanent flux is $-\phi_r$, the secondary voltage is $n(\phi_s - \phi_r)$. The greater voltage reads out as a "one" and the lesser as a "zero." It is now obvious that rectangular hysteresis loops give the best discrimination (see Fig. 15.20).

The switching time from one magnetic configuration to another is important. If the magnetization changes by the motion of Bloch walls, then damping limits the speed of passage of the walls. The eddy current part of the damping is reduced by using high resistivity material or thin ribbons or films.

As we have seen, the mode of magnetization reversal is dependent on the strength of the magnetizing field. At values of drive field just above $H_c$, the coercive force (see Fig. 15.6), the magnetization is by domain wall motion. At high fields the reversal is by magnetization rotation; in this process damping is small and switching times are reduced. A method of utilizing domain moment rotation is to use thin films of the order of $10^{-7}$ m thick, which can contain only a single domain through their thickness.

Figure 15.21 shows switching times of thin films compared with those of ferrite cores. The times depend in the manner described, on the operating conditions. It is seen that rotational mode times for thin films are less by a factor of 10 to 100 than times associated with domain wall motion in ferrite or tape switching.

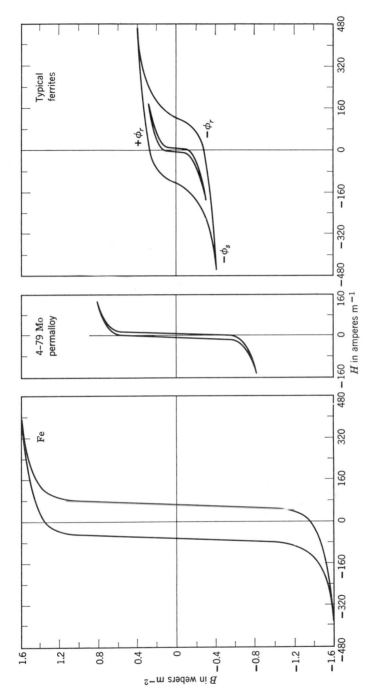

**Fig. 15.20** Hysteresis loops of iron, permalloy, and ferrites. (After Shull, Strauser, and Wollan)

445

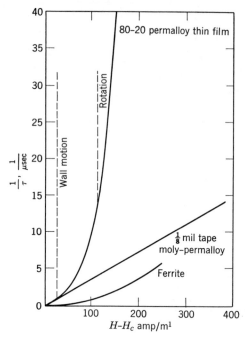

**Fig. 15.21** Inverse switching time versus field for permalloy film, moly-permalloy tape, and bulk ferrite core. (Redrawn from the data of Olson and Pohm, *J. Appl. Phys.*, **29**, 274, 1958)

## References

Bates, L. F., *Modern Magnetism*, 4th ed., Cambridge Univ. Press, 1961.

Bogorth, R. M., *Ferromagnetism*, Van Nostrand, Princeton, N.J., 1951.

Herschberger, W. D., Paramagnetic and Nuclear Resonance, page 35, in *Foundations of Future Electronics*, McGraw-Hill Book Co., New York, 1961.

Morrish, A. H., *Physical Principles of Magnetism*, John Wiley and Sons, New York, 1965.

Suhl, H., Ferromagnetism, page 53 in *Foundations of Future Electronics*, McGraw-Hill Book Co., New York, 1961.

## Exercises

1. A long straight wire carries a current of 10 amps. Calculate the magnetic induction $B$ at a point in vacuum situated 2 m from the axis of the wire.

2. The magnetic susceptibility of copper is $-0.5 \times 10^{-5}$. Calculate the magnetic moment per unit volume in copper when subjected to a field whose magnitude inside the copper is $10^4$ amps $m^{-1}$.

3. Estimate the order of magnitude of the diamagnetic susceptibility of copper from Equation 15.13. Use a value of 1 A as the atomic radius and assume that only one electron per atom contributes. ($a = 3.608$ A).

4. A paramagnetic system of electric spin magnetic dipole moments is placed in an applied field of $10^5$ amp m$^{-1}$. Calculate the average magnetic moment per dipole at $300°$K and at $0.3°$K. Also calculate the fractional number of spins which are parallel and antiparallel to the field.

5. Estimate the frequencies at which we would expect: (*a*) electron spin resonance in sodium with an applied field of $10^6$ amps m$^{-1}$; (*b*) proton spin resonance in ferric nitrate solution with an applied field of $10^6$ amps m$^{-1}$.

6. The Curie temperature of iron is $1043°$K. Assume that iron atoms, when in the metallic form, have moments of two Bohr magnetons per atom. Iron is body-centered cubic with the lattice parameter $a = 2.86$ A. Calculate: (*a*) the saturation magnetization; (*b*) the Curie constant; (*c*) the Weiss field constant; (*d*) the magnitude of the internal field.

7. The ions in the molecule of magnetite are $Fe^{+2}$, $Fe_2^{+3}$, and $O_4^{-2}$, the subscripts giving the number per molecule. In the conventional unit cell, which is cubic with $a = 8.37$ A, there are eight molecules. The $Fe^{+3}$ magnetic moments cancel and the magnetization is that produced by the $Fe^{+2}$ ions alone. If the saturation magnetization of magnetite is $5.2 \times 10^5$ amps m$^{-1}$ calculate the moment per $Fe^{+2}$ ion in Bohr magnetons.

8.         αFe          bcc       $a = 2.86$ A

                    αCo          hcp       $a = 2.51$ A         $c = 4.11$ A

                    αNi          hcp       $a = 2.66$ A         $c = 4.29$ A

Ascribe the magnetic moment in the above elements to the $3d$ electrons and neglect the $4s$ contribution. Calculate the spin magnetic moment per atom for Fe, Co, and Ni. Calculate the maximum magnetic induction (in webers m$^{-2}$) for these elements.

# 16

## *Superconductivity*

As discussed in Section 12.6, the electrical resistivity of a normal metal or alloy decreases with temperature, until at temperatures $\simeq 10°K$ it levels out at the residual value. It was discovered by Kammerlingh Onnes in 1911, however, that at a certain temperature and often within a very narrow temperature range, the resistivity of certain metals becomes zero. The name *superconductivity* was given to the phenomenon; it is illustrated in Fig. 16.1. Superconductivity has now been observed in 25 metals and several hundred alloys and compounds. The temperature at which the resistance disappears, *in zero magnetic field*, is called the *transition temperature*. Transition temperatures for a number of metals, alloys, and compounds are given in Table 16.1.

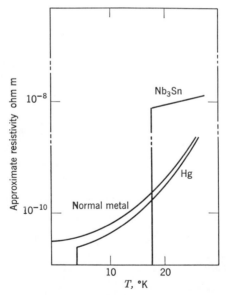

**Fig. 16.1** Variation of resistivity with temperature for a normal metal, Type I super-conductor (Hg), and a high-field high-current superconductor ($Nb_3Sn$).

*448*

**Table 16.1**   Critical Temperatures $T_c$ and Critical Magnetic Fields $H_0$ (at $0°K$) for Some Elements and Compounds

| Element | $T_c$ (°K) | $H_0$ (amp m$^{-1}$) | Compound | $T_c$ (°K) | $H_0$ (amp m$^{-1}$) |
|---|---|---|---|---|---|
| Al | 1.196 | $7.9 \times 10^3$ | $BaBi_3$ | 5.69 | $59 \times 10^3$ |
| Cd | 0.56 | 2.4 | $Bi_2Pt$ | 0.16 | 0.8 |
| Hg | 4.153 | 33 | $CoSi_2$ | 1.40 | 8.4 |
| Hg | 3.949 | 27 | $Nb_3Sn$ | 18.07 | |
| In | 3.407 | 23.5 | | | |
| Nb | 9.25 | 159 | | | |
| Pb | 7.175 | 64 | | | |
| Sn | 3.74 | 24.5 | | | |
| Ta | 4.483 | 62 | | | |

The width of the transition region in a particular specimen depends on a number of factors, such as the purity and metallurgical history, and can be as sharp as one millidegree or spread over several degrees.

## 16.1   Critical Magnetic Field

It was also discovered that superconductivity could be destroyed by the application of a certain magnetic field of magnitude $H_c$, termed the *critical* field. This critical field is a function of the temperature, and for many superconductors (Type I, Section 16.9) in thin, rod-shaped form the relation is approximately

$$H_c = H_0\left(1 - \frac{T^2}{T_c^{\,2}}\right) \tag{16.1}$$

where $H_0$, the critical field at $0°K$, has a specific value for each material (Table 16.1). $H_c$ is the critical field at temperature $T$ and $T_c$ is the critical temperature in zero field. Figure 16.2 shows the field-temperature behavior for a number of superconducting elements. The region inside the curve represents the superconducting phase and the region outside the normal phase.

## 16.2   The Meissner Effect

The destruction of superconductivity by a field is rather different when specimens of shape other than that of thin rods are used. The problem arises

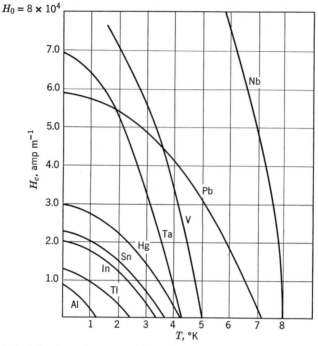

**Fig. 16.2** The dependence of critical field on temperature for a number of materials. These measurements were made with the field along the axis of a rod-shaped specimen. (Redrawn from D. A. Buck, *Proc. IRE*, **44**, 482, 1956)

in the following way. From electromagnetic field theory it is easy to deduce that perfect conductivity leads to the condition

$$\frac{\partial B}{\partial t} = 0$$

where $B$ is the magnetic induction threading the material and $t$ is the time. The condition can be rewritten

$$B = \text{constant}$$

The constant value of $B$ should be the one used at the time when the perfectly conducting state is initiated. Suppose then that we take a cylindrical specimen of superconductor at a temperature below $T_c$ and impose on it a small transverse magnetic field. The initial value of $B$ inside the superconductor is zero, so that $B$ must remain zero inside as the field grows. The material behaves in a perfectly diamagnetic fashion. The flux lines outside are shown in Fig. 16.3.

The concentration of the flux lines at the points $X$ and $X$ means that the field is higher there than it is at a great distance from the superconductor.

Thus, if the field is increased, it will reach a value $H_c$ at points $X$ and $X$ before the field at infinity has this value. For this geometry the field at $X$ is just $H_c$ when the field at infinity is $\frac{1}{2}H_c$. The critical condition just described is, in fact, adequate to initiate the transition from superconducting to normal phase. From then on, with increased field, the specimen exists in a rather complex mixture of superconductive and normal regions known as the *intermediate state*. If the field is increased further, the proportion of normal material grows at the expense of that of superconducting material until, when the external field equals $H_c$, the material is wholly normal and the transition is complete.

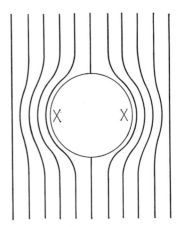

**Fig. 16.3** The flux lines around a superconducting cylinder in a transverse field.

Suppose that a long thin superconductor is cooled below its critical temperature. A longitudinal field of magnitude greater than $H_c$ will make all of the specimen normal. If the external field is then removed, the superconductor does not behave like a perfect conductor in which the flux stays at the value it had on initiation of the state. Instead, the flux is actually ejected. This effect is reversible in simple (Type I) superconductors; that is, if the sample is cooled and then brought into a field the end result is the same as on applying a field and then cooling. If a pure strain-free material is used, the flux ejection can be almost complete. This is called the *Meissner* effect. If impurities and stresses exist in the cylinder, the ejection of flux can be incomplete, leaving a certain fraction of the flux as trapped flux. Metallurgically hard superconductors and alloys tend to trap flux more than soft superconductors. However, the effect is used to specify a condition for the superconducting material, that is, the flux value is not merely constant but is identically zero. Thus the conditions defining the superconducting state are

$$\mathscr{E} = 0 \qquad \text{(from the absence of resistivity)}$$

$$(16.2)$$

$$B = 0 \qquad \text{(from the Meissner effect)}$$

where $\mathscr{E}$ is the electric field.

## 16.3   The Penetration Depth

A phenomenological picture of the superconducting state supposes supercurrents flowing over the surface of the conductor with their associated magnetic fields shielding the interior of the specimen. The prediction of a *penetration depth* for the supercurrent follows from an application of Maxwell's electromagnetic equations and the two conditions (16.2) specifying the superconducting state. The analysis in one dimension leads to the differential equation

$$\frac{d^2J_s}{dx^2} = \frac{J_s}{\lambda^2} \tag{16.3}$$

where $J_s$ is the supercurrent density and $x$ is the distance from the surface into the superconducting material. The parameter $\lambda$ is called the *penetration depth* and is given by

$$\lambda^2 = \frac{m}{\mu_0 n_s e^2} \tag{16.4}$$

where $m$ is the mass, $e$ the charge of the electron, and $n_s$ is the number of superconducting electrons per unit volume. A solution of Equation 16.3 is of the form

$$J_s = Ce^{x/\lambda} + De^{-x/\lambda} \tag{16.5}$$

where the constants $C$ and $D$ depend on boundary conditions. The solution with the negative index is realistic since the other would lead to infinite currents.

The current density $J_0$ at the surface is the value of $D$ and

$$J_s = J_0 e^{-x/\lambda} \tag{16.6}$$

The penetration depth is thus the distance into the superconductor at which the current has fallen to $1/e$ of its value at the surface. On substituting the mass of the electron for $m$ and the number of electrons per unit volume for $n_s$ in (16.4), we obtain a rough estimate of the magnitude of $\lambda$—of the order of 200 A.

The number of superconducting electrons $n_s$ would be expected to vary with temperature from a maximum value at $T = 0°K$ to the value zero at $T = T_c$. Pippard has shown that the variation of $n_s$ with $H$ is small. It should be emphasized that at this point the theory is applicable to the superconducting state and will be a good representation of experimental data only with simple superconductors. The behavior of real superconducting solids is generally more complicated.

## 16.4  Free Energy Difference

Experimental evidence shows that the specific heat in the normal and superconducting states differs markedly in the temperature region $T = 0°K$ to $T = T_c$. In Fig. 16.4 the specific heat of vanadium is plotted as a function of temperature. The peaked nature of the curve at the transition temperature is typical of a *second order* phase change. The measurements on normal vanadium below $T_c$ are made with the use of a magnetic field greater than $H_c$. If the measurements are made through the transition in the presence of a magnetic field, then a heat of transition is involved, thus making it typical of a *first order* transition. This will now be discussed from an elementary thermodynamics viewpoint.

The differential Gibbs free energy $dG$ of a material with a magnetization $M$ may be written

$$dG = -S \, dT + V \, dp - \mu_0 M \, dH$$

Neglecting the $V \, dp$ term, at constant temperature the free energy difference, *because of the presence of a magnetic field*, is found by integration, thus,

$$G(T, H) - G(T, 0) = -\int_0^H \mu_0 M \, dH$$

$$(16.7)$$

From Equations 15.3 and 15.7, we have

$$M = (\mu_r - 1)H \qquad (16.8)$$

*For a superconductor*, it follows from Equation 16.2 that

$$M = -H \qquad (16.9)$$

On substituting into Equation 16.7, integrating gives

$$G_s(T, H) - G_s(T, 0) = \frac{\mu_0 H^2}{2} \qquad (16.10)$$

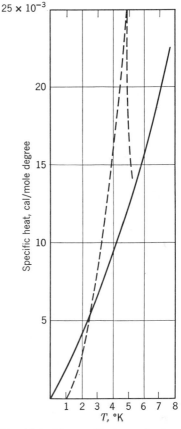

**Fig. 16.4** The specific heat of vanadium in the normal (solid line) and superconducting (dashed line) states.

where $G_s$ is the free energy of a superconducting phase. A graph line of Fig. 16.2 represents a phase boundary between normal and superconducting states. Along such a phase boundary the *normal* phase must have a free energy indistinguishable from that of the *superconducting* phase. Therefore

$$G_n(T, H_c) - G_s(T, 0) = \frac{\mu_0 H_c^2}{2} \qquad (16.11)$$

where $G_n$ is the free energy of the normal phase.

Let us now calculate the difference in entropy of the two phases. For solids the entropy $S$ is given by $-dG/dT$. From (16.11)

$$S_n - S_s = -\frac{\partial}{\partial T}\left(\mu_0 \frac{H_c{}^2}{2}\right)$$

$$= \mu_0 H_c \frac{dH_c}{dT} \tag{16.12}$$

where the entropies $S_n$ and $S_s$ refer to normal and superconducting phases, respectively.

An ideally simple superconductor has a parabolic relation (16.1) between $H_c$ and $T_c$, and therefore at $T = T_c$, $dH_c/dT = 0$. Thus it is clear from Equation 16.12 that there is no entropy change involved if the change from superconducting to normal is made by a change in temperature across the value $T_c$ *in the absence of a magnetic field*. The change is second order. On the other hand, examination of Fig. 16.2 shows that $dH_c/dT$ is negative at a temperature $T$ below $T_c$. Then, from Equation 16.12, $S_n - S_s$ must be positive, indicating a first order change with a heat of transition. This change is associated with the filling of the superconductor with magnetic flux.

From the lowered entropy in the superconducting state it can be concluded that superconducting electrons are more ordered. Modern theory indicates that there is a spatial order which, in simple superconductors (Type I), extends over distance of the order of $10^{-6}$ m. This range is called the *coherence length*. In hard or alloy superconductors (Type II) the coherence length takes much smaller values with very striking changes in superconducting properties. This will be discussed later.

Since the free energies of the normal $G_n$ and the superconducting $G_s$ states are equal at the transition temperature $T_c$, it follows from the definition of $G$ (equation 3.6) that the difference in energy $U_n - U_s$ between the two states is

$$U_n - U_s = T_c(S_n - S_s) \tag{16.13}$$

From experiment, $S_n - S_s$ is of the order of $10^{-7}$ eV per atom, so that the energy difference $U_n - U_s$ between the normal and superconducting states is also of the order of $10^{-7}$ eV per atom. This is extremely small in comparison with band energies we have encountered previously.

## 16.5    The Energy Gap

Examination of Fig. 16.4 shows that the specific heat versus temperature curve is exponential for the superconducting state. $C$ varies as $e^{-bT_c/T}$ where $b$ is a constant. This indicates that an energy gap may exist in the superconducting electron levels, separating the lowest excited state from the ground state. We have already seen in many quantum problems that thermal excitation across a gap is exponential with temperature.

The existence of an energy gap in the levels has been confirmed by a number of experiments. It has been shown that the gap decreases from a value of about $3.5\,kT_c$ at $0°K$ to zero at the transition temperature.


## 16.6   Quantum Tunneling

An experiment which directly confirms the existence of the energy gap is that of Giaever on quantum tunneling. Tunneling has been observed in many superconducting junctions. We will take a specific example.

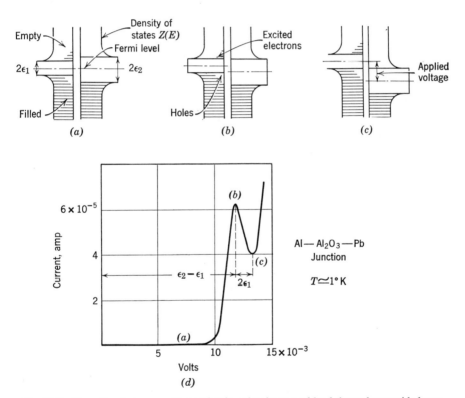

**Fig. 16.5** Tunneling between superconducting aluminum and lead through an oxide layer. (*a*) No voltage applied. A little thermal excitation of electrons and holes. (*b*) Voltage applied. Electrons can tunnel from left to right. After voltage shown, the electrons of the left face a decreasing density of empty states on the right. (*c*) Higher voltage applied. Above this voltage electrons from the left filled band can tunnel to empty states of the right. (From I. Giaever, *Superconductors*, Interscience, New York, 1962)

An aluminum strip is first evaporated onto a glass slide. The aluminum is then allowed to oxidize and a lead strip is evaporated on top. An Al–Al$_2$O$_3$–Pb junction is formed. The oxide layer is of the order of 100 A in thickness. Current measurements are made at 1°K as a function of applied voltage across the junction.

Figure 16.5a shows the density of states of the electrons when no voltage is applied. The Fermi levels line up and some electrons are excited into empty states above the superconducting energy gap. The junction acts like an intrinsic semiconductor (Section 14.2). In b a voltage is applied and current flows because electrons in the left superconductor (Al) can tunnel into the right (Pb). In c the voltage is increased until the bottom of the left gap matches the top of the right gap. Over this region electron tunneling from left to right becomes more restricted as the electrons of the left face a lower density of states on the right superconductor. If the voltage is increased beyond the point c, then electrons from the filled band of the left can tunnel over into the empty levels of the right, thus increasing the current. Figure 16.5d shows the tunneling current as a function of voltage applied between Al and Pb when both are superconducting. The regions of current increase and decrease are related to the band positions.

The density of states function can be simply deduced from the shape of the current-voltage curve. The energy dependence of this function strongly suggests that the electron interactions in superconductivity are associated with the phonon spectrum of the lattice.

### 16.7   The Isotope Effect

There is another effect which suggests that superconductivity is related to lattice properties as well as electron properties. This is the *isotope effect*. It was discovered in 1950 that the superconducting critical temperature for various isotopes of lead was inversely proportional to the square root of the atomic mass. After reviewing the discussion of Section 13.6, this suggests that $T_c$ is proportional to the Debye temperature $\Theta$.

### 16.8   Theory of Superconductivity

Theories of superconductivity have developed along two lines. The phenomenological theories of London, Pippard, Ginzburg, and Landau deal with the existence and order of magnitude of the penetration depth and coherence length and give a qualitative account of some of the electrodynamic properties.

The microscopic theory of Frohlich introduced the concept of an interaction between superconducting electrons and phonons. In 1957 Bardeen, Cooper, and Schrieffer proposed a microscopic theory (BCS theory) which accounts for the observed properties of superconductors which we have described. The phenomenological equations introduced thus far can be derived from the BCS theory, and superconductivity is now understood in terms of the electronic and atomic structures.

Very briefly and qualitatively, the BCS theory proposes that electrons within the range $k\Theta$ about the Fermi surface in the superconducting state are correlated in pairs of equal and opposite momenta and opposite spin. The correlation causes the energy of each pair to be lowered by an amount which is equivalent to a binding energy for the pair. Before excitation of the electrons and the consequent return of resistivity is possible, this energy must be supplied thermally. A gap in the density of states thus comes from the theory and is of the correct magnitude and temperature dependence.

A coherence length also comes naturally from the theory. In simple superconductors this involves grouping in pairs over spatial distances of the order of $10^{-6}$ m.

In alloys the mean free path can be much shorter than in pure metals. Electron scattering may break up the correlated pairs. It is perhaps not surprising to find that superconductivity behavior in materials for which the correlation length is greater than the depth of penetration differs greatly from superconductivity in materials where the opposite is the case. The former class of materials are Type I and the latter Type II.

## 16.9   Type I and Type II Superconductors

A typical Type I superconducting element such as Pb has a critical field $H_0$ at $0°K$ of the order $10^4$ amp $m^{-1}$, whereas a niobium alloy Type II superconductor may have a value of $H_0$ of the order of $10^0$ amp m [1]. The distinction between Type I and Type II materials is difficult to make solely on on chemical grounds. Hard metallic elements are often of Type II and soft Type I metallic elements can be given high $H_0$ values, a Type II characteristic, by severe mechanical strain.

In ideal Type I and Type II rods of large length-diameter ratio, the modes of penetration and expulsion of magnetic flux serve to differentiate between the classes. Figure 16.6 shows the abrupt penetration in Type I of flux at the critical value $H_c$. In ideal Type II superconductors flux penetrates at lower fields but does not completely fill the superconductor until very high fields are reached, at which point the electrical resistance is abruptly restored. Such ideal behavior is dependent on correct geometry as well as on carefully

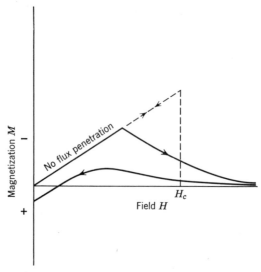

**Fig. 16.6** Flux penetration as a function of applied field in Type I (dashed line) and Type II (solid line) superconductors. Flux penetrates abruptly in Type I at $H_c$, dropping the magnetization. Flux does not completely fill Type II until very high fields. Hysteresis occurs in Type II.

controlled metallurgical conditions and is rarely found in actual specimens. We will now describe in greater detail the magnetic behavior of Type I and Type II superconductors.

## 16.10  Magnetic Flux Penetration in Type I

As the external magnetic field is increased around the superconductor, supercurrents are supposed to flow in the surface penetration depth. The field associated with these supercurrents just cancels out the external field for the material of the interior. We have also seen that the normal state is stable for $H > H_c$ and that over parts of the surface the field may be greater than the external field at an infinite distance. The breakdown of the superconducting state is complicated and normal regions grow at the expense of superconducting regions.

The reverse transition again proceeds, as the field is reduced, in a complicated manner. There is a migration of the normal regions to the surface. The flux expulsion is more hysteretic than the invasion process and is more sensitive to lattice distortion by defects. A grain boundary, for example, can hold up the movement of a portion of normal region. A specimen of such perfection is rarely prepared so that the *trapped flux* is reduced below a few

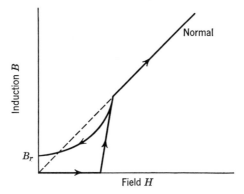

**Fig. 16.7** Flux penetration and expulsion in a solid Type I superconductor showing hysteresis and trapped flux.

per cent of the total flux in the normal state. The variation of $B$ with $H$ will be of the form shown in Fig. 16.7.

The description thus far has referred to a solid specimen. Should there be a hole in the specimen, the circumstances would be different. Consider, for example, a toroid, shown in section in Fig. 16.8. On reducing the field, the flux is expelled until the material of the toroid is wholly superconducting. The space inside still contains the field at which this condition is reached. Further reduction of the external field cannot affect the field threading the toroid, since it is now completely shielded by superconducting material. The trapped flux in this case is genuinely permanent unless the external field is raised once again to a level at which the material of the toroid becomes normal. The trapped flux is in a bistable condition. This device is of obvious importance as a logic and memory element. A bank of such Type I elements can be simply constructed in the form of an evaporated layer of superconductor containing a lattice of holes. A possible memory sheet is shown in Fig. 16.9.

A superconducting wire carrying a current has a magnetic field associated with the current (Equation 15.2). If the field reaches the critical value, the

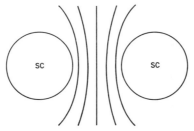

**Fig. 16.8** A superconducting toroid in section showing trapped flux threading the toroid.

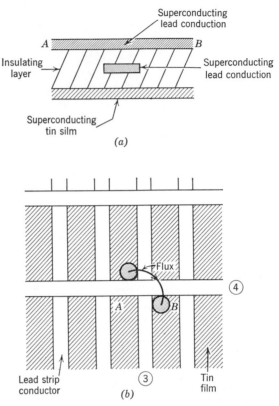

**Fig. 16.9** Memory element using evaporated tin film and lead conductors. The interrogation circuit is not shown. (*a*) *AB* section showing a superconducting tin film overlaid by an insulating film and crossed lead superconducting film strips ③ and ④ . (*b*) A single memory element. When positive signals pass along ③ and ④ a normal "hole" is produced in the superconducting tin. The flux flows in one direction corresponding to "zero" of the bistable memory elements. The flux will shrink and flip to the other direction on reversing the signals.

wire will contain a complicated mixture of normal and superconducting regions. Electrical resistance then reappears; the complete variation of resistance with current is shown in Fig. 16.10.

## 16.11  Magnetic Flux Penetration in Type II

Type II superconductors are mostly hard metals and alloys in a highly strained condition. The coherence length is reduced and the degree of subdivision of the specimen into normal and superconducting regions is much

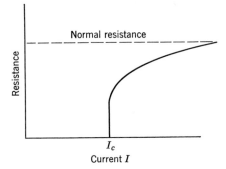

**Fig. 16.10** Current-resistance relation for a superconducting wire. Resistance appears when the magnetic field, associated with the current $I_c$, just reaches the critical value $H_c$ for certain parts of the wire.

finer. It is, in fact, energetically favorable for the subdivision to proceed as far as possible. Theoretically and experimentally the limit of subdivision is the *fluxon* of value $hc/e$ where $c$ is the speed of light. The value of the fluxon is $4 \times 10^{-15}$ weber. In Abrikosov's model of Type II superconductor the flux is arrayed as in Fig. 16.11. There is a continuous variation of field and supercurrent through the array. The spacing of the array adjusts to provide the equilibrium amount of flux commensurate with the external field.

The behavior of real Type II superconductors is rarely ideal, as is the description just given. Fluxons are trapped by defects, and hysteresis between B and $H$ is common.

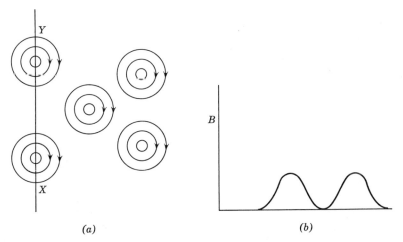

*(a)*             *(b)*

**Fig. 16.11** (a) Flux lines and current contours in a Type II superconductor. (b) The variation of induction B between points X and Y.

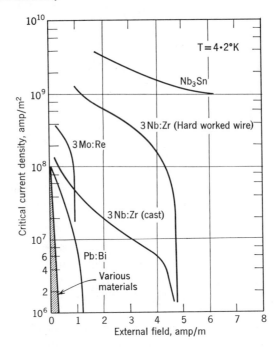

**Fig. 16.12** Critical current versus applied field curves for various Type II superconductors. (Redrawn from J. E. Kunzler, Bell Telephone System Monograph 4991)

A consequence of the fluxon array model is that, even under conditions of almost complete flux penetration, superconducting threads remain throughout the specimen. For certain materials these links can be extremely resistant to destruction by external fields. The possibility then exists of constructing superconducting solenoids which can be operated at very high fields. The obvious advantage of no Joule heating loss in such a device is attractive.

Figure 16.12 shows typical critical current versus applied field curves for several conductors. It is seen that the current density in superconducting $Nb_3Sn$ wire can reach the extremely large value of $10^9$ amp m$^{-2}$. Destruction of superconductivity does not occur in these wires at induction levels of up to 9 weber m$^{-2}$.

It is exciting to consider the possibility of power transmission in such conductors. If the necessary refrigeration proved to be economically possible, then a $Nb_3Sn$ conductor of $10^{-4}$ m$^2$ cross section operating at, say, $10^5$ volts could carry, theoretically without loss, the enormous power of $10^{10}$ watts.

# References

Lynton, E. A., *Superconductivity*, John Wiley and Sons, New York, 1962.
Schoenberg, D., *Superconductivity*, 2nd ed., Cambridge Univ. Press, 1960.
Tanenbaum, M., and W. V. Wright, eds., *Superconductors*, New York Symposium, Interscience, 1962.

# Exercises

1. A short table of $C_{es}/\gamma T$ versus $T_c/T$ is given for vanadium at low temperatures. $C_{es}$ is the electronic specific heat and $\gamma T$ is the electronic specific heat for *norma* vanadium.

| $\dfrac{C_{es}}{\gamma T}$ | $\dfrac{T_c}{T}$ |
|---|---|
| 2.5 | 1.0 |
| 1.0 | 1.5 |
| 0.5 | 2.0 |
| 0.25 | 2.5 |
| 0.10 | 3.0 |
| 0.045 | 3.5 |
| 0.02 | 4.0 |

Show that the relation is

$$\frac{C_{es}}{\gamma T} = a \exp\left(\frac{-bT_c}{T}\right)$$

Estimate $a$ and $b$ and show that for the excitation of *two* electrons at $T = 0$ the energy gap is $\simeq 3\, kT_C$.

2. From Fig. 16.5$d$ estimate the energy gap in Al and Pb at 1°K.

3. Biondi and Garfunkel (*Phys. Rev. Letters*, **2**, 143, 1959) have measured the attenuation of microwaves in aluminum wave guides at low temperatures. They obtain the surface resistance to bulk resistance ratios $R_S/R_B$ as a function of photon energy $h\nu$. Their results are shown in the figure on page 464. Give a qualitative description of the results. Plot the energy gap $\epsilon$ (equal to $h\nu$ where surface resistance is encountered) as a function of $T$ and show that $\epsilon$ varies between zero at $T = T_c$ and approximately $3.5\, kT_C$ at $T = 0$.

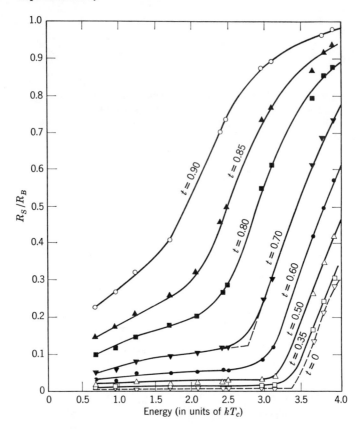

4. A short table of mass numbers of separated isotopes of mercury are given with the associated superconducting transition temperatures.

| Mass Number | $T_c$ °K |
|---|---|
| 203.0 | 4.146 |
| 202.1 | 4.159 |
| 200.7 | 4.174 |
| 199.7 | 4.180 |

Make a log-log plot and test for the isotope effect.

5. From the data of Table 16.1 calculate the critical currents which can flow in long thin superconducting wires of Al, Nb, and $Bi_2$ Pt of diameter $10^{-3}$ m.

# 17

# *The Optical Properties of Dielectrics and Semiconductors*

In this chapter we shall be concerned with the optical properties of dielectric and semiconducting solids. Pure dielectric materials, with the electrons bound to the atoms, are considered first, followed by a description of electrical behavior in a static and then an alternating electric field. This presentation leads to the development of the classical theory of dispersion, dielectric loss, and other properties.

We next extend the discussion to semiconducting solids with additional energy levels between the valence and conduction bands. The possibilities of quantum transitions between these levels give rise to properties such as luminescence, response to radiation, and stimulated emission, which are discussed later.

We shall use simple physical models, which can act only as guides to the complicated mechanisms in real solids.

*Polarization in Static Fields*

## 17.1   Displacement, Field Strength, and Dipole Moment

As mentioned, our first topic will be the static electric properties of dielectrics. For our present purposes a dielectric is considered to have a band structure with a filled valence band and an energy gap large enough that conduction is observed only under exceptional circumstances. We shall find later that conduction can, in certain cases, be extremely important in dielectric materials, but discussion of these cases is postponed. Currently the electrons in the dielectric material are considered permanently bound to the atoms. We shall consider the response to an electric field, first defining the quantities with which we will be working. These quantities bear certain similarities to those defined in the section on magnetism in Chapter 15. The new quantities are the electric displacement **D**, the electric field strength $\mathscr{E}$, and the electric dipole moment **p**.

### The Electric Displacement or Flux Density D

Gauss' theorem states that if a closed surface encloses a total electric charge $\sum Q$, the electric flux $\phi$ which emerges from the surface is given by

$$\phi = \sum Q \tag{17.1}$$

The total flux $\phi$ may be written as the surface integral $\iint \mathbf{D} \cdot d\mathbf{S}$ where **D** is the electric displacement or flux density in coulombs per square meter and $d\mathbf{S}$ is a surface element in square meters, represented by the outwardly directed vector $d\mathbf{S}$. Thus

$$\iint \mathbf{D} \cdot d\mathbf{S} = \sum Q \tag{17.2}$$

This is the definition of the electric displacement **D**.

### The Electric Field Strength $\mathscr{E}$

The *electric field strength* $\mathscr{E}$ is the force acting on unit charge placed in the field. $\mathscr{E}$ is related to the electric displacement by

$$\mathbf{D} = \epsilon_0 \epsilon_r \mathscr{E} \tag{17.3}$$

where $\epsilon_0$ is called the *dielectric constant* or *permittivity* of a *vacuum* and $\epsilon_r$ is the *relative permittivity* or dielectric constant of the medium through which the electric flux threads. The value of $\epsilon_0$ in mks units is $8.854 \times 10^{-12}$ farad $m^{-1}$, and $\epsilon_r$ is a dimensionless number which is equal to unity for a vacuum. The value of $\epsilon_r$ for a solid dielectric medium can be found experimentally relatively easily. It is the ratio of the capacitances of a parallel-plate condenser with and without the dielectric between the plates.

### The Electric Dipole Moment

The electric dipole moment is defined in the following way. Suppose that a system of charges $Q_1, Q_2, Q_3, \ldots, Q_i$ exists at vector displacements $\mathbf{r}_1, \mathbf{r}_2, \mathbf{r}_3, \ldots, \mathbf{r}_i$ from the origin of a coordinate system. The over-all net charge of the system is zero. Then the *total electric dipole moment* of the system is given by

$$\mathbf{p} = \sum_i Q_i \mathbf{r}_i \tag{17.4}$$

The units in which **p** is expressed are coulomb meters. The *dipole moment per unit volume* is called the *polarization* **P** of a dielectric medium and is expressed in coulombs per square meter.

## 17.2 Polarizability

Let us now consider the three types of response of an isolated atom or molecule to an electric field.

### *Electronic Polarizability*

Suppose that in Fig. 17.1*a* an atom is represented by a positive nucleus surrounded by a negative electron cloud. If a static electric field $\mathscr{E}$ is applied in the directions shown in Figs. 17.1*b* and *c*, the field tends to displace the center of gravity of the electrons away from coincidence with the nucleus. The displacement force is counteracted by the attraction of the nucleus and the actual magnitude of the displacement is small. For instance, a field of, say, 30 kV m$^{-1}$ will displace the center of gravity of the electrons by about $10^{-17}$ m. The formula that gives the displacement $d$ in terms of the atomic radius $R$, the electronic charge $e$, and number of electrons $Z$ is

$$d = \frac{4\pi\epsilon_0 R^3}{Ze}\mathscr{E} \tag{17.5}$$

This equation is a simple consequence of Coulomb's law of attraction between electrical charges.

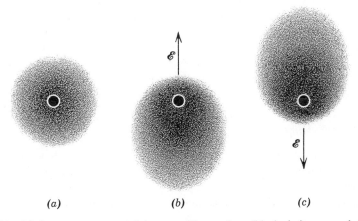

$(a)$            $(b)$            $(c)$

**Fig. 17.1** ($a$) An atom represented by a positive nucleus (black dot) surrounded by a negative electron cloud. In ($b$) and ($c$) the center of gravity of the electron cloud is displaced from coincidence with the nucleus by an electric field.

The two electric charges $+Ze$ and $-Ze$, now displaced by distance $d$, constitute an induced electron dipole moment $\mathbf{p}_e$ where

$$\mathbf{p}_e = Ze \cdot d = 4\pi\epsilon_0 R^3 \cdot \mathscr{E} \tag{17.6}$$

The dipole moment $\mathbf{p}_e$ is also linked to the electric field $\mathscr{E}$ by the definition of *electronic polarizability* $\alpha_e$, since

$$\mathbf{p}_e = \alpha_e \mathscr{E} \tag{17.7}$$

### Orientational Polarizability

For molecules another contribution to the polarizability exists, because some molecules such as water and alcohol exhibit permanent dipole moments. In the liquid form each electric dipole moment is free to rotate. Thus in a static electric field the dipoles tend to line up in the direction of the field. Thermal energy, however, tends to make the distribution of dipole orientations a random one. The orientational polarizability $\alpha_0$ depends on the fractional number of electric dipoles lined up at any temperature.

The calculation of orientational polarizability $\alpha_0$ follows closely the method used to obtain the magnetic susceptibility of a paramagnetic solid in Equation 15.28. Once again a Curie law of temperature dependence is found, namely,

$$\alpha_0 = \frac{C{p_0}^2}{T} \tag{17.8}$$

where $p_0$ is the permanent dipole moment, $T$ the temperature, and $C$ the Curie constant. This equation applies only to polar materials in which the dipole moments are free to rotate with ease into the direction of minimum energy. Whereas this is true in gases and liquids, it is seldom true in solids.

Later in this chapter we shall discuss a class of substance—the ferroelectrics—where the dipoles become completely aligned over regions in the crystal. The ions of ferroelectric crystals are bound together by Coulomb forces (ionic bond), unlike the molecules we discuss in this section, and the mechanism of dipolar saturation is quite different.

### Ionic Polarizability

In molecules an electric field may also displace the individual ions or molecules with respect to one another, thus changing the bond angles or interatomic distances. This is pictured in Fig. 17.2. Again, dipole moments are induced by the field, the *ionic dipole* moment being given by

$$\mathbf{p}_a = \alpha_a \mathscr{E} \tag{17.9}$$

where $\alpha_a$ is the *ionic polarizability*.

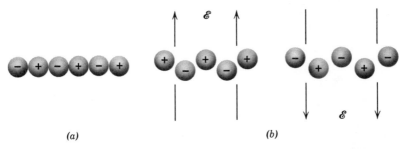

*(a)*                                              *(b)*

**Fig. 17.2** (*a*) Positive and negative ions in a dielectric. (*b*) The ions are displaced with respect to one another by an electric field.


## 17.3  Polarization in Bulk Dielectrics

We have discussed the mechanisms of polarization in atoms and molecules, and shall now extend the discussion to solids. The calculation is more complicated than before, because each atom or molecule is subject not only to the external field but also to a field arising from the induced dipole moments of all the surrounding atoms or molecules. The response of a solid dielectric to an electric field must therefore be made the subject of a special calculation, as was done for the magnetic quantities considered in Chapter 15. To treat the problem of the fields inside a solid dielectric, we consider first the relationship between the quantities $\mathbf{D}$, $\mathscr{E}$, and $\mathbf{p}$.

Let us suppose that a slab of homogeneous isotropic dielectric material is placed, as in Fig. 17.3, between two parallel plates and that an electric voltage is applied across the plates so that the electric field has a value $\mathscr{E}$. The electric displacement $\mathbf{D}$, from Equation 17.3, is $\epsilon_0 \epsilon_r \mathscr{E}$.

Suppose now that a small cylinder of area $dA$ and length $dl$ is removed from the dielectric as shown in the diagram. To produce a field inside the cavity equal to what existed before the material of the cavity was removed necessitates a reduction in electric displacement inside the cavity. In fact, if $\mathbf{D}_c$ is the electric displacement "inside the cavity," the relationship between the original $\mathbf{D}$ and the new $\mathbf{D}_c$ must be

$$\frac{\mathbf{D}_c}{\epsilon_0} = \frac{\mathbf{D}}{\epsilon_0 \epsilon_r} = \mathscr{E} \qquad (17.10)$$

The electric displacement may be reduced, according to Equation 17.2, by reducing the sum of the electric charges on the end faces of the cavity. By placing a negative charge, as in Fig. 17.3*b*, of $(\mathbf{D} - \mathbf{D}_c)\, dA$ on one end face and a positive charge of the same magnitude on the opposite end, the electric displacement is reduced from $\mathbf{D}$ to $\mathbf{D}_c$. The field in the cavity is thus

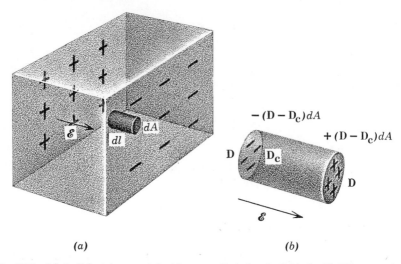

(a)                                   (b)

**Fig. 17.3**  (a) A dielectric material with an applied electric field $\mathscr{E}$. (b) When a volume element is removed, charges $\pm(\mathbf{D} - \mathbf{D_c})\, dA$ must be placed as shown to keep the field strength in the cavity at the original value.

maintained at the original value of $\mathscr{E}$. Now positive and negative charges on the respective ends of the small cylindrical cavity correspond according to Equation 17.4 to an electric dipole moment from left to right in the figure, that is in the same direction as $\mathscr{E}$. The magnitude of the dipole moment is given by

$$\mathbf{p} = (\mathbf{D} - \mathbf{D_c})\, dA\, dl \tag{17.11}$$

We can thus conclude that to maintain an unchanged electric field inside a dielectric when a portion of the dielectric is removed necessitates providing the vacant portion with an electric dipole moment. It would appear, therefore, that the portion of dielectric material before removal must have carried an electric dipole moment.

Per unit volume the dipole moment is $(\mathbf{D} - \mathbf{D_c})$. That is, $\mathbf{P}$, the polarization, is given by

$$\mathbf{P} = \mathbf{D} - \mathbf{D_c}$$

and from Equation 17.10 this becomes

$$\mathbf{P} = \epsilon_0 \mathscr{E}(\epsilon_r - 1) \tag{17.12}$$

This relationship obviously applies to dielectric materials in which the polarization is produced by the applied field. If polarization exists in zero field, as it does in the ferroelectric materials, a unique relationship does not exist between $\mathbf{P}$ and $\mathscr{E}$. In fact, just as in the ferromagnetic materials, hysteretic behavior is observed.

We are now in a position to relate the macroscopic quantity $\epsilon_r$ to the quantity that characterizes the polarization of an individual atom or molecule. Before doing so, however, we should look more closely into the detailed nature of the electric field. The value of $\mathscr{E}$ thus far in the discussion has been an average value over a volume element large in comparison with molecular volumes.

Suppose that the field which the molecule actually experiences is a local field $\mathscr{E}_{loc}$. Then it is customary to write the induced molecular dipole moment as $\mathbf{p}_m$, where

$$\mathbf{p}_m = \alpha \mathscr{E}_{loc} \tag{17.13}$$

and $\alpha$ is called the polarizability of the molecule and describes the ease of polarization. If there are $N_d$ dipoles per unit volume, then

$$\mathbf{P} = N_d \mathbf{p}_m = N_d \alpha \mathscr{E}_{loc} \tag{17.14}$$

It now follows from Equation 17.3 that

$$\epsilon_r - 1 = \frac{\mathbf{P}}{\epsilon_0 \mathscr{E}} = \frac{N_d \alpha \mathscr{E}_{loc}}{\mathscr{E}} \tag{17.15}$$

This equation relates the experimentally observed quantity $\epsilon_r$ to the molecular quantity $\alpha$. It is important to first calculate the magnitude of the local field which the molecule experiences.

### 17.4 The Local Electric Field

The local electric field which acts on any particular molecule can be regarded as made up of four parts.

$$\mathscr{E}_{loc} = \mathscr{E}_0 + \mathscr{E}_1 + \mathscr{E}_2 + \mathscr{E}_3 \tag{17.16}$$

where $\mathscr{E}_0$ is the externally applied electric field, and $\mathscr{E}_1$ is the depolarization field that results from polarization charges *on the outer surface of the specimen*.

To give a meaning to the components $\mathscr{E}_1$ and $\mathscr{E}_2$, first imagine a small sphere of dielectric material removed from around the site of the molecule $A$, as in Fig. 17.4. The *Lorentz field* $\mathscr{E}_2$ is then the field due to the polarization charges on the inside of the spherical cavity. If the radius of the sphere is considerably greater than that of the molecule, then the remainder of the dielectric around the sphere can be treated on a macroscopic basis. Thus both $\mathscr{E}_1$ and $\mathscr{E}_2$ are treated on this basis, their magnitudes being calculated from Equations 17.2 and 17.3 where integration over the outer surface gives $\mathscr{E}_1$ and integration over the surface of the spherical cavity gives $\mathscr{E}_2$. The *field of the adjacent dipoles* $\mathscr{E}_3$ is the field due to the molecules within

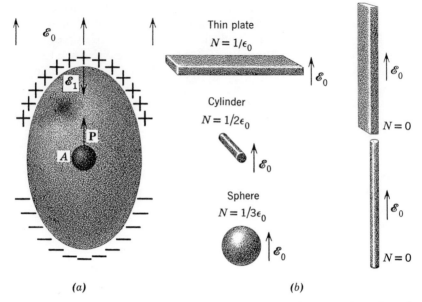

**Fig. 17.4**  (*a*) The depolarization field $\mathcal{E}_1$ due to the induced charges on the surface of an ellipsoid placed in the electric field $\mathcal{E}_0$. (*b*) The values of $N$, the depolarization factor, for dielectric specimens of various shapes placed in a field $\mathcal{E}_0$.

the spherical cavity, and this summation must be made on a microscopic basis. The field components will now be discussed separately and in some more detail.

### The Depolarization Factor

A dielectric specimen of simple geometry such as the sphere, cylinder, or ellipsoid or revolution, when placed in a uniform electric field $\mathcal{E}_0$, becomes uniformly polarized. The charges that are induced on the surface reduce the field strength inside the surface from the value $\mathcal{E}_0$. The reduction in field, that is, $\mathcal{E}_1$, is proportional to the polarization, the constant of proportionality $N$ being known as the *depolarization factor $N$* and dependent on the specimen geometry.

We have, therefore, that

$$\mathcal{E}_1 = -N\mathbf{P} \tag{17.17}$$

Figure 17.4*a* shows the depolarization field $\mathcal{E}_1$ which arises when a dielectric specimen of ellipsoidal shape is placed in a uniform field $\mathcal{E}_0$. Figure 17.4*b* gives the values of $N$ for other geometries.

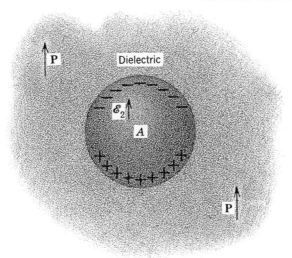

**Fig. 17.5** A small sphere in a dielectric of polarization **P** is subject to a depolarization or Lorentz field $\mathscr{E}_2$. The induced electric charges giving rise to $\mathscr{E}_2$ are shown.

### The Lorentz Field

The induced charges that cause the Lorentz field $\mathscr{E}_2$ are shown in Fig. 17.5. These charges are opposite in sign to those that appear on an outside surface. It is possible to show that the inside field at $A$ is the same whether $A$ is at the center of the spherical cavity or not. The magnitude of this field is given by

$$\mathscr{E}_2 = \frac{\mathbf{P}}{3\epsilon_0} \tag{17.18}$$

Note that the factor $1/3\epsilon_0$ also appears in Fig. 17.4 as the depolarization factor for a sphere.

### Field of Adjacent Dipoles

The field $\mathscr{E}_3$, which is caused by the dipoles within the cavity, must be computed microscopically and will depend on the crystal structure. The calculation is complex. If the environment of the molecule $A$ is cubic, however, it can be shown that $\mathscr{E}_3$ has the value zero. Although this is always true for a pure element, in a solid cubic compound like barium titanate the symmetry of the oxygen atoms is not cubic, and a contribution to the local field from these atoms does exist.

## Polarization in Alternating Fields

Our study of polarization in static fields has served to define the fundamental parameters. We will now discuss polarization in alternating fields. The range of application of the theory is enormous, covering the response of a dielectric in a capacitor at, say, 60 Hz right up to the response of a glass under ultraviolet light.

### 17.5 Electronic Polarization in Alternating Fields

Let us first consider a simple situation in which only electronic polarization is included. Consider a model in which an electron in an atom is bound by forces that we consider to be *elastic*. This is equivalent to the assumption that the permittivity is independent of field strength. We obtain a classical model in which the displacement of the electron about the atom occurs at a natural or resonant frequency. This classical model of a naturally oscillating system is related to a quantum model with absorption of energy up to the first excited state. A more complex model with several excited states would be identified with a classical model of several different natural frequencies.

If the natural frequency of the electron about the atom is $\omega_0$, then the displacement $x$, assumed linear for simplicity, will be given by the equation

$$\ddot{x} + \omega_0{}^2 x = 0$$

Under the influence of a periodically varying field of frequency $\omega$, the displacement of the electron will be given by

$$\ddot{x} + \omega_0{}^2 x = \frac{e \mathscr{E}_0}{m} \exp{(i\omega t)} \tag{17.19}$$

where $\mathscr{E}_0$ is the maximum value of the field and $m$ is the mass of the electron. This equation ignores the possibility that the response of the electron to the electric field may not be instantaneous. If there is indeed a time of response, then, just as in Chapter 6 when we considered anelastic behavior of solids, we now must write the total equation with a damping term included, that is,

$$\ddot{x} + 2K\dot{x} + \omega_0^2 x = \frac{e \mathscr{E}_0}{m} \exp{(i\omega t)} \tag{17.20}$$

Note that in the following discussion we shall consider each electron acting independently, that is, there are no electron-electron interactions.

Before solving this differential equation (17.20), let us briefly examine the possible application. We are discussing a bound electron, because of the

$\omega_0^2 x$ term, and thus the material under consideration is a dielectric. The dielectric shows dissipation or damping loss because of the $2K\dot{x}$ term.

Suppose, on the other hand, that the $\omega_0^2 x$ term is not important. Then we have an equation that describes the motion of *free charges*. This would give a good model for plasmas, conduction electrons, X-ray scattering (because the binding is negligible compared with the X-ray energy), and other examples.

### Case of Small Damping

Let us now consider the solution for the case of *small damping*. The dielectric constant $\epsilon_r$ is related to the index of refraction $n$ by an equation due to Maxwell,

$$\epsilon_r = n^2 \tag{17.21}$$

And from Equation 17.15 we have

$$\epsilon_r = 1 + \frac{\mathbf{P}}{\epsilon_0 \mathscr{E}}$$

If there are $N_e$ electrons per unit volume and each is displaced by the field a distance $x$ from its equilibrium position, then the dipole moment per unit volume or polarization $\mathbf{P}$ is

$$\mathbf{P} = N_e e x \tag{17.22}$$

It is clear then that we must get a solution for $x$ in Equation 17.19 in order to calculate the polarization.

Since the motion of the electrons will obviously be at the frequency $\omega_0$ of the applied field, we can make a trial solution,

$$x = x_0 \exp(i\omega t) \tag{17.23}$$

where we must determine the value of $x_0$, the amplitude of motion. Substituting the trial solution in Equation 17.19 gives

$$-\omega^2 x_0 + \omega_0^2 x_0 = \frac{e\mathscr{E}_0}{m}$$

from which we get

$$x_0 = \frac{e\mathscr{E}_0}{m} \frac{1}{\omega_0^2 - \omega^2}$$

Thus

$$\mathbf{P} = \frac{N_e e^2 \mathscr{E}_0}{m} \frac{1}{\omega_0^2 - \omega^2} \exp(i\omega t) \tag{17.24}$$

Also

$$\epsilon_r = 1 + \frac{N_e e^2}{\epsilon_0 m (\omega_0^2 - \omega^2)} \tag{17.25}$$

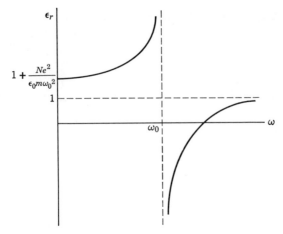

**Fig. 17.6**  The dependence of relative permittivity $\epsilon_r$ on frequency $\omega$ for small damping in a dielectric solid.

This equation is plotted in Fig. 17.6.  It enables us to consider the frequency dependence of the index of refraction (i.e., $\epsilon_s^{\frac{1}{2}}$) of the dielectric.

At *low* frequencies of applied field, $\epsilon_r$ starts at the value $1 + Ne^2/\epsilon_0 m\omega_0^2$ and rises gradually with increase of $\omega$.  $\epsilon_r$ is positive and the index of refraction $n$ is real.  This is the familiar region of transparent dielectric behavior with indices of refraction slightly over the value unity.

As the frequency $\omega$ is increased toward $\omega_0$, Equation 17.25 gives a singularity with a large increase in $n$.  This is the region of *dispersion* in glasses and other dielectrics.  Dispersion is the term denoting change of index of refraction with wavelength.  In most of the familiar dielectric materials the value of $\omega_0$ lies in the ultraviolet.  For a quantum model the energy gap is large enough to require ultraviolet excitation.

On the high frequency side of the singularity the optical behavior of the dielectric is less obvious.  Since $\epsilon_r$ is initially negative, the value of $n$ must be imaginary.  In texts on optics* it is shown that this situation corresponds to a condition of total reflection.  Reflection over a certain frequency range is experimentally found in certain dielectrics and plasmas.

Above a certain definite frequency for which

$$\frac{N_e e^2}{\epsilon_0 m(\omega_0^2 - \omega^2)} = -1 \tag{17.26}$$

the value of $\epsilon_r$ again becomes positive and the material regains its transparency.  This behavior is familiar in the ionosphere, which reflects signals

* See, for example, B. Rossi, *Optics*, Addison-Wesley. Co., Reading, Mass., 1957.

**Table 17.1**  Optical Transparency of the Alkali Metals ($\lambda_0$ is the wavelength in A at which the metal becomes transparent, and $N_e$ is the effective number of free electrons per atom, calculated from Equation 17.26)

| Metal | Cs | Rb | K | Na | Li |
|---|---|---|---|---|---|
| $\lambda_0$ (observed) | 4400 | 3600 | 3150 | 2100 | 2050 |
| $N_e$ (calculated) | 0.85 | 0.94 | 0.97 | 1.1 | 0.55 |

below a certain frequency while transmitting those of a higher frequency. The frequency which marks the onset of transparency is relatively easily measured and is important since, as is seen from Equation 17.26, it gives a value for $N_e$, the number of electrons involved.

If this theory is applied to a plasma or the conduction electrons in a metal, the binding term is negligible and $\omega_0 = 0$. The onset of transparency has been observed in the alkali metals to occur in the ultraviolet. Some values are given in Table 17.1 with the calculated numbers of free electrons per atom.

Our elementary treatment has ignored the damping term. It is quite a good approximation for glasses, provided the frequency is not too close to the resonant value $\omega_0$. The main purpose in first working out the simple case was, however, to illustrate the principles of the method. When we include damping it will turn out that there are two main consequences. First, the singularity at $\omega_0$ will be eliminated and the two branches of $\epsilon_r$ will join smoothly as $\omega$ passes through $\omega_0$. Second, we shall see that energy can be absorbed from the incident electric field. So far this has not been the case. The motion of the electron has been exactly in phase with the applied field when $\omega < \omega_0$ and exactly in antiphase when $\omega > \omega_0$. No absorption of energy by the medium has taken place. This statement may appear confusing since the energy in a light beam clearly diminishes as the ray passes through a transparent solid. This process, however, involves a scattering mechanism, not an absorption mechanism. Energy loss, shown by our model on inclusion of the $2K\dot{x}$ term, is responsible for losses in dielectric filled transmission lines, the heat generated in dielectric cooking, and many other examples.

### Case of Appreciable Damping

If we again consider the trial solution (Equation 17.23) now substituted in Equation 17.20, we have

$$-\omega^2 x_0 + 2Ki\omega x_0 + \omega_0^2 x_0 = \frac{e\mathscr{E}_0}{m}$$

which gives

$$x_0 = \frac{e\mathscr{E}_0}{m} \frac{1}{\omega_0^2 + 2iK\omega - \omega_0^2}$$

The significant feature of this value is that it is a complex quantity. Rationalization gives

$$x = \frac{e\mathscr{E}_0}{m}\left[\frac{\omega_0{}^2 - \omega^2}{(\omega_0{}^2 - \omega^2) + 4K^2\omega^2} - i\frac{2k\omega}{(\omega_0{}^2 - \omega^2) + 4K^2\omega^2}\right] \quad (17.27)$$

We now have for the displacement an *in-phase* and a "90° out-of-phase" or *quadrature* component. Of course, the polarization **P** was essentially defined in terms of the moment induced by the field $\mathscr{E}$ and so is automatically associated with the in-phase component of the displacement. Thus the first term in the bracket of Equation 17.27 gives us the polarization and dielectric constant. From the second term we get the *power* dissipated and hence the damping loss. This follows if we recall that power is a potential-current product. Here the potential is the electric field and the current the velocity of the moving charges or the time derivative of the charge displacement. This latter parameter is proportional to the second term of the bracket of Equation 17.27.

Figure 17.7 shows the dielectric constant and power loss as a function of applied frequency. In most materials several resonant frequencies exist. The resultant dispersion curve is then more complicated, being the sum of a number of curves of the form of Fig. 17.7. The whole dispersion curve for a dipolar substance is shown in Fig. 17.8.

We have now discussed the effect of inclusion of the damping term in the analysis of the dependence of dielectric constant on the frequency of the applied electric field. If the polarization is electronic, the damping is not generally of great importance since the electron displacement is usually almost in-phase with the applied field. To a certain extent, however, even in electronic polarization, thermally generated collisions do affect the free response of the electrons. These delay effects, however, are of greater importance in orientation polarization.

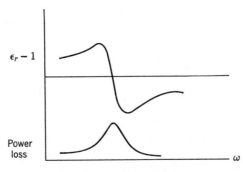

**Fig. 17.7** Dielectric constant versus applied frequency. Power loss versus applied frequency.

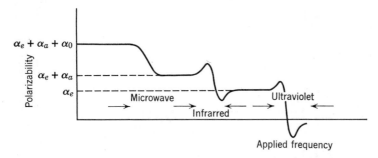

**Fig. 17.8** The polarizability of a dipole material with an ionic and electronic resonance.

## 17.6 Orientational Polarization in Alternating Fields

The physical mechanisms involved in some aspects of orientational polarization are rather different from those in electronic polarization. In electronic polarization an equilibrium position existed for the electron. In orientational polarization, however, the electric dipoles may be subject to no restoring force and assume a quite random orientation. This situation would exist, for instance, in a polar liquid. Then the polarization in an alternating field would be greatly influenced by the inertia of the polar molecule or dipole and the damping of the motion involved. The damping would again be affected by thermal motion. The situation in a liquid is complicated, and it is even more so in a solid where certain restriction to the orientation motion is present. Because of the complication, the phenomenon of orientational polarization is usually treated empirically by introducing the concept of a relaxation time. The treatment again follows the mathematical form we encountered in the treatment of anelastic behavior of solids in Chapter 6.

Let us consider, for simplicity, a liquid of dipole molecules which are randomly oriented. An electric field is suddenly applied. The molecules will be reoriented by the field while thermal disturbances delay the approach to complete orientation. The growth of polarization of the liquid is shown in Fig. 17.9a. Similarly, termination of the applied field results in a delayed return of the dipoles to a condition of random orientation and no over-all polarization, as shown in Fig. 17.9b. On the assumption that both growth and decay of polarization can be described by exponential curves, a *relaxation time* $\tau$ is defined as the time required for the polarization to rise to $1/e$ of its final value or to fall to $1/e$ of its initial value. We can write for growth

$$\mathbf{P}(t) = \mathbf{P}_0(1 - e^{-t/\tau}) \qquad (17.28)$$

and for decay

$$\mathbf{P}(t) = \mathbf{P}_0 e^{-t/\tau} \qquad (17.29)$$

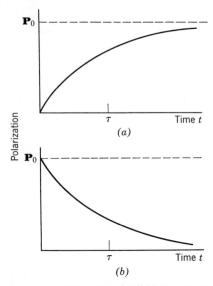

**Fig. 17.9**   Growth and decay of polarization. $\tau$ is the relaxation time.

The calculation of the dielectric constant follows the former pattern. The real part (in-phase) of the polarization turns out to be proportional to $1/(1 + \omega\tau)$ and the imaginary part (quadrature) to $\omega\tau/(1 + \omega\tau)$. The former is proportional to the dielectric constant and the latter to the absorption loss. Both are plotted as a function of frequency in Fig. 17.10.

As can be seen, the total orientational polarization is greatest at low frequencies. At high frequencies, where the dipole molecules are unable to orient themselves rapidly enough to follow the field, the orientational polarization is not observed.

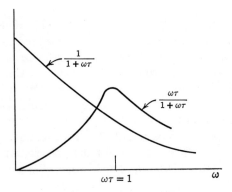

**Fig. 17.10**   Real and imaginary parts of dielectric constant plotted as a function of frequency.

The phase difference between the field and the polarization direction is greatest at a frequency value such that $\omega\tau = 1$. Then the dielectric loss is a maximum. This condition is similar to the one we found in Chapter 6 to govern the maximum values of loss in relaxation damping. Again, since the reorientation of the dipoles in their characteristic relaxation time occurs because of thermal activation, the dielectric loss is highly temperature dependent.

For practical electrical work at high frequencies low loss dielectric materials are favored, and thus the material should have no orientational polarizability. The molecular dipoles, if they exist, should be fixed in the lattice. The worth of the dielectric is quoted frequently in terms of the phase angle $\delta$

$$\tan \delta = \frac{\text{imaginary part}}{\text{real part}}$$

and values as low as $\simeq 10^{-4}$ are achieved. Typical values for common materials are given in Table 17.2.

**Table 17.2** Relative Permittivities and Losses in Dielectrics at Frequencies of $10^6$ to $10^9$ Hz

|  | $\epsilon_r$ | $\tan \delta$ |
|---|---|---|
| Ceramics |  |  |
| Electrical porcelain | 5.7 | 0.007 to 0.02 |
| Steatites | 9 | 0.001 |
| Forsterites | 6 to 6.5 | 0.0005 |
| Glasses |  |  |
| Fused silica | 3.8 | 0.0002 |
| Soda glass | 7.6 | 0.009 |
| Lead glass | 7.5 | 0.009 |
| Borasilicate | 4.5 | 0.01 |
| Micas |  |  |
| Mica (muscovite) | 6.5 to 8.7 | 6 to 10 × $10^{-4}$ |
| Mica (phlogopite) | 5 to 6 | 1.5 to 8 × $10^{-4}$ |
| Ferroelectrics |  |  |
| Rutile titanium oxide | 80 | 0.0005 |
| Barium titanate | 1200 | 0.0014 |
| Barium/strontium titanate | 3000 | 0.005 |
| Plastics |  |  |
| Polystyrene | 2.55 | 0.0012 |
| Lucite | 2.57 | 0.0032 |

There are some special applications in which use is made of dielectric loss. Dielectric cooking makes use of the heating effects of such losses. Unlike induction heating in conductors, dielectric heating has the advantage that it occurs throughout the volume of the treated specimen.

### 17.7    Ferroelectricity

Thus far we have assumed that the orientation of an electric dipole or the development of atomic polarization is a consequence solely of the applied field, which is similar to the development of paramagnetism by an external applied magnetic field. Just as an internal magnetic field exists in ferromagnetic solids, internal electric fields exist in *ferroelectric* crystals. Spontaneous and permanent polarization occur in these materials. We shall discuss the phenomena by analogy with the magnetic case.

The polarization of a ferroelectric crystal is always dependent to a certain extent on the history of the crystal. Figure 17.11 shows the relationship between polarization and field for a ferroelectric crystal. In a nonpolarized specimen the polarization first rises rapidly with applied field to a value above which the dependence is linear. Linear extrapolation to zero field gives $P_s$, the saturation or spontaneous polarization. On subsequently reducing the field to zero a *remanent polarization* $P_r$ remains. The negative field to reduce the polarization to zero is called the *coercive field* and is represented by $\mathscr{E}_c$. Ferroelectric crystals, like ferromagnetics, have Curie temperatures and a Curie-Weiss dependence of polarization with temperature.

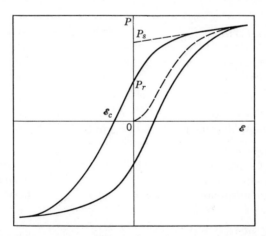

**Fig. 17.11**   The hysteretic relationship between electric field and polarization for a ferroelectric crystal. The dotted curve from the origin shows the initial behavior.

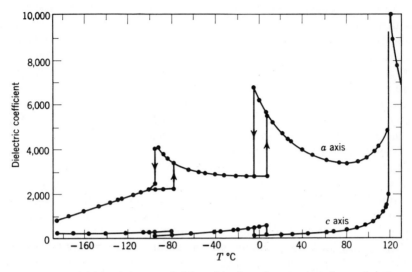

**Fig. 17.12**  The initial relative permittivity of barium titanate plotted as a function of temperature.  The arrows refer to the direction in which the temperature is changing. (After Merz)

They also reveal domain structure.  The similarity in nomenclature used to describe ferroelectric and ferromagnetic phenomena is, however, somewhat misleading since the fundamental processes are quite different.

At temperatures below the ferroelectric Curie temperature, where the polarization is a function of field strength, it is obviously impossible to apply Equation 17.15 directly.  This equation was developed on the assumption that $\epsilon_r$ was independent of $\mathscr{E}$.  We can, however, define a *differential relative permittivity* from the slope of the polarization versus field strength curve.  That is, from

$$\epsilon_0(\epsilon_r - 1) = \frac{d\mathbf{P}}{d\mathscr{E}} \tag{17.30}$$

The simplest of the ferroelectric crystals are the titanates, of which the best known is ceramic barium titanate, $BaTiO_3$.  The dielectric constant defined by Equation 17.30 at the *origin of the* $\mathbf{P}$ versus $\mathscr{E}$ curve is shown in Fig. 17.12 as a function of temperature.  As can be seen, there are anomalies in the dielectric constant at the temperatures of 120°C, 0°C, and −100°C. At temperatures above 120°C, which is the Curie temperature, the dielectric constant of barium titanate varies with temperature according to a Curie-Weiss law, namely,

$$\epsilon_r = \frac{C}{T - \theta} \tag{17.31}$$

where $C$ is a constant and $\theta$ is the Curie temperature characteristic of the particular ferroelectric crystal.

Below 120°C, barium titanate is spontaneously polarized. The spontaneous polarization is associated with a displacement of charge, corresponding to a lattice expansion in the direction of polarization. Thus at the Curie temperature and also at the other two transition temperatures, structural changes in the crystal take place. The Curie temperature structural change reduces the polarization to zero, and at the other two transition temperatures changes in the direction of spontaneous polarization take place.

Free energy differences exist between the barium titanate structures below and above each of the transition temperatures. Energy is required to drive the structure from one form to another. As a consequence, the dielectric constant, which is dependent on the structure, measured with the temperature increasing does not follow the same path when the temperature is decreasing. Loops occur at each of the transition temperatures, as shown in Fig. 17.12.

Let us now look more closely into the nature of the spontaneous dipole moment in barium titanate. The crystal structure is called *perovoskite* after the name of the prototype calcium titanate. The structure above the Curie temperature is shown in Fig. 17.13. It is cubic with each of the titanium $Ti^{4+}$ ions surrounded by six oxygen $O^{2-}$ ions in an octahedral configuration. At temperatures above 120°C, the $TiO_6$ octahedron is symmetrical, and the center of gravity of the negative charges coincides with that of the positive charges. The net dipole moment is therefore zero. As the temperature falls through the Curie temperature, the titanium and barium ions move with respect to the oxygen ions so that a dipole moment results. From neutron diffraction studies it is now known that the $O'$ and $O''$ type oxygen ions (see Fig. 17.13) move in the same direction, whereas the Ti and Ba ions move in the opposite direction. The titanium ions move considerably further than the barium ions. The distance that the titanium ion moves with respect to the oxygen ion can be roughly computed from the known value of the saturation polarization $P_s$ of barium titanate.

The lattice constant of $BaTiO_3$ is $4 \times 10^{-10}$ m and the saturation polarization $P_s$ is 0.16 coulomb $m^{-2}$. There is one titanium ion per unit cell carrying a charge of $4e$. If it is assumed that the dipole moment is due to the displacement $d$ of the titanium ion only, the dipole moment per unit cell is

$$4e \times d = 0.16 \times (4 \times 10^{-10})^3 \simeq 10^{-29}$$

Thus

$$d \simeq 1.6 \times 10^{-11} \text{ m}$$

We have assumed that the spontaneous polarization below the Curie temperature is due largely to the strong interaction between the Ti and $O'$ ions. The buildup process of polarization is cumulative and is called the

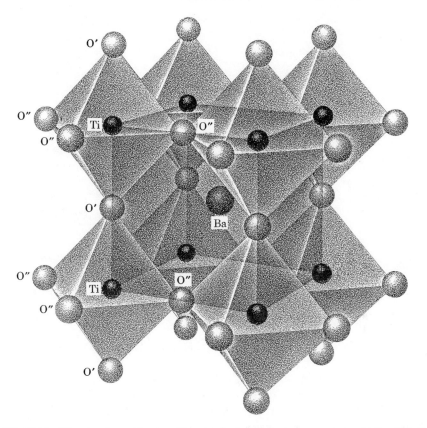

**Fig. 17.13** The structure of barium titanate above the Curie temperature. (After Kittel)

*polarization catastrophe.* This means that the polarization of the Ti ions increases the local field at the O′ ion sites, which increases the polarization of the O′ ions and which in turn increases the polarization of the Ti ions.

## 17.8 Domain Structure in Ferroelectric Crystals

In our discussion of ferromagnetism it was shown that the concept of domains magnetized in different directions enabled us to account for the possibility of a net magnetization of zero, even if each domain is spontaneously magnetized. A similar concept is used to account for net polarizations of zero in ferroelectric crystals below the Curie temperature.

We have seen that the cubic structure of barium titanate just above the Curie temperature becomes slightly tetragonal as the temperature falls.

**Fig. 17.14**   Wedge-shaped laminar domains in barium titanate. (After Forsbergh)

The polar direction in the crystal is the *c* axis of the tetragonal cell which coincided with one of the former cube axes. Often in a specimen crystal the tetragonal axes of different regions correspond with different cube directions. This means that different regions have different directions of spontaneous polarization. These different regions are called *domains*.

The index of refraction of barium titanate parallel to the tetragonal *c* axis differs from the index at right angles to the *c* axis. Since the crystal is transparent to ordinary light, it is possible to send polarized light through a specimen plate and view the emergent light with an analyzer. The domains then show up as dark and light bands. Figure 17.14 shows wedge-shaped laminar domains in barium titanate rendered visible by this technique. It is found that the *domain wall*, unlike the magnetic domain wall, is only a few atomic spacings thick.

Another difference between ferroelectric and ferromagnetic domains concerns the growth process. The growth of ferroelectric domains is brought about by the formation of a great number of new antiparallel domains of thickness about one micron. If an external electric field is applied in a direction that tends to reverse the polarization in a domain, these narrow spikes grow out from the edges of the specimen plate. There is little or no sideways growth. The number of spikes nucleated is dependent on the magnitude of the applied field.

## 17.9 Piezoelectricity

We have seen that an applied electric field, in inducing an electric dipole moment in a dielectric, displaces ions relative to each other. The structural dimensions of the crystal have been changed by the applied field. Figure 17.15 shows an ion array with and without an applied field. The dimensions of the crystal have increased in the field direction. This physical property is called *electrostriction*.

Now let us consider the effect on the polarization of changing the dimensions of the crystal by means of a *mechanical strain*. We consider two kinds of crystals, namely, those with a *center of symmetry* and those without. First a word about the nature of a center of symmetry. If the unit cell of a dielectric is such that we can draw from a central point a vector to one charged ion, and on drawing an equal and opposite vector from the point we also find a similar ion, then the structure has a center of symmetry at the central point. Of the thirty-two crystal classes which exist in nature (point groups), twelve have a center of symmetry.

We will now consider the effect of mechanically changing the spacing in very simple two-dimensional ion arrays with and without centers of symmetry.

### *Array with a Center of Symmetry*

Figure 17.16 shows an array of ions in which the position of the ion $A$ is obviously a center of symmetry. In Fig. 17.16*b* the array has been compressed by a mechanical force. Ion $B$ has been moved closer to ion $A$, thus decreasing the $BA$ dipole moment. However, atom $C$ has also been moved closer to

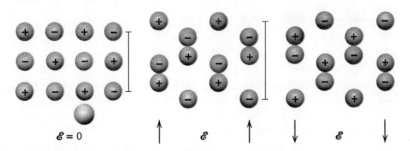

**Fig. 17.15** Electrostriction. Displacement of the ions by the applied electric field increases the dimension of the crystal in the field direction.

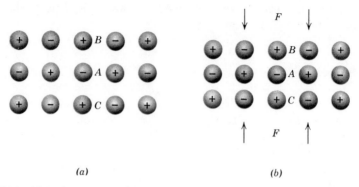

*(a)*                                        *(b)*

**Fig. 17.16**  (*a*) Ionic structure with a center of symmetry. (*b*) Structure compressed by force.  No net change in polarization.

atom *A*, which decreases the *CA* dipole moment by the same amount and, moreover, in the opposite direction to the decrease in the *BA* moment.  Thus no net change in polarization results from mechanical deformation of a crystal with a center of symmetry.

### *Array without a Center of Symmetry*

Figure 17.17*a* shows a very simple two-dimensional array of ions with no center of symmetry.  A compressive force is applied to this array in 17.17*b* and a tensile force in 17.17*c*.  The total electric dipole moment has been

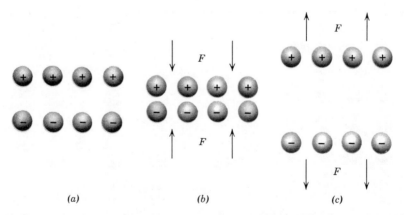

*(a)*                        *(b)*                        *(c)*

**Fig. 17.17**  (*a*) Ionic structure with no center of symmetry. (*b*) Structure compressed. Polarization decreased.  (*c*) Structure extended.  Polarization increased.

decreased in *b* and increased in *c*. Materials that exhibit this phenomenon are called *piezoelectric*.

Since both the strain and the polarization are characteristically directional in a crystal, complex relationships exist between these quantities. For example, quartz crystals cut in wafers whose faces are parallel to the basal plane (X cut) will contract or expand in a direction parallel to an electric field perpendicular to the faces.

Transducers are now often fabricated from polycrystalline ceramic materials based on barium or zinc titanate. These ferroelectric materials must be prepolarized by cooling through a transition temperature in the presence of a polarizing electric field.

A few of the many uses of piezoelectric behavior in crystals will now be mentioned.

A piezoelectric crystal will vibrate naturally in several mechanical modes, the frequencies of vibration being dependent on the dimensions of the specimen and the elastic constants of the material. If the crystal is placed between electrodes and an alternating voltage at one of the resonant frequencies is applied, the amplitude of oscillation will build up at this frequency. The stability of the oscillator system will be controlled by the constancy of the elastic constants of the crystal. Specially cut quartz disks are generally used for this purpose, the stability being particularly high since the coefficient of thermal expansion of quartz is very low. The use of quartz crystal oscillators is electronic circuitry is already very great.

Another application of piezoelectric oscillators lies in the conversion of mechanical pulses into electrical ones, and vice versa. The crystal is here used as a *transducer*. Acoustic pulses are used in underwater search and other applications. In almost all such cases the acoustic pulses are produced by piezoelectric transducers shock excited by electric fields.

A final application lies in the use of piezoelectric materials as delay lines. If an electrical signal is converted into an acoustic one at one end of a quartz rod, the signal will pass along the rod as an acoustic wave. It will travel in the quartz with the appropriate *sound velocity*. On reaching the end of the rod, the acoustic wave may be picked off as an electrical signal. The initial electrical signal has been delayed, a requirement often found in communication devices.

### Quantum Electronic Properties

So far in this chapter we have assumed that the only response of a dielectric material to an electric field is the induction of a dipole moment. We will now discuss conduction and other properties which depend on electron energy transitions.

## 17.10   Photoconductivity in Dielectric Solids

Both semiconductors and insulators have the property that electrons can be excited by irradiation with photons across the energy gap to form electron-hole pairs. In a semiconductor (see Chapter 14) other conductive processes, such as electron excitation from impurity levels into the conduction band, obscure the simple photoconductive process. Let us deal therefore with a pure photocurrent in a dielectric, ignoring other contributions to the conductivity.

Consider a slab of photoconductive material between electrodes which are a distance $d$ apart. Consider that the incident light generates $R$ electron-hole pairs per unit volume per second. Now consider the conduction due to the electrons only. (In many photoconductive devices this is a valid assumption.) The *lifetime* of the electrons in the conduction band is $\tau$ seconds. In equilibrium the number of electrons per unit volume will be

$$N_e = R\tau \tag{17.32}$$

Now let a potential difference be applied to the electrodes so that an electron would take a time $t_d$, the *transit time*, to travel from one electrode to the other. The photocurrent is then

$$I = \frac{N_e e}{t_d} = \frac{Re\tau}{t_d} \tag{17.33}$$

This equation is frequently written

$$I = ReG \tag{17.34}$$

where $G$ is called the *photoconductive gain*.

The quantity $t_d$ can obviously be varied by changing the thickness of the slab of material and the applied voltage. Subsequent improvement in performance is subject to two limitations. The first is the familiar influence of space charge, which will not be discussed further. The second is found in most photoconductive materials. We have assumed in Equation 17.33 that the whole time $t_d$ was available for conduction; this is not necessarily so. In Section 15.7 we saw in our discussion of extrinsic semiconductors that electrons can become trapped at local impurity levels before becoming excited back into the conduction band. Clearly, the time spent in a trap adds to the transit time $t_d$ and so acts to reduce the photocurrent. Discussion of the practical application of photoconductivity will be given in Section 17.12.

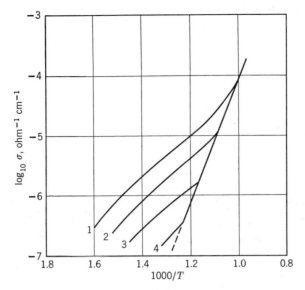

**Fig. 17.18** The ionic conductivity of KCl containing various amounts of $SrCl_2$. Curve 1, $8.7 \times 10^{-5}$ mole fraction; curve 2, $3.5 \times 10^{-5}$ mole fraction; curve 3, $1.2 \times 10^{-5}$ mole fraction; curve 4, 0 mole fraction. (From H. Kelting and H. Witt, *Z. Physik*, **126**, 697, 1949)

## 17.11 Ionic Conductivity in Dielectric Solids

In an ionic solid, such as one of the alkali halides, any migration of the ions throughout the lattice is necessarily accompanied by transport of electric charge. We have already seen in Chapter 4 that appreciable ion migration is possible only if defects such as vacancies are present. There the kinetics of vacancy diffusion were fully discussed.

In the case of the alkali halides any method of increasing the vacancy concentration will increase the ionic conduction. Thus radiation damage results in increased conductivity. Suppose also that into a lattice of an alkali halide, which contains monovalent metal ions, a divalent metal impurity is introduced. An imbalance in the lattice binding results since each divalent metal atom can now satisfy the binding requirements of two halogen atoms. The lattice adjusts to this situation by leaving one metal atom site vacant adjacent to each divalent impurity atom. The increase in conduction resulting from these impurity-vacancy pairs is shown in Fig. 17.18. In the figure, where, as usual, the logarithm of the conductance is plotted against reciprocal temperature, the lower temperature region is largely impurity controlled and the higher temperature region dependent on pure vacancy concentration.

The slopes of the lines should give a measure of the migration energies involved in the two processes.

## 17.12   Localized Energy Levels in Dielectrics

In this section we shall consider electron energy levels associated with specific centers in the crystal, first treating the levels associated with electron-hole pairs and then with chemical impurities.

### Exciton Levels

Consider a hole in the valence band to be a center of positive charge. An electron in the vicinity of this positive charge has energy configurations available to it. It need not annihilate the hole by recombination. The system can be considered to behave in some respects like a hydrogen atom (or, more closely, a positronium atom, i.e., a positron-electron combination), and similar energy states will be available to it. If energies are measured from the bottom of the conduction band, which corresponds to the ionization level $E = 0$ in the hydrogen atom, then the bound states of the combination will have energies $E_n$ given by

$$E_n = -\frac{m'e^4}{8\epsilon_0^2 h^2} \frac{1}{n^2} \tag{17.35}$$

Here $m'$ is the "reduced mass" of the electron defined to compensate for the finite mass of the positive charge center. An elementary treatment gives

$$\frac{1}{m'} = \frac{1}{m} + \frac{1}{M}$$

where $m$ is the mass of the electron and $M$ is the mass of the positive charge center. In a simple case $M$ may be similar to $m$, but the effective masses of electrons and holes differ if the Fermi surface is markedly nonspherical. The exciton spectrum is detectable only to the extent that the levels can be accommodated within the energy gap. For this reason we have discussed dielectric materials in this chapter rather than with semiconductors since in dielectrics the band gap is wider. Transitions due to exciton levels can be distinguished from transitions across the total energy gap since absorption in those due to exciton levels do not result in photoconductivity. In this way the first few absorption bands in crystals like KBr between the visible and ultra-violet have been attributed to exciton levels. Exciton spectra are usually difficult to observe, but fine examples in CuO have been obtained by Gross, which are illustrated in Fig. 17.19.

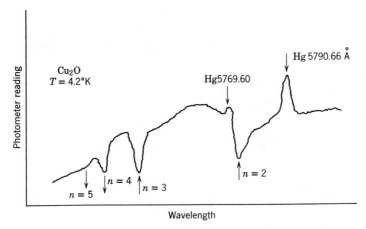

**Fig. 17.19** Transmission through $Cu_2O$ at 4.2°K. The absorption is high at the wavelengths of the exciton series. The mercury lines are included for calibration. (After Apfel and Hadley)

One important and unique feature of excitons is that they are not fixed in the lattice and can move, although perhaps without the electron or hole mobility. Such mobility can be significant since energy can be transferred to stationary and localized levels such as $F$ centers or trapping sites.

### Trapping and Recombination Centers

We have already discussed the role of traps and recombination centers in semiconduction (Section 14.7). We found that in the elemental semiconductors Ge and Si electron-hole recombination was generally accomplished at centers with the energy released as phonons. In GaAs and the Group III-V compounds, on the other hand, the energy release was usually photoemissive. This is also true in Group II-VI compounds such as ZnS. In these materials, impurity levels near the valence band act as recombination centers or hole traps. Levels near the conduction band act as electron traps. Transitions between these localized levels can give photoemission in the optical range ($\simeq$ 2 to 3 eV). In all these processes electron transport is involved. However, in certain dielectric materials typically of an ionic nature, certain impurities may have electronic states that lie within the energy gap. These impurities may act as excited photoemissive centers without electron transport between the conduction and valence band being involved.

### Color Centers

It has been observed that certain crystals as, for example, the alkali halides, which are normally transparent and colorless, become colored when

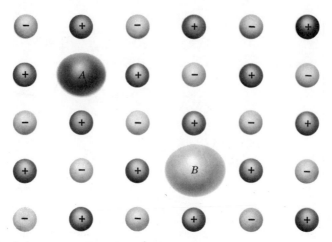

**Fig. 17.20**  Anion vacancy at *A*. Anion vacancy with associated electron, that is, *F* center at *B*.

subjected to certain treatments. We shall try to give simple treatments of these phenomena in terms of the elementary mechanisms already discussed.

The coloring can be achieved in the following ways:

1. By heating the alkali halide crystal in an atmosphere of one of the constituent atoms and quenching, thereby producing a stochiometric excess of one of the atoms.

2. By radiation with X-rays, $\gamma$-rays, or energetic particles.

The coloring is caused by electron or hole trapping at a negative ion or positive ion vacancy, respectively. Let us consider the trapping of an electron at a negative ion vacancy. Figure 17.20 shows the electric charge distribution around such a defect and makes clear how it becomes a trapping site for an electron or negative ion. The electron at such a site has a ground energy state and excited states. The wave function is centered at the vacancy and is, to some extent, distributed over the neighboring atoms. The center has quite well-defined energy levels, but because of the solid nature of the matrix some broadening of the levels into bands is generally found. This broadening is, of course, fundamentally similar in nature to that discussed in Chapter 10. Thus absorption of light is extended over a range of wavelengths.

The binding of an electron at a vacancy site depends, as one might expect, on the thermal expansion of the lattice, and both the width and the position of the peaks in the absorption spectra are influenced by temperature. This is shown in Fig. 17.21. The elementary *color center* we have described with an electron trapped at a negative ion vacancy is known as an *F center*.

The formation of *F* centers by radiation is easy to understand. Formation by stochiometric excess was first described by de Boer. Let us consider an alkali halide crystal heated in a vapor of the corresponding metal atoms. Adsorption of a metal atom on the crystal surface attracts to the newly deposited atom (if ionized) a negative ion from the crystal surface. A negative ion vacancy is thus created and can diffuse into the crystal. The electron, surrendered by the metal ion on joining the surface, may join the negative ion vacancy, thus forming the complete *F* center.

The corresponding process for positive ions is also possible. To facilitate this process the crystal is located in a vapor of the halogen atoms. If a hole is then trapped at a positive ion vacancy, identifiable energy levels are again experimentally found. This combination is called a *V* center.

Many different optical phenomena are associated with color centers. We shall mention only a few. When a crystal containing *F* centers is irradiated with light of wavelength within the absorption band, the *F* center becomes ionized. The trapped electrons are returned to the conduction band and photoconductivity is observed. Simultaneously, the loss of the *F* center causes the crystal to regain its transparency. This is referred to as "bleaching." Other possibilities can, however, result. For instance, *two* electrons may be bound at the negative ion vacancy. The binding is naturally weaker than for one electron, but bound levels are, in fact, found experimentally, especially

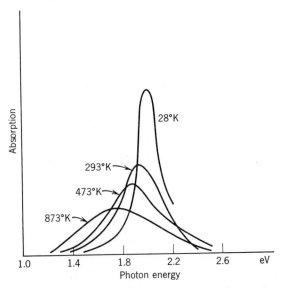

**Fig. 17.21**  The optical absorption of KBr with excess potassium for photons of different energies. The measurements are made at various temperatures. (From E. Mollwo; *Z. Physik.*, **85**, 56, 1933.)

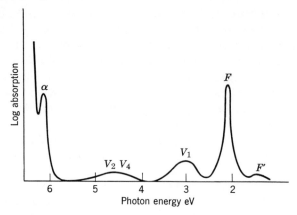

**Fig. 17.22**    Absorption bands in X-irradiated KBr crystal. The types of defects giving rise to the absorption peaks are marked. (Redrawn from H. Pick; *Suppl. Nuovo Cimento,* **7,** 498, 1958)

at lower temperatures. Such centers are called *F′ centers*, and absorption due to them has been found after crystal irradiation. Figure 17.22 shows absorption bands in a crystal of KBr after irradiation with X-rays. The wavelengths and energies associated with a number of different centers are given.

### 17.13   Luminescence

Many dielectric and semiconducting materials can emit radiation which is in excess of their thermal radiation, a phenomenon called *luminescence*. Before luminescent emission the material must first be excited, the excitation agency giving the name to the phenomenon.

*Photoluminescence* depends upon excitation by photons.
*Cathodoluminescence* follows bombardment of the material by electrons, as in a television tube.

*Electroluminescence* occurs upon the application of an alternating electric field to the material.

*Chemiluminescence* occurs following certain chemical reactions.

The time delay between absorption of the excitation energy and re-emission of the luminescent radiation serves to differentiate luminescent materials into two classes. If the time is less than about $10^{-8}$ s the material is *fluorescent*; if longer, it is called *phosphorescent*. Commercially useful *phosphors* have delay times which are often several milleseconds, although delay times of minutes or even hours are found in some natural phosphors. There are a very great number of energy transition schemes encountered in luminescent materials. We shall discuss the physical principles of these transitions with reference to three important examples.

### Photoluminescence in Zinc Sulphide Phosphors

Zinc sulfide is a compound semiconductor with a large band gap of 3.7 eV. Impurities such as Cu, Ag, or Au, when introduced in a few parts per million, occupy Zn sites and introduce *activator* levels just above the valence band. Some of these activator levels will be empty and act as *acceptors* in semiconductor terminology. Other impurities such as Ga or In at Zn sites or Cl at S sites introduce levels close to the conduction band. These are called *coactivators* and can act as *donor* levels.

Figure 17.23a shows donor *D* and acceptor *A* levels and two possible transitions. Let us suppose than an incident light photon is absorbed and produces an electron in the conduction band and a hole in the valence band. The electron in scheme 1 may fall into an *A* level producing luminescent radiation. A transition, as in scheme 2, from the lowest donor level to the highest acceptor level would produce an emission band of longer wavelength. The subsequent short fall from *A* into the valance band is nonradiative, the energy being absorbed as lattice vibrations or phonons.

In Fig. 17.23b donor levels which are not associated with acceptor levels have been drawn. The electron may be trapped at these levels and re-emitted back into the conduction band. The time that the electron stays in the trap depends on the factor $e^{-E_T/kT}$ where $E_T$ is the depth of the trap. Factors such as these govern all delay times in luminescent processes. The trapping delay times are therefore strongly influenced by the nature of the coactivator impurity. Figure 17.23a shows that the activator impurity, on the other hand, is largely responsible for the emission spectrum. Figure 17.24 shows emission bands for various zinc sulfide phosphors.

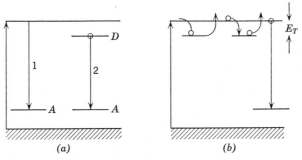

**Fig. 17.23**   Energy band structures and electron transitions in phosphors.

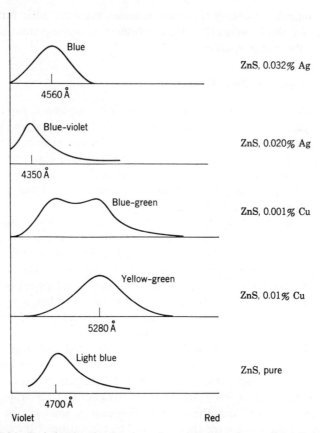

**Fig. 17.24** Emission bands of various zinc sulfide phosphors. (After Leverenz)

### Photoluminescence in Ionic Crystals

The alkali halides are luminescent if doped with certain impurities or if they contain lattice defects. Figure 17.25 shows both the absorption and emission spectrum of thallium doped potassium chloride. An impurity ion in an ionic solid may have ground and excited energy states. These energies are dependent on the environment of the ion. Figure 17.26 shows the energy levels as a function of the distance apart of the chlorine and thallium ions. A radiative transfer of an electron from one energy level to another will alter its wave function and, consequently, the spread of the electronic cloud. The Coulomb force between the ions will then be changed and the distance apart altered. Suppose now that the electron absorbs energy $h\nu$, and makes the transition from ground to excited state. The distance between the ions may now relax from distance $r_1$ to $r_2$. Energy is absorbed as phonons,

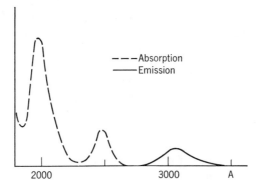

**Fig. 17.25**   Absorption and emission spectra of thallium doped potassium chloride.

the relaxation process taking much longer than the electron transition. If the electron then drops to the ground state the energy emitted is $hv_2$, which from the figure is less than $hv_1$. The arrows show the direction of final relaxation of the ions. The value of $hv_1 - hv_2$ is called the *Stokes shift* and in this case is about 1 eV. The broadening of the levels by the crystalline field and the effect of thermal motion on the distance apart of the ions account for the band nature of the spectrum shown in Fig. 17.25.

### Electroluminescence in Zinc Sulfide Crystals

Electroluminescent phosphors are manufactured by introducing segregations of a relatively good conductor such as zinc oxide into copper doped

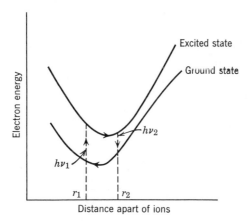

**Fig. 17.26**   Energy levels and distance apart of ions in thallium doped KCl. The arrows show possible transitions and relaxations.

zinc sulfide crystals. The Cu introduces activator levels as discussed previously. If an alternating electric field of about $10^6$ V m$^{-1}$ is applied to a sheet of the material, then local fields of up to $10^6$ V m$^{-1}$ may be present in the neighborhood of the segregations. Electrons may be liberated and accelerated to collide and ionize the activators. These then act as luminescent centers in the manner already described. The electroluminescence in ZnS increases with voltage and with the frequency of the applied field up to a saturation frequency of about $10^5$ Hz. Electroluminescent lamps have an efficiency of about 10 per cent that of fluorescent lamps. They are, however, area sources and have a number of specific uses because of this feature.

It is important to first distinguish between stimulated emission and luminescence in solids. Let us suppose that an atom can exist in two energy states $E_1$ and $E_2$, where $E_2 > E_1$. The photon energy $h\nu_{21}$ emitted when a permitted transition between the states occurs is given by

$$h\nu_{21} = E_2 - E_1$$

Moreover, if the atom is in state 1 then it can absorb a photon of frequency $\nu_{21}$ and be excited to state 2. Such a transition of the atom between energy states may be excited by the electric or magnetic field component of the incident electromagnetic radiation, depending on whether the change in energy is electric or magnetic in nature.

The probability of an absorption of energy taking place in unit time is $\rho_\nu B_{12}$, where $\rho_\nu$ is the energy density of the radiation and $B_{12}$ is the probability of the transition. The absorption is *phase coherent* with the incident radiation. *There also exists a probability $\rho_\nu B_{21}$ that an atom in state 2 will be stimulated to emit a photon $h\nu_{21}$ and fall to state 1.* This process is also phase coherent with the incident radiation. Einstein was the first to show on thermodynamic grounds, that the probability $B_{12}$ of absorption is equal to the probability $B_{21}$ of stimulated emission.

We have seen in our discussion on luminescence that the atom, if in the upper state 2, may also *spontaneously* revert to state 1. This is a random process and is *phase incoherent* with the incident radiation. The spontaneous expression is independent of the electromagnetic radiation interacting with the atom. Suppose that the probability of such a spontaneous transition is $A_{21}$; then the members $N_1$ and $N_2$ of atoms in the two states 1 and 2, respectively, may be calculated.

The Boltzmann probabilities give us

$$N_1 \propto \exp\left[-\frac{E_1}{kT}\right]$$

and

$$N_2 \propto \exp\left[-\frac{E_2}{kT}\right]$$

(17.36)

since, in equilibrium, the atoms may not make a net gain of energy from the electromagnetic field, the number of downward transitions must equal the number of upward transitions. Thus

$$N_1 B_{12} \rho_v = N_2 A_{21} + N_2 B_{21} \rho_v \tag{17.37}$$

and from Equation 17.36

$$\frac{N_2}{N_1} = \frac{B_{12}\rho_v}{A_{21} + B_{21}\rho_v} = \exp\left[-\frac{(E_2 - E_1)}{kT}\right] \tag{17.38}$$

## 17.14   The Nature of Spontaneous and Stimulated Emission

### Spontaneous Emission

As discussed, the probability of spontaneous emission is independent of the radiation density. Furthermore, spontaneously emitted photons are random in direction and have a random phase relationship to one another since the time of emission is statistical. The probability of spontaneous emission $A$ is the reciprocal of a characteristic time $\tau$, which is called the spontaneous lifetime. We have

$$A = \frac{1}{\tau} \tag{17.39}$$

Directly associated with this time is the linewidth of the excited energy level. The uncertainty principle gives

$$\Delta E \, \Delta t \simeq h$$

with the uncertainty $\Delta E$ in energy of the excited atom in level 2 associated with an uncertainty $\Delta t$ in time of emission of a photon. An uncertainty $\Delta E$ in energy level implies a spread or linewidth in frequency $\Delta v$ of the emitted photon. This is the natural linewidth of the transition frequency $v_{21}$.

In addition to this natural linewidth we have already seen in our discussion of photoluminescence in ionic crystals that line-broadening can be produced by interaction with thermal phonons. It is also of interest to note that, when gases are considered, the effects of Doppler shift and collisions between molecules and the wall may also broaden the spectral lines: the former broadens the linewidth directly and the latter may produce transitions to the lower state which, by shortening the lifetime in the state, so broaden the linewidth.

### Stimulated Emission

Let us now consider the nature of stimulated emission. If a photon of frequency $v_s$ with a linewidth $\Delta v_s$ interacts with an atom which is in an excited state of energy $h\nu_s$ above the ground state then the photon will stimulate the atom to emit a photon with the following properties:

1. Its frequency is also $\nu_s$.
2. Its phase is the same as that of the stimulating photon.
3. Its direction is that of the stimulating photon.

Let us now consider an assembly of excited atoms placed in a lossless cavity, that is, one that contains all of the electromagnetic energy. Suppose one atom de-excites spontaneously, liberating a photon of frequency $\nu_s$. This photon will interact with other atoms of energy $E_s$ above the ground state, causing further photon emission. One might expect that the emission would tend to "eat-a-hole" in the line. This does not happen. Rather, lattice phonons, whose vibration frequencies are of the order of $10^{12}$ s$^{-1}$ tend to relax the rest of the emission line into the exact stimulated emission frequency $\nu_s$. The spectrum in the lossless cavity is thus composed of a spectrum over a frequency $\Delta\nu_s$ with a large peak at $\nu_s$, the only depletion of the line being by spontaneous emission.

## 17.15   The Maser Cavity

The length of a microwave maser cavity may be a small integral number of wavelengths. A single oscillation mode may be sustained in it. The cavity for an optical maser, on the other hand, as shown in Fig. 17.27, may sustain many different modes because of the much shorter optical wavelengths.

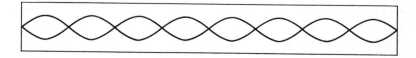

**Fig. 17.27**   Two possible standing wave (axial mode) patterns in an optical maser crystal.

Let us consider a cavity which will support many axial modes, particularly those modes whose frequencies are near the maser frequency $v_s$. If $l$ is the length of the cavity, then

$$n\lambda = 2l \qquad (17.40)$$

for standing waves where $n$ takes integral values. The frequencies of the cavity resonances are given by

$$v = \frac{nv}{2l} \qquad (17.41)$$

where $v$ is the velocity of the electromagnetic radiation in the cavity. The separation of cavity resonances is therefore $v/2l$.

For

$$l \simeq 5 \text{ cm}$$

$$\frac{v}{2l} \simeq 3 \times 10^9 \text{ Hz}$$

$$\simeq 10^{-2} \text{ m}^{-1}$$

Thus a large number of such modes whose frequencies lie within the normal linewidth of luminescent radiation may be supported.

As the temperature is decreased, the luminescent linewidth decreases. Consequently the number of oscillating modes within the linewidth decreases and a mode then is more easily maintained since more atoms are available for the excitation of a particular mode.

The frequency of the cavity modes is "pulled" by the narrowing spectral line. The full theory predicts that the oscillation frequency is determined by the linewidths of the cavity and luminescent spectra $\Delta v_c$ and $\Delta v_m$ respectively, these being centered on frequencies $v_c$ and $v_m$.

Quantitatively the oscillation frequency $v_{osc}$ is given by

$$v_{osc} = \frac{Q_c + Q_m}{Q_c/v_c + Q_m/v_m} \qquad (17.42)$$

where $Q_c$ is the cavity quality factor, $Q_m$ is the luminescent quality factor, each being a measure of $v/\Delta v$. If the luminescent spectrum is broad, $\Delta v_m$ is large and $Q_m$ small. Then

$$v_{osc} \simeq \frac{Q_c}{Q_c/v_c} \simeq v_c \qquad (17.43)$$

We have seen that shortening the cavity or lowering the temperature reduces the number of axial modes. Radial modes of oscillation are discriminated against by the nature of the cavity. If a resonant cavity is to have a low loss (or high $Q$) in a particular mode, then the propagating electromagnetic wave within the cavity must undergo many internal reflections. The modes propagating with low loss must then be those propagating in an axial direction.

There are, of course, stringent requirements for the end-faces of the maser crystal that is acting as the resonant cavity. These must be flat to within $\lambda/4$ and parallel to one another to within a few minutes of arc.

## 17.16  Pumping in the Optical Maser

The upper excited state is populated by absorption of photons, the process being known as optical pumping. In general, high power light sources with a broad spectral region are used. The spectral efficiency will be low since much of the light is not absorbed. The pumping light, however, must maintain more atoms in the upper excited states than in the ground state, that is, the population must be *inverted* from the normal. This is the criterion for maser action, namely, the system must emit rather than absorb energy. The pump itself need not, of course, give coherent light; it merely maintains the population inversion.

## 17.17  The Two-level, Three-level and Four-level Optical Maser

Figure 17.28 shows two-level, three-level, and four-level energy diagrams for possible optical masers. The pumping process and the maser amplifying process must be separated in space and time. Spatial separation is achieved by pumping the system outside the maser cavity or crystal. Intermittent operation can separate in time the pumping and maser amplification.

The two-level maser suffers from two severe disadvantages. First, only a small part of the pump spectrum, that around $\nu_{12}$, the stimulating frequency, is effective, thus the spectral efficiency is low. Second, as we have already seen, narrow line widths are desirable, and this is a difficult condition to meet in the pumped light.

The three-level maser has several advantages. Here the pumping is carried out between levels 1 and 3 in the figure. Then maser action may take place between levels 3 and 2 with a fast nonradiative decay from 2 to 1. Such a decay is phonon-assisted and the time for the process is of the order of $10^{-12}$ sec. An alternative is for fast nonradiative decay from 3 to 2, with maser action between levels 2 and 1.

The advantage of the former scheme is that the terminal level 2 is empty, or nearly so, and thus achieving a population inversion is not difficult. Also, the fast decay from level 2 to level 1 removes atoms from level 2 so that the population $N_2$ is small and the inversion ratio large. However, if the lifetime $\gamma$ is to be long, then level 3, the pumping level, must be sharp so the spectral efficiency is reduced.

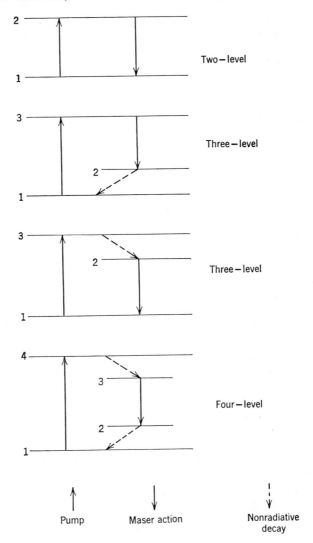

**Fig. 17.28** Maser systems.

The latter scheme has the advantage that level 3 may be quite broad and hence give higher spectral efficiencies. Level 2 may now be sharp. Now, however, more than half the atoms from the ground state 1 must be pumped into level 3 and hence to level 2 in order to maintain a population inversion between 2 and 1.

The four-level maser combines the advantages of both three-level configurations. The pump operates between levels 1 and 4. Atoms in level 4 decay rapidly to level 3 by a phonon-assisted transition. Maser action takes place between levels 3 and 2 and a fast nonradiative transition to the ground state depopulates the terminal level 2. Now level 4 may be quite broad for efficient pumping and level 3 sharp for a long lifetime $\tau$. Level 2 may be very nearly depopulated at steady state, so that a population inversion is easily achieved. Finally, atoms do not build up in the terminal state to decrease the population inversion.

Solids exhibiting such properties are found in the rare earths and actinides. The transitions involve inner level electrons which are shielded from crystalline field line-broadening.

We conclude this discussion of maser action by writing the dynamic equation for a general case. The following probabilities are defined:

1. The probability of electrons *arriving* in state $i$ by *stimulated* emission from state $j$ is $S_{ji}$.

2. The probability of electrons *leaving* state $i$ by *stimulated emission* and making a transition to state $j$ by $S_{ij}$.

3. The probability of electrons *arriving* in state $i$ via *spontaneous* emission is $A_{ji}$ $(j > i)$.

4. The probability of electrons *leaving* state $i$ via *spontaneous* emission is $A_{ij}$ $(i > j)$.

5. The probability of electrons *arriving* in state $i$ by *thermal relaxation* processes is $\mathbf{P}_{ji}$.

6. The probability of electrons *leaving* state $i$ by *thermal relaxation* processes is $\mathbf{P}_{ij}$.

The net change of numbers of atoms in state $i$ is now given by the dynamic equation for the $i$th state:

$$\frac{dN_i}{dt} = \sum_j S_{ij}(N_j - N_i) + \sum_{j>i} A_{ji}N_j - \sum_{j<i} A_{ij}N_i + \sum_i (\mathbf{P}_{ji}N_j - \mathbf{P}_{ij}N_i) \quad (17.44)$$

In any steady state or thermal equilibrium condition, $dN_i/dt$ is zero. Moreover, for equilibrium,

$$\mathbf{P}_{ij}N_i = \mathbf{P}_{ji}N_j \quad (17.45)$$

From Equation 17.38, this condition may be written

$$\mathbf{P}_{ji} = \mathbf{P}_{ij}e^{(E_j - E_i)/kT} \quad (17.46)$$

## 17.18    The Ruby Optical Maser

Ruby is aluminum oxide $Al_2O_3$ in which $Cr^{3+}$ ions substitutionally replace the $Al^{3+}$ ions in the octahedral holes in the hexagonal close-packed structure of $Al_2O_3$.

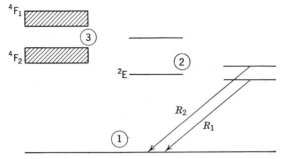

**Fig. 17.29** Energy levels in ruby optical maser. The splitting of the level 2 doublet is exaggerated on the right.

The energy levels of the $Cr^{3+}$ ions are shown in Fig. 17.30. This is a three-level optical maser system. The pump band 3 is a broad band in the green centered at $\sim$5600 A ($^4F_2$) supplemented by another broad band at 4100 A ($^4F_1$). A metastable 2 level ($^2E$) lies between these pump bands. This is a doublet and transitions to the ground state 1 are labelled $R_1$(6943 A) and $R_2$(6929 A).

For the three level ruby system $A_{21} \simeq 200$ sec$^{-1}$ corresponding to a spontaneous decay time from level 2 to level 1 of $\tau = 5 \times 10^{-3}$ sec. In comparison with this, the relaxation from the band to the intermediate state is very rapid. In fact, $P_{32} \simeq 2 \times 10^7$ sec$^{-1}$. Spontaneous emission from the band to the ground state gives $A_{31} \simeq 3 \times 10^5$, whereas relaxation effects $P_{31}$ and $P_{21}$ are negligible compared with spontaneous emission.

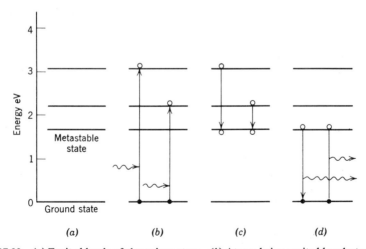

**Fig. 17.30** (a) Excited levels of chromium atom. (b) Atoms being excited by photons into higher states. (c) Fall from metastable to ground state. Emission of photons.

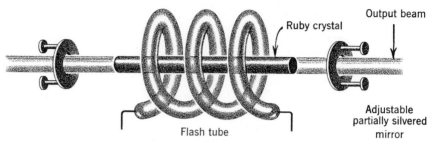

**Fig. 17.31**   Pulsed ruby optical maser.

When the appropriate probabilities for the ruby optical maser are inserted in the dynamic equation (17.44), it can be shown that

$$\frac{N_2 - N_1}{N_0} \simeq \frac{S_{13} - A_{21}}{S_{13} + A_{21} + 2S_{12}} \qquad (17.47)$$

where

$$N_0 = N_1 + N_2 + N_3$$

For a population inversion, $N_2 > N_1$ and the minimal requirement for pump power must therefore be $S_{13} > A_{21}$. In fact, transmission and other losses must also be taken into account, giving a final condition for maser action,

$$S_{13} > A_{21} + \text{losses} \qquad (17.48)$$

Ruby optical maser apparatus is shown in Fig. 17.31. A ruby rod of specific size, with the end faces polished, is placed near an electronic flash tube. The flash tube provides broad band pumping light. Up to a certain flash intensity ordinary luminescence results. Above this critical intensity, stimulated and non luminescent emission dominates, and a powerful beam of red light flashes out from the ends of the ruby rod. This red light has the enormous power output of more than $10^4$ watts over a beam of cross section $10^{-4}$ square meter. The emitted band is within a wavelength interval of about 0.02 A. The beam from the end face of the ruby rod has an angular spread of less than one degree.

The light is reflected back and forth through the crystal by two planar and partially silvered mirrors. The maser emission adjusts to one of many cavity resonances established by the mirrors.

In the ruby *microwave maser* the $Cr^{3+}$ level may be split into several components by a magnetic field. We have already discussed this splitting in Section 15.6. The $Al^{3+}$ and $O^{2-}$ ions have no magnetic moment and are not split. The populations in the split $Cr^{3+}$ levels can be inverted by a local oscillator and maser action produced. The separation of the levels in a field of about 1 weber $m^{-2}$ gives coherent emission in the microwave region.

A considerable variety of crystals containing paramagnetic ions can be employed as microwave masers. The paramagnetic ion must, of course, have a suitable zero field splitting with the separation of the levels preferably greater than the maser transition. The atoms of the host structure should have low nuclear magnetic moments in order not to interact with the paramagnetic ion. Such an interaction would split the levels and increase the number of transitions. The pumping power would then have to be increased to produce the necessary inversion of population. The matrix crystal should be strong and chemically stable. Large single crystals which can withstand the necessary reduction of temperature are advantageous. Table 17.3 gives a short list of some maser materials.

**Table 17.3**  Maser Materials and Wavelengths in $10^{-6}$ m

| Lattice | Ion | Maser Wavelength |
|---------|-----|------------------|
| $Al_2O_3$ | $Cr^{3+}$ | 0.7 |
| $CaF_2$ | $U^{3+}$ | 2.6 |
|  | $Nd^{3+}$ | 1.06 |
|  | $Ho^{3+}$ | 2.05 |
|  | $Sm^{2+}$ | 0.71 |
|  | $Dy^{2+}$ | 2.36 |
|  | $Tm^{2+}$ | 1.12 |
| $SrF_2$ | $U^{3+}$ | 2.6 |
|  | $Nd^{3+}$ | 1.06 |
|  | $Tm^{3+}$ | 1.91 |
|  | $Sm^{2+}$ | 0.71 |
| $BaF_2$ | $U^{3+}$ | 2.6 |
|  | $Nd^{3+}$ | 1.06 |
| $LaF^3$ | $Nd^{3+}$ | 1.06 |
| $CaWO_4$ | $Nd^{3+}$ | 1.06 |
|  | $Pr^{3+}$ | 1.05 |
|  | $Tm^{3+}$ | 1.91 |
|  | $Ho^{3+}$ | 2.05 |
|  | $Er^{3+}$ | 1.61 |
| $SrWO_4$ | $Nd^{3+}$ | 1.06 |
| $CaMoO_4$ | $Nd^{3+}$ | 1.06 |
| $SrMoO_4$ | $Nd^{3+}$ | 1.06 |
| $PbMoO_4$ | $Nd^{3+}$ | 1.06 |
| Glass | $Nd^{3+}$ | 1.06 |
| Glass | $Yb^{3+}$ | 1.01 |

## 17.19 The Semiconductor Optical Maser

Recently maser action has been successfully produced in a number of III–V semiconducting *p-n* junction diodes similar to that shown in Fig. 17.32. The necessary population inversion and photon emission is brought about by forward biasing the junction. This injects large numbers of minority carriers across the junction which then combine. In Fig. 17.33*a* the valence and conduction bands with zero and forward bias are shown. Figure 17.33*b* shows the density of energy states in *n*-type, *p*-type, and compensated material. A major part of the recombination in GaAs, InAs, and InP is associated with photon emission (Section 14.7).

Once population inversion has been established, one photon induces an electron to make a transition from the higher to the lower state with emission of a second photon. A cascade process is established in which the phase of any photon is fixed relative to the phase of the preceding photon. If the wave is reflected between the ends of the diode, a coherent radiation pattern is set up.

The diode is operated at liquid nitrogen (77°K) or helium (4.2°K) temperature. Large current pulses of about 100 amp at 77°K and of microsecond

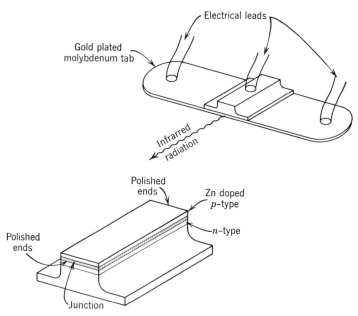

**Fig. 17.32** Gallium arsenide diode laser. (Redrawn from B. Lax, "Semiconducting Lasers," *Science*, **141**, 1249, 1963)

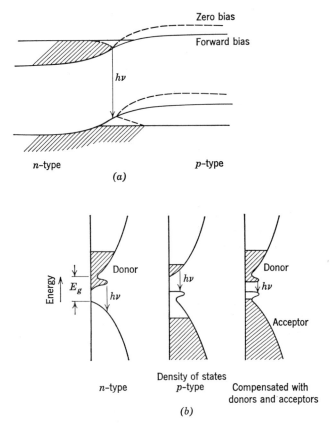

**Fig. 17.33** (*a*) Forward bias in *p-n* junction giving population inversion and photon emission. Bias lowers bands on *p*-side relative to *n*-side. (*b*) Density states in *n*-type, *p*-type, and compensated material. (From Lax)

duration are applied. Figure 17.34 shows the radiation intensity as a function of current, and Fig. 17.35 gives the spectrum in a typical gallium arsenide diode.

Many modifications of semiconductor lasers and masers are possible. Some of these utilize tunnel diodes with the transition levels modified or tuned by the application of a magnetic field.

## 17.20 Radiation Detectors

We have already discussed most of the physical principles which govern the dielectric and optical response of solids to irradiation by photons or by

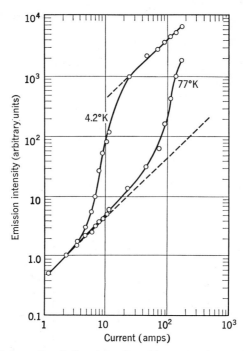

**Fig. 17.34** Variation of radiation intensity with current in a gallium arsenide diode. (From Lax)

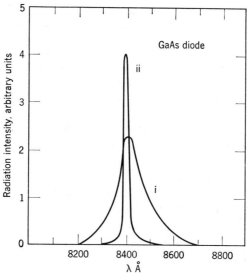

**Fig. 17.35** Spectrum of radiation as a function of wavelength at 77°K in a typical gallium arsenide diode, (i) below threshold current, and (ii) above threshold current to operate as a maser. (From Lax)

nuclear particles. In this section we shall list some of these detectors, giving a brief reference to their mode of operation.

*Photovoltaic cells* have been manufactured for some time in the form of thin layers of *copper oxide, selenium,* or *lead sulfide* on a metal surface. The layer is covered by a transparent, conducting film. Currents are generated on illumination with a spectral response close to that of ordinary photographic emulsions.

*Photoconductive cells* operate because of a change in conductance on irradiation. Lead sulfide, lead selenide, and lead telluride as well as indium antimonide and doped germanium are examples.

The devices mentioned operate because of the excitation of electrons to a higher energy level by the irradiating photons. In many cases the separation of the levels is a fraction of an electron volt. Equating this to the photon energy puts the peak response well into the infrared. Detectors with a response to wavelengths greater than about $5 \times 10^{-6}$ m have very small energy gaps and must be cooled to inhibit thermal excitation.

The lifetimes of the excited electrons in these photoconductive cells depend on trapping and recombination and often lie between $10^{-6}$ and $10^{-4}$ s. Table 17.4 gives characteristics of a few solid state detectors.

*Junction photodevices* may be used in the forms of diodes or transistors. The simplest use of the diode is with reverse bias. The photons are made to impinge close to the junction. Electron-hole pairs are produced and the minority carriers diffuse to the junction. The diffusion length must be, of course, above a certain value for this to occur, and care is taken in preparation to eliminate defects. Transport of the minority carriers across the junction gives a current in the external circuit.

**Table 17.4**

| | Maximum Sensitivity Wavelength | Long Wavelength Limit |
|---|---|---|
| Cb–Sb (photoemissive) | $0.4 \times 10^{-6}$ m | $0.65 \times 10^{-6}$ m |
| Cs–O–Ag (photoemissive) | 0.8 | 1.2 |
| CdS (photoconductive) | 0.68 | 0.9 |
| Ge (phototransistor) | 1.6 | 2 |
| PbS | 2.4 | 3.5 |
| PbSe | 3.3 | 5 |
| PbTe | 4.4 | 6 |
| InSb | 6.5 | 8 |
| Ge (doped with Au) | | 9.5 |
| Ge (doped with Au and Sb) | | 6 |

Silicon diodes are used as photovoltaic generators in the "solar cell" with an appropriate circuit. Silicon is preferred because of the wide band gap which matches well to the solar spectrum and the ease of manufacture of oxidized wafers with low surface recombination properties.

*Photoemissive detectors* are now often used in the form of *photomultipliers*. On irradiation, electrons are released from the low work function surface of the photocathode. Surfaces such as Cs–O–Ag are often used. The electrons are then accelerated by an electric field and focused on a second surface or *dynode*. Each primary electron produces several secondary electrons, which are then ejected. In practice, a number of dynodes are employed to amplify the initial photocurrent. With accelerating fields of several thousand volts and several dynodes the amplification factor can be as high as $10^8$.

Photomultipliers are generally used in conjunction with a *scintillator* in the detection and counting of nuclear radiation. The requirements are for high counting rates and short resolving times. The nuclear particle being detected produces a flash of fluorescent light in the scintillator crystal. This light is transmitted to the photocathode of a photomultiplier tube. The resulting current pulse produces a pulse at the input of the preamplifier in the counting circuit. Good scintillators must have high efficiency of conversion of the nuclear particle energy to that of luminescent radiation. They should be transparent to their own fluorescent radiation and have short fluorescent delay times.

Liquid, gaseous, organic crystal, and liquid scintillators are in use. Inorganic crystal scintillators are often doped alkali halide crystals. The theory of luminescence in these crystals has been discussed in Section 17.12. Inorganic crystals are transparent to their own luminescent radiation since the photon energy is less than the width between the valence and conduction bands and it is transitions between these bands which produce normal optical absorption. Decay times for NaI doped with Tl are about $10^{-7}$ s. Faster response times are possible with some organic crystals such as trans-stilbene.

High energy charged particles can be detected by *crystal counters*. Opposite faces of the crystals are coated with electrodes, across which an electric field is applied. Ionizing radiation is stopped in the crystal and raises electrons to the conduction band. Conductivity changes are recorded as pulses in the external circuit. Again trapping sites limit the passage of the electrons to the electrodes. Suitable crystals are diamond, CdS, AgBr, ThI, and ZnS.

## References

Beam, W. R., *Electronics of Solids*, McGraw-Hill Book Co., New York, 1965.
Bloembergen, N., Masers, on page 80 of *Foundations of Future Electronics*, McGraw-Hill Book Co., New York, 1961.

## Exercises

1. Calculate the electric dipole moments of the following charge configurations. (*a*) Charges of $+1$ microcoulombs are located at the points $(0, 0)$, $(1, 0)$ and $(2, 0)$ and charges of $-1$ microcoulombs are located at $(4, 0)$, $(5, 0)$ and $(6, 0)$. The number referring to meters. (*b*) Charges of $+3$ microcoulombs at $(0, 0)$; $+6$ microcoulombs at $(1, 1)$; $-3$ microcoulombs at $(1, 0)$; and $-6$ microcoulombs at $(0, 1)$.

2. A charge of $Q$ coulombs is distributed homogeneously throughout the volume of a sphere of radius $R$ meters. The sphere is in vacuum. Find the electric displacement $D$ and the electric field strength $\mathcal{E}$ as a function of the distance from the center of the sphere.

3. Two square parallel plates of side 0.1 m are separated by a sulfur ($\epsilon_r = 4.0$) slab 0.01 m thick and are connected to a 200-volt battery. (*a*) What is the capacitance of this capacitor? (*b*) What is the charge on the plates? (*c*) What is the induced electric dipole moment per unit volume of dielectric? (*d*) What is the electric field strength in the sulfur?

4. The relative permittivity of argon at $0°C$ and 1 atmosphere pressure is 1.000435. Calculate the polarizability of the argon atom.

5. A long narrow cylindrical rod is composed of atoms each with polarizability $10^{-40}$ farad m$^2$. The solid contains $5 \times 10^{28}$ atoms per cubic meter. An electric field is applied parallel to the length of the rod. Calculate the ratio of local to applied field.

6. The critical wavelength for transparency in sodium is 2100 A. Calculate the number of free electrons per atom which this implies.

7. The resonant frequency of a piezoelectric quartz crystal given by

$$f_0 = \frac{1}{2b}\sqrt{\frac{E}{\rho}}$$

   where $b$ is the dimension that determines the mode of oscillation of the crystal, $E$ is Young's modulus, and $\rho$ the density of quartz. Calculate useful sizes of crystal for oscillators in the kilocycle and megacycle ranges. For quartz, $E = 10^{10}$n m$^{-2}$, $\rho = 2500$ kg m$^{-3}$.

8. The fractional number of electrons released per second from traps in a particular phosphor is equal to $10^8 e^{-E_T/kT}$. If the intensity of phosphorescent light drops to half the value at the time of excitation in 0.02 second at $300°K$, calculate the depth of trap $E_T$ in electron volts. What is the time interval to half intensity at $-50°C$?

9. What is the decay time and line width associated with a transition probability of $10^4$ sec$^{-1}$ in a *solid*. *Gas* atoms emit photons of energy 1.8 eV. If the gas atoms are moving at velocities corresponding to a temperature of $5000°K$ calculate the *Doppler* line width.

10. A two-level maser system has the following characteristics:

$$E_2 - E_1 = 1 \text{ eV}$$
$$A_{21} \simeq B_{21} \simeq 10^4 \text{ sec}^{-1}$$
$$S_{12} \simeq S_{21} \simeq 10^5 \text{ sec}^{-1}$$
$$N_0 = N_1 + N_2 = 10^{24} \text{ m}^{-3}$$

The distribution is in thermal equilibrium at 300°K when pump light is switched on. Calculate $N_1$ and $N_2$ as functions of time from that moment.

11. In a three-level microwave maser spontaneous emission may be neglected. Confirm the following dynamic equations:

$$\frac{dN_1}{dt} = (-N_1 P_{12} + N_2 P_{21}) + (-N_1 P_{13} + N_3 P_{31}) + S_{12}(N_1 - N_1) + S_{13}(N_3 - N_1)$$

$$\frac{dN_2}{dt} = (-N_2 P_{21} + N_1 P_{12}) + (-N_2 P_{23} + N_3 P_{32}) + S_{12}(N_1 - N_2) + S_{23}(N_3 - N_2)$$

$$\frac{dN_3}{dt} = (-N_3 P_{31} + N_1 P_{13}) + (-N_3 P_{32} + N_2 P_{23}) + S_{13}(N_1 - N_2) + S_{23}(N_2 - N_3)$$

The transition probabilities and frequencies in a solid system are as follows:

$$P_{12} \simeq P_{13} \simeq P_{23} \simeq 10^3 \text{ sec}^{-1}$$
$$S_{23} \simeq 0$$
$$\nu_{12} = 10 \text{ GHz}; \qquad \nu_{23} = 15 \text{ GHz}$$

(a) Express $(N_2 - N_1)$ as a function of $S_{12}$ and $S_{13}$.
(b) Express $(N_3 - N_1)$ as a function of $S_{12}$ and $S_{13}$.
(c) Show that the frequency-power conversion between pump and emitted light is

$$\frac{\nu_{12} S_{12}(N_2 - N_1)}{\nu_{13} S_{13}(N_3 - N_1)}$$

(d) Express the conversion faction as a function of $S_{12}$ and $S_{13}$.

12. A GaAs diode has the following characteristics:

| | |
|---|---|
| $E_g = 1.58 \text{ eV (at } 0°K)$ | $\mu_n = 0.85 \text{ m}^2/\text{volt sec}$ |
| $\dfrac{m_n^*}{m_e} = 0.072$ | $\mu_p = 0.04 \text{ m}^2/\text{volt sec}$ |
| $\dfrac{m_p^*}{m_e} = 0.65$ | Minority carrier $\tau = 80 \ \mu\text{sec}$ |

$$N_a = N_d = 10^{24} \text{ m}^{-3}$$

What is the "population inversion" (minority-majority carrier) on the $p$ side at a forward bias current density of $10^5$ amp m$^{-2}$?

# General References

Following are some recent introductory texts on solid state physics listed in order of increasing sophistication.

Van Vlack, L. H., *Elements of Materials Science*, Addison-Wesley, Reading, Mass., 1960.

Hemenway, C. L., R. W. Henry, and M. Caulton, *Physical Electronics*, John Wiley and Sons, New York, 1962.

Wulff, J. et al., *Structure and Properties of Materials*, John Wiley and Sons, New York, 1964. Vol. 1, Structure; Vol. II, Thermodynamics of Structure; Vol. III, Mechanical Behavior; Vol. IV, Electronic Properties.

Adler, R. B., A. C. Smith, and R. L. Longini, *Introduction to Semiconductor Physics*, John Wiley and Sons, New York, 1964.

Sproull, R. L., *Modern Physics*, 2d ed., John Wiley and Sons, New York, 1963.

Azaroff, L. V., and J. J. Brophy, *Electronic Processes in Materials*, McGraw-Hill Book Co., New York, 1963.

Kittel, C., *Elementary Solid State Physics*, John Wiley and Sons, New York, 1962.

Langmuir, D. B., and W. D. Hershberger, eds., *Foundations of Future Electronics*, McGraw-Hill Book Co., New York, 1961.

Beam, W. R., *Electronics of Solids*, McGraw-Hill Book Co., New York, 1965.

McKelvey, J. P., *Solid State and Semiconductor Physics*, Harper and Row, New York, 1966.

Kittel, C., *Introduction to Solid State Physics*, 3d ed., John Wiley and Sons, New York, 1966.

# Appendix

## A.1 The Physical Constants

Speed of light $\qquad$ $c = 2.998 \times 10^8$ m sec$^{-1}$

Electronic charge $\qquad$ $e = 1.602 \times 10^{-19}$ coulomb

Electronic rest mass $\qquad$ $m = 9.108 \times 10^{-31}$ kg

Proton rest mass $\qquad$ $m = 1.672 \times 10^{-27}$ kg

Planck's constant $\qquad$ $h = 6.625 \times 10^{-34}$ joule sec

Boltzmann's constant $\qquad$ $k = 1.380 \times 10^{-23}$ joule deg$^{-1}$

$\qquad\qquad\qquad\qquad = 8.616 \times 10^{-5}$ eV deg$^{-1}$

Gas constant $\qquad$ $R = 8.317 \times 10^3$ joule (kg mole)$^{-1}$ deg$^{-1}$

Avogadro's number $\qquad$ $N = 6.025 \times 10^{26}$ (kg mole)$^{-1}$

Bohr magneton $\qquad$ $\beta = 9.273 \times 10^{-24}$ amp m$^2$

Permittivity of free space $\qquad$ $\epsilon_0 = 8.854 \times 10^{-12}$ farad m$^{-1}$

Permeability of free space $\qquad$ $\mu_0 = 4\pi \times 10^{-7}$ henry m$^{-1}$

## A.2 Conversion Factors

eV-joule conversion $\qquad$ $1 \text{ eV} = 1.602 \times 10^{-19}$ joule

Magnetic induction conversion $\qquad$ $1 \text{ gauss} = 10^{-4}$ weber m$^{-2}$

Magnetic field conversion $\qquad$ $1 \text{ oersted} = 7.96$ amps m$^{-1}$

# Answers to Exercises

### Chapter 1

2. 7.76 eV per molecule
   180 kcal per mole
   20 kcal per mole

3. Nearest Neighbor Distance $R$      Number of Neighbors

| Nearest Neighbor Distance $R$ | Number of Neighbors |
|---|---|
| 2.81 A | 6 opposite |
| $\sqrt{2}R$ | 12 same |
| $\sqrt{3}R$ | 8 opposite |

$$\alpha = \frac{6}{1} - \frac{12}{\sqrt{2}} + \frac{8}{\sqrt{3}} - \frac{6}{2} + \cdots$$

Special methods of arranging make the series converge.
Then   Coulomb energy $= (\alpha 14.4/2.81)eV$

4. (a) $[10\bar{1}]$
   (b) $[0\bar{1}2]$
   (c) $[\bar{1}\bar{1}2]$

5. 
| | | | |
|---|---|---|---|
| Cu | 2.552 A | 2.083 A | 1.614 A |
| Fe | 2.023 A | 1.652 A | 1.280 A |

7. 
| | |
|---|---|
| 7920 | kg m$^{-3}$ |
| 8990 | kg m$^{-3}$ |
| 7180 | kg m$^{-3}$ |
| 3530 | kg m$^{-3}$ |

9. Coordinates $\frac{1}{2}\,\frac{1}{2}\,0$

   $r = 0.154\,R$     where $R$ is radius of atom

   Coordinates $\frac{1}{2}\,\frac{1}{4}\,0$

   $r = 0.291\,R$     where $R$ is radius of atom

10. (a) $1.73 \times 10^{19}$ atoms m$^{-2}$
    (b) $1.77 \times 10^{19}$ atoms m$^{-2}$
         $1.09 \times 10^{19}$ atoms m$^{-2}$
    (c) $1.63 \times 10^{19}$ atoms m$^{-2}$

## Chapter 2

1. (a) $3.85 \times 10^{-10}$ m
   (b) $2.52 \times 10^{-10}$ m
   (c) $0.41 \times 10^{-10}$ m
2. (a) 2.3 m
   (b) $2.9 \times 10^{-6}$ m
3. $6.23 \times 10^{26}$ atoms per kg atomic weight
4. $20.0 \times 10^{-6}$ °K$^{-1}$
5. 3.304 A
6. (111)  (220)  (311)  (400)  (331)  (422)  (511, 333)  (440)  (531)

## Chapter 3

1. fav.       fav.       fav.
   fav.       fav.       res.
   fav.       fav.       fav.
   fav.       fav.      · fav.
   res.       res.       res.
2. 1,2        1,2        1,1
   1,2        1,2        1,1
   1,2        1,3        1,4
   1,2        1,3        1,4
   1,2        1,3        1,3
   0,3        1,4        1,3
3. Interstitial
4. Approximately       88 per cent nickel
                       70 per cent nickel
                       24 per cent nickel
                       0.37 kg solid
5. 93 per cent α
   (a) Liquid and β phases of which 61 per cent is β
   (b) Eutectic microconstituent of which 20 per cent is α
7. $K_0 \simeq 0.5$
   Ultimate purity is approx. $10^{-5}$ per cent by weight of copper
   In approximately 13 passes

## Chapter 4

1. $10^{-6}$ m

2. (a) $\dfrac{N!}{(N - n)!n!}$

   (b) $\dfrac{N'!}{(N' - n)!n!}$

   $\simeq 10^{31}$

3. $10^{-15}$ atomic per cent for interstitials
   $10^{-4}$ atomic per cent for vacancies

5. *D*               $2 \times 10^{-28 \cdot 5}$ m$^2$ sec$^{-1}$
   *D* (volume)        $0.72 \times 10^{-36 \cdot 5}$ m$^2$ sec$^{-1}$
   *D* (grain boundary)    $0.14 \times 10^{-19 \cdot 5}$ m$^2$ sec$^{-1}$

7. For $D_0 \simeq 10^{-2}$:   $S_f + S_m \simeq 10^{-2}$ eV deg$^{-1}$

## Chapter 5

1. $\sigma_1 + \sigma_2 = \dfrac{E}{\nu}\left(\dfrac{d_s - d_u}{d_u}\right)$

   where $d_s$ and $d_u$ are the spacings of atomic planes lying parallel to the surface in the stressed and unstressed condition, respectively. (511) plane.

2. $2 \times 10^6$ nm$^{-2}$

4. $7.6 \times 10^{-10}$ m

5. 137 calories

6. 0.59 min.

7. $10^7$ dislocations cm.$^{-2}$

9. $1.5 \times 10^5$ nm$^{-2}$

10. $3 \times 10^{-10}$ m

## Chapter 6

3. $10^{-2}$ sec
   20 Hz

5. $\nu(90°\text{K}) \; = 9.9 \times 10^5$ Hz
   $\nu(300°\text{K}) = 12.9 \times 10^{10}$ Hz
   $\nu(500°\text{K}) = 97.6 \times 10^{10}$ Hz

7. 100°K
   192°K

8. $\alpha\left(\dfrac{\text{db}}{\mu\text{sec}}\right) = \dfrac{2\pi^2 \nu Q^{-1}}{0.722}$

   where $\nu$ is in MHz

9. 4 $\mu$sec
   Ratio 1.26

## Chapter 7

2. Au $\simeq 2000$
   Ge $\simeq 5000$

3.

| 76 eV | 325 Ev | 638 eV | 1263 eV |
|---|---|---|---|
| 0.10 MeV | 0.41 MeV | 0.68 MeV | 1.10 MeV |
| 31 eV | 91 eV | 169 eV | 325 eV |
| 76 eV | 28 eV | 25 eV | 28 eV |

Your answers will be order of magnitude only.

These are more accurately calculated values from G. J. Dienes and H. G. Vineyard, *Radiation Effects in Solids*, Interscience, New York, 1957.

## Chapter 8

1. Radius: $1.07 \times 10^{-4}$ m
   Pitch: $6.72 \times 10^{-4}$ m
   Frequency: $1.4 \times 10^{10}$ sec$^{-1}$

2. $2.38 \times 10^{17}$ sec$^{-1}$

3. $1.24 \times 10^4$ volts

4. 0.11 A

5. $5.05 \times 10^{-15}$ m

6. 5.47 A

7. 1.3 per cent

8. $10^{-8.5}$

9. (a) Energy difference     $7.16 \times 10^{-19}$ joules
         Wavelength          2770 A
   (b) Energy difference     $180.0 \times 10^{-35}$ joules
         Wavelength          $1.1 \times 10^8$ m

10. (a) $6.6 \times 10^{-24}$ joule
         $20 \times 10^{-24}$ joule
    (b) $1.6 \times 10^{-34}$ joule
         $4.8 \times 10^{-34}$ joule

## Chapter 9

1. $1.97 \times 10^6$ m sec$^{-1}$

2. Energy: $-2.42 \times 10^{-19}$ joule
   Angular momentum: $1.49 \times 10^{-34}$ kg m$^2$ sec$^{-1}$
                         $2.58 \times 10^{-34}$ kg m$^2$ sec$^{-1}$
   Wavelength: 1030 A

4. Momentum: $1.10 \times 10^{-24}$ kg m sec$^{-1}$
   Energy: $6.63 \times 10^{-19}$ joule

5. $\pm\kappa_x \pm 2\kappa_y = \dfrac{\pi}{a} \cdot 5, \quad \pm 2\kappa_x \pm \kappa_y = \dfrac{\pi}{a} \cdot 5, \quad \pm\kappa_x \pm \kappa_x = \dfrac{\pi}{a} \cdot 2$

6. $\pm\kappa_x \pm \kappa_y = \dfrac{\pi}{a} \cdot 2, \quad \pm\kappa_x \pm \kappa_z = \dfrac{\pi}{a} \cdot 2, \quad \pm\kappa_z = \dfrac{\pi}{a} \cdot 2$

7. Surface is hexagonal with faces parallel to those of the conventional unit cell. The dimensions of the zone are inversely proportional to those of the cell.

## Chapter 10

1. 1260°K
2. 0.684 eV, 25 per cent
3. $5.1 \times 10^{23}$
4. Fermi energy: 4.67 eV
   Fermi temperature: 54,200°K
6. $2.8 \times 10^{-9}$
7. Wavelength: 1.38 A
8. $0.97 \times 10^{-18}$ joule
9. $2.9 \times 10^{-9}$ n

## Chapter 11

1. 2760 A
2. Current: $4.40 \times 10^{-7}$ amp m$^{-2}$
   Potential: 0.48 volt

5.

| $n$ | $l$ | $j$ |
|-----|-----|-----|
| 1 | 0 | $\frac{1}{2}$ |
| 2 | 0 | $\frac{1}{2}$ |
| 2 | 1 | $\frac{1}{2}$ |
| 2 | 1 | $\frac{3}{2}$ |
| 3 | 0 | $\frac{1}{2}$ |
| 3 | 1 | $\frac{1}{2}$ |
| 3 | 1 | $\frac{3}{2}$ |
| 3 | 2 | $\frac{3}{2}$ |
| 3 | 2 | $\frac{5}{2}$ |
| 4 | 0 | $\frac{1}{2}$ |
| 4 | 1 | $\frac{1}{2}$ |
| 4 | 1 | $\frac{3}{2}$ |
| 4 | 2 | $\frac{3}{2}$ |
| 4 | 2 | $\frac{5}{2}$ |
| 4 | 3 | $\frac{5}{2}$ |
| 4 | 3 | $\frac{7}{2}$ |

6. 367 $\mu a$
7. Current: 399 $\mu a$
   Change in $\phi$: 0.015 eV
8. 3.4 volts
   11 $ma$
9. 0.08 volt
11. $1.51 \times 10^2$, 0.63 per cent

## Chapter 12

2. $5.31 \times 10^{-8}$ m

3. $\dfrac{m^*}{m} = 0.755$

4. 1.5 watts m$^{-2}$ m$^{-1}$ °K$^{-1}$

6. Use estimate of $L_T$ in Equation 12.27

## Chapter 13

2. $\simeq 2.5 \times 10^{12}$ Hz

$h\nu_{max} \simeq 10^{-2}$ eV

$\Theta \simeq 115$°K

5. $\simeq 10^4$ m sec$^{-1}$

First estimate mean free path

## Chapter 14

1. 1.94 mhos m$^{-1}$

0.091 mho m$^{-1}$ °K$^{-1}$

2. $E_g - E_F = 0.16$ eV

3120 mhos m$^{-1}$

3. $E_F = 0.20$ eV

304 mhos m$^{-1}$

4. Carry out calculation with $4 \times 10^{22}$ donors

5. $1.6 \times 10^{22}$ carriers m$^{-3}$

0.04 m$^2$ volt sec$^{-1}$

6. $2.3 \times 10^{-4}$ volt

8. 0.18 volt

9. (a) $h\nu = 3.1$ eV, Gap $= 2.4$ eV (check momentum)

(b) $16.1 \times 10^{13}$

(c) $\Delta\sigma = 2.6 \times 10^{-10}$ mho m$^{-1}$

10. (e) Calculate $E_F$ for $n$ and $p$ sides as in Section 14.5

## Chapter 15

1. $B = \dfrac{\mu_0 \mu_r I}{2\pi a} = 10^{-6}$ webers m$^{-2}$

2. $-0.05$ amp m$^{-1}$

3. $\simeq -5 \times 10^{-6}$

4. At 300°K: $2.6 \times 10^{-27}$ amp m$^2$: $\simeq 50$ per cent

At 0.3°K: $2.23 \times 10^{-27}$ amp m$^2$: $\simeq 62$ per cent

5. (a) 35,200 MHz

(b) 53.5 MHz

6. (a) $15.8 \times 10^5$ amps m$^{-1}$
   (b) 0.66
   (c) 1580
   (d) 3140 webers m$^{-2}$

7. $4\beta$

## Chapter 16

5. $3 \times 10^{-3}$ Ho

## Chapter 17

1. (a) 12 $\mu$cm in $-x$ direction
   (b) 3 $\mu$cm in $x$ direction

2. $r < R$:  $D = \dfrac{Qr}{4\pi R^3}$ : $\mathscr{E} = \dfrac{Qr}{4\pi\epsilon_0 R^3}$

   $r > R$:  $D = \dfrac{Q}{4\pi r^2}$ : $\mathscr{E} = \dfrac{Q}{4\pi\epsilon_0 r^2}$

3. (a) $35.4 \times 10^{-12}$ farad
   (b) $7.08 \times 10^{-9}$ coulomb on each plate
   (c) $5.31 \times 10^{-7}$ C m$^{-2}$
   (d) $2 \times 10^4$ V m$^{-1}$

4. $1.43 \times 10^{-40}$ farad m$^{-2}$

5. $\dfrac{\mathscr{E}_{loc}}{\mathscr{E}} = 1.23$

6. 1 electron per atom

7.  1 KHz: 1 m
    10 KHz: 0.1 m
    1 MHz: $10^{-3}$ m
    10 MHz: $10^{-4}$ m

8. 0.38 eV
   3.3 sec

# Index